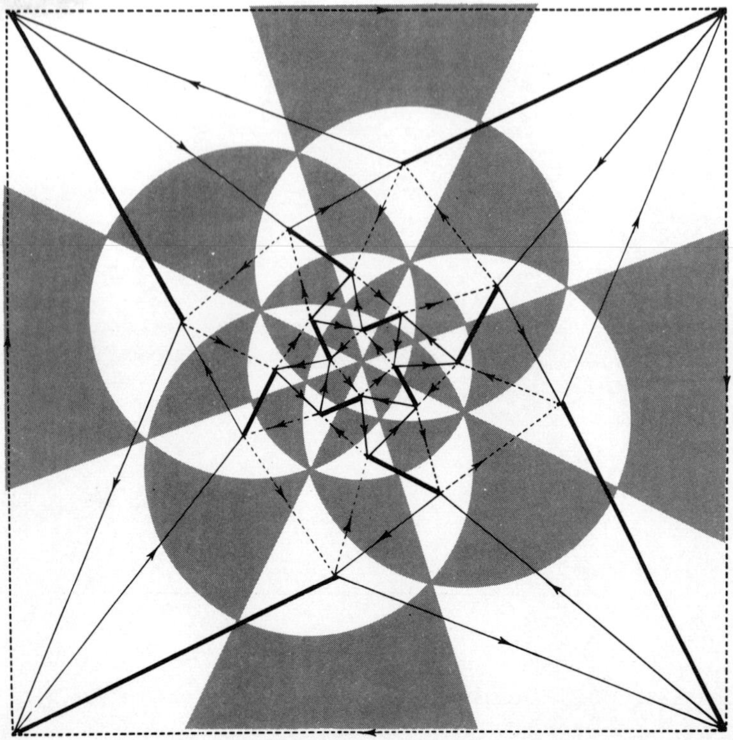

The octohedral group represented as a colour-group

Heavy line = red.
Dotted line = green.
Light line = yellow.

THEORY OF GROUPS

OF

FINITE ORDER

BY

W. BURNSIDE, M.A., F.R.S.

D.Sc. (Dublin), LL.D. (Edinburgh)

HONORARY FELLOW OF PEMBROKE COLLEGE, CAMBRIDGE

PROFESSOR OF MATHEMATICS AT THE ROYAL NAVAL COLLEGE, GREENWICH

SECOND EDITION

DOVER PUBLICATIONS, INC.

This new Dover edition, first published in 1955,
is an unabridged republication of the second edition,
published in 1911.
It is published through special arrangement
with Cambridge University Press.

Manufactured in the United States of America.

PREFACE TO THE SECOND EDITION

VERY considerable advances in the theory of groups of finite order have been made since the appearance of the first edition of this book. In particular the theory of groups of linear substitutions has been the subject of numerous and important investigations by several writers; and the reason given in the original preface for omitting any account of it no longer holds good.

In fact it is now more true to say that for further advances in the abstract theory one must look largely to the representation of a group as a group of linear substitutions. There is accordingly in the present edition a large amount of new matter. Five Chapters, XIII to XVII, are devoted to the theory of groups of linear substitutions, including their invariants. In Chapter IV, which is also new, certain properties of abstract groups, to which no reference was made in the first edition, are dealt with; while Chapter XII develops more completely the investigation of the earlier sections of Chapter IX of the first edition.

All the chapters dealing with the abstract theory, including that of the group of isomorphisms, have been brought together in the earlier part of the book; while from Chapter X onwards various special modes of representing a group are investigated. The last Chapter of the first edition has none to correspond to it in the present, but all results of importance which it contained are given in connections in which they naturally occur. With this exception there are no considerable changes in the matter of the first edition though there is some re-arrangement, and in places additions have been made.

A number of special questions, most of which could not have been introduced in the text without somewhat marring the scheme of the work, have been dealt with in the notes.

Some of the examples, especially in the earlier part of the book, are suitable exercises for those to whom the subject is new. The examples as a whole, however, have not been inserted with this object, but rather (i) to afford further illustration of points dealt with in the text, (ii) where references are given, to call attention to points of importance not mentioned in the text, and (iii) to suggest subjects of investigation.

A separate index to the definitions of all technical terms has been prepared which it is hoped may be of considerable service to readers.

I owe my best thanks to the Rev. Alfred Young, M.A., Rector of Birdbrook, Essex, and formerly Fellow of Clare College, Cambridge, who read the whole of the book as it passed through the press. His careful criticism has saved me from many errors and his suggestions have been of great help to me. Mr Harold Hilton, M.A., Lecturer in Mathematics at Bedford College, University of London, and formerly Fellow of Magdalen College, Oxford, gave me great assistance by reading and criticising the chapters on groups of linear substitutions; and Dr Henry Frederick Baker, F.R.S., Fellow of St John's College, Cambridge, helped me with most valuable suggestions on the chapter dealing with invariants. To both these gentlemen I offer my sincere thanks. I must further not omit to thank correspondents, both English and American, for pointing out to me errors in the first edition. All these have, I hope, been corrected.

Finally I would again express my gratitude to the officers and staff of the University Press for their courtesy and for the care with which the printing has been carried out.

W. BURNSIDE

March 1911

PREFACE TO THE FIRST EDITION

THE theory of groups of finite order may be said to date from the time of Cauchy. To him are due the first attempts at classification with a view to forming a theory from a number of isolated facts. Galois introduced into the theory the exceedingly important idea of a self-conjugate sub-group, and the corresponding division of groups into simple and composite. Moreover, by shewing that to every equation of finite degree there corresponds a group of finite order on which all the properties of the equation depend, Galois indicated how far reaching the applications of the theory might be, and thereby contributed greatly, if indirectly, to its subsequent developement.

Many additions were made, mainly by French mathematicians, during the middle part of the century. The first connected exposition of the theory was given in the third edition of M. Serret's "*Cours d'Algèbre Supérieure*," which was published in 1866. This was followed in 1870 by M Jordan's "*Traité des substitutions et des équations algébriques.*" The greater part of M. Jordan's treatise is devoted to a developement of the ideas of Galois and to their application to the theory of equations.

No considerable progress in the theory, as apart from its applications, was made till the appearance in 1872 of Herr Sylow's memoir "*Théorèmes sur les groupes de substitutions*" in the fifth volume of the *Mathematische Annalen*. Since the date of this memoir, but more especially in recent years, the theory has advanced continuously.

In 1882 appeared Herr Netto's "*Substitutionentheorie und ihre Anwendungen auf die Algebra*," in which, as in M. Serret's and M. Jordan's works, the subject is treated entirely from the point of view of groups of substitutions. Last but not least among the works which give a detailed account of the subject must be mentioned Herr Weber's "*Lehrbuch der Algebra*," of which the first volume appeared in 1895 and the second in 1896. In the last section of the first volume some of the more important properties of substitution groups are given. In the first section of the second volume, however, the subject is approached from a more general point of view, and a theory of finite groups is developed which is quite independent of any special mode of representing them.

The present treatise is intended to introduce to the reader the main outlines of the theory of groups of finite order apart from any applications. The subject is one which has hitherto attracted but little attention in this country; it will afford me much satisfaction if, by means of this book, I shall succeed in arousing interest among English mathematicians in a branch of pure mathematics which becomes the more fascinating the more it is studied.

Cayley's dictum that "a group is defined by means of the laws of combination of its symbols" would imply that, in dealing purely with the theory of groups, no more concrete mode of representation should be used than is absolutely necessary. It may then be asked why, in a book which professes to leave all applications on one side, a considerable space is devoted to substitution groups; while other particular modes of representation, such as groups of linear transformations, are not even referred to. My answer to this question is that while, in the present state of our knowledge, many results in the pure theory are arrived at most readily by dealing with properties of substitution groups, it would be difficult to find a result that could be most directly obtained by the consideration of groups of linear transformations.

The plan of the book is as follows. The first Chapter has been devoted to explaining the notation of substitutions. As this notation may not improbably be unfamiliar to many English readers, some such introduction is necessary to make the illustrations used in the following chapters intelligible. Chapters II to VII deal with the more important properties of groups which are independent of any special form of representation. The notation and methods of substitution groups have been rigorously excluded in the proofs and investigations contained in these chapters; for the purposes of illustration, however, the notation has been used whenever convenient. Chapters VIII to X deal with those properties of groups which depend on their representation as substitution groups. Chapter XI treats of the isomorphism of a group with itself. Here, though the properties involved are independent of the form of representation of the group, the methods of substitution groups are partially employed. Graphical modes of representing a group are considered in Chapters XII and XIII. In Chapter XIV the properties of a class of groups, of great importance in analysis, are investigated as a general illustration of the foregoing theory. The last Chapter contains a series of results in connection with the classification of groups as simple, composite, or soluble.

A few illustrative examples have been given throughout the book. As far as possible I have selected such examples as would serve to complete or continue the discussion in the text where they occur.

In addition to the works by Serret, Jordan, Netto and Weber already referred to, I have while writing this book consulted many original memoirs. Of these I may specially mention, as having been of great use to me, two by Herr Dyck published in the twentieth and twenty-second volumes of the *Mathematische Annalen* with the title "*Gruppentheoretische Studien*"; three by Herr Frobenius in the *Berliner Sitzungsberichte* for 1895 with the titles, "*Ueber endliche Gruppen*," "*Ueber auflösbare Gruppen*," and "*Verallgemeinerung des Sylow'schen Satzes*"; and one by Herr Hölder in the forty-sixth volume of the *Mathematische Annalen* with the title "*Bildung zusammengesetzter Gruppen*." Whenever a result is taken from an original memoir I have given a full reference; any omission to do so that may possibly occur is due to an oversight on my part.

To Mr A. R. Forsyth, Sc.D., F.R.S., Fellow of Trinity College, Cambridge, and Sadlerian Professor of Mathematics, and to Mr G. B. Mathews, M.A., F.R.S., late Fellow of St John's College, Cambridge, and formerly Professor of Mathematics in the University of North Wales, I am under a debt of gratitude for the care and patience with which they have read the proof-sheets. Without the assistance they have so generously given me, the errors and obscurities, which I can hardly hope to have entirely escaped, would have been far more numerous. I wish to express my grateful thanks also to Prof. O. Hölder of Königsberg who very kindly read and criticized parts of the last chapter. Finally I must thank the Syndics of the University Press of Cambridge for the assistance they have rendered in the publication of the book, and the whole Staff of the Press for the painstaking and careful way in which the printing has been done.

W. BURNSIDE

July 1897

CONTENTS

CHAPTER I.

ON PERMUTATIONS.

CHAPTER II.

THE DEFINITION OF A GROUP.

CHAPTER III.

ON THE SIMPLER PROPERTIES OF A GROUP WHICH ARE INDEPENDENT OF ITS MODE OF REPRESENTATION.

CHAPTER IV.

FURTHER PROPERTIES OF A GROUP WHICH ARE INDEPENDENT OF ITS MODE OF REPRESENTATION.

CHAPTER V.

ON THE COMPOSITION-SERIES OF A GROUP.

CHAPTER VI.

ON THE ISOMORPHISM OF A GROUP WITH ITSELF.

CHAPTER VII.

ON ABELIAN GROUPS.

CHAPTER VIII.

ON GROUPS WHOSE ORDERS ARE THE POWERS OF PRIMES.

CHAPTER IX.

ON SYLOW'S THEOREM.

CHAPTER X.

ON PERMUTATION-GROUPS: TRANSITIVE AND INTRANSITIVE GROUPS: PRIMITIVE AND IMPRIMITIVE GROUPS.

CHAPTER XI.

ON PERMUTATION-GROUPS: TRANSITIVITY AND PRIMITIVITY: (CONCLUDING PROPERTIES).

CHAPTER XII.

ON THE REPRESENTATION OF A GROUP OF FINITE ORDER AS A PERMUTATION-GROUP.

CHAPTER XIII.

ON GROUPS OF LINEAR SUBSTITUTIONS; REDUCIBLE AND IRREDUCIBLE GROUPS.

CHAPTER XIV.

ON THE REPRESENTATION OF A GROUP OF FINITE ORDER AS A GROUP OF LINEAR SUBSTITUTIONS.

CHAPTER XV.

ON GROUP-CHARACTERISTICS.

CHAPTER XVI.

SOME APPLICATIONS OF THE THEORY OF GROUPS OF LINEAR SUBSTITUTIONS AND OF GROUP-CHARACTERISTICS.

CHAPTER XVII.

ON THE INVARIANTS OF GROUPS OF LINEAR SUBSTITUTIONS.

CHAPTER XVIII.

ON THE GRAPHICAL REPRESENTATION OF A GROUP.

CHAPTER XIX.

ON THE GRAPHICAL REPRESENTATION OF GROUPS: GROUPS OF GENUS ZERO AND UNITY: CAYLEY'S COLOUR-GROUPS.

CHAPTER XX.

ON CONGRUENCE GROUPS.

THEORY OF GROUPS

OF

FINITE ORDER

CHAPTER I.

ON PERMUTATIONS.

1. Among the various notations used in the following pages, there is one of such frequent recurrence that a certain readiness in its use is very desirable in dealing with the subject of this treatise. We therefore propose to devote a preliminary chapter to explaining it in some detail.

2. Let $a_1, a_2, \ldots, a_n$ be a set of n distinct letters. The operation of replacing each letter of the set by another, which may be the same letter or a different one, when carried out under the condition that no two distinct letters are replaced by one and the same letter, is called a *permutation* performed on the n letters. Such a permutation will change any given arrangement

$$a_1, a_2, \ldots, a_n$$

of the n letters into a definite new arrangement

$$b_1, b_2, \ldots, b_n$$

of the same n letters.

3. One obvious form in which to write the permutation is

$$\begin{pmatrix} a_1, & a_2, \ldots\ldots, & a_n \\ b_1, & b_2, \ldots\ldots, & b_n \end{pmatrix},$$

thereby indicating that each letter in the upper line is to be replaced by the letter standing under it in the lower. The disadvantage of this form is its unnecessary complexity, each of the n letters occurring twice in the expression for the permutation; by the following process, the expression of the permutation may be materially simplified.

Let p be any one of the n letters, and q the letter in the lower line standing under p in the upper. Suppose now that r is the letter in the lower line that stands under q in the upper, and so on. Since the number of letters is finite, we must arrive at last at a letter s in the upper line under which p stands. If the set of n letters is not thus exhausted, take any letter p' in the upper line, which has not yet occurred, and let $q', r', \ldots$ follow it as $q, r, \ldots$ followed p, till we arrive at s' in the upper line with p' standing under it. If the set of n letters is still not exhausted, repeat the process, starting with a letter p'' which has not yet occurred. Since the number of letters is finite, we must in this way at last exhaust them; and the n letters are thus distributed into a number of sets

$$\begin{array}{l} p,\ q,\ r, \ldots,\ s\,; \\ p',\ q',\ r', \ldots,\ s'\,; \\ p'',\ q'',\ r'', \ldots,\ s''\,; \\ \ldots\ldots\ldots\ldots\ldots\ldots\,; \end{array}$$

such that the permutation replaces each letter of a set by the one following it in that set, the last letter of each set being replaced by the first of the same set.

If now we represent by the symbol

$$(pqr \ldots s)$$

the operation of replacing p by q, q by $r, \ldots$, and s by p, the permutation will be completely represented by the symbol

$$(pqr \ldots s)\,(p'q'r' \ldots s')\,(p''q''r'' \ldots s'') \ldots\ldots$$

The advantage of this mode of expressing the permutation is that each of the letters occurs only once in the symbol.

4. The separate components of the above symbol, such as $(pqr \ldots s)$, are called the *cycles* of the permutation. In particular cases, one or more of the cycles may contain a single letter; when this happens, the letters so occurring singly are unaltered by the permutation. The brackets enclosing single letters may clearly be omitted without risk of ambiguity, as also may the unaltered letters themselves. Thus the permutation

$$\begin{pmatrix} a, & b, & c, & d, & e \\ c, & b, & d, & a, & e \end{pmatrix}$$

may be written $(acd)(b)(e)$, or $(acd)\,be$, or simply (acd). If for any reason it were desirable to indicate that permutations of the five letters a, b, c, d, e were under consideration, the second of these three forms would be used.

5. The form thus obtained for a permutation is not unique. The symbol $(qr\ldots sp)$ clearly represents the same permutation as $(pqr\ldots s)$, if the letters that occur between r and s in the two symbols are the same and occur in the same sequence; so that, as regards the letters inside the bracket, any one may be chosen to stand first so long as the cyclical order is preserved unchanged.

Moreover the order in which the brackets are arranged is clearly immaterial, since the operation denoted by any one bracket has no effect on the letters contained in the other brackets. This latter property is characteristic of the particular expression that has been obtained for a permutation; it depends upon the fact that the expression contains each of the letters once only.

6. When we proceed to consider the effect of performing two or more permutations successively, it is seen at once that the order in which the permutations are carried out in general affects the result. Thus to give a very simple instance, the permutation (ab) followed by (ac) changes a into b, since b is unaltered by the second permutation. Again, (ab) changes b into a and (ac) changes a into c, so that the two permutations performed successively change b into c. Lastly, (ab) does not affect c and (ac) changes c into a. Hence the two permutations performed successively change a into b, b into c, c into a, and affect no other symbols. The result of the two permutations performed successively is therefore equivalent to the permutation (abc); and it may be similarly shewn that (ac) followed by (ab) gives (acb) as the resulting permutation. To avoid ambiguity it is therefore necessary to assign, once for all, the meaning to be attached to such a symbol as $s_1 s_2$, where s_1 and s_2 are the symbols of two given permutations. We shall always understand by the symbol $s_1 s_2$ *the result of carrying out first the* *permutation s_1 and then the permutation s_2*. Thus the two simple examples given above may be expressed in the form

$$(ab)(ac) = (abc),$$
$$(ac)(ab) = (acb),$$

the sign of equality being used to represent that the permutations are equivalent to each other.

If now

$$s_1 s_2 = s_4 \text{ and } s_2 s_3 = s_5,$$

the symbol $s_1 s_2 s_3$ may be regarded as the permutation s_4 followed by s_3 or as s_1 followed by s_5. But if s_1 changes *any* letter a into b, while s_2 changes b into c and s_3 changes c into d, then s_4 changes a into c and s_5 changes b into d. Hence $s_4 s_3$ and $s_1 s_5$ both change a into d; and therefore, a being any letter operated upon by the permutations,

$$s_4 s_3 = s_1 s_5.$$

Hence the meaning of the symbol $s_1 s_2 s_3$ is definite; it depends only on the component permutations s_1, s_2, s_3 and their sequence, and it is independent of the way in which they are associated when their sequence is assigned. And the same clearly holds for the symbols representing the successive performance of any number of permutations. To avoid circumlocution, it is convenient to speak of the permutation $s_1 s_2 \ldots s_n$ as the *product* of the permutations $s_1, s_2, \ldots, s_n$ in the sequence given. The product of a number of permutations, thus defined, always obeys the associative law but does not in general obey the commutative law of algebraical multiplication.

7. The permutation which replaces every symbol by itself is called the *identical permutation*. The *inverse* of a given permutation is that permutation which, when performed after the given permutation, gives as result the identical permutation. Let s_{-1} be the permutation inverse to s, so that, if

$$s = \begin{pmatrix} a_1, a_2, \ldots, a_n \\ b_1, b_2, \ldots, b_n \end{pmatrix},$$

then

$$s_{-1} = \begin{pmatrix} b_1, b_2, \ldots, b_n \\ a_1, a_2, \ldots, a_n \end{pmatrix}.$$

Let s_0 denote the identical permutation which can be represented by

$$\begin{pmatrix} a_1, a_2, \ldots, a_n \\ a_1, a_2, \ldots, a_n \end{pmatrix}.$$

Then $$ss_{-1} = s_0 \text{ and } s_{-1}s = s_0,$$
so that s is the permutation inverse to s_{-1}.

Now if $$ts = t's,$$
then $$tss_{-1} = t'ss_{-1},$$
or $$ts_0 = t's_0.$$

But ts_0 is the same permutation as t, since s_0 produces no change; and therefore

$$t = t'.$$

In exactly the same way, it may be shewn that the relation

$$st = st'$$
involves $$t = t'.$$

8. The result of performing r times in succession the same permutation s is represented symbolically by s^r. Since, as has been seen, products of permutations obey the associative law of multiplication, it follows that

$$s^{\mu}s^{\nu} = s^{\mu+\nu} = s^{\nu}s^{\mu}.$$

Now since there are only a finite number of distinct permutations that can be performed on a given finite set of symbols, the series of permutations $s, s^2, s^3, \ldots$ cannot be all distinct. Suppose that s^{m+n} is the first of the series which is the same as one that precedes it, and let that one be s^n. Then

$$s^{m+n} = s^n,$$
and therefore $$s^m s^n (s^n)_{-1} = s^n (s^n)_{-1},$$
or $$s^m = s_0.$$

Hence n must be 1. Moreover there is no index μ smaller than m for which this relation holds. For if

$$s^{\mu} = s_0,$$
then $$s^{\mu+1} = ss_0 = s,$$
contrary to the supposition that s^{m+1} is the first of the series which is the same as s.

Moreover the $m-1$ permutations $s, s^2, \ldots, s^{m-1}$ must be all distinct. For if

$$s^\mu = s^\nu, \qquad \nu < \mu < m,$$

then

$$s^{\mu-\nu}s^\nu (s^\nu)_{-1} = s^\nu (s^\nu)_{-1},$$

or

$$s^{\mu-\nu} = s_0,$$

which has just been shewn to be impossible.

The number m is called the *order* of the permutation s. In connection with the order of a permutation, two properties are to be noted. First, if

$$s^n = s_0,$$

it may be shewn at once that n is a multiple of m the order of s; and secondly, if

$$s^\alpha = s^\beta,$$

then

$$\alpha - \beta \equiv 0 \text{ (mod. } m).$$

If now the equation

$$s^{\mu+\nu} = s^\mu s^\nu$$

be assumed to hold, when either or both of the integers μ and ν is a negative integer, a definite meaning is obtained for the symbol s^{-r}, implying the negative power of a permutation; and a definite meaning is also obtained for s^0. For

$$s^\mu s^{-\nu} = s^{\mu-\nu} = s^{\mu-\nu}s^\nu (s^\nu)_{-1} = s^\mu (s^\nu)_{-1},$$

so that

$$s^{-\nu} = (s^\nu)_{-1}.$$

Similarly it can be shewn that

$$s^0 = s_0.$$

9. If the cycles of a permutation

$$s = (pqr\ldots s)(p'q'\ldots s')(p''q''\ldots s'')\ldots$$

contain $m, m', m'', \ldots$ letters respectively, and if

$$s^\mu = s_0,$$

μ must be a common multiple of $m, m', m'', \ldots$. For s^μ changes p into a letter μ places from it in the cyclical set $p, q, r, \ldots, s$; and therefore, if it changes p into itself, μ must be a multiple of m. In the same way, it must be a multiple of $m', m'', \ldots$. Hence the order of s is the least common multiple of $m, m', m'', \ldots$.

In particular, when a permutation consists of a single cycle, its order is equal to the number of letters which it interchanges. Such a permutation is called a *circular permutation*.

A permutation, all of whose cycles contain the same number of letters, is said to be *regular* in the letters which it interchanges; the order of such a permutation is clearly equal to the number of letters in one of its cycles.

10. Two permutations, which contain the same number of cycles and the same number of letters in corresponding cycles, are called *similar*. If s, s' are similar permutations, so also clearly are s^r, s'^r; and the orders of s and s' are the same.

Let now $$s = (a_p a_q \ldots a_s)(a_{p'} a_{q'} \ldots a_{s'})\ldots$$

and $$t = \begin{pmatrix} a_1, & a_2, \ldots, & a_n \\ b_1, & b_2, \ldots, & b_n \end{pmatrix}$$

be any two permutations. Then

$$t^{-1}st = \begin{pmatrix} b_1, & b_2, \ldots, & b_n \\ a_1, & a_2, \ldots, & a_n \end{pmatrix} (a_p a_q \ldots a_s)(a_{p'} a_{q'} \ldots a_{s'})\ldots \begin{pmatrix} a_1, & a_2, \ldots, & a_n \\ b_1, & b_2, \ldots, & b_n \end{pmatrix}$$
$$= (b_p b_q \ldots b_s)(b_{p'} b_{q'} \ldots b_{s'})\ldots,$$

the latter form of the permutation being obtained by actually carrying out the component permutations of the earlier form. Hence s and $t^{-1}st$ are similar permutations.

Since $$s_2 s_1 = s_1^{-1} s_1 s_2 s_1,$$

it follows that $s_1 s_2$ and $s_2 s_1$ are similar permutations and therefore that they are of the same order. Similarly it may be shewn that $s_1 s_2 s_3 \ldots s_{n-1} s_n$, $s_2 s_3 \ldots s_{n-1} s_n s_1, \ldots,$ $s_n s_1 s_2 s_3 \ldots s_{n-1}$ are all similar permutations.

It may happen in particular cases that s and $t^{-1}st$ are the same permutation. When this is so, t and s are *permutable*, that is, st and ts are equivalent to one another; for if

$$s = t^{-1}st,$$

then $$ts = st.$$

This will certainly be the case when none of the symbols that are interchanged by t are altered by s; but it may happen when s and t operate on the same symbols. Thus if

$$s = (ab)(cd), \quad t = (ac)(bd),$$

then $$st = (ad)(bc) = ts.$$

Ex. 1. Shew that every regular permutation is some power of a circular permutation.

Ex. 2. If s, s' are permutable regular permutations of the same mn letters of orders m and n, these numbers being relatively prime, shew that ss' is a circular permutation in the mn letters.

Ex. 3*. If

$$s = (123)(456)(789),$$
$$s_1 = (147)(258)(369),$$
$$s_2 = \qquad (456)(798),$$

shew that s is permutable with both s_1 and s_2, and that it can be formed by a combination of s_1 and s_2.

Ex. 4. Shew that the only permutations of n given letters which are permutable with a circular permutation of the n letters are the powers of the circular permutation.

Ex. 5. Determine all the permutations of the ten symbols involved in

$$s = (abcde)(\alpha\beta\gamma\delta\epsilon)$$

which are permutable with s.

11. A circular permutation of order two is called a *transposition*. It may be easily verified that

$$(pqr \ldots s) = (pq)(pr) \ldots (ps),$$

so that every circular permutation can be represented as a product of transpositions; and thence, since every permutation is the product of a number of circular permutations, every permutation can be represented as a product of transpositions. It must be remembered, however, that, in general, when a permutation is represented in this way, some of the letters will occur more than once in the symbol, so that the sequence in which the constituent transpositions occur is essential. There is thus a fundamental difference from the case when the symbol of a permutation is the product of circular permutations, no two of which contain a common letter.

Since

$$(p'q') = (pp')(pq')(pp'),$$

every transposition, and therefore every permutation of n letters, can be expressed in terms of the $n-1$ transpositions

$$(a_1a_2),\ (a_1a_3), \ldots,\ (a_1a_n).$$

* It is often convenient to use digits rather than letters for the purpose of illustration.

The number of different ways in which a given permutation may be represented as a product of transpositions is evidently unlimited; but it may be shewn that, however the representation is effected, the number of transpositions is either always even or always odd. To prove this, it is sufficient to consider the effect of a transposition on the square root of the discriminant of the n letters, which may be written

$$D = \prod_{r=1}^{r=n-1} \left\{ \prod_{s=r+1}^{s=n} (a_r - a_s) \right\}.$$

The transposition $(a_r a_s)$ changes the sign of the factor $a_r - a_s$. When q is less than either r or s, the transposition interchanges the factors $a_q - a_r$ and $a_q - a_s$; and when q is greater than either r or s, it interchanges the factors $a_r - a_q$ and $a_s - a_q$. When q lies between r and s, the pair of factors $a_r - a_q$ and $a_q - a_s$ are interchanged and are both changed in sign. Hence the effect of the single transposition on D is to change its sign. Since any permutation can be expressed as the product of a number of transpositions, the effect of any permutation on D must be either to leave it unaltered or to change its sign. If a permutation leaves D unaltered it must, when expressed as a product of transpositions in any way, contain an even number of transpositions; and if it changes the sign of D, every representation of it, as a product of transpositions, must contain an odd number of transpositions. Hence no permutation is capable of being expressed both by an even and by an odd number of transpositions.

A permutation is spoken of as *odd* or *even*, according as the transpositions which enter into its representation are odd or even in number.

Further, an even permutation can always be represented as a product of circular permutations of order three. For any even permutation of n letters can be represented as the product of an even number of the $n-1$ transpositions

$$(a_1 a_2),\ (a_1 a_3), \ldots,\ (a_1 a_n),$$

in appropriate sequence and with the proper number of occurrences; and the product of any consecutive pair of these $(a_1 a_r)(a_1 a_s)$ is the circular permutation $(a_1 a_r a_s)$.

Now
$$(a_1 a_2 a_s)(a_1 a_2 a_r)(a_1 a_2 a_s)^2$$
$$=(a_1 a_2 a_s)(a_1 a_2 a_r)(a_1 a_s a_2)$$
$$=(a_1 a_r a_s),$$

so that every circular permutation of order three displacing a_1, and therefore every even permutation of n letters, can be expressed in terms of the $n-2$ permutations

$$(a_1 a_2 a_3),\ (a_1 a_2 a_4), \ldots,\ (a_1 a_2 a_n)$$

and their powers.

Ex. 1. Shew that every even permutation of n letters can be expressed in terms of

$$(a_1 a_2 a_3),\ (a_1 a_4 a_5), \ldots\ldots,\ (a_1 a_{n-1} a_n),$$

when n is odd; and in terms of

$$(a_1 a_2 a_3),\ (a_1 a_4 a_5), \ldots\ldots,\ (a_1 a_{n-2} a_{n-1}),\ (a_1 a_2 a_n),$$

when n is even.

Ex. 2. If $n+1$ is odd and m is greater than 1, shew that every even permutation of $mn+1$ letters can be expressed in terms of

$$(a_1 a_2 \ldots\ldots a_{n+1}),\ (a_1 a_{n+2} \ldots\ldots a_{2n+1}), \ldots\ldots,\ (a_1 a_{(m-1)n+2} \ldots\ldots a_{mn+1});$$

and if $n+1$ is even, that every permutation of $mn+1$ letters can be expressed in terms of this set of m circular permutations.

The reader, who is not familiar with the notation explained in this chapter, may be advised to study in detail some of the simplest cases that present themselves. The permutations of four symbols are neither too simple nor too complicated for such a purpose. Moreover the fact that to each permutation of four symbols there corresponds a projective transformation of points in a plane, completely defined by the permutation of four arbitrarily chosen points, gives a geometrical interest to the discussion of this case.

CHAPTER II.

THE DEFINITION OF A GROUP.

12. In the present chapter we shall enter on our main subject and we shall begin with definitions, explanations and examples of what is meant by a group.

Definition. Let

$$A, B, C, \ldots$$

represent a set of operations, which can be performed on the same object or set of objects. Suppose this set of operations has the following characteristics.

(α) The operations of the set are all distinct, so that no two of them produce the same change in every possible application.

(β) The result of performing successively any number of operations of the set, say A, B,..., K, is another definite operation of the set, which depends only on the component operations and the sequence in which they are carried out, and not on the way in which they may be regarded as associated. Thus A followed by B and B followed by C are operations of the set, say D and E; and D followed by C is the same operation as A followed by E.

(γ) A being any operation of the set, there is always another operation A_{-1} belonging to the set, such that A followed by A_{-1} produces no change in any object. The operation A_{-1} is called the *inverse* of A.

The set of operations is then said to form a *Group*.

From the definition of the inverse of A given in (γ), it follows directly that A is the inverse of A_{-1}. For if A changes any object Ω into Ω', A_{-1} must change Ω' into Ω. Hence A_{-1} followed by A leaves Ω', and therefore every object, unchanged.

The operation resulting from the successive performance of the operations $A, B, \ldots, K$ in the sequence given is denoted by the symbol $AB\ldots K$; and if Ω is any object on which the operations may be performed, the result of carrying out this compound operation on Ω is denoted by $\Omega . AB\ldots K$.

If the component operations are all the same, say A, and r in number, the abbreviation A^r will be used for the resultant operation, and it will be called the rth *power* of A.

Definition. Two operations, A and B, are said to be *permutable* when AB and BA are the same operation.

13. If AB and AC are the same operation, so also are $A_{-1}AB$ and $A_{-1}AC$. But the operation $A_{-1}A$ produces no change in any object and therefore $A_{-1}AB$ and B, producing the same change in every object, are the same operation. Hence B and C are the same operation.

This is expressed symbolically by saying that, if

$$AB = AC,$$

then

$$B = C;$$

the sign of equality being used to imply that the symbols represent the same operation.

In a similar way, if

$$BA = CA,$$

it follows that

$$B = C.$$

From conditions (β) and (γ), AA_{-1} must be a definite operation of the group. This operation, by definition, produces no change in any possible object, and it must, by condition (α), be unique. It is called the *identical* operation. It will always be represented by E, and if A be any other operation, then

$$EA = AE = A,$$

and for every integer r,

$$E^r = E.$$

14. The number of distinct operations contained in a group may be either finite or infinite. When the number is infinite, the group may contain operations which produce an infinitesimal change in every possible object or operand.

Thus the totality of distinct displacements of a rigid body evidently forms a group, for they satisfy conditions (α), (β) and (γ) of the definition. Moreover this group contains operations of the kind in question, namely infinitesimal twists; and each operation of the group can be constructed by the continual repetition of a suitably chosen infinitesimal twist.

Next, the set of translations, that arise by shifting a cube parallel to its edges through distances which are any multiples of an edge, forms a group containing an infinite number of operations; but this group contains no operation which effects an infinitesimal change in the position of the cube.

As a third example, consider the set of displacements by which a complete right circular cone is brought to coincidence with itself. It consists of rotations through any angle about the axis of the cone, and rotations through two right angles about any line through the vertex at right angles to the axis. Once again this set of displacements satisfies the conditions (α), (β) and (γ) of the definition and forms a group.

This last group contains infinitesimal operations, namely rotations round the axis through an infinitesimal angle; and every finite rotation round the axis can be formed by the continued repetition of an infinitesimal rotation. There is however in this case no infinitesimal displacement of the group by whose continued repetition a rotation through two right angles about a line through the vertex at right angles to the axis can be constructed. Of these three groups with an infinite number of operations, the first is said to be a *continuous* group, the second a *discontinuous* group, and the third a *mixed* group.

Continuous groups and mixed groups lie entirely outside the plan of the present treatise; and though, later on, some of the properties of discontinuous groups with an infinite number of operations will be considered, such groups will be approached from a point of view suggested by the treatment of groups containing a finite number of operations. We pass on then at once to the case of groups which contain a finite number only of distinct operations.

15. Definition. If the number of distinct operations contained in a group be finite, the number is called the *order* of the group.

Let S be an operation of a group of finite order N. Then the infinite series of operations

$$S, S^2, S^3, \ldots\ldots$$

must all be contained in the group, and therefore a finite number of them only can be distinct. If S^{m+n} is the first of the series which is the same as one that precedes it, say S^n, and if $S^n{}_{-1}$ is the operation inverse to S^n, then

$$S^{m+n} S^n{}_{-1} = S^n S^n{}_{-1} = E,$$

or

$$S^m = E.$$

Exactly as in § 8, it may be shewn that, if

$$S^\mu = E,$$

μ must be a multiple of m, and that the operations $S, S^2, \ldots\ldots, S^{m-1}$ are all distinct.

Since the group contains only N distinct operations, m must be equal to or less than N. It will be seen later that, if m is less than N, it must be a factor of N.

The integer m is called the *order* of the operation S. The order m' of the operation S^x is the least integer for which

$$S^{xm'} = E,$$

that is, for which

$$xm' \equiv 0 \,(\text{mod. } m).$$

Hence, if g is the greatest common factor of x and m,

$$gm' = m.$$

In particular, if m is prime, all the powers of S, whose indices are less than m, are of order m.

Since

$$S^x S^{m-x} = S^m = E, \quad (x < m),$$

and

$$S^x (S^x)_{-1} = E,$$

it follows that

$$(S^x)_{-1} = S^{m-x}.$$

If now a meaning be attached to S^{-x}, by assuming that the equation

$$S^{x+y} = S^x S^y$$

holds when either x or y is a negative integer, then

$$S^{m-x} = S^m S^{-x} = S^{-x},$$

and
$$(S^x)_{-1} = S^{-x},$$

so that S^{-x} denotes the inverse of the operation S^x.

Ex. If $S_a, S_b, \ldots\ldots, S_c, S_d$ are operations of a group, shew that the operation inverse to $S_a^{\alpha} S_b^{\beta} \ldots\ldots S_c^{\gamma} S_d^{\delta}$ is $S_d^{-\delta} S_c^{-\gamma} \ldots\ldots S_b^{-\beta} S_a^{-\alpha}$.

16. If
$$S_1 (= E),\ S_2,\ S_3, \ldots,\ S_N$$
are the N operations of a group of order N, the set of N operations
$$S_r S_1,\ S_r S_2,\ S_r S_3 \ldots,\ S_r S_N$$
are (§ 13) all distinct; and their number is equal to the order of the group. Hence every operation of the group occurs once and only once in this set.

Similarly every operation of the group occurs once and only once in the set
$$S_1 S_r,\ S_2 S_r,\ S_3 S_r, \ldots,\ S_N S_r.$$

Every operation of the group can therefore be represented as the product of two operations of the group, and either the first factor or the second factor can be chosen at will.

A relation of the form
$$S_p = S_q S_r$$
between three operations of the group will not in general involve any necessary relation between the order of S_p and the orders of S_q and S_r. If however the two latter are permutable the relation requires that, for all values of x,
$$S_p^x = S_q^x S_r^x;$$
and in that case the order of S_p is equal to or is a factor of the least common multiple of the orders of S_q and S_r.

Suppose now that S, an operation of the group, is of order mn, where m and n are relatively prime. Then we may shew that, of the various ways in which S may be represented as the product of two operations of the group, there is just one in which the operations are permutable and of orders m and n respectively.

Thus let
$$S^n = M,$$
and
$$S^m = N,$$
so that M, N are operations of orders m and n. Since S^m and S^n are permutable, so also are M and N, and powers of M and N.

If x_0, y_0 are integers satisfying the equation
$$xn + ym = 1,$$
every other integral solution is given by
$$x = x_0 + tm, \quad y = y_0 - tn,$$
where t is an integer.

Now
$$M^x N^y = S^{xn+ym} = S;$$
and since x and m are relatively prime, as also are y and n, M^x and N^y are permutable operations of orders m and n, so that S is expressed in the desired form.

Moreover, it is the only expression of this form; for let
$$S = M_1 N_1,$$
where M_1 and N_1 are permutable and of orders m and n.

Then $S^n = M_1{}^n$, since $N_1{}^n = E$.

Hence
$$M_1{}^n = M,$$
or
$$M_1{}^{xn} = M^x,$$
or
$$M_1{}^{1-ym} = M^x.$$
But $M_1{}^m = E$, and therefore $M_1{}^{-ym} = E$; hence
$$M_1 = M^x.$$
In the same way it is shewn that N_1 is the same as N^y. The representation of S in the desired form is therefore unique.

17. Two given operations of a group successively performed give rise to a third operation of the group which, when the operations are of known concrete form, may be determined by actually carrying out the two given operations. Thus the set of finite rotations, which bring a regular solid to coincidence with itself, evidently form a group; and it is a purely geometrical problem to determine that particular rotation of the group which arises from the successive performance of two given rotations of the group.

When the operations are represented by symbols, the relation in question is represented by an equation of the form

$$AB = C;$$

but the equation indicates nothing of the nature of the actual operations. Now it may happen, when the operations of two groups of equal order are represented by symbols,

$$\text{(i)}\quad E,\ A,\ B,\ C, \ldots\ldots$$

$$\text{(ii)}\quad E',\ A',\ B',\ C', \ldots\ldots$$

that, to every relation of the form

$$AB = C$$

between operations of the first group, there corresponds the relation

$$A'B' = C'$$

between operations of the second group. In such a case, although the nature of the actual operations in the first group may be entirely different from the nature of those in the second, the laws according to which the operations of each group combine among themselves are identical. The following series of groups of operations, of order six, will at once illustrate the possibility just mentioned, and will serve as concrete examples to familiarize the reader with the conception of a group of operations.

I. *Group of inversions.* Let P, Q, R be three circles with a common radical axis and let each pair of them intersect at an angle $\frac{1}{3}\pi$. Denote the operations of inversion with respect to P, Q, R by U, V, W; and denote successive inversions at P, R and at P, Q by S and T. The object of operation may be any point in the plane of the circles, except the two common points in which they intersect. Then it is easy to verify, from the geometrical properties of inversion, that the operations

$$E,\ S,\ T,\ U,\ V,\ W$$

are all distinct, and that they form a group. For instance, VW represents successive inversions at Q and R. But successive inversions at Q and R produce the same displacement of points as successive inversions at P and Q, and therefore

$$VW = T.$$

II. *Group of rotations.* Let POP', QOQ', ROR' be three concurrent lines in a plane such that each of the angles POQ and QOR is $\frac{1}{3}\pi$, and let IOI' be a perpendicular to their plane. Denote by S a rotation round II' through $\frac{2}{3}\pi$ bringing PP' to $Q'Q$; and by T a rotation round II' through $\frac{4}{3}\pi$ bringing PP' to $R'R$. Denote also by U, V, W rotations through two right angles round PP', QQ', RR'. The object of the rotations may be any point or set of points in space. Then it may again be verified, by simple geometrical considerations, that the operations

$$E,\ S,\ T,\ U,\ V,\ W$$

are distinct and that they form a group.

III. *Group of linear transformations of a single variable.* The operation of replacing x by a given function $f(x)$ of itself is sometimes represented by the symbol $(x, f(x))$. With this notation, if

$$S=\left(x,\ \frac{1}{1-x}\right),\quad T=\left(x,\ \frac{x-1}{x}\right),\quad U=(x, 1-x),\quad V=\left(x,\ \frac{1}{x}\right),$$

$$W=\left(x,\ \frac{x}{x-1}\right),\quad E=(x,\ x),$$

it may again be verified without difficulty that these six operations form a group.

IV. *Group of linear transformations of two variables.* With a similar notation, the six operations

$$S=(x,\ \omega x\ ;\ y,\ \omega^2 y),\quad T=(x,\ \omega^2 x\ ;\ y,\ \omega y),\quad U=(x,\ \omega^2 y;\ y,\ \omega x),$$
$$V=(x,\ y\ ;\ y,\ x),\quad W=(x,\ \omega y\ ;\ y,\ \omega^2 x),\quad E=(x,\ x\ ;\ y,\ y)$$

form a group, if ω is an imaginary cube root of unity.

V. *Group of linear transformations to a prime modulus.* The six operations defined by

$$S=(x,\ x+1),\qquad T=(x,\ x+2),\qquad U=(x,\ 2x+2),$$
$$V=(x,\ 2x),\qquad W=(x,\ 2x+1),\qquad E=(x,\ x),$$

where each transformation is taken to modulus 3, form a group.

VI. *Group of permutations of 3 symbols.* The six permutations

$$E,\ S=(xyz),\quad T=(xzy),\quad U=x\,(yz),\quad V=y\,(zx),\quad W=z\,(xy)$$

are the only permutations that can be formed with three symbols; they must therefore form a group.

VII. *Group of permutations of 6 symbols.* The permutations

$$E,\ S=(xyz)(abc),\quad T=(xzy)(acb),\quad U=(xb)(ya)(zc),$$
$$V=(xa)(yc)(zb),\quad W=(xc)(yb)(za)$$

may be verified to form a group.

VIII. *Group of permutations of 6 symbols.* The permutations

$$E,\ S=(xaybzc),\quad T=(xyz)(abc),\quad U=(xb)(yc)(za),$$
$$V=(xzy)(acb),\quad W=(xczbya)$$

form a group.

The operations in the first seven of these groups, as well as the objects of operation, are quite different from one group to another; but it may be shewn that the laws according to which the operations, denoted by the same letters in the different groups, combine together are identical for all seven. There is no difficulty in verifying that in each instance

$$S^3=E,\quad T=S^2,\quad U^2=E,\quad V=SU=US^2,\quad W=S^2U=US;$$

and from these relations the complete system, according to which the six operations in each of the seven groups combine together, may be at once constructed. This is given by the following multiplication table, where the left-hand vertical column gives the first factor and the top horizontal line the second factor in each product; thus the table is to be read $SE=S$, $ST=E$, $SU=V$, and so on.

	E	S	T	U	V	W
E	E	S	T	U	V	W
S	S	T	E	V	W	U
T	T	E	S	W	U	V
U	U	W	V	E	T	S
V	V	U	W	S	E	T
W	W	V	U	T	S	E

But, though the operations of the seventh and eighth groups are of the same nature and though the operands are identical, the laws according to which the six operations combine together are quite distinct for the two groups. Thus, for the last group, it may be shewn that

$$T=S^2, \quad U=S^3, \quad V=S^4, \quad W=S^5, \quad S^6=E,$$

so that the operations of this group may, in fact, be represented by

$$E, S, S^2, S^3, S^4, S^5.$$

18. If we pay no attention to the nature of the actual operations and operands, and consider only the number of the former and the laws according to which they combine, the first seven groups of the preceding paragraph are identical with each other. From this point of view a group, abstractly considered, is completely defined by its multiplication table; and, conversely, the multiplication table must implicitly contain all properties of the group which are independent of any special mode of representation.

It is of course obvious that this table cannot be arbitrarily constructed. Thus, if

$$AB=P \text{ and } BC=Q,$$

the entry in the table for PC must be the same as that for AQ. Except in the very simplest cases, the attempt to form a consistent multiplication table, merely by trial, would be most laborious.

The very existence of the table shews that the symbols denoting the different operations of the group are not all independent of each other; and since the number of symbols is finite, it follows that there must exist a set of symbols $S_1, S_2, \ldots, S_n$ no one of which can be expressed in terms of the remainder, while every operation of the group is expressible in terms of the set. Such a set is called a set of *fundamental* or *generating* operations of the group. Moreover though no one of the generating operations can be expressed in terms of the remainder, there must be relations of the general form

$$S_m{}^a S_n{}^b \ldots\ldots S_p{}^c = E$$

among them, as otherwise the group would be of infinite order; and the number of these relations, which are independent of one another, must be finite. Among them there necessarily occur the relations

$$S_1^{a_1} = E, \quad S_2^{a_2} = E, \ldots\ldots, \quad S_n^{a_n} = E,$$

giving the orders of the fundamental operations.

We thus arrive at a virtually new conception of a group; it can be regarded as arising from a finite number of fundamental operations connected by a finite number of independent relations. But it is to be noted that there is no reason for supposing that such an origin for a group is unique; indeed, in general, it is not so. Thus there is no difficulty in verifying that the group, whose multiplication table is given in § 17, is completely specified either by the system of relations

$$S^3 = E, \quad U^2 = E, \quad (SU)^2 = E, \quad \text{ie generators}$$
$$\text{+ relations.}$$

or by the system

$$U^2 = E, \quad V^2 = E, \quad (UV)^3 = E.$$

In other words, it may be generated by two operations of orders 2 and 3, or by two operations of order 2. So also the last group of § 17 is specified either by

$$S^6 = E,$$

or by

$$T^3 = E, \quad U^2 = E, \quad TU = UT.$$

19. Definition. Let G and G' be two groups of equal order. If a correspondence can be established between the operations of G and G', so that to every operation of G there corresponds a single operation of G' and to every operation of G' there corresponds a single operation of G, while to the product AB of any two operations of G there corresponds the product $A'B'$ of the two corresponding operations of G', the groups G and G' are said to be *simply isomorphic**. Two simply isomorphic groups are, abstractly considered, identical.

In discussing the properties of groups, some definite mode of representation is, in general, indispensable; and as long as we are dealing with the properties of a group *per se,* and not with properties which depend on the form of representation, the group may, if convenient, be replaced by

---

* We shall sometimes use the phrase that two groups are of the same *type* to denote that they are simply isomorphic.

any group which is simply isomorphic with it. For the discussion of such properties, it would be most natural to suppose the group given either by its multiplication table or by its fundamental operations and the relations connecting them. Unfortunately, however, these purely abstract modes of representing a group are by no means the easiest to deal with. It thus becomes an important question to determine as far as possible what different concrete forms of representation any particular group may be capable of; and we shall accordingly end the present chapter with a demonstration of the following general theorem bearing on this question.

20. THEOREM. *Every group of finite order N can be represented as a group of regular permutations of N symbols**.

Let
$$S_1 (=E),\ S_2,\ldots,\ S_i,\ldots,\ S_N$$
be the N operations of the group. Then
$$S_1S_i,\ S_2S_i,\ldots,\ S_i^2,\ldots,\ S_NS_i$$
are the N operations in some altered sequence, and
$$\begin{pmatrix} S_1 & , S_2 & ,\ldots, & S_i & ,\ldots, & S_N \\ S_1S_i, & S_2S_i, & \ldots, & S_i^2, & \ldots, & S_NS_i \end{pmatrix}$$
is a permutation s_i performed on the symbols of the N operations. If m is the order of S_i, this permutation replaces
$$S_p \text{ by } S_pS_i,\quad S_pS_i \text{ by } S_pS_i^2,\ldots,\text{ and } S_pS_i^{m-1} \text{ by } S_p,$$
whatever operation S_p may be. It is therefore a regular permutation of the N symbols. Moreover it may clearly be represented in the abbreviated form
$$\begin{pmatrix} S \\ SS_i \end{pmatrix}.$$
Corresponding to the N operations of the group there thus arises a set of N regular permutations on the N symbols, viz.
$$s_i \text{ or } \begin{pmatrix} S \\ SS_i \end{pmatrix},\quad (i=1, 2,\ldots, N).$$
The N permutations are all distinct: for if
$$s_i = s_j,$$
then
$$\begin{pmatrix} S \\ SS_i \end{pmatrix} = \begin{pmatrix} S \\ SS_j \end{pmatrix},$$
and
$$S_i = S_j.$$

* Jordan, *Traité des Substitutions* (1870), pp. 60, 61.

Moreover the product of any two of the permutations is another permutation of the set; for

$$s_i s_j = \begin{pmatrix} S \\ SS_i \end{pmatrix} \begin{pmatrix} S \\ SS_j \end{pmatrix} = \begin{pmatrix} S \\ SS_i \end{pmatrix} \begin{pmatrix} SS_i \\ SS_i S_j \end{pmatrix}$$

$$= \begin{pmatrix} S \\ SS_i S_j \end{pmatrix} = \begin{pmatrix} S \\ SS_r \end{pmatrix} = s_r,$$

if $S_i S_j = S_r$.

Hence the N regular permutations constitute a group of regular permutations simply isomorphic with the given group. This group has been arrived at by what may be called *post-multiplication*, i.e. in forming the permutation that corresponds to S_i, viz. $\begin{pmatrix} S \\ SS_i \end{pmatrix}$, S_i has been taken as the second factor. If *pre-multiplication* be used, and the regular permutation

$$\begin{pmatrix} S_1 \;, & S_2 \;,\ldots, & S_i \;,\ldots, & S_N \\ S_i^{-1}S_1, & S_i^{-1}S_2,\ldots, & S_i^{-1}S_i,\ldots, & S_i^{-1}S_N \end{pmatrix}$$

or

$$\begin{pmatrix} S \\ S_i^{-1}S \end{pmatrix}$$

be denoted by s_i'; then, again, corresponding to the N operations of the group there arises a set of N regular permutations, viz.

$$s_i' \text{ or } \begin{pmatrix} S \\ S_i^{-1}S \end{pmatrix}, \; (i = 1, 2, \ldots, N),$$

which are as before all distinct. Moreover the product of any two permutations of this set is another of the set; for

$$s_i' s_j' = \begin{pmatrix} S \\ S_i^{-1}S \end{pmatrix} \begin{pmatrix} S \\ S_j^{-1}S \end{pmatrix} = \begin{pmatrix} S \\ S_i^{-1}S \end{pmatrix} \begin{pmatrix} S_i^{-1}S \\ S_j^{-1}S_i^{-1}S \end{pmatrix}$$

$$= \begin{pmatrix} S \\ S_j^{-1}S_i^{-1}S \end{pmatrix} = \begin{pmatrix} S \\ S_r^{-1}S \end{pmatrix} = s_r',$$

if $S_i S_j = S_r$.

This second set of permutations therefore constitute a group of regular permutations of the N symbols simply isomorphic with the given group.

The two representations of a group of order N as a group of regular permutations of N symbols are in general different from each other. In fact, if

$$s_i = s_j'$$

then
$$\begin{pmatrix} S \\ SS_i \end{pmatrix} = \begin{pmatrix} S \\ S_j^{-1}S \end{pmatrix},$$
and
$$SS_i = S_j^{-1}S,$$
for each operation S of the group. Hence
$$S_i = S_j^{-1},$$
and
$$SS_i = S_iS,$$
or S_i must be permutable with every operation of the group. The two groups will therefore consist of the same permutations only when every pair of operations of the group are permutable. The two groups moreover have the remarkable property that every permutation of the one is permutable with every permutation of the other. Thus
$$s_i s_j' = \begin{pmatrix} S \\ SS_i \end{pmatrix}\begin{pmatrix} S \\ S_j^{-1}S \end{pmatrix} = \begin{pmatrix} S \\ S_j^{-1}SS_i \end{pmatrix} = s_j' s_i.$$

Further, since the N permutations of the second group change S_1 respectively into each of the symbols $S_1, S_2, \ldots, S_N$, if there were another permutation permutable with every permutation of the first group and changing S_1 into S_i, there would be a permutation leaving S_1 unchanged and permutable with every permutation of the first group. But such a permutation must obviously leave each of the symbols unchanged. Hence the N permutations of the second group are the only ones which are permutable with every permutation of the first.

21. It will be seen later that there are many other concrete forms in which it is always possible to represent a group of finite order. None, however, are so directly and simply related to the multiplication table of the group as the representation in the form of a regular permutation group.

CHAPTER III.

ON THE SIMPLER PROPERTIES OF A GROUP WHICH ARE INDEPENDENT OF ITS MODE OF REPRESENTATION.

22. In this chapter we proceed to discuss some of the simplest of the properties of groups of finite order which are independent of their mode of representation.

If among the operations of a group G a certain set can be chosen which do not exhaust all the operations of the group G, yet which at the same time satisfy all the conditions of § 12 so that they form another group H, this group H is called a *sub-group* of the group G. Thus if S be any operation, order m, of G, the operations

$$E, S, S^2, \ldots\ldots, S^{m-1}$$

evidently form a group; and when the order of G is greater than m, this group is a sub-group of G. A sub-group of this nature, which consists of the different powers of a single operation, is called a *cyclical sub-group*; and a group, which consists of the different powers of a single operation, is called a *cyclical group*.

Theorem I. *If H is a sub-group of G, the order n of H is a factor of the order N of G.*

Let $$T_1 (=E),\ T_2, \ldots\ldots, T_n$$

be the n operations of H; and let S_2 be any operation of G which is not contained in H.

Then the operations

$$T_1 S_2,\ T_2 S_2, \ldots\ldots, T_n S_2$$

are all distinct from each other and from the operations of H.

For if
$$T_p S_2 = T_q S_2,$$
then
$$T_p = T_q,$$
contrary to supposition; and if
$$T_p = T_q S_2,$$
then
$$S_2 = T_q^{-1} T_p,$$
and S_2 would be contained among the operations of H.

If the $2n$ operations thus obtained do not exhaust all the operations of G, let S_3 be any operation of G not contained among them.

Then it may be shewn, by repeating the previous reasoning, that the n operations
$$T_1 S_3,\ T_2 S_3, \ldots\ldots,\ T_n S_3$$
are all different from each other and from the previous $2n$ operations. If the group G is still not exhausted, this process may be repeated; so that finally the N operations of G can be exhibited in the form
$$\begin{array}{llll} T_1 &, T_2 &, \ldots\ldots, & T_n \ ; \\ T_1 S_2 &, T_2 S_2 &, \ldots\ldots, & T_n S_2 \ ; \\ T_1 S_3 &, T_2 S_3 &, \ldots\ldots, & T_n S_3 \ ; \\ \multicolumn{4}{c}{\ldots\ldots\ldots\ldots\ldots\ldots\ldots\ldots} \\ T_1 S_m &, T_2 S_m &, \ldots\ldots, & T_n S_m . \end{array}$$
Hence $N = mn$, and n is therefore a factor of N.

Corollary. If S is an operation of G, the order n of S is a factor of the order N of G.

For the order of S is also the order of the cyclical sub-group generated by S.

When N is a prime p, the group G can have no sub-group other than one of order unity consisting of the identical operation alone. Every operation S of the group, other than the identical operation, is of order p, and the group consists of the operations
$$E,\ S,\ S^2, \ldots\ldots,\ S^{p-1}.$$
A group whose order is prime is therefore necessarily cyclical.

The set of operations
$$T_1 S_i,\ T_2 S_i\ , \ldots\ldots,\ T_n S_i,$$
where
$$T_1\ ,\ T_2\ , \ldots\ldots,\ T_n\ ,$$

constitute a group H, may be conveniently represented by the abbreviation HS_i. In using this notation it must be remembered that, H being a group, the operation S_i is in no way distinguished from the other operations of the set. In fact

$$T_1T_jS_i, \ T_2T_jS_i, \ldots\ldots, \ T_nT_jS_i$$

is the same set, so that

$$HS_i = HT_jS_i.$$

With this notation, when H is a sub-group of G, the operations of G may, *in respect of* H, be arranged in the sets

$$H, \ HS_2, \ldots\ldots, \ HS_m,$$

where mn is the order of G.

Moreover pre-multiplication instead of post-multiplication might have been used in forming the sets. Thus if U_i is an operation of G which does not belong to H, the operations

$$U_iT_1, \ U_iT_2, \ldots\ldots, \ U_iT_m$$

are distinct from each other and from the operations of H. The operations of G may thus also be arranged in the sets

$$H, \ U_2H, \ldots\ldots, \ U_mH.$$

These latter sets are however, except the first, in general quite different from those formed by post-multiplication. A similar notation will be found convenient even when

$$T_1, \ T_2, \ldots\ldots, \ T_n$$

do not constitute a group. If this set be denoted by the abbreviation R, then the sets

$$ST_1, \ ST_2, \ldots\ldots, \ ST_n,$$

and

$$T_1S, \ T_2S, \ldots\ldots, \ T_nS,$$

will be denoted by the abbreviations SR and RS respectively. In this more general case, however, S will not usually belong to either of the sets SR or RS; while SR and ST_jR (or RS and RT_jS) are not usually the same set.

23. THEOREM II. *The operations common to two groups G_1, G_2 themselves form a group g, whose order is a factor of the orders of G_1 and G_2.*

For if S, T are any two operations common to G_1 and G_2, ST is also common to both groups; and hence the common operations satisfy conditions (α) and (β) of the definition in § 12. But their orders are finite and they must therefore satisfy also condition (γ), and form a group g. Moreover g is a sub-group of both G_1 and G_2, and therefore by Theorem I its order is a factor of the orders of both these groups.

If G_1 and G_2 are sub-groups of a third group G, then g is also clearly a sub-group of G.

The set of operations, that arise by combining in every way the operations of the groups G_1 and G_2, evidently satisfy the conditions of § 12 and form a group; but this will not necessarily or generally be a group of finite order. If however G_1 and G_2 are sub-groups of a group G of finite order, the group g' that arises from their combination will necessarily be of finite order; it may either coincide with G or be a sub-group of G. In either case, the order of g' will be a multiple of the orders of G_1 and G_2.

It is convenient here to explain a notation that enables us to avoid an otherwise rather cumbrous phraseology. Let $S_1, S_2, S_3, \ldots\ldots$ be a given set of operations, and $G_1, G_2, \ldots\ldots$ a set of groups. Then the symbol

$$\{S_1, S_2, S_3, \ldots\ldots, G_1, G_2, \ldots\ldots\}$$

will be used to denote the group that arises by combining in every possible way the given operations and the operations of the given groups.

Thus, for instance, the group g' above would be represented by

$$\{G_1, G_2\};$$

the cyclical group that arises from the powers of an operation S by

$$\{S\};$$

and, as a further example, the sixth group of § 17 may be represented by

$$\{(xy), (xz)\}.$$

24. Definition. If S and T are any two operations of a group, the operations S and $T^{-1}ST$ are called *conjugate* operations; while $T^{-1}ST$ is spoken of as the result of *transforming* the operation S by T.

The two operations S and $T^{-1}ST$ are identical only when S and T are permutable. For if

$$S = T^{-1}ST,$$

then
$$TS = ST.$$

Two conjugate operations are always of the same order. For

$$(T^{-1}ST)^n = T^{-1}ST \,.\, T^{-1}ST \ldots\ldots T^{-1}ST$$
$$= T^{-1}S^nT.$$

Therefore, if
$$S^n = E,$$
$$(T^{-1}ST)^n = T^{-1}T = E;$$

and conversely, if
$$(T^{-1}ST)^n = E,$$

then
$$S^n = T \,.\, T^{-1}S^nT \,.\, T^{-1} = T(T^{-1}ST)^n\, T^{-1} = TT^{-1} = E.$$

The operations ST and TS are always conjugate and therefore of the same order; for

$$ST = T^{-1}T \,.\, ST = T^{-1} \,.\, TS \,.\, T.$$

Ex. Shew that the operations $S_1S_2\ldots\ldots S_{n-1}S_n$ and $S_rS_{r+1}\ldots\ldots S_nS_1\ldots\ldots S_{r-1}$ are conjugate within the group $\{S_1, S_2, \ldots\ldots, S_n\}$.

Definitions. An operation S of a group G, which is identical with all its conjugate operations, is called a *self-conjugate* operation. Such an operation must evidently be permutable with each of the operations of G. ie S in the centre of G.

If every pair of operations of a group are permutable, every operation is self-conjugate. Such a group is called an *Abelian* group.

If all the operations of a group be transformed by a given operation, the set of transformed operations form a group. For if T_1 and T_2 are any two operations of the group, so that T_1T_2 is also an operation of the group, then

$$S^{-1}T_1S \,.\, S^{-1}T_2S = S^{-1}T_1T_2S;$$

hence the product of any two operations of the transformed set is another operation belonging to the transformed set, and the set therefore forms a group. Moreover the preceding equation shews that the new group is simply isomorphic to the original group. If G is the given group, the symbol

this is inner automorphism.

$S^{-1}GS$ will be used for the new group. When S belongs to the group G, the groups G and $S^{-1}GS$ are evidently the same.

Now unless S is a self-conjugate operation of G, the pairs of operations T and $S^{-1}TS$ will not all be identical when for T the different operations of G are put in succession. Hence the process of transforming all the operations of a group by one of themselves is equivalent to establishing a correspondence between the operations of the group, which exhibits it as simply isomorphic with itself.

Definitions. When H is a sub-group of G and S is any operation of G, the groups H and $S^{-1}HS$ are called *conjugate* sub-groups of G.

If H and $S^{-1}HS$ are identical, S is said to be permutable with the sub-group H. This does not necessarily involve that S is permutable with each of the operations of H.

If H and $S^{-1}HS$ are identical, whatever operation S is of G, H is said to be a *self-conjugate* sub-group of G.

A group is called *composite* or *simple*, according as it does or does not possess at least one self-conjugate sub-group other than that formed of the identical operation alone.

Every sub-group of an Abelian group is a self-conjugate sub-group.

When H is a self-conjugate sub-group of G, the sets into which the operations of G fall, in respect of H, by pre-multiplication and by post-multiplication are the same.

For since
$$S_i^{-1}HS_i = H,$$
$$HS_i = S_iH,$$
whatever operation of G S_i may be.

Conversely, if the sets into which the operations of G fall in respect of H by pre- and post-multiplication are the same, H must be a self-conjugate sub-group. In fact, if the sets
$$H,\ HS_2, \ldots\ldots,\ HS_m,$$
and
$$H,\ U_2H, \ldots\ldots,\ U_mH,$$
are the same (except of course as regards sequence), then for each i it must be possible to find j so that
$$U_iH = HS_j,$$
or
$$H = U_i^{-1}S_j \,.\, S_j^{-1}HS_j.$$

Since $S_j^{-1}HS_j$ is a group and H is a group, $U_i^{-1}S_j$ must belong to the group $S_j^{-1}HS_j$, and therefore

$$H = S_j^{-1}HS_j,$$

for every j; in other words, H is a self-conjugate sub-group of G.

25. THEOREM III. *The operations of a group G, which are permutable with a given operation T, form a sub-group H; and the order of G divided by the order of H is the number of operations conjugate to T*.* ce the centralizer of T. or normalizer of T.

If R_1 and R_2 are any two operations permutable with T, so that $$R_1T = TR_1 \text{ and } R_2T = TR_2;$$
then $$R_1R_2T = R_1TR_2 = TR_1R_2,$$

and therefore R_1R_2 is permutable with T. The operations permutable with T therefore form a group H. Let m be its order and

$$R_1(=E), R_2,\ldots, R_m$$

its operations. Then if S is any operation of G not contained in H, the operations

$$R_1S, R_2S,\ldots\ldots, R_{m-1}S, R_mS$$

all transform T into the same operation T'.

For $$(R_iS)^{-1}TR_iS = S^{-1}R_i^{-1}TR_iS = S^{-1}TS.$$

Also the m operations thus obtained are the only operations which transform T into T'; for if

$$S'^{-1}TS' = T',$$

then $$SS'^{-1}TS'S^{-1} = ST'S^{-1} = T;$$ $S'S^{-1} = R_i$ $S' = R_iS$.

and therefore $S'S^{-1}$ belongs to H. The number of operations which transform T into any operation conjugate to it is therefore equal to the number that transform T into itself, that is, to the order of H. If then N is the order of G, the operations of G may be divided into N/m sets of m each, such that the operations of each set transform T into a distinct operation, those of the first set, namely the operations of H, transforming T into itself. The number of operations conjugate to T, including itself, is therefore N/m.

---

* Among these T is of course included.

\# el. conj. to T = $|G : N(T)|$.

Since $$T = ST'S^{-1},$$

therefore $$R_i^{-1}TR_i = R_i^{-1}ST'S^{-1}R_i;$$

hence $T' = S^{-1}TS = S^{-1}R_i^{-1}TR_iS = S^{-1}R_i^{-1}S \,.\, T' \,.\, S^{-1}R_iS,$

so that every operation of the form $S^{-1}R_iS$ is permutable with T'. Hence if H is the group of operations permutable with T, and if

$$S^{-1}TS = T',$$

then $S^{-1}HS$ is the group of operations permutable with T'.

THEOREM IV. *The operations of a group G which are permutable with a sub-group H form a sub-group I, which is either identical with H or contains H as a self-conjugate sub-group. The order of G divided by the order of I is the number of sub-groups conjugate to H**. $I = N(H) \supseteq H,\ N(H) \triangleright H.$

If S_1, S_2 are any two operations of G which are permutable with H, then

$$S_1^{-1}HS_1 = H,\ S_2^{-1}HS_2 = H,$$

and therefore $$S_2^{-1}S_1^{-1}HS_1S_2 = H,$$

so that S_1S_2 is permutable with H. The operations of G which are permutable with H therefore form a group I, which may be identical with H and, if not identical with H, must contain it. Also, if S is any operation of I,

$$S^{-1}HS = H,$$

and therefore H is a self-conjugate sub-group of I.

If now Σ is any operation of G not contained in I, it may be shewn, exactly as in the proof of Theorem III, that the operations $I\Sigma$ and no others transform H into a conjugate sub-group H' which is not identical with H; and therefore that the number of sub-groups in the conjugate set to which H belongs is the order of G divided by the order of I. □

The operations of G which are permutable with H' may also be shewn to form the group $\Sigma^{-1}I\Sigma$.

It is perhaps not superfluous to point out that two distinct conjugate sub-groups may have some operations in common with one another.

* Among these sub-groups H is included.

subgroups conj. to $H = |G:N(H)|$.

26. Let S_1 be any operation of G, and

$$S_1, S_2, \ldots\ldots, S_h$$

the distinct operations obtained on transforming S_1 by every operation of G. The number, h, of these operations is, by Theorem III, a factor of N, the order of G. Moreover if, instead of transforming S_1, we transform any other operation of the set, S_i, by every operation of G, the same set of h distinct operations of G will result. Such a set of operations we call a *complete set* of conjugate operations. If T is any operation of G which does not belong to this complete set of conjugate operations, no operation that is conjugate to T can belong to the set. Hence the operations of G may be distributed into a number of distinct sets such that every operation belongs to one set and no operation belongs to more than one set; while any set forms by itself a complete set of conjugate operations. If r is the number of complete sets of conjugate operations and $h_1, h_2, \ldots\ldots, h_r$ are the numbers of operations in the different sets, then

$$N = h_1 + h_2 + \ldots\ldots + h_r;$$

and, since the identical operation is self-conjugate, one at least of the h's must be unity.

Similarly, if H_1 is any sub-group of G, and

$$H_1, H_2, \ldots\ldots, H_p$$

the distinct sub-groups obtained on transforming H_1 by every operation of G, we call the set a *complete set* of conjugate sub-groups. If K is a sub-group of G not contained in the set, no sub-group conjugate to K can belong to the set. If the operation S_1 belongs to one or more of a complete set of conjugate sub-groups, $\Sigma^{-1}S_1\Sigma$ must also belong to one or more sub-groups of the set, Σ being any operation of G. Hence among the operations contained in the complete set of conjugate sub-groups, the complete set of conjugate operations

$$S_1, S_2, \ldots\ldots, S_h$$

occurs.

No sub-group of G can contain operations belonging to every one of the complete sets of conjugate operations of G. For if such a sub-group H existed, the complete set of conjugate sub-groups, to which H belongs, would contain all the operations of G. Let m be the order of H and n $(\geqslant m)$ the order of the sub-group I formed of those operations of G which are permutable with H. Then H is one of N/n conjugate sub-groups, each of which contains m operations. The identical operation is common to all these sub-groups, and they therefore cannot contain more than

$$1+\frac{N(m-1)}{n}$$

distinct operations in all. This number is less than N, and therefore the complete set of conjugate sub-groups cannot contain all the operations of G.

27. If a group contains self-conjugate operations, it must contain self-conjugate sub-groups. For the cyclical sub-group generated by any self-conjugate operation must be self-conjugate. The only exception to this statement is the case of the cyclical groups of prime order. Every operation of such a group is clearly self-conjugate; but since the cyclical sub-group generated by any operation coincides with the group itself, there can be no self-conjugate sub-group*.

If every operation of a group is not self-conjugate, or, in other words, if the operations of a group are not all permutable with each other, the totality of the self-conjugate operations forms a self-conjugate sub-group. For, if S_1 and S_2 are permutable with every operation of the group, so also is S_1S_2. This sub-group has been called the *central* of the group.

THEOREM V. *The operations common to a complete set of conjugate sub-groups form a self-conjugate sub-group.*

It is an immediate consequence of Theorem II that the operations common to a complete set of conjugate sub-groups form a sub-group. The set of conjugate sub-groups, when transformed by any operation of the group, is changed into itself. Hence their common sub-group must be self-conjugate.

It may of course happen that the identical operation is the only one which is common to every sub-group of the set.

* Strictly speaking, this statement should be qualified by the addition "except that formed by the identical operation alone." No real ambiguity however will be introduced by always leaving this exception unexpressed.

Corollary. The operations permutable with each of a complete set of conjugate sub-groups form a self-conjugate sub-group.

For, if the operations permutable with the sub-group H form a sub-group I, the operations permutable with every sub-group of the conjugate set to which H belongs are the operations common to every sub-group of the conjugate set to which I belongs.

Further, the operations which are permutable with every operation of a complete set of conjugate sub-groups form a self-conjugate sub-group.

THEOREM VI. *If $T_1, T_2, \ldots, T_h$ are a complete set of conjugate operations of G, the group $\{T_1, T_2, \ldots, T_h\}$, if it does not coincide with G, is a self-conjugate sub-group of G; and it is the self-conjugate sub-group of smallest order that contains T_1.*

Since the operations $T_1, T_2, \ldots, T_h$ are merely rearranged in a new sequence when the set is transformed by any operation of G, it follows that

$$S^{-1}\{T_1, T_2, \ldots, T_h\} S = \{T_1, T_2, \ldots, T_h\},$$

whatever operation of G may be represented by S. Hence $\{T_1, T_2, \ldots, T_h\}$ is a self-conjugate sub-group. Also any self-conjugate sub-group of G that contains T_1 must contain $T_2, T_3, \ldots, T_h$; and therefore any self-conjugate sub-group of G which contains T_1 must contain $\{T_1, T_2, \ldots, T_h\}$.

In exactly the same way it may be shewn that, if

$$H_1, H_2, \ldots, H_s$$

form a complete set of conjugate sub-groups of G, the group $\{H_1, H_2, \ldots, H_s\}$, if it does not coincide with G, is the smallest self-conjugate sub-group of G which contains the sub-group H_1.

The theorem just proved suggests a process for determining whether any given group is simple or composite. To this end, the groups $\{T_1, T_2, \ldots, T_h\}$ corresponding to each set of conjugate operations in the group are formed. If any one of them differs from the group itself, it is a self-conjugate sub-group and the group is composite; but if each group so formed coincides with the original group, the latter is simple. If the order of T_1 contains more than one prime factor and if T_1^m is of prime order, it is easy to see that the distinct operations of the set $T_1^m, T_2^m, \ldots, T_h^m$ form a complete set of conjugate operations, and that the group $\{T_1, T_2, \ldots, T_h\}$ contains the group $\{T_1^m, T_2^m, \ldots, T_h^m\}$. Hence practically it is sufficient to form the groups $\{T_1, T_2, \ldots, T_h\}$ for all conjugate sets of operations whose orders are prime.

With the notation of § 26 (p. 33), the order of any self-conjugate sub-group of G must be of the form $h_\alpha + h_\beta + \ldots\ldots$; for if the sub-group contains any given operation, it must contain all the operations conjugate with it. Moreover one at least of the numbers $h_\alpha, h_\beta, \ldots\ldots$ must be unity, since the sub-group must contain the identical operation. It may happen that the numbers h_i are such that the only factors of N of the form $h_\alpha + h_\beta + \ldots\ldots$, one of the h's being unity, are N itself and unity. When this is the case, G is necessarily a simple group. It must not however be inferred that, if N has factors of this form, other than N itself and unity, then G is necessarily composite.

If G_1 and G_2 are sub-groups of G, it has already been seen (§ 23) that the operations common to G_1 and G_2 form a sub-group g of G; and it is now obvious that, when G_1 and G_2 are self-conjugate sub-groups, so also is g. Moreover the group $\{G_1, G_2\}$ is a self-conjugate sub-group unless it coincides with G. For

$$S^{-1}\{G_1, G_2\}S = \{S^{-1}G_1S, S^{-1}G_2S\} = \{G_1, G_2\}.$$

Again, with the same notation, if T_1 is an operation of G not contained in the self-conjugate sub-group G_1, and if $T_1, T_2, \ldots, T_h$ is a complete set of conjugate operations, the group $\{G_1, T_1, T_2, \ldots, T_h\}$ is a self-conjugate sub-group, unless it coincides with G.

Definitions. If G_1, a self-conjugate sub-group of G, is such that the group

$$\{G_1, T_1, T_2, \ldots, T_h\}$$

coincides with G, when $T_1, T_2, \ldots, T_h$ is any complete set of conjugate operations not contained in G_1, then G_1 is said to be a *maximum* self-conjugate sub-group of G. This does not imply that G_1 is the self-conjugate sub-group of G of absolutely greatest order; but that there is no self-conjugate sub-group of G, distinct from G itself, which contains G_1 and is of greater order than G_1.

If H is a sub-group of G, and if, for every operation S of G which does not belong to H, the group $\{H, S\}$ coincides with G, H is said to be a *maximum* sub-group of G.

28. **Definition.** When a correspondence can be established between the operations of a group G and the operations of a group G', whose order is smaller than the order of G, such that to each operation S of G there corresponds a single operation S' of G', while to the operation S_pS_q there corresponds the operation $S_p'S_q'$, the group G is said to be *multiply isomorphic* with the group G'.

THEOREM VII. *If a group G is multiply isomorphic with a group G', then* (i) *the operations of G, which correspond to the identical operation of G', form a self-conjugate sub-group of G;* (ii) *to each operation of G' there correspond the same number of operations of G;* (iii) *the order of any operation of G is equal to or is a multiple of the order of the corresponding operation of G';* and (iv) *the order of G is a multiple of the order of G'.*

Let $$S_1, S_2, \ldots, S_{n-1}, S_n$$

be the set of operations of G which correspond to the identical operation E' of G'. These operations must form a group, since to S_pS_q corresponds the operation $E'E'$, i.e. the identical operation of G'; and therefore S_pS_q must belong to the set.

Again, to the operation $T^{-1}S_pT$ of G corresponds the operation $T'^{-1}E'T'$, that is, the identical operation of G'. Hence, whatever operation of G is taken for T,

$$T^{-1}\{S_1, S_2, \ldots, S_n\}\,T = \{S_1, S_2, \ldots, S_n\}.$$

The sub-group H of G formed of the operations

$$S_1, S_2, \ldots, S_{n-1}, S_n$$

is therefore self-conjugate.

Again, if T and T_1 are two operations of G which correspond to the operation T' of G', the operation $T^{-1}T_1$ corresponds to the identical operation of G', and therefore belongs to H. Hence the operations that correspond to T' are all contained in the set TH. The operations of this set are all distinct and equal in number to the order of H. Hence if n is the order of H, to each operation of G' there correspond n operations of G.

If p is the order of T', so that p is the least index for which

$$T'^p = E',$$

then p is the least index for which the distinct operations of the set $(TH)^p$ belong to H.

Hence $$T^p = S_i,$$

where S_i is some operation of H; and therefore the order of T is equal to or is a multiple of p.

Finally, since to each operation of G there corresponds only one of G', while to each operation of G' there correspond n of G, the order of G is n times the order of G'.

To any sub-group of G' of order μ, there corresponds a sub-group of G of order μn. For if $T_p'T_q'$ forms one of the set

$$T_1', \ldots, T_p', \ldots, T_q', \ldots, T_\mu',$$

at least one, and therefore all, of the set $T_p T_q H$ must occur among

$$H, \ldots, T_p H, \ldots, T_q H, \ldots, T_\mu H,$$

and hence these operations form a group. Moreover, if the sub-group of G' is self-conjugate, so also is the corresponding sub-group of G.

It should be noticed that no correspondence is thus established between a sub-group of G which does not contain H and any sub-group of G'.

29. The group G' of the previous paragraph is completely determinate, that is to say, its multiplication table may be constructed, from a knowledge of the group G alone.

Let $$H, T_2 H, \ldots\ldots, T_m H$$

be the sets into which the operations of G fall in respect of H, mn being the order of G. Then

$$T_i H \,.\, T_j H = T_i T_j \,.\, T_j^{-1} H T_j H = T_i T_j H \,.\, H,$$

since H is a self-conjugate sub-group. Now the set $H.H$ gives each operation of H repeated n times, so that

$$T_iH.T_jH = nT_iT_jH;$$

and if T_iT_j belongs to the set T_kH, then T_iT_jH is the same set as T_kH. Therefore

$$T_iH.T_jH = nT_kH,$$

or

$$\frac{1}{n}T_iH.\frac{1}{n}T_jH = \frac{1}{n}T_kH.$$

The symbols $\frac{1}{n}T_iH \ (i = 1, 2, \ldots, m)$

therefore combine by multiplication according to exactly the same laws as the operations $T_i' \ (i = 1, 2, \ldots, m)$ of the group G'.

It follows that a group G' with which a group G is multiply isomorphic, in such a way that to the identical operation of G' there corresponds a given self-conjugate sub-group H of G, is completely defined (as an abstract group) when G and H are given. This being so it is natural to use a symbol to denote directly the group thus defined in terms of G and H. Herr Hölder* has introduced the symbol

$$G/H$$

to represent this group; he calls it the *quotient of G by H*, and a *factor-group* of G. We shall in the sequel make constant use both of the symbol and of the phrase thus defined.

It may not be superfluous to notice that the symbol G/H has no meaning†, unless H is a self-conjugate sub-group of G. Moreover, it may happen that G has two simply isomorphic self-conjugate sub-groups H and H'. When this is the case, there is no necessary relation between the factor-groups G/H and G/H' (except of course that their orders are equal); in

* "Zur Reduction der algebraischen Gleichungen," *Math. Ann.* XXXIV (1889), p. 31.

† Herr Frobenius has extended the use of the symbol to the case in which H is any group, whether contained in G or not, with which every operation of G is permutable: "Ueber endliche Gruppen," *Berliner Sitzungsberichte*, 1895, p. 169. We shall always use the symbol in the sense defined in the text.

other words, the type of the factor-group G/H depends on the actual self-conjugate sub-group of G which is chosen for H and not merely on the type of H.

Further, though in relation to its definition by means of G and H we call G/H a factor-group of G, we may without ambiguity, since the symbol represents a group of definite type, omit the word factor and speak of the group G/H. It is also to be observed that G has not necessarily a sub-group simply isomorphic with G/H. This may or may not be the case.

30. If G is multiply isomorphic with G' so that the self-conjugate sub-group H of G corresponds to the identical operation of G', it was shewn, at the end of § 28, that to any self-conjugate sub-group of G' there corresponds a self-conjugate sub-group of G containing H. Hence, unless G/H is a simple group, H cannot be a maximum self-conjugate sub-group of G. If g_1 is any self-conjugate sub-group of G/H, and G_1 the corresponding (necessarily self-conjugate) sub-group of G, containing H, we may form the factor-group G/G_1, and determine again whether this group is simple or composite. By continuing this process a maximum self-conjugate sub-group of G, containing H, must at last be reached.

31. Though G/H is completely defined by G and H, where H is any given self-conjugate sub-group of G, the reader will easily verify that G is not in general determined when H and G/H are given.

We shall have in the sequel to consider the solution of this problem in various particular cases. There is, however, in every case one solution of it which is immediately obvious. We may take any two groups G_1 and G_2, simply isomorphic with the given groups H and G/H, such that G_1 and G_2 have no common operation except identity, while each operation of one is permutable with each operation of the other. The group $\{G_1, G_2\}$, formed by combining these two, is clearly such that $\{G_1, G_2\}/G_1$ is simply isomorphic with G/H; it therefore gives a solution of the problem.

Definition. If two groups G_1, G_2 have no common operation except identity, and if each operation of G_1 is permutable with each operation of G_2, the group $\{G_1, G_2\}$ is called the *direct product* of G_1 and G_2.

Ex. If H, h are self-conjugate sub-groups of G, and if h is contained in H, so that H/h is a self-conjugate sub-group of G/h, shew that the quotient of G/h by H/h is simply isomorphic with G/H.

32. If H is a self-conjugate sub-group of G, of order n, and if H' is a self-conjugate sub-group of G', of order n', and if G/H and G'/H' are simply isomorphic, a correspondence of the most general kind may be established between the operations of G and G'. To every operation of G (or G') there will correspond n' (or n) operations of G' (or G), in such a way that to the product of any two operations of G (or G') there corresponds a definite set of n' (or n) operations of G' (or G). Let

$$G = H\,,\ S_1H,\quad S_2H,\ldots\ldots,\quad S_{m-1}H,$$

and

$$G' = H',\ S_1'H',\ S_2'H',\ldots\ldots,\ S'_{m-1}H';$$

and in the simple isomorphism between G/H and G'/H', let S_r and S_r' $(r = 0, 1,\ldots, m-1)$ be corresponding operations. Then if we take the set $S_r'H'$ as the n' operations of G' that correspond to any operation of the set S_rH of G, and the set S_rH as the n operations of G that correspond to any operation of the set $S_r'H'$ of G', the correspondence is, in fact, established.

For, if h_1' and h_2' are any two operations of H', the set of operations $S_r'h_1'S_s'h_2'$ includes n' distinct operations only, namely those of the set $S_r'S_s'H'$. Hence to the product of any given operation of the set S_rH by any given operation of the set S_sH, there corresponds the set of n' operations $S_r'S_s'H'$; at the same time the product of the two given operations belongs (in consequence of the isomorphism between G/H and G'/H') to the set S_rS_sH. The same statements clearly hold when we interchange accented and unaccented symbols.

We still speak of G and G' as isomorphic groups, and the correspondence between their operations is said to give an n'-to-n isomorphism of the two groups. We shall return to this general form of isomorphism in dealing with intransitive permutation groups.

33. Definition. Two groups G and G' are said to be permutable with each other when the distinct operations of the set S_iS_j', where for S_i every operation of the group G is put in turn and for S_j' every operation of the group G', coincide with the distinct operations of the set $S_j'S_i$ except possibly as regards arrangement.

If the two groups G and G' are permutable, the group $\{G, G'\}$ must be of finite order. For, by the definition, every operation

$$\ldots S_p S_q' S_r S_t' \ldots$$

can be reduced to the form $S_i S_j'$; and therefore the number of distinct operations of the group $\{G, G'\}$ cannot exceed the product of the orders of G and G'. Let g be the group formed of the common operations of G and G'. Divide the operations of these groups into the sets

$$g,\ \Sigma_1 g.\ \Sigma_2 g, \ldots,\ \Sigma_{m-1} g$$

and

$$g,\ g\Sigma_1',\ g\Sigma_2', \ldots\ldots\ldots\ldots,\ g\Sigma'_{m'-1}.$$

Then every operation of the set $S_i S_j'$ can clearly be expressed in the form

$$\Sigma_p \gamma \Sigma_q',$$

where γ is some operation of g. And no two operations of this form can be identical, for if

$$\Sigma_p \gamma_1 \Sigma_q' = \Sigma_r \gamma_2 \Sigma_t',$$

then

$$\gamma_2^{-1} \Sigma_r^{-1} \Sigma_p \gamma_1 = \Sigma_t' \Sigma_q'^{-1};$$

so that $\Sigma_t' \Sigma_q'^{-1}$ belongs to g. But this is only possible if

$$\Sigma_t' = \Sigma_q',$$

which leads to

$$\Sigma_r = \Sigma_p,$$

and

$$\gamma_2 = \gamma_1.$$

The order of $\{G, G'\}$ is therefore the product of the orders of G and G', divided by the order of g.

If every operation of G is permutable with G', then g must be a self-conjugate sub-group of G. For G and G' are transformed, each into itself, by any operation of G; and therefore their common sub-group g must be transformed into itself by any operation of G.

Moreover those operations of G, which are permutable with every operation of G', form a self-conjugate sub-group of G. For if T is an operation of G, which is permutable with every operation S' of G', so that

$$T^{-1} S' T = S',$$

and if S is any operation of G, then

$$S^{-1}T^{-1}S \,.\, S^{-1}S'S \,.\, S^{-1}TS = S^{-1}S'S,$$

so that $S^{-1}TS$ is permutable with every operation of G'. Hence every operation of G, which is conjugate to T, is permutable with every operation of G'; and the operations of G, which are permutable with every operation of G', therefore form a self-conjugate sub-group.

If G is a simple group, g must consist of the identical operation only; and either all the operations of G, or none of them, must be permutable with every operation of G'.

A special case is that in which the two groups G' and G are respectively a self-conjugate sub-group I and any sub-group H of some third group; for then every operation of H is permutable with I. If H is a cyclical sub-group generated by an operation S of order n, and if S^m is the lowest power of S which occurs in I, then m must be a factor of n. For if m' is the greatest common factor of m and n, integers x and y can be found such that

$$xm + yn = m'.$$

Now $$S^{m'} = S^{xm+yn} = S^{xm},$$

and therefore $S^{m'}$ belongs to I. Hence m' cannot be less than m, and therefore m is a factor of n. Moreover, since $\{S^m\}$ is a sub-group of I, the order of I must be divisible by n/m. Hence:—

THEOREM VIII. *If an operation S, of order n, is permutable with a group G, and if S^m is the lowest power of S which occurs in G; then m is a factor of n, and n/m is a factor of the order of G.*

The operations of $\{G, S\}$ can clearly be distributed in the sets

$$G,\ GS,\ GS^2, \ldots,\ GS^{m-1};$$

and no two of the operations $S, S^2, \ldots, S^{m-1}$ are conjugate in $\{G, S\}$.

34. A still more special case, but it is most important, is that in which the two groups are both of them self-conjugate sub-groups of some third group. If in this case the two groups are G and H, while S and T are any operations of the two groups respectively, then

$$S^{-1}HS = H,$$

and

$$T^{-1}GT = G;$$

so that every operation of G is permutable with H and every operation of H is permutable with G.

Consider now the operation $S^{-1}T^{-1}ST$. Regarded as the product of S^{-1} and $T^{-1}ST$ it belongs to G, and regarded as the product of $S^{-1}T^{-1}S$ and T it belongs to H. Every operation of this form therefore belongs to the common group of G and H. If G and H have no common operation except identity, then

$$S^{-1}T^{-1}ST = E,$$

or

$$ST = TS;$$

and S and T are permutable. Hence:—

THEOREM* IX. *If every operation of G transforms H into itself and every operation of H transforms G into itself, and if G and H have no common operation except identity; then every operation of G is permutable with every operation of H.*

Corollary. If every operation of G transforms H into itself and every operation of H transforms G into itself, and if either G or H is a simple group; then G and H have no common operation except identity, and every operation of G is permutable with every operation of H.

For, by § 33, if G and H had a common sub-group, it would be a self-conjugate sub-group of both of them; and neither of them could then be simple, contrary to hypothesis. Consequently, the only sub-group common to G and H is the identical operation.

Ex. 1. Shew that, in the group whose defining relations are

$$A^4 = E, \quad B^3 = E, \quad (AB)^2 = E,$$

the three operations A^2, $B^{-1}A^2B$, BA^2B^{-1} are permutable and that they form a complete set of conjugate operations. Hence shew that $\{A^2, B\}$ is a self-conjugate sub-group, and that the order of the group is 24.

* Dyck, "Gruppentheoretische Studien," *Math. Ann.* Vol. XXII (1883), p. 97.

Ex. 2. Shew that the cyclical group generated by the permutation (1234567) is permutable with the group

$$\{(243756)\},$$

and that the order of the group resulting from combining them is 42.

Ex. 3. If g_1 and g_2 are the orders of the groups G_1 and G_2, γ the order of their greatest common sub-group and g the order of $\{G_1, G_2\}$, shew that

$$g\gamma \geqslant g_1 g_2,$$

and that, if $g\gamma = g_1 g_2$, then G_1 and G_2 are permutable. (Frobenius.)

Ex. 4. If G_1 and G_2 are two sub-groups of G of orders g_1 and g_2, and S any operation of G, prove that the number of distinct operations of G contained in the set $S_1 S S_2$, when for S_1 and S_2 are put in turn every pair of operations of G_1 and G_2 respectively, is $g_1 g_2/\gamma$; γ being the order of the greatest sub-group common to $S^{-1} G_1 S$ and G_2.

If T is any other operation of G, shew also that the sets $S_1 S S_2$ and $S_1 T S_2$ are either identical or have no operation in common. (Frobenius.)

Ex. 5. If a group G of order mn has a sub-group H of order n, and if n has no prime factor which is less than m, shew that H must be a self-conjugate sub-group. (Frobenius.)

Ex. 6. If G is the direct product of G_1 and G_2, and if H is a self-conjugate sub-group of G; prove that either (i) H is Abelian or (ii) H has operations, other than E, in common with either G_1 or G_2. (Maclagan-Wedderburn.)

CHAPTER IV.

FURTHER PROPERTIES OF A GROUP WHICH ARE INDEPENDENT OF ITS MODE OF REPRESENTATION.

35. We have seen in § 22 that the order of any sub-group or operation of a group is a factor of the order of the group. The complete converse of this theorem, viz. the statement that if n is a factor of N, then a group of order N has a sub-group of order n is not generally true. We are however now in a position to prove a limited converse of great importance.

THEOREM I. *If p is a prime and if p^m is less than, and divides, the order of a group, then the group has at least one sub-group, distinct from itself, whose order is divisible by p^m.*

Suppose the theorem true for all groups of order less than N. If G, of order N, has no self-conjugate operation except E, the relation (§ 26)

$$N = h_1 + h_2 + \dots + h_r,$$

in which each term on the right, except h_1, is greater than unity, shews that at least one of the h's, say h_i, is not divisible by p. Hence N/h_i, the order of a sub-group, is divisible by p^m.

If G has self-conjugate operations, let S be one of an order as small as possible and therefore prime.

Suppose first that the order of S is p. Then $G/\{S\}$, a group whose order is less than N and is divisible by p^{m-1}, has an actual sub-group whose order is divisible by p^{m-1}. Therefore G has an actual sub-group whose order is divisible by p^m.

Suppose next that the order of S is q, a prime different from p. Then the order of $G/\{S\}$ is divisible by p^m; and if it is not equal to p^m the result follows as in the previous case. Finally if G, of order p^mq, has a self-conjugate operation S of order q every operation of $\{S\}$ is self-conjugate, so that G contains at least q self-conjugate operations. Moreover in the relation

$$p^m q = h_1 + h_2 + \dots + h_r,$$

no h is divisible by q since every operation is permutable with S. Hence more than q h's must be unity; i.e. there is a self-conjugate operation T not contained in $\{S\}$. The order of T cannot be a power of q, since G has no sub-group of order q^2. Hence in this case G has a self-conjugate operation P of order p. Then $G/\{P\}$, of order $p^{m-1}q$, has a sub-group of order p^{m-1}, and G has a sub-group of order p^m.

Hence if the theorem is true for groups whose order is less than N, it is true for groups of order N; and therefore it is true for all groups of finite order.

Corollary I. If p^m divides the order of a group, the group has at least one sub-group of order p^m.

For the group has an actual sub-group whose order is divisible by p^m. This again has a sub-group whose order is divisible by p^m, and so on. Since the order of the group is finite this process must terminate in a group of order p^m.

Corollary II. If p, a prime, divides the order of a group, the group has operations of order p*. For the group has a sub-group of order p^m $(m \geqslant 1)$; any operation of this sub-group has a power of p for its order, and a suitably chosen power of this operation has p for its order.

36. As a simple illustration of this theorem we will consider groups of order p^2 and pq where p and q are primes.

If a group of order p^2 contains an operation of order p^2 it is cyclical. If not, its $p^2 - 1$ operations, other than E, are all of order p. A sub-group of order p contains $p-1$ operations of order p which enter in no other such sub-group. There must therefore be $p+1$ sub-groups of order p, and hence at least one of them is self-conjugate. If this is $\{P\}$ and if P' is an operation of order p which is not a power of P,

$$P'^{-1}\{P\}P' = \{P\}.$$

Hence $$P'^{-1}PP' = P^{\alpha}, \quad P'^{-p}PP'^{p} = P^{\alpha^p},$$

$$\alpha^p \equiv 1 \quad (\text{mod. } p),$$

$$\alpha = 1,$$

and $$PP' = P'P.$$

* This result is due to Cauchy, *Exercices d'Analyse*, III, p. 250 (1844).

The group is therefore an Abelian group, generated by two permutable operations of order p.

A group of order pq must contain a sub-group of order p and a sub-group of order q. If the latter is not self-conjugate it must be one of p conjugate sub-groups, which contain $p(q-1)$ distinct operations of order q. The remaining p operations must constitute a sub-group of order p, which is therefore self-conjugate. A group of order pq has therefore either a self-conjugate sub-group of order p, or one of order q. Take $p<q$, and suppose first that there is a self-conjugate sub-group $\{P\}$ of order p. Let Q be an operation of order q. Then

$$Q^{-1}PQ = P^{\alpha},$$

$$Q^{-q}PQ^{q} = P^{\alpha^q},$$

$$\alpha^q \equiv 1 \pmod{p},$$

and therefore $$\alpha \equiv 1 \pmod{p}.$$

In this case P and Q are permutable and the group is cyclical. Suppose secondly that there is no self-conjugate sub-group of order p. There is then necessarily a self-conjugate sub-group $\{Q\}$ of order q; and if P is an operation of order p,

$$P^{-1}QP = Q^{\beta},$$

$$P^{-p}QP^{p} = Q^{\beta^p},$$

$$\beta^p \equiv 1 \pmod{q}.$$

If $q \not\equiv 1 \pmod{p}$, this would involve $\beta = 1$, and $\{P\}$ would be self-conjugate, contrary to supposition. Hence if the group is non-cyclical,

$$q \equiv 1 \pmod{p}$$

and $$P^{-1}QP = Q^{\beta},$$

where β is a root, other than unity, of the congruence

$$\beta^p \equiv 1 \pmod{p}.$$

Between the groups defined by

$$P^p = E, \quad Q^q = E, \quad P^{-1}QP = Q^{\beta},$$

and $$P'^p = E, \quad Q'^q = E, \quad P'^{-1}Q'P' = Q^{\beta^a},$$

a simple isomorphism is established by taking P' and P^a, Q' and Q, as corresponding operations. Hence when $q \equiv 1 \pmod{p}$ there is a single type of non-cyclical group of order pq.

37. If N is the order of a group G every operation of the group satisfies the relation

$$S^N = E,$$

and if n is any factor N, it follows from the preceding theorem and its corollaries that there are operations of the group satisfying the relation

$$S^n = E.$$

Herr Frobenius* has shewn that the number of such operations is always a multiple of n, and he has generalised† this result in the form of the following:—

THEOREM II. *The number of operations of a group of order N whose nth powers belong to a given conjugate set is zero or a multiple of the highest common factor of N and n.*

If N is a small number the truth of this theorem is easily verified by direct calculation. We shall therefore suppose the theorem true for all groups whose order is less than N. Let p^a (p prime) be a factor of N, and let T be a given operation of a group G of order N. We begin by considering those operations S of G which satisfy the relation

$$S^{p^a} = T.$$

Suppose first that the order of T is divisible by p. Then (§ 16) we may put $T = PQ$, where P and Q are permutable, the order of P is $p^b\,(b \geqslant 1)$ and the order m of Q is prime to p. Similarly we may put $S = P'Q'$, where P' and Q' are permutable while the order of P' is a power of p and the order of Q' is prime to p. Then

$$P'^{p^a} Q'^{p^a} = PQ.$$

Hence (§ 16) $$P'^{p^a} = P, \quad Q'^{p^a} = Q.$$

If $$p^a m' \equiv 1, \quad (\text{mod. } m)$$

$$Q' = Q^{m'},$$

and $$S = P'Q^{m'},$$

where $$P'^{p^a} = P.$$

From this relation it follows that P' is of order p^{a+b} $(b \geqslant 1)$, and unless G contains operations of order p^{a+b} permutable with T, there are no operations satisfying

$$S^{p^a} = T.$$

* "Verallgemeinerung des Sylow'schen Satzes," *Berliner Sitzungsberichte* (1895), pp. 984, 985.

† "Ueber einen Fundamentalsatz der Gruppentheorie," *Berliner Sitzungsberichte* (1903), pp. 987—991.

If P' is an operation of G, permutable with T, and satisfying

$$P'^{p^a} = P,$$

then each of the operations P'^{1+kp^b}, $(k = 1, 2, \ldots\ldots, p^a)$ satisfy these conditions, and they are the only operations belonging to $\{P'\}$ which satisfy the conditions. Similarly every other cyclical sub-group of G of order p^{a+b} contains either 0 or p^a operations satisfying the conditions; while no two distinct cyclical sub-groups of order p^{a+b} can have common operations of order p^{a+b}. Hence the number of operations of G satisfying

$$S^{p^a} = T$$

is zero or a multiple of p^a. If T' is any operation conjugate to T, the operations of G satisfying

$$S^{p^a} = T'$$

are distinct from and equal in number to those satisfying the previous relation. Hence if the order of T is divisible by p, the number of operations of G whose p^ath powers belong to the conjugate set containing T is zero or a multiple of $p^a h_T$, h_T being the number of operations in the conjugate set.

(b) Suppose next that the order m of T is prime to p. Then with the same notation

$$P'^{p^a} Q'^{p^a} = T,$$

and $$P'^{p^a} = E, \quad Q'^{p^a} = T.$$

Hence $$S = P' T^{m'},$$

where $$P'^{p^a} = E,$$

while P' is permutable with T.

Let $p^{a_1}s$, where s is prime to p, be the order of the sub-group G_T constituted of the operations of G which are permutable with T. The order of $G_T/\{T\}$ is $p^{a_1}s/m$, which is less than N. Therefore the number of operations of this group which satisfy the relation

$$S^{p^a} = E$$

is a multiple of the highest common factor of p^a and $p^{a_1}s/m$; i.e. is a multiple of p^a or p^{a_1} according as $a \leqslant a_1$, or $a > a_1$. The same statement is true of the operations of G_T whose p^ath powers belong to $\{T\}$. Now if S is an operation of G_T such that

$$S^{p^a} = T^i,$$

then
$$(ST^j)^{p^a} = T^{i+jp^a} = E$$

if
$$i + jp^a \equiv 0 \text{ (mod. } m).$$

Hence of the operations

$$S, ST, \ldots\ldots, ST^{m-1}$$

just one is such that its p^ath power is E.

The number of operations P' of G_T which satisfy the relation

$$P'^{p^a} = E$$

is therefore the same as the number of operations of $G_T/\{T\}$ which satisfy the same relation. Hence in this case the number of operations S such that

$$S^{p^a} = T$$

is a multiple of p^a or of p^{a_1} according as $a \leqslant a_1$ or $a > a_1$. As in the former case, if T' is conjugate to T, the operations satisfying

$$S^{p^a} = T'$$

are distinct from and equal in number to those satisfying the previous relation. Hence the number of operations whose p^ath power is conjugate to T is a multiple of $p^a h_T$ or $p^{a_1} h_T$ according as $a \leqslant a_1$ or $a > a_1$. If $N = p^\alpha N_1$, where N_1 is prime to p,

$$h_T = p^{\alpha - a_1} N_1/s.$$

The number of operations whose p^ath power is conjugate to T is then finally a multiple of $p^{\alpha - a_1 + a} N_1/s$ or of $p^\alpha N_1/s$ according as $a \leqslant a_1$ or $a > a_1$. In either case it is necessarily a multiple of p^a.

Suppose next that n is any factor of N, and that $n = p^a n_1$, where n_1 is prime to p. If S^n is conjugate to T, and if

$$S^{p^a} = S'$$

then S'^{n_1} is conjugate to T. The operations S' for which this is true must form one or more complete conjugate sets. The number of operations for which S^{p^a} is conjugate to S' is zero or a multiple of p^a. Hence the number of operations for which S^n

is conjugate to T is zero or a multiple of p^a. The same reasoning may be applied to the other primes dividing n; and therefore the number of operations whose nth powers are conjugate to T is zero or a multiple of n.

Lastly, let $n = n_1 n_2$, where the prime factors of n_1 are, and those of n_2 are not prime factors of N, and suppose that

$$n_2 n_2' \equiv 1 \text{ (mod. } N\text{)}.$$

If $$S^n = T,$$

then $$S^{n_1} = T^{n_2'};$$

and conversely if $$S^{n_1} = T^{n_2'}$$

then $$S^n = S^{n_1 n_2} = T^{n_2 n_2'} = T.$$

The number of operations whose nth powers belong to the conjugate set containing T is therefore the same as the number whose n_1th powers belong to the set containing $T^{n_2'}$. If the highest power of p dividing n_1, say p^a, is not greater than p^α, the highest power of p dividing N, the number of operations whose n_1th powers are conjugate to $T^{n_2'}$ has been shewn to be a multiple of p^a. If $a > \alpha$, the relation

$$S^{n_1} = T^{n_2'}$$

may be written

$$S^{p^\alpha} = S', \quad S'^{n_1 p^{-\alpha}} = T^{n_2'};$$

and it follows that the number of operations whose n_1th power is conjugate to $T^{n_2'}$ is a multiple of p^α. Hence the number of operations whose n_1th powers are conjugate to a given operation is a multiple of the greatest common factor of n_1 and N. This is the same as the greatest common factor of n and N; and the theorem is therefore true for a group of order N.

Corollary I. If n is a factor of N, the order of G, then the number of operations of G satisfying the relation

$$S^n = E$$

is a multiple of n.

For it has been seen in § 35 that there are always operations of the group satisfying this relation, and the number cannot therefore be zero.

Corollary II. If $n\,(=p^a q^b \ldots)$ is a factor of $N\,(=p^\alpha q^\beta \ldots)$, and if the number of operations of G, of order N, which satisfy the relation

$$S^n = E$$

is equal to n, then either $a=\alpha$ or G must contain operations of order p^{a+1}. If $a<\alpha$, the number of operations which satisfy

$$S^{pn} = E$$

is a multiple of pn, and is therefore greater than the number which satisfy

$$S^n = E.$$

There must therefore be operations whose orders divide pn and do not divide n; and the orders of these operations are multiples of p^{a+1}.

Corollary III.* If a group of order mn, where m and n are relatively prime, contains a self-conjugate sub-group of order n, the group contains just n operations whose orders divide n.

For if G had an operation S, whose order divides n, which is not contained in the self-conjugate sub-group H of order n, $\{S, H\}$ would be a sub-group whose order is greater than n and relatively prime to m. Such a sub-group cannot exist, since its order does not divide the order of G.

Corollary IV.* If G has a self-conjugate sub-group H of order mn, where m and n are relatively prime, and if H has a self-conjugate sub-group K of order n, then K is a self-conjugate sub-group of G.

For, by the preceding Corollary, H contains just n operations whose orders divide n, namely those of K; and every operation of G, since it transforms H into itself, must therefore transform K into itself.

Ex. If m and n are relatively prime factors of the order of a group G, and if the number of operations of G whose orders divide m and n are m and n respectively; then every operation whose order is a factor of m is permutable with every operation whose order is a factor of n, and the number of operations of G whose orders divide mn is equal to mn. (Frobenius.)

* Frobenius: "Ueber endliche Gruppen," *Berliner Sitzungsberichte* (1895), p. 170.

38. If S and T are any two operations of a group, the operation $S^{-1}T^{-1}ST$ is called *a commutator*. The identical operation E is always a commutator; for a group necessarily contains permutable operations, and if S and T are permutable

$$S^{-1}T^{-1}ST = E.$$

If every pair of operations of a group are permutable, then E is the only commutator.

A commutator can always be expressed as such in a variety of ways. In fact if U is any operation of the sub-group G_S, which consists of all the operations permutable with S, then since

$$U^{-1}SU = S,$$

$$R = S^{-1}T^{-1}ST = S^{-1}T^{-1}U^{-1}SUT$$
$$= S^{-1}(UT)^{-1}S(UT).$$

Conversely, if $S^{-1}T^{-1}ST = S^{-1}V^{-1}SV,$

then $(TV^{-1})S(TV^{-1})^{-1} = S,$

and therefore TV^{-1} belongs to G_S.

Hence $S^{-1}T^{-1}ST$ can be expressed in N/h_S distinct ways as a commutator with S^{-1} for its first factor; h_S being the number of operations in the set to which S belongs. The last factors in these distinct forms of $S^{-1}T^{-1}ST$ are the operations of the set G_ST. If U is any one of them and h_U the number of operations in the conjugate set to which U belongs, then $S^{-1}T^{-1}ST$ can be expressed in a form in which U is the last factor in N/h_U distinct ways. Hence $S^{-1}T^{-1}ST$ can be expressed as a commutator in at least $\sum_U N/h_U$ distinct ways, where the summation is extended to all operations of the set G_ST. This obviously does not necessarily exhaust all the ways in which $S^{-1}T^{-1}ST$ can be expressed as a commutator, but it gives a lower limit to the number of such ways.

If h_m is the greatest number of operations in any conjugate set, then $\sum_U N/h_U$ is certainly not less than $(N/h_m)^2$. Now the number of distinct forms $S^{-1}T^{-1}ST$ is N^2. Hence if

$$N(N/h_m)^2 > N^2,$$

or

$$h_m < \sqrt{N},$$

these are certainly operations which cannot be expressed as commutators.

39. The product of two commutators, in which the last factor of the first and the first factor of the second are inverse operations is another commutator; for

$$S^{-1}T^{-1}ST.T^{-1}U^{-1}TU = (S^{-1}TS)^{-1}(S^{-1}U)^{-1}(S^{-1}TS)(S^{-1}U);$$

but without some further knowledge of the group concerned it is obviously not possible in general to express the product of any two commutators as a commutator. The totality of the commutators of a group G do not therefore necessarily constitute a group. They however necessarily generate a group, which may or may not be identical with G.

Definition. The group generated by the commutators of a group G is called the *commutator sub-group* or the *derived group* of G.

THEOREM III. *The derived group of G is that self-conjugate sub-group H of smallest order such that the factor-group G/H is Abelian.*

That the derived group is a self-conjugate sub-group follows at once from the fact that if R is a commutator so also is $S^{-1}RS$, where S is any operation of G; so that the derived group is generated by a certain number of complete conjugate sets of operations.

If it is distinct from G let S, T be operations of G which do not belong to H. Then

$$S^{-1}T^{-1}ST = R,$$

or

$$ST = TSR,$$

where R belongs to H. Hence

$$STH = TSH,$$

$$SHT = THS,$$

and

$$SH.TH = TH.SH.$$

Now (§ 29) the operations of G/H combine according to the same laws, as the sets

$$H,\ S_2H,\ S_3H,\ \ldots\ldots,\ S_mH$$

into which the operations of G fall in respect of H. Hence since these sets are permutable, every pair of operations of G/H are permutable; i.e. G/H is Abelian.

Conversely, if H' is any self-conjugate sub-group such that G/H' is Abelian, and if S, T are any two operations of G; then

$$SH' . TH' = TH' . SH',$$

so that $S^{-1}T^{-1}ST$ belongs to H', and H' therefore contains H.

40. The derived group H has itself a commutator sub-group or derived group, which may or may not coincide with H. Suppose now that starting with a given group G, of finite order, G_1 is the derived group of G, and actually distinct from it; G_2 is the derived group of G_1 and actually distinct from it: and so on. Since the order of each of these groups is less than the preceding, the series must terminate. This may happen in one of two ways. We may either arrive at a group which is identical with its derived group, or we may arrive at an Abelian group, whose derived group is the identical operation. In either case the series of groups

$$G_1, G_2, \ldots\ldots, G_\nu,$$

is spoken of as the series of *derived groups* arising from G; and when G_ν is E, G is said to be *soluble*.

Each group of the series is necessarily a self-conjugate sub-group of G, and the following theorem holds in respect of the groups of the series.

THEOREM IV. *If K is a self-conjugate sub-group of G, and if G/K is a soluble group with i terms in its derived series, then K contains G_i, the ith derived group of G, and does not contain G_{i-1}.*

Let G/K be denoted by G', and let

$$G'_1, G'_2, \ldots\ldots, G'_{i-1}, E,$$

be its derived series. The corresponding series of sub-groups of G may be denoted by

$$H_1, H_2, \ldots\ldots, H_{i-1}, K.$$

In the series of derived groups of G,

$$G_1, G_2, \ldots\ldots, G_\nu,$$

let G_{s+1} be the first which does not contain K. Then since H_1 is the smallest self-conjugate sub-group of G, containing K, such that G/H_1 is Abelian, $H_1 = G_1$. In the same way it is shewn that $H_2 = G_2$, ..., $H_s = G_s$. Further H_{s+1} being the smallest self-conjugate sub-group of G_s, containing K, such that G_s/H_{s+1} is Abelian, $H_{s+1} = \{G_{s+1}, K\}$. In the same way it is shewn that $H_{s+2} = \{G_{s+2}, K\}$,......, $H_{i-1} = \{G_{i-1}, K\}$, $K = \{G_i, K\}$. Now by supposition H_{i-1} and K are distinct groups; and therefore K contains G_i and does not contain G_{i-1}.

In the particular case in which the derived group G_1 is Abelian, so that the derived series is G_1, E, the group G is said to be *metabelian*.

41. In the case of an Abelian group, whose operations are all permutable with each other, the conjugate sets each consist of a single operation, and the product of any two conjugate sets (or operations) is another conjugate set (or operation). We now proceed to consider how, in the case of non-Abelian groups, the conjugate sets combine among themselves by multiplication.

Let $$S_1,\ S_2, \ldots\ldots, S_{h_i},$$
and $$T_1,\ T_2, \ldots\ldots, T_{h_j},$$
be two complete conjugate sets of operations in a group G. By multiplication there arises a set of $h_i h_j$ operations of G, viz.

$$S_x T_y,\ (x = 1, 2, \ldots\ldots h_i;\ \ y = 1, 2, \ldots\ldots, h_j).$$

Since
$$S_x^{-1} T_1 S_x,\ S_x^{-1} T_2 S_x, \ldots\ldots,\ S_x^{-1} T_{h_j} S_x,$$
differ only from
$$T_1,\ T_2, \ldots\ldots, T_{h_j}$$
in the sequence in which they occur, the same is true of
$$T_1 S_x,\ T_2 S_x, \ldots\ldots,\ T_{h_j} S_x,$$
and $$S_x T_1,\ S_x T_2, \ldots\ldots,\ S_x T_{h_j}.$$

Hence, except as regards the sequence in which they occur, the set of operations
$$S_x T_y\ (x = 1, 2, \ldots\ldots h_i;\ y = 1, 2, \ldots\ldots, h_j)$$
is the same as the set
$$T_y S_x\ (x = 1, 2, \ldots\ldots h_i;\ y = 1, 2, \ldots\ldots, h_j).$$

If the operation R occurs just t times in the set $S_x T_y$, and if Σ is any operation of G, then $\Sigma^{-1} R \Sigma$ must occur just t times in the set $\Sigma^{-1}S_x\Sigma . \Sigma^{-1}T_y\Sigma$, which, since the S's and T's are conjugate sets, is the same as the set S_xT_y. Hence in the set of operations S_xT_y each operation of the conjugate set, to which R belongs, occurs the same number of times.

This fact may be conveniently expressed in a symbolical form as follows. Let

$$\begin{array}{c} E, \\ A_1,\ A_2,\ldots\ldots,\ A_{h_2}, \\ B_1,\ B_2,\ldots\ldots,\ B_{h_3}, \\ \ldots\ldots\ldots\ldots\ldots\ldots \\ K_1,\ K_2,\ldots\ldots,\ K_{h_r} \end{array}$$

be the complete conjugate sets of operations of G in any order, except that the set consisting of the identical operation alone (for which h_1 is unity) is put first. Denote the sum of the operations in the ith set by C_i, their number being h_i, so that

$$E = C_1$$

$$A_1 + A_2 + \ldots + A_{h_2} = C_2,$$

$$\ldots\ldots\ldots\ldots\ldots\ldots$$

$$K_1 + K_2 + \ldots + K_r = C_r.$$

Then

$$C_iC_j = \sum_k c_{ijk} C_k,$$

where each c_{ijk} is either zero or a suitable positive integer, expresses that in the set S_xT_y each operation of any conjugate set occurs the same number of times. In fact, if the multiplications indicated are carried out and the multiplication table of the group taken account of, the relation

$$C_iC_j = \sum_k c_{ijk} C_k$$

becomes an identity.

42. The coefficients c_{ijk} which enter in these relations obviously depend on the particular group considered; but they are subject to certain conditions which are the same in all cases.

Since

$$C_iC_j = C_jC_i, \quad \text{from * 57.}$$

$$c_{ijk} = c_{jik}.$$

Again, since the multiplication of operations of a group is associative

$$C_iC_j \,.\, C_k = C_i \,.\, C_jC_k.$$

Now $$C_iC_j \,.\, C_k = \sum_s c_{ijs}C_sC_k = \sum_{s,t} c_{ijs}c_{skt}C_t,$$

and $$C_i \,.\, C_jC_k = \sum_s c_{jks}C_iC_s = \sum_{s,t} c_{jks}c_{ist}C_t.$$

Hence for each t, i, j, k

$$\sum_s c_{ijs}c_{skt} = \sum_s c_{jks} \,.\, c_{ist}.$$

If $$S_2 = R^{-1}S_1R,$$

$$S_2C_j = R^{-1}S_1R \,.\, C_j = R^{-1}S_1C_jR,$$ from (**) 57.

and the set of operations S_2C_j contains the same number belonging to any conjugate set that S_1C_j does. Hence $c_{ijk}h_k$, if not zero, is a multiple of both h_i and h_j, and therefore of their least common multiple. Moreover, by counting the number of operations on each side of the relation

$$C_iC_j = \sum_s c_{ijs}C_s,$$

we obtain $$h_ih_j = \sum_s c_{ijs}h_s.$$

43. If $$S_1, S_2, \ldots, S_{h_i}$$

is a complete conjugate set, so also obviously is

$$S_1^{-1}, S_2^{-1}, \ldots, S_{h_i}^{-1}.$$

The number of operations in this second set is necessarily the same as that in the first. If the second set is distinct from the first, the two sets are called *inverse* sets. If they are the same the set is said to be *self-inverse*. A convenient notation, which will be adhered to here, is to take the ith and i'th sets as inverse, which involves for a self-inverse set $i = i'$. In any case $h_i = h_{i'}$.

If S_1 is an operation of the ith conjugate set, the operations of the set

$$S_1C_j$$

are all distinct, and of these $c_{ijk}h_k/h_i$ belong to the kth set. Let these be

$$S_1T_1, S_1T_2 \ldots, S_1T_\mu, \quad \mu = c_{ijk}h_k/h_i,$$

or $$K_1, K_2, \ldots, K_\mu.$$

Then $\qquad S_1 = K_1 T_1^{-1} = K_2 T_2^{-1} = \ldots = K_\mu T_\mu^{-1}$,

and these are the only ways in which S_1 can be expressed as the product of an operation of the kth set with one of the j'th set.   Hence

$$\frac{c_{ijk}h_k}{h_i} = \mu = c_{kj'i},$$

and $\qquad\qquad \Rightarrow c_{ijk}h_k = c_{kj'i}h_i.$

Further since, if $\qquad ST = K,$

then $\qquad\qquad\qquad T^{-1}S^{-1} = K^{-1},$

it follows that $\qquad\qquad c_{ijk} = c_{i'j'k'}.$

The immediately previous relation may therefore be written

$$c_{jik}h_k = c_{j'ki}h_i = c_{jk'i'}h_i.$$

When one of the suffixes is 1, the value of c is obviously given by the equations $\quad c_{jik}h_k = c_{j'ki} = c_{jk'i}$

$$\begin{vmatrix} c_{1jk} = c_{1kj} = 0, & k \neq j, \\ c_{1jj} & = 1, \\ c_{ij1} & = 0, & j \neq i', \\ c_{ii'1} & = h_i. \end{vmatrix}$$

Ex. 1.   In the case of the group of § 17, shew that if

$$E = C_1, \quad S + T = C_2, \quad U + V + W = C_3,$$

then $\qquad C_2^2 = 2C_1 + C_2, \ \ C_2 C_3 = 2C_3, \ \ C_3^2 = 3C_1 + 3C_2.$

Ex. 2.   Prove that if h_i and h_j are relatively prime, every operation of $C_i C_j$ belongs to the same conjugate set.

44.   The system of relations

$$C_i C_j = \sum_{k=1}^{k=r} c_{ijk} C_k,$$

may be called the multiplication table of the conjugate sets of a group.   Its great importance will appear later when we consider the theory of groups of linear substitutions.

No direct information in regard to the ordinary sub-groups of a group is given by the multiplication table of the conjugate sets; but all the self-conjugate sub-groups are determined by a mere inspection of the table.   The operations of a self-conjugate sub-group fall into a certain number, less than the whole, of complete conjugate sets; and since the operations combine among themselves by multiplication, the conjugate sets into which they fall must also do so.

Conversely if a number, less than the whole, of the conjugate sets combine among themselves by multiplication, so also do the operations forming these sets; and therefore the sets in question constitute a self-conjugate sub-group. The totality of the self-conjugate sub-groups of a given group will therefore be determined by finding from the table those various sets of conjugate operations which combine among themselves by multiplication.

45. The distinction between commutators and non-commutators is also given immediately by the table. A commutator is by definition an operation which can be expressed in the form $S^{-1}T^{-1}ST$, i.e. as a product of operations S^{-1} and $T^{-1}ST$ belonging to inverse sets.

Now the relation

$$C_{i'}C_i = C_iC_{i'} = \sum_s c_{ii's}C_s,$$

expresses that any operation of the sth set can be expressed in $c_{ii's}$ distinct ways as a product of an operation of the i'th set by an operation of the ith set. Let

$$S^{-1}T^{-1}ST$$

be one of these ways, where S is some operation of the ith set. Without altering S or the operation which is being represented as a commutator, T may be any one of N/h_i operations. Hence the operation in question can be represented in the form

$$S_i^{-1}TS_iT,$$

where S_i belonging to the ith set is $c_{ii's}N/h_i$ distinct ways; and therefore any operation of the sth set can be represented as a commutator in

$$\sum_{i=1}^{i=r} c_{ii's}N/h_i$$

ways. Since (§ 43),

$$c_{ii's}h_s = c_{ii's'}h_s = c_{isi}h_i,$$

$$\sum_{i=1}^{i=r} c_{ii's}N/h_i = \sum_{i=1}^{i=r} c_{isi}N/h_s;$$

and each operation of the sth set can be represented as a commutator in

$$N/h_s \times \sum_i c_{isi}$$

ways. In particular, an operation of the sth set is not a commutator if, and only if, c_{isi} (or $c_{ii's}$) is zero for each i.

46. The coefficients c_{ijk} in the multiplication table of the conjugate sets are, when not zero, in general greater than unity. If for given i and j, each c_{ijk} is either zero or unity, no operation occurs twice in the product C_iC_j. Let S be an operation of C_i and T one of C_j. If S and T were not permutable, the operation ST would occur again in the product C_iC_j in the form

$$T^{-1}ST\,.\,(ST)^{-1}T(ST),$$

hence every operation of C_i must be permutable with every operation of C_j. When this is not the case some of the c's are necessarily greater than unity. Denoting by G_S the sub-group formed by all the operations which are permutable with S, the only operations permutable with both S and T are those of the sub-group $G_{S,\,T}$ of order $n_{S,\,T}$ common to G_S and G_T. If ST belongs to the kth conjugate set, it is permutable with every operation of G_{ST}, of order N/h_k. Hence when the operations S and T are transformed by all the operations of G_{ST}, $N/h_kn_{S,\,T}$ distinct pairs of operations arise, and therefore

$$c_{ijk} \nless N/h_kn_{S,\,T},$$

where S and T are operations of C_i and C_j whose product belongs to C_k. If C_i and C_j contain operations S' and T' such that

$$S'T' = ST,$$

while there is no operation of the group that transforms S into S' and T into T',

$$c_{ijk} \nless N/h_kn_{S,\,T} + N/h_kn_{S',\,T'};$$

and continuing thus the actual value of c_{ijk} is arrived at.

47. A pair of operations S, T of a group (where the sequence in which the pair is written is essential; i.e. the pairs S, T and T, S are distinct unless $S = T$) when transformed by all the operations of the group will give rise to a set of $N/n_{S,\,T}$ pairs, where $n_{S,\,T}$ is the order of $G_{S,\,T}$, the sub-group formed of all the operations permutable both with S and with T. If

$$R^{-1}SR = S_1 \text{ and } R^{-1}TR = T_1,$$

then the operations of the set $G_{S,T}R$, and no others, transform the pair S, T into the pair S_1, T_1; and the pair S_1, T_1 remains unchanged only by the operations of the sub-group $R^{-1}G_{S,T}R$. Hence, when the $N/n_{S,T}$ pairs of the set are transformed by the N operations of the group, the number of unchanged pairs in the N permutations that arise is N.

Suppose now that, when the N^2 pairs S, T are transformed by the operations of the group, they fall into m conjugate sets of pairs. The total number of unchanged pairs in the N permutations that arise will be mN. On the other hand, the number of unchanged pairs when the N^2 pairs are transformed by any operation of the ith set is equal to the number of pairs of operations in a sub-group of order N/h_i. Hence

$$mN = \sum_i h_i (N/h_i)^2$$

or

$$m = N\sum_i \frac{1}{h_i}.$$

This then is the number of distinct conjugate sets of pairs of operations defined as above. Moreover, if by the *product* of the pair S, T by the pair S', T' we understand the pair SS', TT', the conjugate sets of pairs of operations will combine among themselves on multiplication, but the multiplication will not necessarily be commutative.

Ex. If $S, S', \ldots\ldots, S^{(t-1)}$ is a system of t operations, distinct or not, in which the sequence of the individual operations is essential to the system, prove that the number of distinct conjugate sets of such systems is

$$N^{t-1} \sum_i \frac{1}{h_i^{t-1}}.$$

CHAPTER V.

ON THE COMPOSITION-SERIES OF A GROUP.

48. LET G_1 be a maximum self-conjugate sub-group (§ 27) of a given group G, G_2 a maximum self-conjugate sub-group of G_1, and so on. Since G is a group of finite order, we must, after a finite number of sub-groups, arrive in this way at a sub-group G_{n-1}, whose only self-conjugate sub-group is that formed of the identical operation alone, so that G_{n-1} is a simple group.

Definitions. The series of groups

$$G, G_1, G_2, \ldots, G_{n-1}, E,$$

obtained in the manner just described is called a *composition-series* of G.

The set of groups

$$G/G_1, G_1/G_2, \ldots, G_{n-2}/G_{n-1}, G_{n-1},$$

is called a set of *factor-groups* of G, and the orders of these groups are said to form a set of *composition-factors* of G.

Each of the set of factor-groups is necessarily (§ 30) a simple group.

The set of groups forming a composition-series of G is not, in general, unique. Thus G may have more than one maximum self-conjugate sub-group, in which case the second term in the series may be taken different from G_1. Moreover the groups succeeding G_1 are not all necessarily self-conjugate in G; and when some of them are not so, we obtain a new composition-series on transforming the whole set by a suitably chosen operation of G. That the new set thus obtained is again a composition-series is obvious; for if G_{r+1} is a maximum self-conjugate sub-group of G_r, so also is $S^{-1}G_{r+1}S$ of $S^{-1}G_rS$. We proceed to prove that, if a group has two different composition-series, the number of terms in them is the same and the factor-groups derived from them are identical except as regards the sequence in which they occur.

This result, which is of great importance in the subsequent theory, is due to Herr Hölder*; and the proof we here give does not differ materially from his.

The less general result, that, however the composition-series may be chosen, the composition-factors are always the same except as regards their sequence, had been proved by M. Jordan† some years before the date of Herr Hölder's memoir.

49. THEOREM I. *If H is any self-conjugate sub-group of a group G; and if K, K' are two self-conjugate sub-groups of G contained in H, such that there is no self-conjugate sub-group of G contained in H and containing either K or K' except H, K and K' themselves; and if L is the greatest common sub-group of K and K', so that L is necessarily self-conjugate in G; then the groups H/K and K'/L are simply isomorphic, as also are the groups H/K' and K/L.*

Since K and K' are self-conjugate sub-groups of G contained in H, $\{K, K'\}$ must also be a self-conjugate sub-group of G contained in H; and since, by supposition, there is in H no self-conjugate sub-group of G other than H itself, which contains either K or K', $\{K, K'\}$ must coincide with H. Hence (§ 33) the product of the orders of K and K' is equal to the product of the orders of H and L. $|K||K'| = |H|\cdot|L|$. —— *

If the order of K/L is m, the operations of K may be divided into the m sets

$$L,\ S_1L,\ S_2L, \ldots,\ S_{m-1}L,$$

such that any operation of one set multiplied by any operation of a second gives some operation of a definite third set, and the group K/L is defined by the laws according to which the sets combine.

* "Zurückführung einer beliebigen algebraischen Gleichung auf eine Kette von Gleichungen," *Math. Ann.* XXXIV, (1889), p. 33.

† "Traité des substitutions," (1870), p. 42.

Consider now the m sets of operations

$$K', \; S_1K', \; S_2K', \ldots, \; S_{m-1}K'.$$

No two operations of any one set can be identical. If operations from two different sets are the same, say

$$S_pk_1' = S_qk_2',$$

where k_1' and k_2' are operations of K', then

$$S_q^{-1}S_p = k_2'k_1'^{-1},$$

some operation of K'. But $S_q^{-1}S_p$ is an operation of K; hence, as it belongs both to K and K', it must belong to L, so that

$$S_p = S_ql,$$

where l is some operation of L. This however contradicts the supposition that the operations S_pL and S_qL are all distinct. It follows that the operations of the above m sets are all distinct.

Now they all belong to the group H; and their number, being the order of K' multiplied by the order of K/L, is equal to the order of H. Hence in respect of the self-conjugate sub-group K', which H contains, the operations of the group H can be divided into the sets

$$K', \; S_1K', \; S_2K', \ldots, \; S_{m-1}K',$$

and the group H/K' is defined by the laws according to which these sets combine. But if

$$S_pL \, . \, S_qL = S_rL,$$

then necessarily

$$S_pK' \, . \, S_qK' = S_rK'.$$

Hence the groups H/K' and K/L are simply isomorphic. In precisely the same way it is shewn that H/K and K'/L are simply isomorphic.

Corollary. If H coincides with G, K and K' are maximum self-conjugate sub-groups of G. Hence if K and K' are maximum self-conjugate sub-groups of G, and if L is the greatest group common to K and K', then G/K and K'/L are simply isomorphic; as also are G/K' and K/L.

Now G/K and G/K' are simple groups; and therefore, K/L and K'/L being simple groups, L must be a maximum self-conjugate sub-group of both K and K'.

50. We may now at once proceed to prove by a process of induction the properties of the composition-series of a group stated at the end of § 48. Let us suppose that, for groups whose orders do not exceed a given number n, it is already known that any two composition-series contain the same number of groups and that the factor-groups defined by them are the same except as regards their sequence. If G, a group whose order does not exceed $2n$, has more than one composition-series, let two such series be

$$G,\ G_1,\ G_2, \ldots, E;$$

and

$$G,\ G_1',\ G_2', \ldots, E.$$

If H is the greatest common sub-group of G_1 and G_1', and if

$$H,\ I,\ J, \ldots, E$$

is a composition-series of H, then, by the Corollary in the preceding paragraph,

$$G,\ G_1,\ H,\ I,\ J, \ldots, E,$$

and

$$G,\ G_1',\ H,\ I,\ J, \ldots, E$$

are two composition-series of G which contain the same number of terms and give the same factor-groups. For it has there been shewn that G/G_1 and G_1'/H are simply isomorphic; as also are G/G_1' and G_1/H. Now the order of G_1, being a factor of the order of G, cannot exceed n. Hence the two composition-series

$$G_1,\ G_2,\quad \ldots, E,$$

and

$$G_1,\ H,\ I, \ldots, E,$$

by supposition contain the same number of groups and give the same factor-groups; and the same is true of the two composition-series

$$G_1',\ G_2',\quad \ldots, E,$$

and

$$G_1',\ H,\ I, \ldots, E.$$

Hence finally, the two original series are seen, by comparing them with the two new series that have been formed, to have the same number of groups and to lead to the same factor-groups. The property therefore, if true for groups whose order does not exceed n, is true also for groups whose order does not exceed $2n$. Now the simplest group, which has more than one composition-series, is that defined by

$$A^2 = E,\ B^2 = E,\ AB = BA.$$

For this group there are three distinct composition-series, viz.

$$\{A, B\},\ \{A\},\quad E;$$
$$\{A, B\},\ \{B\},\quad E;$$

and $$\{A, B\},\ \{AB\},\ E:$$

and for these the theorem is obviously true. It is therefore true generally. Hence:—

THEOREM II. *Any two composition-series of a group consist of the same number of sub-groups, and lead to two sets of factor-groups which, except as regards the sequence in which they occur, are identical with each other.*

The definite set of simple groups, which we thus arrive at from whatever composition-series we may start, are essential constituents of the group: the group is said to be *compounded* from them. The reader must not, however, conclude either that the group is defined by its set of factor-groups, or that it necessarily contains a sub-group simply isomorphic with any given one of them.

51. It has been already pointed out that the groups in a composition-series of G are not necessarily, all of them, self-conjugate sub-groups of G.

Suppose now that a series of groups, each contained in the preceding one,

$$G,\ H_1,\ H_2, \ldots,\ H_{m-1},\ E$$

are chosen so that each one is a self-conjugate sub-group of G, while there is no self-conjugate sub-group of G contained in any one group of the series and containing the next group.

Definition. The series of groups, obtained in the manner just described, is called a *chief-composition-series*, or a *chief-series* of G.

It should be noticed that such a series is not necessarily obtained by dropping out from a composition-series those of its groups which are not self-conjugate in the original group. It will be seen later that the composition-series of a group whose order is the power of a prime can be chosen, either (i) so that every group of the series is a self-conjugate sub-group, or (ii) so as to contain any given sub-group, self-conjugate or not.

A chief composition-series of a group is not necessarily unique; and when a group has more than one, the following theorem, exactly analogous to Theorem II, holds:

THEOREM III. *Any two chief-composition-series of a group consist of the same number of terms and lead to two sets of factor-groups, which, except as regards the sequence in which they occur, are identical with each other.*

The formal proof of this theorem would be a mere repetition of the proof of § 50, Theorem I itself being used to start from instead of its Corollary; it is therefore omitted.

Although it is not always possible to pass from a composition-series to a chief-series, the process of forming a composition-series on the basis of a given chief-series can always be carried out. Thus if, in a chief-series, H_{r+1} is not a maximum self-conjugate sub-group of H_r, the latter group must have a maximum self-conjugate sub-group $G_{r,1}$ which contains H_{r+1}. If H_{r+1} is not a maximum self-conjugate sub-group of $G_{r,1}$, then such a group, $G_{r,2}$, may be found still containing H_{r+1}; and this process may be continued till we arrive at a group $G_{r,s-1}$, of which H_{r+1} is a maximum self-conjugate sub-group. A similar process may be carried out for each pair of consecutive terms in the chief-series; the resulting series so obtained is a composition-series of the original group.

52. The factor-groups H_r/H_{r+1} arising from a chief-series are not necessarily simple groups. If between H_r and H_{r+1} no groups of a corresponding composition-series occur, the group H_r/H_{r+1} is simple; but when there are such intermediate groups, H_r/H_{r+1} cannot be simple. We proceed to discuss the nature of this group in the latter case.

Let G be multiply isomorphic with G', so that the self-conjugate sub-group H_{r+1} of G corresponds to the identical operation of G'. Also let

$$H_1', H_2', \ldots, H_p', H'_{p+1}, \ldots, H_r', E$$

be the sub-groups of G' which correspond to the sub-groups

$$H_1, H_2, \ldots, H_p, H_{p+1}, \ldots, H_r, H_{r+1}$$

of G. Since H_p contains H_{p+1}, H_p' must contain H'_{p+1}; and since H_{p+1} is self-conjugate in G, H'_{p+1} is self-conjugate in G'. Also if G' had a self-conjugate sub-group contained in H_p' and containing H'_{p+1}, G would have a self-conjugate sub-group contained in H_p and containing H_{p+1}. This is not the case, and therefore

$$G', H_1', H_2', \ldots, H_r', E$$

is a chief-series of G'. Hence H_r/H_{r+1} is simply isomorphic with H_r', the last group but one in the chief-series of G'.

Definition. If Γ is a self-conjugate sub-group of G, and if G has no self-conjugate sub-group, contained in Γ, whose order is less than that of Γ, then Γ is called a *minimum* self-conjugate sub-group of G.

Making use of the phrase thus defined, the discussion of the factor-groups H_r/H_{r+1} of a chief-series is the same as that of the minimum self-conjugate sub-groups of a given group.

53. To simplify the notation as much as possible, let I be a minimum self-conjugate sub-group of G; and, if I is not a simple group, suppose that i_1 is a minimum self-conjugate sub-group of I. Then i_1 must be one of a set of $m\,(>1)$ conjugate sub-groups in G, say

$$i_1, i_2, \ldots, i_m,$$

each of which is self-conjugate in I.

If i_1 and i_2 had a common sub-group j, it would be a self-conjugate sub-group of I contained in i_1, i.e. i_1 would not be a minimum sub-group of I. Hence no two of the groups $i_1, i_2, \ldots, i_m$ have a common sub-group other than E. Consider now the direct product $\{i_1, i_2\}$ of i_1 and i_2. It is a self-conjugate sub-group of I. If it contains all the m sub-groups of the set, it contains a self-conjugate sub-group of G and must therefore coincide with I. If it does not contain i_3, it can have no sub-group in common with i_3, or else i_3 would not be a minimum sub-group. In this latter case consider the direct product $\{i_1, i_2, i_3\}$ of i_1, i_2 and i_3. If it contains all the m sub-groups of the set it coincides with I. If it does not contain i_4, it can have no sub-group in common with i_4, and the direct product $\{i_1, i_2, i_3, i_4\}$ is a self-conjugate sub-group of I. Continuing thus, it must be possible to select a certain set of s sub-groups from the conjugate set of m, such that I is the direct product of $i_1, i_2, \ldots, i_s$. If i_1 were not a simple group and if j were a minimum self-conjugate sub-group of i_1, then each of the groups $i_1, i_2, \ldots, i_s$ would be the direct product of $t\,(>1)$ groups isomorphic with j and I would be the direct product of st groups simply isomorphic with j, so that i_1 would not be a minimum self-conjugate sub-group of I. Hence i_1 must be a simple group; and I is the direct product of s simply isomorphic simple groups.

Hence:—

THEOREM IV. *If between two consecutive terms H_r and H_{r+1} in the chief-composition-series of a group there occur the groups $G_{r,1}, G_{r,2}, \ldots, G_{r,s-1}$ of a composition-series; then* (i) *the factor groups*

$$H_r/G_{r,1},\ G_{r,1}/G_{r,2}, \ldots, G_{r,s-1}/H_{r+1}$$

are all simply isomorphic, and (ii) *H_r/H_{r+1} is the direct product of s groups of the type $H_r/G_{r,1}$.*

Corollary. If the order of H_r/H_{r+1} is a power, p^s, of a prime, H_r/H_{r+1} must be an Abelian group whose operations, except E, are all of order p.

54. A chief-series of a group G can always be constructed which shall contain among its terms any given self-conjugate sub-group of G. For if Γ is a self-conjugate sub-group of G, and if G/Γ is simple, we may take Γ for the group which follows G in the chief-series. If on the other hand G/Γ is not simple, it must contain a minimum self-conjugate sub-group. Then Γ_1, the corresponding self-conjugate sub-group of G, contains Γ; and if there were a self-conjugate sub-group of G contained in Γ_1 and containing Γ, the self-conjugate sub-group of G/Γ, which corresponds to Γ_1, would not be a minimum self-conjugate sub-group. We may now repeat the same process with Γ_1, and so on; the sub-groups thus introduced will, with G and Γ, clearly form the part of a chief-series extending from G to Γ. The series may be continued from Γ, till we arrive at the identical operation, in the usual way.

55. It will perhaps assist the reader if we illustrate the foregoing theory by one or two simple examples. We take first a group of order 12, defined by the relations

$$A^2 = E, \quad B^2 = E, \quad AB = BA,$$
$$R^3 = E, \quad R^{-1}AR = B, \quad R^{-1}BR = AB^*.$$

From the last two equations, it follows that

$$R^{-1}ABR = A,$$

and therefore R transforms the sub-group $\{A, B\}$ of order 4 into itself; so that this sub-group is self-conjugate, and the order of the group is 12 as stated. The self-conjugate sub-group $\{A, B\}$ thus determined is clearly a maximum self-conjugate sub-group. Also it is the only one. For if there were another its order would be 6, and it would contain all the operations of order 3 in the group. Now since $\{R\}$ is only permutable with its own operations, the group contains 4 sub-groups of order 3, and therefore there can be no self-conjugate sub-group of order 6. The three cyclical sub-groups $\{A\}$, $\{B\}$ and $\{AB\}$ of order 2 are transformed into each other by R, and therefore no one of them is self-conjugate.

Hence the only chief-series is

$$\{R, A, B\}, \quad \{A, B\}, \quad E,$$

and there are three composition-series, viz.

$$\{R, A, B\}, \quad \{A, B\}, \quad \{A\}, \quad E;$$
$$\{R, A, B\}, \quad \{A, B\}, \quad \{B\}, \quad E;$$
and
$$\{R, A, B\}, \quad \{A, B\}, \quad \{AB\}, \quad E.$$

The orders of the factor-groups in the chief series are 3 and 2^2, and the group of order 2^2 is, as it should be, an Abelian group whose operations are all of order 2. The composition-factors are 3, 2, 2 in the order written.

56. As a rather less simple instance, we will now take a group generated by four permutable independent operations A, B, P, Q, of orders 2, 2, 3, 3 respectively and an operation R of order 3, for which

$$R^{-1}AR = B, \quad R^{-1}BR = AB, \quad R^{-1}PR = P, \quad R^{-1}QR = QP\dagger.$$

The sub-group $\{A, B, P, Q\}$, of order 36, is clearly a maximum self-conjugate sub-group, and therefore the order of the group is 108.

* The reader will notice that B can be eliminated from these relations, and that the group can be defined by $A^2 = E$, $R^3 = E$, $(AR)^3 = E$. The structure of the group however is given, at a glance, by the equations in the text.

† Here again the group can clearly be defined in terms of A, Q and R.

Since A, B and AB are conjugate operations, every self-conjugate sub-group that contains A must contain B; and since Q and QP are conjugate, every self-conjugate sub-group that contains Q must contain P. Hence the only other possible maximum self-conjugate sub-groups are those of the form $\{A, B, P, RQ^{\alpha}\}$; and since

$$Q^{-1}RQ^{\alpha}Q = RQ^{\alpha}P^{-1},$$

these groups actually are self-conjugate. The same reasoning shews that the only maximum self-conjugate sub-group of $\{A, B, P, Q\}$ or of $\{A, B, P, RQ^{\alpha}\}$, which is self-conjugate in the original group, is $\{A, B, P\}$; and the only maximum self-conjugate sub-groups of the latter, which are self-conjugate in the original group, are $\{A, B\}$ and $\{P\}$. Hence all the chief-series of the group are given by

$$\{R, A, B, P, Q\}, \quad \begin{matrix}\{A, B, P, Q\}, \\ \text{or} \\ \{A, B, P, RQ^{\alpha}\},\end{matrix} \quad \{A, B, P\}, \quad \begin{matrix}\{A, B\}, \\ \text{or} \\ \{P\}.\end{matrix} \quad E.$$

Since $\{A, B, P, Q\}$ is an Abelian group, all of its sub-groups are self-conjugate. Hence if G_1, G_2, and G_3 are *any* maximum sub-groups of $\{A, B, P, Q\}$, G_1 and G_2 respectively, then

$$\{R, A, B, P, Q\}, \quad \{A, B, P, Q\}, \quad G_1, G_2, G_3, \quad E$$

is a composition-series.

Again, since A and B are conjugate in $\{A, B, P, RQ^{\alpha}\}$, the only maximum self-conjugate sub-groups of this group are those of the form $\{A, B, P^x (RQ^{\alpha})^y\}$. If y is zero, this sub-group is Abelian; and we may take for the next term in the composition-series any maximum sub-group g_2 of this Abelian sub-group, and for the last term but one any sub-group g_3 of g_2. But if y is not zero, $\{A, B, P^x (RQ^{\alpha})^y\}$ can only be followed by $\{A, B\}$. Hence the remaining composition-series are of the forms:—

$$\{R, A, B, P, Q\}, \quad \{A, B, P, RQ^{\alpha}\}, \quad \{A, B, P\}, \quad g_2, g_3, \quad E,$$

and

$$\{R, A, B, P, Q\}, \quad \{A, B, P, RQ^{\alpha}\}, \quad \{A, B, P^x (RQ^{\alpha})^y\},$$
$$\{A, B\}, \quad \{A\} \text{ or } \{B\} \text{ or } \{AB\}, \quad E.$$

It should be noticed that if, in the last of these series, we drop out the terms which are not self-conjugate in the original group, here the third and fifth terms, we do not arrive at a chief-series. This illustrates a remark made in § 51.

57. THEOREM V. *If H is a sub-group of G, each composition-factor of H must be equal to or be a factor of some composition-factor of G.*

If G is simple, its only composition-factor is equal to its order: the theorem in this case is obvious.

If G is not simple, let G_{r+1} be the first term in a composition-series of G which does not contain H; and let G_r be the term preceding G_{r+1}. If H_1 is the greatest common sub-group of G_{r+1} and H, then H_1 is a self-conjugate sub-group of H. For every operation of H transforms both H and G_{r+1} into themselves; and therefore every operation of H transforms H_1, the greatest common sub-group of H and G_{r+1}, into itself. Now the order of $\{H, G_{r+1}\}$ is equal to the product of the orders of H and G_{r+1} divided by the order of H_1; and $\{H, G_{r+1}\}$ is contained in G_r. Hence the order of H/H_1 is equal to or is a factor of the order of G_r/G_{r+1}. If then a composition-series of H be taken, containing the term H_1, the orders of the factor-groups, formed by those terms of the series terminating with H_1, are equal to or are factors of the order of G_r/G_{r+1}. The same reasoning may now be used for H_1 that has been applied to H; and the theorem is therefore true.

Corollary. If all the composition-factors of G are primes, so also are the composition-factors of every sub-group of G.

58. When a group G does not coincide with its derived group G_1, a chief-series may be formed in which G_1 occurs. Since G/G_1 is Abelian, each factor-group of the corresponding composition-series between G and G_1 has a prime for its order. Hence if G is a soluble group (§ 40), i.e. if its series of derived groups terminate with E, all of its composition-factors are primes. The converse is obviously true, for if all the composition-factors are primes, neither the group itself nor any self-conjugate sub-group can coincide with its derived group. A soluble group might therefore be equally well defined as one all of whose composition-factors are primes.

A soluble group of order $p^\alpha q^\beta \ldots r^\gamma$, where $p, q, \ldots, r$ are distinct primes, has $\alpha+\beta+\ldots+\gamma$ composition-factors; these are capable of $\dfrac{(\alpha+\beta+\ldots+\gamma)!}{\alpha!\,\beta!\ldots\gamma!}$ distinct arrangements.

For a specified group the composition-factors may, as we have already seen, occur in two or more distinct arrangements;

but it is immediately obvious that two groups of the same order cannot be of the same type, i.e. simply isomorphic, unless the distinct arrangements, of which the composition-factors are capable, are the same for both. A first step therefore towards the enumeration of all distinct types of soluble groups of a given order, will be to classify them according to the distinct arrangements of which the composition-factors are capable; for no two groups belonging to different classes can be of the same type.

The case, in which the composition-factors are capable of all possible arrangements, is one which will always occur. Taking in this case β q's followed by α p's for the last $\alpha+\beta$ composition-factors, the group contains a sub-group G' of order $p^\alpha q^\beta$. In the composition-series of this group, with the composition-factors taken as proposed, there is a sub-group H of order p^α contained self-conjugately in a sub-group H_1 of order $p^\alpha q$. This sub-group H_1 is contained self-conjugately in a group H_2 of order $p^\alpha q^2$. Hence (Theorem II, Cor. IV, § 37) H is contained self-conjugately in H_2. Again, H_2 is contained self-conjugately in a group H_3 of order $p^\alpha q^3$, and therefore again H is self-conjugate in H_3. Proceeding thus, we shew that H is self-conjugate in G'. It follows that n, the number of conjugate sub-groups of order p^α contained in the group, is not a multiple of q. Now q may be any one of the distinct primes other than p that divide the order of the group. Hence finally the group contains a self-conjugate sub-group of order p^α. In the same way we shew that it contains self-conjugate sub-groups of orders $q^\beta, \dots, r^\gamma$. The group must therefore be the direct product of groups whose orders are $p^\alpha, q^\beta, \dots, r^\gamma$.

Hence:—

THEOREM VI. *A soluble group, the composition-factors of which may be taken in any order, is the direct product of groups whose orders are powers of primes.*

59. In illustration of the preceding paragraph, and in part for the value of the results themselves, we will now determine all distinct types of group whose orders are of the form p^2q, where p and q are distinct primes. A discussion of the case where the order is of the form pq has already been given in § 36. It will here be assumed, as is actually the case, that such groups are soluble. The truth of this statement, which is not difficult to verify directly, follows immediately from Sylow's theorem (Chap. IX).

If the composition-factors are susceptible of all possible arrangements, the group is the direct product of groups of orders p^2 and q, and therefore (§ 36) is Abelian.

If the two arrangements p, p, q and q, p, p are possible, there are self-conjugate sub-groups of orders p^2 and q; the group again is Abelian, and all three arrangements are possible.

There are now five other possibilities.

I. p, p, q and p, q, p, the only possible arrangements.

There must be here a sub-group of order pq, containing self-conjugate sub-groups of orders p and q and therefore Abelian. Let this be generated by operations P and Q, of orders p and q. Since the group has sub-groups of order p^2, there must be operations of orders p or p^2, not contained in the sub-group of order pq, and permutable with P. Let R be such an operation, so that R^p belongs to the sub-group $\{P, Q\}$. R cannot be permutable with Q, as the group would be then Abelian; hence

$$R^{-1}QR = Q^{\alpha},$$

so that
$$R^{-p}QR^{p} = Q^{\alpha^p},$$

and
$$\alpha^p \equiv 1 \pmod{q}.$$

This case can therefore only occur if p is a factor of $q-1$. There are two distinct types, according as R is of the order p or of order p^2; i.e. according as the sub-groups of order p^2 are non-cyclical or cyclical. If α and β are any two distinct primitive roots of the congruence

$$\alpha^p \equiv 1 \pmod{q},$$

the relations
$$R^{-1}QR = Q^{\alpha},$$

and
$$R^{-1}QR = Q^{\beta},$$

do not lead to distinct types, since the latter is reduced to the former on replacing R by R^x, where

$$\beta \equiv \alpha^x \pmod{q}.$$

The two types are respectively defined by the relations

$$Q^q = E, \quad P^p = E, \quad R^p = E, \quad P^{-1}QP = Q,$$

$$R^{-1}PR = P, \quad R^{-1}QR = Q^{\alpha};$$

and
$$Q^q = E, \quad R^{p^2} = E, \quad R^{-1}QR = Q^{\alpha}.$$

In each case, α is a primitive root of the congruence $\alpha^p \equiv 1 \pmod{q}$.

II. p, q, p and q, p, p, the only possible arrangements.

There must be a self-conjugate sub-group of order pq, in which the sub-group of order q is not self-conjugate, and a self-conjugate sub-group of order p^2. The sub-group of order pq must be given by

$$P^p = E, \quad Q^q = E, \quad Q^{-1}PQ = P^{\alpha},$$

$$\alpha^q \equiv 1 \text{ (mod. } p);$$

so that in this case q must be a factor of $p-1$. If the sub-group of order p^2 is not cyclical, there must be an operation R of order p, not contained in the sub-group $\{P, Q\}$. Any such operation must be permutable with P. Moreover since the sub-group of order pq is self-conjugate and contains only p sub-groups of order q, the sub-group $\{Q\}$ must be permutable with some operation of order p. Hence we may assume that R is permutable with $\{Q\}$, and, since $p > q$, with Q.

We thus obtain a single type defined by

$$P^p = E, \quad Q^q = E, \quad Q^{-1}PQ = P^{\alpha},$$
$$R^p = E, \quad QR = RQ, \quad PR = RP.$$

It is the direct product of $\{R\}$ and $\{P, Q\}$.

If the sub-group of order p^2 is cyclical, all the operations, which have powers of p for their orders and are not contained in the sub-group $\{P, Q\}$, must be of order p^2. There can therefore be no operation of order p, which is permutable with $\{Q\}$; and there is no corresponding type.

III. p, p, q, the only possible arrangement.

There must be a self-conjugate sub-group of order pq, which has no self-conjugate sub-group of order p; it is therefore defined by

$$P^p = E, \quad Q^q = E, \quad P^{-1}QP = Q^{\alpha},$$

$$\alpha^p \equiv 1 \text{ (mod. } q);$$

so that here p must be a factor of $q-1$.

If the sub-groups of order p^2 are not cyclical, there must be an operation R' of order p, not contained in this sub-group and permutable with P. Hence

$$R'^{-1}QR' = Q^{\beta};$$

and if

$$\beta \equiv \alpha^x \text{ (mod. } q),$$

then $R'P^{-x}$ is an operation of order p, which is not contained in the sub-group of order pq and is permutable with Q. It is therefore a self-conjugate operation of order p. Hence p, q, p is a possible arrangement of the composition-factors, and there is in this case no type.

If the sub-groups of order p^2 are cyclical, there must be an operation R of order p^2, such that

$$R^p = P.$$

Hence
$$R^{-1}QR = Q^\beta,$$

where β is a primitive root of the congruence

$$\beta^{p^2} = 1 \text{ (mod. } q).$$

This case then can only occur when p^2 is a factor of $q-1$; and we again have a single type defined by

$$R^{p^2} = E, \quad Q^q = E, \quad R^{-1}QR = Q^\beta.$$

IV. p, q, p, the only possible arrangement.

Here the self-conjugate sub-group of order pq must be given by

$$P^p = E, \quad Q^q = E, \quad Q^{-1}PQ = P^\alpha,$$

$$\alpha^q \equiv 1 \text{ (mod. } p),$$

and q must be a factor of $p-1$. As in II, there must be an operation R of order p, permutable with $\{Q\}$ and therefore with Q; and since R transforms $\{P, Q\}$ into itself, it must be permutable with P. This however makes the sub-group $\{P, R\}$ self-conjugate, which requires q, p, p to be a possible arrangement of the composition-factors. Hence there is no type corresponding to this case.

V. q, p, p, the only possible arrangement.

If the sub-group of order p^2 is cyclical, and is generated by P, while Q is an operation of order q, we must have

$$Q^{-1}PQ = P^\alpha,$$

where
$$\alpha^q \equiv 1 \text{ (mod. } p^2).$$

Here q must be a factor of $p-1$; since the congruence has just $q-1$ primitive roots, there is a single type of group.

If the sub-group of order p^2 is not cyclical, it can be generated by two permutable operations P_1 and P_2 of order p, and it contains $p+1$ sub-groups of order p. If an operation Q of order q is permutable with no sub-group of order p, $p+1$ must be divisible by q. If on the other hand, Q is permutable with one sub-group of order p, it is necessarily permutable with one of the remaining sub-groups of that order.

Taking the latter case first, P_1 and P_2 may be so chosen that

$$Q^{-1}P_1Q = P_1^\alpha, \quad Q^{-1}P_2Q = P_2^\beta.$$

Now if either α or β, say β, were unity, then $\{Q, P_1\}$ would be a self-conjugate sub-group and p, q, p would be a possible arrangement of the composition-factors. Hence neither α nor β can be unity, and we may take

$$Q^{-1}P_1Q = P_1^{\alpha}, \quad Q^{-1}P_2Q = P_2^{\alpha^x},$$

where α is a primitive root of

$$\alpha^q \equiv 1 \pmod{p},$$

and x is not zero.

It remains to determine how many distinct types these equations contain. When $q = 2$, the only possible value of x is unity; and there is a single type. When q is an odd prime, and we take

$$Q^y = Q', \quad P_1 = P_2', \quad P_2 = P_1', \quad xy \equiv 1 \pmod{q},$$

the equations become

$$Q'^{-1}P_1'Q' = P_1'^{\alpha}, \quad Q'^{-1}P_2'Q' = P_2'^{\alpha^y},$$

and therefore the values x and y of the index of α, where

$$xy \equiv 1 \pmod{q},$$

give the same type. Now the only way, in which the two equations can be altered into two equations of the same form, is by replacing Q by some other operation of the group whose order is q and by either interchanging P_1 and P_2 or leaving each of them unchanged. Moreover the other operations of the group whose orders are q are those of the form $Q^lP_1^mP_2^n$, where l is not zero, and this operation transforms P_1 and P_2 in the same way as Q^l. Hence finally, the values x and y of the index will only give groups of the same type when

$$xy \equiv 1 \pmod{q}.$$

There are therefore $\frac{1}{2}(q+1)$ distinct types, when q is an odd prime; they are given by the above equations.

Suppose next, that Q is permutable with no sub-group of order p. We may then, by suitably choosing the generating operations of the group of order p^2, assume that

$$Q^{-1}P_1Q = P_2, \quad Q^{-1}P_2Q = P_1^{\alpha}P_2^{\beta}.$$

If now
$$Q^{-x-1}P_1Q^{x+1} = P_1^{\alpha_x}P_2^{\beta_x},$$

then
$$\alpha_{x+1} \equiv \alpha\beta_x, \quad \beta_{x+1} \equiv \alpha_x + \beta\beta_x \pmod{p},$$

and therefore
$$\beta_{x+1} - \beta\beta_x - \alpha\beta_{x-1} \equiv 0 \pmod{p}.$$

Hence if ι_1 and ι_2 are the roots of the congruence

$$\iota^2 - \beta\iota - \alpha \equiv 0 \pmod{p},$$

then
$$\beta_x \equiv \frac{\iota_2^{x+1} - \iota_1^{x+1}}{\iota_2 - \iota_1}.$$

Now since Q^q is the lowest power of Q that is permutable with P_1, β_{q-1} must be the first term of the series $\beta_1, \beta_2, \ldots$ which vanishes. Hence q is the least value of z for which

$$\iota_2^{\ z} \equiv \iota_1^{\ z},$$

and therefore the congruence

$$\iota^2 - \beta\iota - \alpha \equiv 0$$

is irreducible. Moreover α_{q-1} must be congruent to unity, and therefore

$$1 \equiv -\iota_1\iota_2 \frac{\iota_2^{\ q-1} - \iota_1^{\ q-1}}{\iota_2 - \iota_1} \equiv \iota_1^{\ q}.$$

From the quadratic congruence satisfied by ι, it follows that

$$\alpha \equiv -\iota^{p+1} \equiv -1, \quad \beta \equiv \iota^p + \iota \ (\text{mod. } p);$$

and thence $$\alpha_x \equiv -\frac{\iota^{px} - \iota^x}{\iota^p - \iota}, \quad \beta_x \equiv \frac{\iota^{p(x+1)} - \iota^{x+1}}{\iota^p - \iota}.$$

Finally, we may shew that, when q is a factor of $p+1$, the equations

$$P_1^p = E, \quad P_2^p = E, \quad Q^q = E, \quad P_1P_2 = P_2P_1,$$

$$Q^{-1}P_1Q = P_2, \quad Q^{-1}P_2Q = P_1^{-1}P_2^{\iota^p+\iota},$$

where ι is a primitive root of the congruence

$$\iota^q \equiv 1 \ (\text{mod. } p),$$

define a single type of group, whatever primitive root of the congruence is taken for ι.

Thus from the given equations it follows that

$$Q^{-x}P_1Q^x = P_1^{\alpha_{x-1}}P_2^{\beta_{x-1}} = P_3, \text{ say,}$$

and $$Q^{-x}P_3Q^x = (P_1^{\alpha_{x-1}}P_2^{\beta_{x-1}})^{\alpha_{x-1}}(P_1^{\alpha_x}P_2^{\beta_x})^{\beta_{x-1}}$$

$$= P_1^{\alpha_x\beta_{x-1} - \alpha_{x-1}\beta_x}P_3^{\alpha_{x-1}+\beta_x}$$

$$= P_1^{-1}P_3^{\iota^{px}+\iota^x}.$$

If then we take P_1, P_3 and Q^x as generating operations in the place of P_1, P_2 and Q, the defining relations are reproduced with ι^x in the place of ι. The relations therefore define a single type of group*.

We have, for the sake of brevity, in each case omitted the verification that the defining relations actually give a group of order p^2q. This presents no difficulty, even for the last type; for the previous types it is immediately obvious.

* On groups whose order is of the form p^2q the reader may consult; Hölder, "Die Gruppen der Ordnungen p^3, pq^2, pqr, p^4," *Math. Ann.* XLIII (1893), in particular pp. 335—360; and Cole and Glover, "On groups whose orders are products of three prime factors," *Amer. Journal*, XV (1893), pp. 202—214. Groups of order p^3q are classified by Western, "Groups of order p^3q," *Proc. L. M. S.* Vol. XXX. (1899), pp. 209—263.

CHAPTER VI.

ON THE ISOMORPHISM OF A GROUP WITH ITSELF.

60. It is shewn in § 24 that, if all the operations of a group are transformed by one of themselves, which is not self-conjugate, a correspondence is thereby established among the operations of the group which exhibits the group as simply isomorphic with itself. (ie inner auto⁻⁰ˢ.) $x \to y^{-1}xy$

In an Abelian group every operation is self-conjugate, and the only correspondence established in the manner indicated is that in which every operation corresponds to itself. If however in an Abelian group we take, as the operation which corresponds $S \to S$ to any given operation S, its power S^μ, where μ is any number relatively prime to the order of the group, then to ST will correspond $S^\mu T^\mu$ or $(ST)^\mu$; and the correspondence exhibits the group as simply isomorphic with itself. In these ways it is possible for every group, except one whose operations are all of order 2, to establish a correspondence between the operations of the group, which shall exhibit the group as simply isomorphic with itself. Moreover, we shall see that in general there are such correspondences which cannot be established by either of the processes above given. We devote the present Chapter to a discussion of the isomorphism of a group with itself. It will be seen that, for many problems of group-theory, and in particular for the determination of the various types of group which are possible when the factor-groups of the composition-series are given, this discussion is most important.

61. Definition. A correspondence between the operations of a group, such that to every operation S there corresponds a single operation S', while to the product ST of two operations there corresponds the product $S'T'$ of the corresponding operations, is said to define an *isomorphism of the group with itself*. That isomorphism in which each operation corresponds to itself is called the *identical isomorphism*.

In every isomorphism of a group with itself, the identical operation corresponds to itself; and the orders of two corresponding operations are the same. For if E and S were corresponding operations, so also would be E and S^n; and therefore more than one operation would correspond to E. Again, if S and S', of orders n and n', are corresponding operations, so also are S^n and S'^n; and therefore n must be a multiple of n'. Similarly n' must be a multiple of n; and therefore n and n' are equal.

If the operations of a group of order N are represented by

$$S_1(=E),\ S_2, \ldots, S_{N-1},\ S_N,$$

and if, for a given isomorphism of the group with itself, S_r' is the operation that corresponds to $S_r\,(r=1, 2, \ldots, N)$, the isomorphism will be completely represented by the symbol

$$\begin{bmatrix} S_1, & S_2, & \ldots, & S_{N-1}, & S_N \\ S_1', & S_2', & \ldots, & S'_{N-1}, & S'_N \end{bmatrix}.$$

In this symbol, two operations in the same vertical line are corresponding operations. When no risk of confusion is thereby introduced, the simpler symbol

$$\begin{bmatrix} S \\ S' \end{bmatrix}$$

is used.

62. An isomorphism of a group with itself, thus defined, is not an operation. The symbol of an isomorphism however defines an operation. It may, in fact, be regarded as a permutation performed upon the N letters which represent the operations of the group. Corresponding to every isomorphism there is thus a definite operation; and it is obvious that the operations, which correspond to two distinct isomorphisms, are themselves distinct. The totality of these operations form a group. For let

$$\begin{bmatrix} S \\ S' \end{bmatrix} \text{ and } \begin{bmatrix} S' \\ S'' \end{bmatrix}$$

be any two isomorphisms of the group with itself. Then if, as hitherto, we use curved brackets to denote a permutation, we have

$$\begin{pmatrix} S \\ S' \end{pmatrix} \begin{pmatrix} S' \\ S'' \end{pmatrix} = \begin{pmatrix} S \\ S'' \end{pmatrix}.$$

But since $\begin{bmatrix} S \\ S' \end{bmatrix}$ is an isomorphism, the relation

$$S_p S_q = S_r$$

requires that $$S_p' S_q' = S_r'.$$

And since $\begin{bmatrix} S' \\ S'' \end{bmatrix}$ is an isomorphism, the relation

$$S_p' S_q' = S_r'$$

requires that $$S_p'' S_q'' = S_r''.$$

Hence if $$S_p S_q = S_r,$$

then $$S_p'' S_q'' = S_r'';$$

and therefore $\begin{bmatrix} S \\ S'' \end{bmatrix}$ is an isomorphism.

The product of the permutations which correspond to two isomorphisms is therefore the permutation which corresponds to some other isomorphism.

The set of permutations which correspond to all the isomorphisms of a given group with itself, therefore form a group.

Definition. A group, which is simply isomorphic with the group thus derived from a given group, is called *the group of isomorphisms* of the given group.

It is not, of course, necessary always to regard this group as a group of permutations performed on the symbols of the operations of the given group. But however the group of isomorphisms may be represented, each one of its operations corresponds to a definite isomorphism of the given group. To avoid an unnecessarily cumbrous phrase, we may briefly apply the term "isomorphism" to the operations of the group of isomorphisms. So long as we are dealing with the properties of a group of isomorphisms, no risk of confusion is thereby introduced. Thus we shall use the phrase "the isomorphism $\begin{pmatrix} S \\ S' \end{pmatrix}$" as equivalent to "the operation of the group of isomorphisms which corresponds to the isomorphism $\begin{bmatrix} S \\ S' \end{bmatrix}$."

63. If Σ is some operation of a group G, while for S each operation of the group is put in turn, the symbol

$$\begin{bmatrix} S \\ \Sigma^{-1}S\Sigma \end{bmatrix}$$

defines an isomorphism of the group. For if

$$S_pS_q = S_r,$$

then $$\Sigma^{-1}S_p\Sigma \,.\, \Sigma^{-1}S_q\Sigma = \Sigma^{-1}S_pS_q\Sigma = \Sigma^{-1}S_r\Sigma\,;$$

and $\Sigma^{-1}S_r\Sigma$ is an operation of the group. An isomorphism of a group, which is thus formed on transforming the operations of the group by one of themselves, is called an *inner* isomorphism. All others are called *outer** isomorphisms. If $\begin{bmatrix} S \\ S' \end{bmatrix}$ is an outer isomorphism, the isomorphisms

$$\begin{bmatrix} S \\ S' \end{bmatrix}\begin{bmatrix} S \\ \Sigma^{-1}S\Sigma \end{bmatrix},$$

when for Σ each operation of the group is taken successively, are said to form a *class* of outer isomorphisms.

THEOREM I. *The totality of the inner isomorphisms of a group G form a group isomorphic with G; this group is a self-conjugate sub-group of the group of isomorphisms of G*†.

The product of the isomorphisms

$$\begin{pmatrix} S \\ \Sigma^{-1}S\Sigma \end{pmatrix} \text{ and } \begin{pmatrix} S \\ \Sigma'^{-1}S\Sigma' \end{pmatrix}$$

is given by

$$\begin{pmatrix} S \\ \Sigma^{-1}S\Sigma \end{pmatrix}\begin{pmatrix} S \\ \Sigma'^{-1}S\Sigma' \end{pmatrix} = \begin{pmatrix} S \\ \Sigma^{-1}S\Sigma \end{pmatrix}\begin{pmatrix} \Sigma^{-1}S\Sigma \\ \Sigma'^{-1}\Sigma^{-1}S\Sigma\Sigma' \end{pmatrix}$$

$$= \begin{pmatrix} S \\ \Sigma'^{-1}\Sigma^{-1}S\Sigma\Sigma' \end{pmatrix}$$

$$= \begin{pmatrix} S \\ \Sigma''^{-1}S\Sigma'' \end{pmatrix},$$

where $$\Sigma\Sigma' = \Sigma''.$$

The product of two inner isomorphisms is therefore another

* Inner and outer isomorphisms are also sometimes called cogredient and contragredient.

† Hölder, "Bildung zusammengesetzter Gruppen," *Math. Ann.* Vol. XLVI (1895), p. 325.

inner isomorphism; hence the inner isomorphisms form a group. Moreover, if we take the isomorphism

$$\begin{pmatrix} S \\ \Sigma^{-1}S\Sigma \end{pmatrix}$$

as corresponding to the operation Σ of the group G, then to every operation of G there will correspond a definite inner isomorphism, so that to the product of any two operations of G there corresponds the product of the two corresponding isomorphisms. The group G and its group of inner isomorphisms are therefore isomorphic. If G contains no self-conjugate operation, identity excepted, no two isomorphisms corresponding to different operations of G can be identical; and therefore, in this case, G is simply isomorphic with its group of inner isomorphisms. If however G contains self-conjugate operations, forming a self-conjugate sub-group H, then to every operation of H there corresponds the identical isomorphism; and the group of inner isomorphisms is simply isomorphic with G/H.

Let now $$\begin{pmatrix} S \\ S' \end{pmatrix}$$

be any isomorphism. Then

$$\begin{pmatrix} S \\ S' \end{pmatrix}^{-1} \begin{pmatrix} S \\ \Sigma^{-1}S\Sigma \end{pmatrix} \begin{pmatrix} S \\ S' \end{pmatrix} = \begin{pmatrix} S' \\ S \end{pmatrix} \begin{pmatrix} S \\ \Sigma^{-1}S\Sigma \end{pmatrix} \begin{pmatrix} S \\ S' \end{pmatrix}$$

$$= \begin{pmatrix} S' \\ \Sigma^{-1}S\Sigma \end{pmatrix} \begin{pmatrix} \Sigma^{-1}S\Sigma \\ \Sigma'^{-1}S'\Sigma' \end{pmatrix}$$

$$= \begin{pmatrix} S' \\ \Sigma'^{-1}S'\Sigma' \end{pmatrix}.$$

The isomorphism $\begin{pmatrix} S \\ S' \end{pmatrix}$ therefore transforms every inner isomorphism into another inner isomorphism. It follows that the group of inner isomorphisms is self-conjugate within the group of isomorphisms.

64. Let G be a group of order N, whose operations are

$$S_1 (=E),\ S_2, \ldots, S_{N-1},\ S_N;$$

and let L be the group of isomorphisms of G. We have seen in § 20 that G may be represented as a group of regular permutations performed on the N symbols

$$S_1,\ S_2, \ldots,\ S_{N-1},\ S_N;$$

and that, when it is so represented, the permutation which corresponds to the operation S_x is

$$\begin{pmatrix} S_1, & S_2, & \ldots, & S_{N-1}, & S_N \\ S_1S_x, & S_2S_x, & \ldots, & S_{N-1}S_x, & S_NS_x \end{pmatrix},$$

or more shortly

$$\begin{pmatrix} S \\ SS_x \end{pmatrix}.$$

When G is thus represented, we will denote it by G'. We have already seen that L can be represented as a permutation group of the same N symbols; a typical substitution of L, when it is so represented, is

$$\begin{pmatrix} S_1, & S_2, & \ldots, & S_{N-1}, & S_N \\ S_1', & S_2', & \ldots, & S'_{N-1}, & S'_N \end{pmatrix},$$

or more shortly

$$\begin{pmatrix} S \\ S' \end{pmatrix}.$$

When L is thus represented, we will denote it by L'. It is clear that the two permutation groups G' and L' have no permutation in common except identity. For every permutation of L' leaves the symbol S_1 unchanged; and no permutation of G', except identity, leaves S_1 unchanged.

Now
$$\begin{pmatrix} S \\ S' \end{pmatrix}^{-1} \begin{pmatrix} S \\ SS_x \end{pmatrix} \begin{pmatrix} S \\ S' \end{pmatrix} = \begin{pmatrix} S' \\ SS_x \end{pmatrix} \begin{pmatrix} SS_x \\ S'S_x' \end{pmatrix}$$
$$= \begin{pmatrix} S' \\ S'S_x' \end{pmatrix}$$
$$= \begin{pmatrix} S \\ SS_x' \end{pmatrix}.$$

Every operation of L' is therefore permutable with G'. Hence if M is the order of L, the group $\{G', L'\}$, which we will call K', is a permutation group of order NM on the N symbols, containing G' self-conjugately. Further $\begin{pmatrix} S \\ S' \end{pmatrix}$ transforms $\begin{pmatrix} S \\ SS_x \end{pmatrix}$ into $\begin{pmatrix} S \\ SS_x' \end{pmatrix}$; and these two permutations of G' correspond to the operations S_x and S_x' of G. Hence the isomorphism, established on transforming the permutations of G' by any permutation $\begin{pmatrix} S \\ S' \end{pmatrix}$ of L', is the isomorphism denoted by the symbol $\begin{pmatrix} S \\ S' \end{pmatrix}$.

Since $\begin{pmatrix} S \\ S_x S S_x^{-1} \end{pmatrix}$ is a permutation of L', the permutation $\begin{pmatrix} S \\ S_x S S_x^{-1} \end{pmatrix} \begin{pmatrix} S \\ S S_x \end{pmatrix}$, or $\begin{pmatrix} S \\ S_x S \end{pmatrix}$, belongs to K'. Hence K' contains the set of permutations

$$\begin{pmatrix} S \\ S_x S \end{pmatrix}, \; (x = 1, 2, \ldots\ldots, N-1, N).$$

These form (§ 20) a group G'', simply isomorphic with G' and such that every permutation of G'' is permutable with every permutation of G'. Moreover (*l.c.*), the permutations of G'' are the only permutations of the N symbols which are permutable with each of the permutations of G'.

Suppose now that Σ is any permutation of the N symbols which is permutable with G'. When the permutations of G' are transformed by Σ, the resulting isomorphism is identical with that given by some permutation, say $\begin{pmatrix} S \\ S' \end{pmatrix}$, of L'. Hence $\Sigma \begin{pmatrix} S \\ S' \end{pmatrix}^{-1}$ is a permutation of the N symbols which is permutable with every permutation of G'. It therefore belongs to G''; and hence Σ belongs to K'. It follows that K' contains every permutation of the N symbols which is permutable with G'.

The only permutations common to G' and G'' are the self-conjugate permutations of either. The factor-group $K'/\{G', G''\}$ is simply isomorphic with L/g, where g is the group of inner isomorphisms of G contained in L. The groups G' and G'' are identical only when G' is Abelian; in this case, g consists of the identical operation alone.

Definition. A group K, simply isomorphic with the permutation group K' which has just been constructed, we shall call the *holomorph* of G.

$K = \{A(G) \cup P(G)\}$.

The permutation group K' contains both G' and G'' self-conjugately and consists of every permutation of the N symbols which is permutable with both G' and G''. Now

$$\begin{pmatrix} S \\ S^{-1} \end{pmatrix}$$

is a permutation of the N symbols which, when G' is not Abelian, so that G' and G'' are not identical, is not an isomorphism of G and is therefore not contained in K'. Moreover

$$\begin{pmatrix} S^{-1} \\ S \end{pmatrix} \begin{pmatrix} S \\ SS_x \end{pmatrix} \begin{pmatrix} S \\ S^{-1} \end{pmatrix} = \begin{pmatrix} S \\ S_x^{-1}S \end{pmatrix},$$

so that the permutation $\begin{pmatrix} S \\ S^{-1} \end{pmatrix}$ transforms G' into G'' and G'' into G'. It therefore transforms the permutations that are permutable with G' into those that are permutable with G''; i.e. it must transform K' into itself. The group K' is therefore, when G' is not Abelian, contained self-conjugately in the group $\left\{K', \begin{pmatrix} S \\ S^{-1} \end{pmatrix}\right\}$ of double its order, and in this group G' and G'' are conjugate sub-groups.

65. An isomorphism must change any set of operations, which are conjugate to each other, into another set which are conjugate. For if

$$\begin{pmatrix} S \\ S' \end{pmatrix}$$

be the isomorphism, and if

$$S_z^{-1}S_xS_z = S_y,$$

then

$$S_z'^{-1}S_x'S_z' = S_y',$$

so that S_x' and S_y' are conjugate operations when S_x and S_y are conjugate. An inner isomorphism changes every set of conjugate operations into itself; and all the members of a class of outer isomorphisms permute the conjugate sets in the same way. If

$$\begin{pmatrix} S \\ S' \end{pmatrix}$$

is an isomorphism which changes every conjugate set of operations of G into itself, and if

$$\begin{pmatrix} S \\ S'' \end{pmatrix}$$

is any isomorphism of G, then the isomorphism

$$\begin{pmatrix} S \\ S'' \end{pmatrix}^{-1} \begin{pmatrix} S \\ S' \end{pmatrix} \begin{pmatrix} S \\ S'' \end{pmatrix}$$

changes every conjugate set into itself. It follows that those isomorphisms, which change every conjugate set of operations into itself, form a self-conjugate sub-group of the complete group of isomorphisms. This sub-group clearly contains the group of inner isomorphisms and may be identical with it.

No case is known of an outer isomorphism which changes each conjugate set of operations into itself. On the other hand, it is still an open question whether or no such isomorphisms exist.

If now $\begin{pmatrix} S \\ S' \end{pmatrix}$ is any isomorphism of G of order n, the permutations

$$\begin{pmatrix} S \\ S' \end{pmatrix} \text{ and } \begin{pmatrix} S \\ SS_x \end{pmatrix}, \ (x = 1, 2, \ldots\ldots, N),$$

generate a group of order Nn. When J is used to represent the isomorphism, this group may be denoted by $\{J, G\}$; as shewn above, it contains G self-conjugately. Suppose that n is prime and is not a factor of N. The operation J is not permutable with every operation of G; and therefore (§ 26) there must be operations S of G which are permutable with no operation of the conjugate set to which J belongs. The number of operations which in $\{J, G\}$ are conjugate to such an operation S must be a multiple of n; and since n is not a factor of N, this conjugate set of operations must be made up of n distinct conjugate sets of operations in G. The isomorphism J must therefore interchange some of the conjugate sets of G.

The same result is clearly true if the order n of J has any prime factor not contained in N. Hence:—

THEOREM II. *An isomorphism of a group G, whose order contains a prime factor which does not occur in the order of G, must interchange some of the conjugate sets of G.*

66. If the isomorphism $\binom{S}{S'}$ or J leaves no operation except identity unchanged, it must in $\{J, G\}$ be one of N conjugate operations. For if

$$S_x^{-1}JS_x = S_y^{-1}JS_y,$$

J would be permutable with $S_yS_x^{-1}$, which is not the case.

These N conjugate operations are

$$J, JS_2, JS_3 \ldots\ldots JS_N,$$

and since the first transforms every operation of G, except identity, into a different one, the same must be true of all the set. If now J transformed any operation S into a conjugate operation $\Sigma^{-1}S\Sigma$, $J\Sigma^{-1}$ would transform S into itself; hence J must transform every conjugate set of G into a different conjugate set.

The special cases in which the order of J is two or three may here be considered. Representing the N operations conjugate to J by

$$J, J_1, J_2, \ldots\ldots, J_{N-1},$$

the N operations of G, when the order of J is 2, are

$$J^2, JJ_1, JJ_2, \ldots\ldots, JJ_{N-1}.$$

Now $$J \,.\, JJ_x \,.\, J = J_xJ = (JJ_x)^{-1},$$

so that J transforms every operation of G into its inverse. But if

$$S' = S^{-1},$$

and $$T' = T^{-1},$$

then $$S'\,T' = S^{-1}T^{-1} = (TS)^{-1}.$$

Now as $S'\,T'$ is the operation into which the isomorphism transforms ST, it must be $(ST)^{-1}$, and therefore

$$ST = TS.$$

The group G is therefore an Abelian group of odd order.

When the order of J is 3, let $S', S'', \ldots\ldots, S^{(h)}$ or C be a set of h conjugate operations in G. In $\{J, G\}$ the set forms part of a conjugate set of $3h$ operations, consisting of C, $J^{-1}CJ$, JCJ^{-1}.

Now $$S' \,.\, J^{-1}S'J \,.\, JS'J^{-1} = (S'J^{-1})^3 = E,$$

and $$S' \,.\, JS'J^{-1} \,.\, J^{-1}S'J = (S'J)^3 = E.$$

Hence $J^{-1}S'J$ and $JS'J^{-1}$ are permutable, and each is similarly shewn to be permutable with S'. Also since, for J, any one of its N conjugates may be used, S' is permutable with every operation of each of the sets $J^{-1}CJ$ and JCJ^{-1}. Moreover since S' is permutable with $J^{-1}S''J$ and with $JS''J^{-1}$, it is permutable with S''. Hence G must be such that every two of its operations which are conjugate are permutable. It is easy to shew from this that G must be the direct product of groups whose orders are powers of primes; these groups themselves being subject to definite limitations*.

67. Any sub-group H of G is transformed by an isomorphism into a simply isomorphic sub-group H': but H and H' are not necessarily conjugate within G. If however the set of conjugate sub-groups

$$H_1, H_2, \ldots\ldots, H_m,$$

are the only sub-groups of G of a given type, every isomorphism must interchange them among themselves.

Suppose now that this is the case and that no operation of G is permutable with each of the conjugate sub-groups

$$H_1, H_2, \ldots\ldots, H_m.$$

Let J be any operation, of order μ, that transforms G and each of the set of m conjugate sub-groups, into itself. Then J^μ is the lowest power of J that can occur in G, since no operation of G transforms each of the m sub-groups into itself. Now in $\{J, G\}$, the greatest sub-group that contains H_r self-conjugately is $\{J, I_r\}$, I_r being the greatest sub-group of G that contains H_r self-conjugately. Also, in $\{J, G\}$ the set of sub-groups $\{J, I_r\}$, $(r = 1, 2, \ldots, m)$, is a complete conjugate set. Now the set of groups

$$I_1, I_2, \ldots\ldots, I_m$$

have by supposition no common operation except identity; and therefore the greatest common sub-group of

$$\{J, I_1\}, \{J, I_2\}, \ldots\ldots, \{J, I_m\}$$

is $\{J\}$. Hence $\{J\}$ is a self-conjugate sub-group of $\{J, G\}$; and since G is also a self-conjugate sub-group of $\{J, G\}$, while $\{J\}$ and G have no common operation except identity, J must be

* Burnside, "On groups in which every two conjugate operations are permutable," *Proc. L. M. S.* Vol. xxxv (1902), pp. 28—37.

permutable with every operation of G. Every operation therefore which is permutable with G, and with each of the sub-groups

$$H_1, H_2, \ldots\ldots, H_m,$$

is permutable with every operation of G. Thus finally, no outer isomorphism can transform each of the sub-groups $H_r\,(r=1, 2, \ldots\ldots, m)$ into itself. Hence:—

THEOREM III. *If the conjugate set of m sub-groups*

$$H_1, H_2, \ldots\ldots, H_m$$

contains all the sub-groups of G of a given type, and if no operation of G is permutable with each sub-group of the set, then to each isomorphism of G there corresponds a distinct permutation of the m sub-groups.

68. Definition. Any sub-group of a group G which is transformed into itself by every isomorphism of G, is called* a *characteristic sub-group* of G.

A characteristic sub-group of a group G is necessarily a self-conjugate sub-group of G; but a self-conjugate sub-group is not necessarily characteristic. A simple group, having no self-conjugate sub-groups, can have no characteristic sub-groups. Let G be any group, and let K be the holomorph of G. A characteristic sub-group of G is then a self-conjugate sub-group of K; and conversely, every self-conjugate sub-group of K which is contained in G is a characteristic sub-group of G.

Suppose now a chief-series of K formed which contains G. If G has no characteristic sub-group, it must be the last term but one of this series, the last term being identity. It follows by § 53 that G must be the direct product of a number of simply isomorphic simple groups. Hence:—

THEOREM IV. *A group, which has no characteristic sub-group, must be either a simple group or the direct product of simply isomorphic simple groups.*

The converse of this theorem is clearly true.

* Frobenius, "Ueber endliche Gruppen," *Berliner Sitzungsberichte*, 1895, p. 183.

69. Suppose now that G is a group which has characteristic sub-groups; and let

$$G,\ G_1,\ \ldots\ldots,\ G_r,\ G_{r+1},\ \ldots\ldots,\ E$$

be a series of such sub-groups, each containing the one that follows it and chosen so that, for each consecutive pair G_r and G_{r+1}, there is no characteristic sub-group of G contained in G_r and containing G_{r+1}, except G_{r+1} itself. Such a series is called* a *characteristic series* of G.

It may clearly be possible to choose such a series in more than one way. If

$$G,\ G_1',\ \ldots\ldots,\ G_r',\ G'_{r+1},\ \ldots\ldots,\ E$$

be a second characteristic series of G, and if K is the holomorph of G, then

$$K,\ J,\ \ldots\ldots,\ H,\ G,\ G_1,\ \ldots\ldots,\ G_r,\ G_{r+1},\ \ldots\ldots,\ E$$

and $$K,\ J,\ \ldots\ldots,\ H,\ G,\ G_1',\ \ldots\ldots,\ G_r',\ G'_{r+1},\ \ldots\ldots,\ E$$

are two chief-series of K. In fact, if K had a self-conjugate sub-group contained in G_r and containing G_{r+1}, then G would have a characteristic sub-group contained in G_r and containing G_{r+1}. The two chief-series of K coincide in the terms from K to G inclusive. Hence the two sets of factor-groups

$$G/G_1,\ G_1/G_2,\ \ldots\ldots,\ G_r/G_{r+1},\ \ldots\ldots$$

and $$G/G_1',\ G_1'/G_2',\ \ldots\ldots,\ G_r'/G'_{r+1},\ \ldots\ldots$$

must be equal in number and, except possibly as regards the sequence in which they occur, identical in type. Moreover, each factor-group must be either a simple group or the direct product of simply isomorphic simple groups.

70. The isomorphisms of a given group with itself are closely connected with the composition of every composite group in which the given group enters as a self-conjugate sub-group. Let G be any composite group and H a self-conjugate sub-group of G. Then since every operation of G transforms H into itself, to every such operation will correspond an isomorphism of H with itself. If S is an operation of G not contained in H, and if the isomorphism of H arising on

* Frobenius, "Ueber auflösbare Gruppen II," *Berliner Sitzungsberichte*, 1895, p. 1027.

transforming its operations by S is an outer isomorphism, so also is the isomorphism arising from each of the set of operations SH. In this case, no one of this set of operations is permutable with every operation of H. If however the isomorphism arising from S is an inner isomorphism, there must be some operation h of H which gives the same isomorphism as S; and then Sh^{-1} is permutable with every operation of H. In this case, the set of operations SH will give all the inner isomorphisms of H.

Suppose now that H_1 is that sub-group of G which is formed of all the operations of G that are permutable with every operation of H. Then to every operation of G, not contained in $\{H, H_1\}$, must correspond an outer isomorphism of H; and to every operation of the factor-group $G/\{H, H_1\}$ corresponds a class of outer isomorphisms. If then L is the group of isomorphisms of H, and if L_1 is that self-conjugate sub-group of L which gives the inner isomorphisms of H, $G/\{H, H_1\}$ must be simply isomorphic with a sub-group of L/L_1.

If now H contains no self-conjugate operation except identity, H and H_1 can contain no common operation except identity. Hence, since every operation of H is permutable with every operation of H_1, $\{H, H_1\}$ is in this case the direct product of H and H_1.

If, further, L coincides with H, so that H admits of no outer isomorphisms, $G/\{H, H_1\}$ must reduce to identity. In this case, G is the direct product of H and H_1.

Definition. A group, which contains no self-conjugate operation except identity and admits of no outer isomorphism, is called* a *complete* group.

One result of the present paragraph may be expressed in the form:—

THEOREM V. *A group, which contains a complete group as a self-conjugate sub-group, must be the direct product of the complete group and some other group*†.

* Hölder, "Bildung zusammengesetzter Gruppen," *Math. Ann.* Vol. XLVI (1895), p. 325.

† *Ibid.* p. 325.

Ex. If G is a complete group of order N, shew that the order of K, the holomorph of G, is N^2, and that the order of the holomorph of K is $2N^4$.

71. Theorem VI. *If G is a group with no self-conjugate operations except identity; and if the group of inner isomorphisms of G is a characteristic sub-group of L, the group of isomorphisms of G; then L is a complete group*.*

With the notation of § 64, the operations of L may be represented by the permutations

$$\begin{pmatrix} S \\ S' \end{pmatrix}$$

The group of inner isomorphisms, which we will call G', is given by the permutations

$$\begin{pmatrix} S \\ S_x^{-1}SS_x \end{pmatrix}; \ (x = 1, \ \ldots\ldots, \ N-1, \ N),$$

it is simply isomorphic with G.

Now
$$\begin{pmatrix} S \\ S' \end{pmatrix}^{-1} \begin{pmatrix} S \\ S_x^{-1}SS_x \end{pmatrix} \begin{pmatrix} S \\ S' \end{pmatrix} = \begin{pmatrix} S' \\ S_x'^{-1}S'S_x' \end{pmatrix}$$
$$= \begin{pmatrix} S \\ S_x'^{-1}SS_x' \end{pmatrix}:$$

and therefore no operation of L is permutable with every operation of G'. Hence every isomorphism of G' arises on transforming its operations by those of L. Suppose now that J is an operation which transforms L into itself. Since G' is by supposition a characteristic sub-group of L, the operation J transforms G' into itself. If J does not belong to L, we may assume that J is permutable with every operation of G'. For if it is not, it must give the same isomorphism of G' as some operation Σ of L; and then $J\Sigma^{-1}$ is permutable with every operation of G', and is not contained in L. Now J being permutable with every operation of G', we have

$$J^{-1}s^{-1}gsJ = s^{-1}gs,$$

where s is any operation of L, and g any operation of G'.

* Hölder (*loc. cit.* p. 331) gives a theorem which is similar but not quite equivalent to Theorem VI.

Moreover $$JgJ^{-1} = g,$$

and therefore $$J^{-1}s^{-1}JgJ^{-1}sJ = s^{-1}gs.$$

Hence s and $J^{-1}sJ$ give the same isomorphism of G'. Now no two distinct operations of L give the same isomorphism of G', so that s and $J^{-1}sJ$ must be identical; in other words, J is permutable with every operation of L. Hence L admits of no outer isomorphisms. Moreover, G' has no self-conjugate operations, and no operation of L is permutable with every operation of G'; hence L has no self-conjugate operations. It is therefore a complete group.

Corollary. If G is a simple group of composite order, or if it is the direct product of a number of isomorphic simple groups of composite order, the group of isomorphisms L of G is a complete group.

For suppose, if possible, in this case that G is not a characteristic sub-group of L; and that, by an outer isomorphism of L, G is transformed into G_1. Then G_1 is a self-conjugate sub-group of L, and each of the groups G and G_1 transforms the other into itself. Hence (§ 34) either every operation of G is permutable with every operation of G_1, or G and G_1 must have a common sub-group. The former supposition is impossible since no operation of L is permutable with every operation of G. On the other hand, if G and G_1 have a common sub-group, it is a self-conjugate sub-group of L and it therefore is a characteristic sub-group of G. Now (§ 68) G has no characteristic sub-groups, and therefore the second supposition is also impossible. It follows that, in this case, G is a characteristic sub-group of L, and that L is a complete group.

72. THEOREM VII. *If G is an Abelian group of odd order, and if K is the holomorph of G; then when G is a characteristic sub-group of K, the latter group is a complete group.*

Since G is of odd order, there is an isomorphism of order two changing each operation of G into its inverse, leaving E only unchanged. Hence K has no self-conjugate operation except E. If Q is an operation of K of order two giving this isomorphism, then in K there are just N operations conjugate to Q, viz.

$QS_i\ (i = 1, 2, \ldots, N)$, where $S_i\ (i = 1, 2, \ldots, N)$ are the operations of G.

Since G is a characteristic sub-group of K, every isomorphism of K permutes these N operations among themselves; and since no operation of K is permutable with all of them, it follows by § 67 that no isomorphism of K can be permutable with all of them. Let J be an operation which transforms K into itself. As in § 71 we may without loss of generality assume that J is permutable with every operation of G. If

$$J^{-1}QJ = QS_i,$$

there is an operation of G such that

$$S_j^{-1}QS_j = QS_i,$$

and JS_j^{-1} is permutable with Q, and therefore with each of the N operations $QS_t\ (t = 1, 2, \ldots, N)$. But the only isomorphism of K for which this is true is the identical isomorphism. Hence J gives an inner isomorphism of K; or K admits no outer isomorphisms. It has been seen that K has no self-conjugate operation except E, and it is therefore a complete group.

73. We end the present chapter with the following theorem, which, though not directly connected with those that precede it, is of some importance in dealing with groups of isomorphisms.

THEOREM VIII. *If H is a self-conjugate sub-group of G, the order of an isomorphism of G, which transforms every operation of each of the groups G/H and H into itself, is a factor of the order of H.*

If S is any operation of G not contained in H, the isomorphism will change S into Sh, where h is some operation of H. If then m is the order of h, the isomorphism transforms

$$S,\ Sh,\ Sh^2,\ \ldots\ldots,\ Sh^{m-1}$$

cyclically; and therefore it transforms all the operations of the set SH in cycles of m each. If S' is any operation of G not contained in SH, the isomorphism will interchange the operations of the set $S'H$ among themselves in cycles of m' each, where m' again is the order of some operation of H. The isomorphism, when expressed as a permutation performed on the operations of G, will consist of a number of cycles of $m, m', \ldots\ldots$ symbols; and its order is therefore the least common multiple of $m, m', \ldots\ldots$. Now if q is any prime that divides the order of H, and q^n the highest power of q that occurs as the order of an operation of H, no power of q higher than q^n can occur in any of the numbers $m, m', \ldots\ldots$; and q^n is therefore the highest power of q that can occur in their least common multiple. This least common multiple, which is the order of the isomorphism, must therefore divide the order of H.

Ex. 1. If a group G admits an isomorphism, in which more than three quarters of its operations correspond to their inverses, then G must be Abelian. (G. A. Miller.)

Ex. 2. If a group admits an isomorphism in which each operation corresponds to its μth power, where μ is relatively prime to the order of the group, then the $(\mu - 1)$th power of every operation is self-conjugate. (J. W. Young.)

Ex. 3. If a group, of odd order N, admits an isomorphism of order 2, in which n_1 operations correspond to themselves and n_2 to their inverses, prove that

$$N = n_1 (n_2 + 1).$$

Hence shew that if $n_2 \geqslant \frac{1}{3} N$, the group must be Abelian.

Ex. 4. Prove that the group of isomorphisms of the group of order 8, defined by

$$A^2 = E, \quad B^2 = E, \quad (AB)^4 = E,$$

is simply isomorphic with the group itself.

CHAPTER VII.

ON ABELIAN GROUPS*.

74. WE shall now apply the general results, that have been obtained in the previous chapters, to the study of two special classes of groups; in the present chapter we shall deal particularly with Abelian groups (§ 24) whose operations are all permutable with each other.

It is to be expected (and it will be found) that the theory of Abelian groups is much simpler than that of groups in general; for the process of multiplication of the operations of such groups is commutative as well as associative.

Every sub-group of an Abelian group is itself an Abelian group, since its operations are necessarily all permutable. For the same reason, every operation and every sub-group of an Abelian group is self-conjugate both in the group itself and in any sub-group in which it is contained.

If G is an Abelian group and H any sub-group of G, then since H is necessarily self-conjugate, there exists a factor-group G/H, and this again must be an Abelian group. (The reader must not however infer that, if H and G/H are both Abelian,

* On Abelian groups, the reader may consult Frobenius and Stickelberger, "Ueber Gruppen vertauschbarer Elemente," *Crelle's Journal*, Vol. LXXXVI (1879), p. 217; and a very complete discussion in the second volume of Herr Weber's *Lehrbuch der Algebra*.

The name "Abelian group" has been applied by M. Jordan (*Traité des substitutions etc.* pp. 171 et seq.) to an entirely different class of groups, whose operations are not permutable. Most writers, we believe, have used the phrase in the sense defined in the text.

The connection of Abel's name with groups of permutable operations is due to his having been the first to investigate, with complete generality, the application of such groups to the theory of equations, "Mémoire sur une classe particulière d'équations résolubles algébriquement," *Crelle's Journal*, Vol. IV (1829), p. 131; or Collected Works, 1881 edition, Vol. I, p. 478.

then G is also Abelian. It is indeed clear that this is not necessarily the case.)

75. If P and Q are permutable operations of order m and n, the order of their product is equal to or a factor of mn; for

$$(PQ)^{mn} = (P^m)^n (Q^n)^m = E.$$

In particular if the orders of P and Q are powers of p, then PQ is either identity or has a power of p for its order.

Let now G be any Abelian group of finite order $N = p^\alpha q^\beta \ldots r^\gamma$, where $p, q, \ldots, r$ are distinct primes. By § 35 G must have operations of orders $p, q, \ldots, r$. Let

$$P, P', P'', \ldots\ldots,$$
$$Q, Q', Q'', \ldots\ldots,$$
$$\ldots\ldots\ldots\ldots\ldots\ldots,$$
$$R, R', R'', \ldots\ldots,$$

be those operations of G whose orders are respectively powers of $p, q, \ldots, r$. The product of any two of the operations

$$P, P', P'', \ldots\ldots$$

is either E or another operation of the set. Hence

$$E, P, P', P'', \ldots\ldots$$

constitute a sub-group of G, which may be denoted by G_p. Its order is a power of p (§ 35), say $p^{\alpha'}$. Similarly

$$E, Q, Q', Q'', \ldots\ldots$$

constitute a sub-group of G_q of order $q^{\beta'}$; and so on.

Now it has been seen (§ 16) that any operation of order $p^a q^b \ldots r^c$, where $p, q, \ldots, r$ are distinct primes, can be represented in just one way in the form $PQ \ldots R$, where $P, Q, \ldots, R$ are permutable operations of orders $p^a, q^b, \ldots, r^c$. Hence every operation of G can be represented as the product of operations, one being chosen from each of the sub-groups $G_p, G_q, \ldots, G_r$. No two of these sub-groups have a common operation except E, and their operations are all permutable. Their direct product (§ 31) is contained in G, and G is contained in their direct product. Hence G is the direct product of $G_p, G_q, \ldots, G_r$; and $\alpha' = \alpha, \beta' = \beta, \ldots, \gamma' = \gamma$.

THEOREM I. *An Abelian group G of order $p^\alpha q^\beta \ldots r^\gamma$, where $p, q, \ldots, r$ are distinct primes, is the direct product of groups $G_p, G_q, \ldots, G_r$ of orders $p^\alpha, q^\beta, \ldots, r^\gamma$. The sub-group G_p is formed of all the operations of G whose orders are powers of p with the identical operation.*

76. The first problem of pure group-theory that presents itself in connection with Abelian groups is the determination of all distinct Abelian groups of given order N. Let G_p and G_p' be two distinct Abelian groups of order p^α, i.e. two groups which are not simply isomorphic. Then two Abelian groups of order N, whose sub-groups of order p^α are simply isomorphic with G_p and G_p' respectively, are necessarily distinct. Since then G is the direct product of $G_p, G_q, \ldots, G_r$, the general problem for any composite order N will be completely solved when we have determined all distinct types of Abelian groups of orders $p^\alpha, q^\beta, \ldots, r^\gamma$. We may therefore, for the purpose of this problem, confine our attention to those Abelian groups whose orders are powers of primes.

77. If $P_1, P_2, \ldots, P_s$ of orders $p^{m_1}, p^{m_2}, \ldots, p^{m_s}$ are a set of operations between which no other relations exist, except

$$P_i P_j = P_j P_i, \quad (i, j = 1, 2, \ldots, s),$$

they clearly generate an Abelian group of order p^m, where $m = m_1 + m_2 + \ldots + m_s$. For if there are less than p^m distinct operations in the set

$$P_1^{x_1} P_2^{x_2} \ldots P_s^{x_s},$$

there must be relations of the form

$$P_1^{a_1} P_2^{a_2} \ldots P_s^{a_s} = E,$$

contrary to supposition. The s operations $P_1, P_2, \ldots, P_s$ are spoken of as a set of independent generating operations of the group. A fundamental question is whether an Abelian group of finite order always has such a set of independent generating operations. It is answered in the affirmative by the following investigation*.

* This method of shewing that an Abelian group of finite order has a set of independent generating operations is due to Mr Hilton, *Finite Groups* (1908), pp. 126, 127.

Let G be an Abelian group whose order is a power of p, and let P_1 be an operation of G whose order p^{m_1} is not less than that of any other operation. Then every operation of G satisfies the relation

$$S^{p^{m_1}} = E.$$

Consider the factor-group $G/\{P_1\}$, which is Abelian. Let P' be an operation of it, whose order p^{m_2} is not less than that of any other operation, and P a corresponding operation of G. The order of P is (§ 28) equal to or a multiple of p^{m_2}; and therefore m_2 is equal to or less than m_1. Then if S is any operation of G, $S^{p^{m_2}}$ is contained in $\{P_1\}$. If

$$P^{p^{m_2}} = P_1^{x},$$

then
$$E = P^{p^{m_1}} = P_1^{xp^{m_1-m_2}},$$

so that x is divisible by p^{m_2}. If x/p^{m_2} is y, then

$$(PP_1^{-y})^{m_2} = E.$$

Put
$$PP_1^{-y} = P_2;$$

then
$$P_2^{p^{m_2}} = E,$$

and no power of P_2, distinct from E, occurs in $\{P_1\}$.

Consider next the factor-group $G/\{P_1, P_2\}$, which is Abelian. Let Q' be an operation of it, whose order p^{m_3} is not less than the order of any other, and Q a corresponding operation of G. Then, if S is any operation of G, $S^{p^{m_3}}$ is contained in $\{P_1, P_2\}$, so that m_3 is equal to or less than m_2. Moreover

$$Q^{p^{m_3}} = P_1^{x_1}P_2^{x_2},$$

$$Q^{p^{m_2}} = P_1^{x_1p^{m_2-m_3}}P_2^{x_2p^{m_2-m_3}},$$

$$E = Q^{p^{m_1}} = P_1^{x_1p^{m_1-m_3}}P_2^{x_2p^{m_1-m_3}}.$$

Now $Q^{p^{m_2}}$ is contained in $\{P_1\}$. Hence x_2 is a multiple of p^{m_3}, say $x_2/p^{m_3} = y_2$. The last relation now becomes

$$E = P_1^{x_1p^{m_1-m_3}},$$

so that x_1 is a multiple of p^{m_3}, say $x_1/p^{m_3} = y_1$. Put

$$P_3 = QP_1^{-y_1}P_2^{-y_2};$$

then
$$P_3^{p^{m_3}} = E,$$

and no power of P_3, distinct from E, occurs in $\{P_1, P_2\}$.

The operations P_1, P_2, P_3 thus determined are independent; and the process may clearly be continued (considering next the factor-group $G/\{P_1, P_2, P_3\}$) till a set of independent operations which generate G is arrived at. Hence :—

THEOREM II. *The operations of an Abelian group, whose order is a power of p, can always be represented in the form*

$$P_1^{x_1}P_2^{x_2}......P_s^{x_s},$$

$$\begin{pmatrix} x_i = 0, 1, 2, \ldots, p^{m_i}-1 \\ i = \quad 1, 2, \ldots, s \end{pmatrix},$$

where the operations P_1, $P_2, \ldots, P_s$ are connected by the relations

$$\begin{aligned} P_i^{p^{m_i}} &= E, \\ P_iP_j &= P_jP_i, \end{aligned} \quad (i, j = 1, 2, \ldots, s),$$

and by no others.

It is convenient to suppose the m's in descending order, so that

$$m_1 \geqslant m_2 \geqslant m_3 \geqslant ...... \geqslant m_s.$$

78. It is clear, from the synthetic process by which it has been proved that an Abelian group of order p^m can be generated by a set of independent operations, that a considerable latitude exists in the choice of the actual generating operations; and the question arises as to the relations between the numbers and the orders of distinct sets of independent generating operations.

The discussion of this question is facilitated by a consideration of certain special sub-groups of G. If A and B are two operations of G, and if the order of A is not less than that of B, the order of AB is equal to, or is a factor of, the order of A. Hence the totality of those operations of G whose orders do not exceed p^μ, or in other words of those operations which satisfy the relation

$$S^{p^\mu} = E,$$

form a sub-group G_μ. The order of G_μ clearly depends on the orders of the various operations of G and in no way on a special choice of generating operations. Now if

$$P_1^{\alpha_1}P_2^{\alpha_2}......P_s^{\alpha_s}$$

belongs to G_μ, then

$$P_1^{\alpha_1 p^\mu}P_2^{\alpha_2 p^\mu}......P_s^{\alpha_s p^\mu} = E.$$

Hence if m_{i+1} is the first of the series

$$m_1, m_2, \ldots\ldots, m_s,$$

which is less than μ, then $\alpha_{i+1}, \ldots\ldots, \alpha_s$ may have any values whatever; but $\alpha_t\,(t = 1, 2, \ldots\ldots, i)$ must be a multiple of $p^{m_t-\mu}$.

It follows from this that G_μ is generated by the s independent operations

$$P_1^{p^{m_1-\mu}},\ P_2^{p^{m_2-\mu}}, \ldots\ldots, P_i^{p^{m_i-\mu}},\ P_{i+1}, \ldots\ldots, P_s.$$

If then the order of G_μ is p^ν, we have

$$\nu = \mu i + \sum_{i+1}^{s} m_t.$$

The order of G_1, the sub-group formed of all operations of G whose order is p, is clearly p^s.

79. Suppose now that by a fresh choice of independent generating operations, it were found that G could be generated by the s' independent operations

$$P_1', P_2', \ldots\ldots, P'_{s'}$$

of orders $\qquad p^{m_1'}, p^{m_2'}, \ldots\ldots, p^{m'_{s'}},$

where $\qquad m_1' \geqslant m_2' \geqslant \ldots\ldots \geqslant m_s'.$

If $m'_{i'+1}$ is the first of this series which is less than μ, the order of G_μ will be $p^{\nu'}$, where

$$\nu' = \mu i' + \sum_{i'+1}^{s'} m_t'.$$

The order of G_μ is independent of the choice of generating operations; so that for all values of μ

$$\nu = \nu'.$$

Hence, by taking $\mu = 1$,

$$s = s',$$

or the number of independent generating operations is independent of their choice.

If now $\qquad m_t = m_t'\ (t = i+1, i+2, \ldots\ldots, s),$

and $\qquad m_i > m_i',$

and if we choose μ so that

$$m_i \geqslant \mu > m_i';$$

then $$\nu = \mu i + \sum_{i+1}^{s} m_t,$$

and $$\nu' = \mu(i-1) + m_i' + \sum_{i+1}^{s} m_t.$$

The condition $$\nu = \nu'$$

gives $$\mu = m_i',$$

in contradiction to the assumption just made.

Similarly we can prove that the assumption $m_i' > m_i$ cannot be maintained. Hence

$$m_i = m_i';$$

and therefore, however the independent generating operations of G are chosen, their number is always s, and their orders are

$$p^{m_1},\ p^{m_2}, \ldots\ldots,\ p^{m_s}.$$

80. If G' is a second Abelian group of order p^m, simply isomorphic with G, and if

$$P_1',\ P_2', \ldots\ldots,\ P'_{s'}$$

of orders $$p^{m_1'},\ p^{m_2'}, \ldots\ldots,\ p^{m'_{s'}},$$

where $$m_1' \geqslant m_2' \geqslant \ldots\ldots \geqslant m'_{s'}$$

are a set of independent generating operations of G', exactly the same process as that of the last paragraph may be used to shew that

$$s = s',$$

and $$m_i = m_i' \ (i = 1,\ 2, \ldots\ldots,\ s).$$

In fact, since corresponding operations of two simply isomorphic groups have the same order, the order of G_μ must be equal to the order of G_μ'; and this is the condition that has been used to obtain the result of the last paragraph.

Two Abelian groups of order p^m cannot therefore be simply isomorphic unless the series of integers $m_1, m_2, \ldots\ldots, m_3$ is the same for each. On the other hand when this condition is satisfied, it is clear that the two groups are simply isomorphic, since by taking P_i and P_i' $(i = 1, 2, \ldots\ldots, s)$ as corresponding operations, the isomorphism is actually established.

The number of distinct types of Abelian groups of order p^m, where p is a prime, i.e. the number of such groups no one of which is simply isomorphic with any other, is therefore equal to the number of partitions of m. When the prime p is given, each type of group may be conveniently, and without ambiguity, represented by the symbol of the corresponding partition. Thus the typical group G that we have been dealing with would be represented by the symbol $(m_1, m_2, \ldots\ldots, m_s)$.

81. Having thus determined all distinct types of Abelian groups of order p^m, a second general problem in this connection is the determination of all possible types of sub-group when the group itself is given. This will be facilitated by the consideration of a second special class of sub-groups in addition to the sub-groups G_μ already dealt with.

If S and S' are any two operations of G, then

$$S^{p^\mu} S'^{p^\mu} = (SS')^{p^\mu};$$

and therefore the totality of the distinct operations obtained by raising every operation of G to the power p^μ will form a sub-group $G^{(\mu)}$.

If
$$m_i > \mu \geqslant m_{i+1},$$
then (Theorem II, § 77)

$$S^{p^\mu} = P_1^{\alpha_1 p^\mu} P_2^{\alpha_2 p^\mu} \ldots\ldots P_i^{\alpha_i p^\mu},$$

S being any operation of G. Hence $G^{(\mu)}$ is generated by the i independent operations

$$P_1^{p^\mu}, P_2^{p^\mu}, \ldots\ldots, P_i^{p^\mu};$$

and the order of $G^{(\mu)}$ is $p^{\sum_1^i m_t - \mu i}$.

Let now H of type $(n_1, n_2, \ldots\ldots, n_t)$ be any sub-group of G. The order of the group H_1, formed of all the operations of H which satisfy the equation

$$S^p = E,$$

is p^t (§ 79). This group must be identical with or be a sub-group of G_1, whose order is p^s. Hence

$$t \leqslant s,$$

i.e. the number of independent generating operations of any

sub-group of G is equal to or is less than the number of independent generating operations of G itself.

Again the sub-group $H^{(\mu)}$ of H is a sub-group of the sub-group $G^{(\mu)}$ of G; and therefore, as has just been seen, the number of generating operations of $H^{(\mu)}$ must be equal to or less than the number of generating operations of $G^{(\mu)}$. Now the number of generating operations of $H^{(\mu)}$ is i', where

$$n_{i'} > \mu \geqslant n_{i'+1},$$

and the number of generating operations of $G^{(\mu)}$ is i, where

$$m_i > \mu \geqslant m_{i'+1}.$$

Hence for each μ

$$i \geqslant i'.$$

If for each i,

$$m_i \geqslant n_i$$

this condition is obviously satisfied. If however

$$m_i \geqslant n_i \quad (i = 1, 2, \ldots\ldots, a)$$

and

$$m_{a+1} < n_{a+1},$$

then taking $\mu = n_{a+1}$,

$$i = a, \ i' \geqslant a + 1.$$

Hence a necessary condition that G should contain a sub-group of type H is that, for each i,

$$n_i \leqslant m_i;$$

while if this condition is satisfied a sub-group of the given type can be actually constructed. These results may be summed up as follows:

THEOREM III. *The number of distinct types of Abelian groups of order p^m, where p is a prime, is equal to the number of partitions of m; and each type may be completely represented by the symbol $(m_1, m_2, \ldots\ldots, m_s)$ of the corresponding partition. If the numbers in the partition are written in descending order, a group of type $(m_1, m_2, \ldots\ldots, m_s)$ will have a sub-group of type $(n_1, n_2, \ldots\ldots, n_t)$, when the conditions*

$$t \leqslant s,$$

$$n_i \leqslant m_i \quad (i = 1, 2, \ldots\ldots, t)$$

are satisfied; and the type of every sub-group must satisfy these conditions.

82. Every sub-group of an Abelian group is self-conjugate, and if the group is cyclical every sub-group is obviously a characteristic sub-group. In general however an Abelian group will contain sub-groups which are not characteristic. Now it follows immediately from § 68 that the only Abelian groups which have no characteristic sub-group are those of order p^m and type (1, 1,......, to m units). We proceed to form a characteristic series for an Abelian group which is not of this type*. Suppose that the group G is generated by a set of independent operations, of which n_s are of the order

$$p^{m_s}, (s = 1, 2, \ldots\ldots, r),$$

while $$m_1 > m_2 > \ldots\ldots > m_r.$$

The sub-group G_μ (§ 78), formed of the operations of G which satisfy the relation

$$S^{p^\mu} = E,$$

is clearly a characteristic sub-group. As a first step towards forming the characteristic series, we may take the set of groups

$$G_{m_1} (= G), G_{m_1-1}, G_{m_1-2}, \ldots\ldots, G_2, G_1, E;$$

for this is a set of characteristic sub-groups such that each contains the one that follows it.

Now the sub-group $G^{(\nu)}$ (§ 81), formed of the distinct operations that remain when every operation of G is raised to the power p^ν, is also a characteristic sub-group; and since the operations common to two characteristic sub-groups also form a characteristic sub-group, the sub-group $K_{\mu,\nu}$ (common to G_μ and $G^{(\nu)}$) is characteristic. It follows from this that G_1 will be the last group but one of a characteristic series only when $r=1$. If $r>1$, G_1 is not contained in $G^{(m_{r-1}-1)}$, and the common sub-group $K_{1, m_{r-1}-1}$ of these two is characteristic. If $r>2$, this sub-group again is not contained in $G^{(m_{r-2}-1)}$; and the common sub-group $K_{1, m_{r-2}-1}$ of G_1 and $G^{(m_{r-2}-1)}$ is a characteristic sub-group contained in $K_{1, m_{r-1}-1}$. Continuing thus, we form between G_1 and E the series

$$G_1, K_{1, m_{r-1}-1}, K_{1, m_{r-2}-1}, \ldots\ldots, K_{1, m_1-1}, E.$$

* Frobenius, "Ueber auflösbare Gruppen II," *Berliner Sitzungsberichte*, 1895, pp. 1028, 1029.

In a similar way, between G_α and $G_{\alpha-1}$ we introduce such of the series

$$\{G_{\alpha-1}, K_{\alpha, m_{r-1}-\alpha}\}, \{G_{\alpha-1}, K_{\alpha, m_{r-2}-\alpha}\}, \ldots\ldots, \{G_{\alpha-1}, K_{\alpha, m_1-\alpha}\}$$

as are distinct, the symbol $m_s - \alpha$ being replaced by zero where it is negative.

From the original series we thus form a new one, in which again each group is characteristic and contains the following. This series may be shewn to be a characteristic series.

Let $$P_{m_s, 1}, P_{m_s, 2}, \ldots\ldots, P_{m_s, n_s}$$

be the n_s generating operations of G, whose orders are p^{m_s}. Then if $\{G_{\alpha-1}, K_{\alpha, m_s-\alpha}\}$ and $\{G_{\alpha-1}, K_{\alpha, m_{s-1}-\alpha}\}$ are distinct, the generating operations of the latter differ only from those of the former in containing the set

$$P_{m_s, x}^{p^{m_s-\alpha+1}}, \quad (x = 1, 2, \ldots\ldots, n_s),$$

in the place of

$$P_{m_s, x}^{p^{m_s-\alpha}}, \quad (x = 1, 2, \ldots\ldots, n_s).$$

Now any permutation of the n_s generating operations

$$P_{m_s, x}, \quad (x = 1, 2, \ldots\ldots, n_s),$$

among themselves, the remaining generating operations being unaltered, must clearly give an isomorphism of G with itself; and therefore no sub-group of G, contained in $\{G_{\alpha-1}, K_{\alpha, m_s-\alpha}\}$ and containing $\{G_{\alpha-1}, K_{\alpha, m_{s-1}-\alpha}\}$, can be a characteristic sub-group. This result being true for every pair of distinct groups which succeed each other in the series that has been formed, it follows that the series is a characteristic series. It may be noticed that, if Γ and Γ' are any two consecutive sub-groups in a characteristic series of G, the order of Γ/Γ' must be p^ν, where ν is one of the r numbers n_s, and its type is (1, 1,...... to ν units).

83. It is clear that the Abelian group of order p^m and type (1, 1, 1,......, with m units) is of special importance in the general theory, and we shall here discuss one or two of its simpler properties.

Since the generating operations of the group are all of order p, every operation except identity is of order p; and therefore the type of any sub-group of order p^s is (1, 1, 1,...... to s units).

In choosing a set of independent generating operations, we may take for the first, P_1, any one of the $p^m - 1$ operations of the group, other than identity. The sub-group $\{P_1\}$ is of order p; and therefore G has $p^m - p$ operations which are not contained in $\{P_1\}$. If we choose any one of these, P_2, it is necessarily independent of P_1, and may be taken as a second generating operation. The sub-group $\{P_1, P_2\}$ is of order p^2 and type (1, 1); and G has $p^m - p^2$ operations which are not contained in this sub-group. If P_3 be any one of these, no power of P_3 other than identity is contained in $\{P_1, P_2\}$; and P_1, P_2, P_3 are therefore three independent operations which generate a sub-group of order p^3. This process may clearly be continued till all m generating operations have been chosen. If then the position which each generating operation occupies in the set of m, when they are written in order, be taken into account, there are

$$(p^m - 1)(p^m - p)(p^m - p^2)\ldots\ldots(p^m - p^{m-1})$$

distinct ways in which a set may be chosen. If on the other hand the sets of generating operations which consist of the same operations written in different orders be regarded as identical, the number of distinct sets is

$$\frac{(p^m - 1)(p^m - p)\ldots\ldots(p^m - p^{m-1})}{m\,!}.$$

84. No operation P of the group can belong to two distinct sub-groups of order p except the identical operation. Hence since every sub-group of order p contains $p - 1$ operations besides identity, G must contain $(p^m - 1)/(p - 1)$ sub-groups of order p.

Let $N_{m,s}$ be the number of sub-groups of G of order p^s, so that

$$N_{m,1} = \frac{p^m - 1}{p - 1}.$$

There are, in G, $p^m - p^s$ operations not contained in any given sub-group of order p^s. If P occurs among these operations, so also do $P^2, P^3, \ldots\ldots, P^{p-1}$. Hence there are $(p^m - p^s)/(p - 1)$ sub-groups of order p in G which are not contained in a given sub-group of order p^s. Each of these may be combined with the given sub-group to give a sub-group of order p^{s+1}. When every sub-group of order p^s is treated in this way, every sub-group of order p^{s+1} will be formed and each of them the same number, x, of times. Hence

$$xN_{m,\,s+1} = N_{m,\,s}\frac{p^m - p^s}{p-1}.$$

Now a sub-group of order p^{s+1} contains $N_{s+1,\,s}$ sub-groups of order p^s, and $(p^{s+1} - p^s)/(p-1)$ sub-groups of order p which are not contained in any given sub-group of order p^s. Hence

$$x = \frac{p^{s+1} - p^s}{p-1} N_{s+1,\,s},$$

and therefore $$N_{m,\,s+1} = \frac{N_{m,\,s}}{N_{s+1,\,s}} \cdot \frac{p^{m-s} - 1}{p-1}.$$

We will now assume that

$$N_{m,\,t} = \frac{(p^m-1)(p^{m-1}-1)\ldots\ldots(p^{m-t+1}-1)}{(p-1)(p^2-1)\ldots\ldots(p^t-1)},$$

for all values of m and for values of t not exceeding s. This has been proved for $s = 1$. Then it follows, from the above relation, that

$$N_{m,\,s+1} = \frac{(p^m-1)(p^{m-1}-1)\ldots\ldots(p^{m-s}-1)}{(p-1)(p^2-1)\ldots\ldots(p^{s+1}-1)},$$

that is to say, if the result is true for values of t not exceeding s, it is also true when $t = s+1$. Hence the formula is true generally.

It may be noticed that

$$N_{m,\,t} = N_{m,\,m-t}.$$

85. If $P_1, P_2, \ldots\ldots, P_m$ are independent generating operations of an Abelian group G of order p^m and type

$$(1, 1, \ldots\ldots, \text{to } m \text{ units}),$$

an isomorphism of the group with itself is given by

$$\begin{pmatrix} P_1, & P_2, & \ldots\ldots, & P_m \\ P'_1, & P'_2, & \ldots\ldots, & P'_m \end{pmatrix}$$

where $P'_1, P'_2, \ldots, P'_m$ is any other set of generating operations. The order of the group of isomorphisms of G is therefore, by § 83,

$$(p^m-1)(p^m-p)\ldots\ldots(p^m-p^{m-1}),$$

and the order of the holomorph K of G is this number multiplied by p^m. If G were not a characteristic sub-group of K, and if G' were conjugate to G in the group of isomorphisms of K, then $\{G, G'\}$ would be a self-conjugate sub-group of K. Since G has no characteristic sub-group, G and G' can have no common sub-group; and therefore every operation of G' would be permutable with every operation of G. But the only operations of K which are permutable with every operation of G are the operations of G itself. Hence G must be a characteristic sub-group of K, and therefore, § 72, if p is an odd prime, K is complete.

86. If G is any Abelian group whose order is a power of p and if

$$G, \Gamma_1, \Gamma_2, \ldots\ldots, \Gamma_n, E$$

is a characteristic series of G, every isomorphism of G must transform each of these groups into itself; and therefore also must transform each factor-group Γ_r/Γ_{r+1} into itself. Let I be an isomorphism which transforms each operation of Γ_r/Γ_{r+1} and Γ_{r+1} into itself. Then, § 73, the order of I is a power of p. Hence the only isomorphism which transforms each operation of each of the groups

$$G/\Gamma_1, \Gamma_1/\Gamma_2, \ldots\ldots, \Gamma_{n-1}/\Gamma_n, \Gamma_n$$

into itself and is of order prime to p is the identical isomorphism. Now Γ_r/Γ_{r+1} is an Abelian group of type

$$(1, 1, \ldots\ldots \text{ to } \nu \text{ units}).$$

Hence if k be the greatest value of ν for the above series of factor-groups, the order of any isomorphism of G, if prime to p, must divide the order of the group of isomorphisms of an Abelian group of order p^k and type (1, 1,...... to k units). In other words it must be a factor of

$$(p^k - 1)(p^{k-1} - 1)\ldots\ldots(p-1).$$

With the notation of § 82, k is the greatest of the numbers n_s. Hence:

THEOREM IV. *If G is an Abelian group, generated by n_1 operations of order p^{m_1}, n_2 operations of order $p^{m_2}, \ldots\ldots, n_r$ operations of order p^{m_r}, and if k is the greatest of the numbers $n_1, n_2, \ldots\ldots, n_r$, then any operation whose order is relatively* *prime to* $(p^k-1)(p^{k-1}-1)\ldots\ldots(p-1)\,p$ *which is permutable with* G, *is permutable with every operation of* G.

87. An Abelian group G of order $p_1^{a_1}p_2^{a_2}\ldots\ldots p_n^{a_n}$ is the direct product of Abelian groups $G_1, G_2, \ldots\ldots, G_n$ of orders $p_1^{a_1}, p_2^{a_2}, \ldots\ldots, p_n^{a_n}$. If I is any isomorphism of G_1, then G obviously admits an isomorphism in which the operations of G_1 undergo the isomorphism I, while the operations of $G_2, \ldots\ldots, G_n$ undergo the identical isomorphism. This isomorphism is clearly permutable with any isomorphism of G in which the operations of G_1 undergo the identical isomorphism. Hence the group of isomorphisms of G is the direct product of the groups of isomorphisms of $G_1, G_2, \ldots\ldots, G_n$; and similarly the holomorph of G is the direct product of the holomorphs of $G_1, G_2, \ldots\ldots, G_n$.

If m is the least common multiple of the orders of the operations of an Abelian group, or in other words if the group has operations of order m and no operations of order greater than m, and if μ is any number less than and prime to m, then

$$\begin{pmatrix} S \\ S^\mu \end{pmatrix}$$

gives an isomorphism of the group. In fact the operations S^μ, when for S each operation of the group is written in turn, are all distinct, and if

$$ST = U,$$

then

$$S^\mu T^\mu = U^\mu.$$

When for μ each of the $\phi(m)$ numbers, less than and prime to m, is taken in turn, $\phi(m)$ distinct isomorphisms thus arise, and they clearly form a sub-group of the group of isomorphisms.

Let

$$\begin{pmatrix} S \\ S' \end{pmatrix}$$

be any isomorphism of the group. Then

$$\begin{pmatrix} S \\ S' \end{pmatrix}^{-1}\begin{pmatrix} S \\ S^\mu \end{pmatrix}\begin{pmatrix} S \\ S' \end{pmatrix}=\begin{pmatrix} S' \\ S'^\mu \end{pmatrix}=\begin{pmatrix} S \\ S^\mu \end{pmatrix};$$

and therefore each of the isomorphisms $\begin{pmatrix} S \\ S^\mu \end{pmatrix}$ is self-conjugate in the group of isomorphisms.

88. We shall now discuss the groups of isomorphisms of certain Abelian groups, taking first the case of a cyclical group G, of prime order p, generated by an operation P. Every isomorphism of such a group must interchange among themselves the $p-1$ operations

$$P,\ P^2,\ \ldots\ldots,\ P^{p-1},$$

and therefore any isomorphism of the group may be represented by

$$\begin{pmatrix} P \\ P^{\alpha} \end{pmatrix}.$$

Now the nth power of this isomorphism is

$$\begin{pmatrix} P \\ P^{\alpha^n} \end{pmatrix}.$$

Hence if α is a primitive root of the congruence

$$\alpha^{p-1} - 1 \equiv 0, \qquad (\text{mod. } p),$$

the group of isomorphisms is a cyclical group generated by the isomorphism

$$\begin{pmatrix} P \\ P^{\alpha} \end{pmatrix}.$$

Further, if S is an operation satisfying the relations

$$S^{p-1} = E, \quad S^{-1}PS = P^{\alpha},$$

where α is a primitive root of p, $\{S, P\}$ is the holomorph of G.

Since $\{P\}$ is clearly a characteristic sub-group of $\{S, P\}$, the latter is a complete group.

Consider next the case of any cyclical group; and suppose, first, that G is a cyclical group of order p^n, where p is an odd prime; and let it be generated by an operation S. The group contains $p^{n-1}(p-1)$ operations of order p^n; and if S' is any one of these,

$$\begin{pmatrix} S \\ S' \end{pmatrix}$$

defines an isomorphism. The group of isomorphisms is therefore a group of order $p^{n-1}(p-1)$. Moreover, since the congruence

$$\alpha^{p^{n-1}(p-1)} - 1 \equiv 0, \qquad (\text{mod. } p^n),$$

has primitive roots, the group of isomorphisms is a cyclical group. The holomorph of G is defined by

$$S^{p^n} = E, \quad J^{p^{n-1}(p-1)} = E, \quad J^{-1}SJ = S^{\alpha},$$

where α is a primitive root of the congruence

$$\alpha^{p^{n-1}(p-1)} - 1 \equiv 0, \qquad (\text{mod. } p^n).$$

If G is a cyclical group of order 2^n, it follows, in the same way, that the group of isomorphisms is an Abelian group of order 2^{n-1}. In this case, however, the congruence

$$a^{2^{n-1}} - 1 \equiv 0, \qquad (\text{mod. } 2^n), \quad n > 2,$$

has no primitive root, and therefore the group of isomorphisms is not cyclical.

Now $$5^{2^{n-2}} \equiv 1 \ (\text{mod. } 2^n),$$

and $$5^{2^{n-3}} \equiv 1 + 2^{n-1} \ (\text{mod. } 2^n).$$

The powers of the isomorphism

$$\begin{pmatrix} S \\ S^5 \end{pmatrix}$$

then form a cyclical group of order 2^{n-2}; and the only isomorphism of order 2 contained in it is

$$\begin{pmatrix} S \\ S^{1+2^{n-1}} \end{pmatrix}.$$

Hence $$\begin{pmatrix} S \\ S^5 \end{pmatrix} \text{ and } \begin{pmatrix} S \\ S^{-1} \end{pmatrix},$$

the latter not being contained in the sub-group generated by the former, are two permutable and independent isomorphisms of orders 2^{n-2} and 2. They generate an Abelian group of order 2^{n-1}, which is the group of isomorphisms of G. The corresponding holomorph is given by

$$S^{2^n} = E, \quad J_1^{2^{n-2}} = E, \quad J_2^2 = E, \quad J_1J_2 = J_2J_1,$$
$$J_1^{-1}SJ_1 = S^5, \quad J_2SJ_2 = S^{-1}.$$

If G is a cyclical group of order 4, its group of isomorphisms is clearly a group of order 2.

The nature of the group of isomorphisms and of the holomorph of any cyclical group follow from these particular cases by the preceding paragraph.

Ex. 1. Prove that the holomorph of any cyclical group of odd order is a complete group.

Ex. 2. If G is a cyclical group of order 8 and if K is the holomorph of G, prove that G is not a characteristic sub-group of K. With the above notation, and $n = 3$, shew that $\{S, J_1, J_2\}$ admits the outer isomorphism

$$\begin{pmatrix} S, & J_1, & J_2 \\ J_1S, & J_1, & J_1J_2 \end{pmatrix}.$$

89. We shall next consider the group of isomorphisms of an Abelian group of order p^n and type (1, 1, ... to n units). Such a group is generated by n independent permutable operations of order p, say

$$P_1, P_2, \ldots\ldots, P_n.$$

We may therefore begin by determining under what conditions the symbol

$$\begin{pmatrix} P_r \\ P_1^{a_{1r}} P_2^{a_{2r}} \ldots\ldots P_n^{a_{nr}} \end{pmatrix} \quad (r = 1, 2, \ldots\ldots, n),$$

defines an isomorphism. This symbol replaces the operation $P_1^{x_1} P_2^{x_2} \ldots\ldots P_n^{x_n}$ by $P_1^{y_1} P_2^{y_2} \ldots\ldots P_n^{y_n}$, where

$$\left.\begin{aligned} y_1 &\equiv a_{11}x_1 + a_{12}x_2 + \ldots\ldots + a_{1n}x_n, \\ y_2 &\equiv a_{21}x_1 + a_{22}x_2 + \ldots\ldots + a_{2n}x_n, \\ &\ldots\ldots\ldots\ldots\ldots\ldots\ldots\ldots\ldots\ldots \\ y_n &\equiv a_{n1}x_1 + a_{n2}x_2 + \ldots\ldots + a_{nn}x_n, \end{aligned}\right\} \pmod{p}.$$

Unless the p^n operations $P_1^{y_1} P_2^{y_2} \ldots\ldots P_n^{y_n}$ thus formed are all distinct, when for $P_1^{x_1} P_2^{x_2} \ldots\ldots P_n^{x_n}$ is put successively each of the p^n operations of the group, the symbol does not represent an isomorphism. On the other hand, when this condition is satisfied, the symbol represents a permutation of the operations among themselves which leaves the multiplication table of the group unchanged; it is therefore an isomorphism.

If this condition is satisfied, $x_1, x_2, \ldots\ldots, x_n$ must be definite numbers (mod. p), when $y_1, y_2, \ldots\ldots, y_n$ are given; and therefore the above set of n simultaneous congruences must be capable of definite solution with respect to the x's. The necessary and sufficient condition for this is that the determinant

$$\begin{vmatrix} a_{11}, & a_{12}, & \ldots\ldots, & a_{1n} \\ a_{21}, & a_{22}, & \ldots\ldots, & a_{2n} \\ \ldots & \ldots & \ldots & \ldots \\ a_{n1}, & a_{n2} & \ldots\ldots, & a_{nn} \end{vmatrix}$$

should not be congruent to zero (mod. p).

Every distinct set of congruences of the above form, for which this condition is satisfied, represents a distinct isomorphism of the group, two sets being regarded as distinct if the congruence

$$a_{rs} \equiv a'_{rs} \quad (\text{mod. } p)$$

does not hold for each corresponding pair of coefficients. Moreover, to the product of two isomorphisms will correspond the set of congruences which results from carrying out successively the operations indicated by the two sets that correspond to the two isomorphisms.

The group of isomorphisms is therefore simply isomorphic with the group of operations defined by all sets of congruences

$$\left.\begin{array}{l} y_1 \equiv a_{11}x_1 + a_{12}x_2 + \ldots\ldots + a_{1n}x_n, \\ y_2 \equiv a_{21}x_1 + a_{22}x_2 + \ldots\ldots + a_{2n}x_n, \\ \ldots\ldots\ldots\ldots\ldots\ldots\ldots\ldots\ldots\ldots\ldots \\ y_n \equiv a_{n1}x_1 + a_{n2}x_2 + \ldots\ldots + a_{nn}x_n, \end{array}\right\} \pmod{p}$$

for which the relation

$$\begin{vmatrix} a_{11}, & a_{12}, & \ldots\ldots, & a_{1n} \\ a_{21}, & a_{22}, & \ldots\ldots, & a_{2n} \\ \ldots & \ldots & \ldots & \ldots \\ a_{n1}, & a_{n2}, & \ldots\ldots, & a_{nn} \end{vmatrix} \not\equiv 0 \pmod{p}$$

is satisfied. Its order has been determined in § 85.

90. The group thus defined is of great importance in many branches of analysis. It is known as the *linear homogeneous* group. In a subsequent Chapter we shall consider some of its more important properties.

The holomorph of an Abelian group of order p^n and type (1, 1, ... to n units), can similarly be represented as a group of linear transformations to the prime modulus p. Consider, in fact, the set of transformations

$$\left.\begin{array}{l} y_1 \equiv a_{11}x_1 + a_{12}x_2 + \ldots\ldots + a_{1n}x_n + b_1, \\ y_2 \equiv a_{21}x_1 + a_{22}x_2 + \ldots\ldots + a_{2n}x_n + b_2, \\ \ldots\ldots\ldots\ldots\ldots\ldots\ldots\ldots\ldots\ldots\ldots \\ y_n \equiv a_1x_{n1} + a_{n2}x_2 + \ldots\ldots + a_{nn}x_n + b_n, \end{array}\right\} \pmod{p};$$

where the coefficients take all integral values (mod. p) consistent with

$$\begin{vmatrix} a_{11}, & a_{12}, & \ldots\ldots, & a_{1n} \\ a_{21}, & a_{22}, & \ldots\ldots, & a_{2n} \\ \ldots & \ldots & \ldots & \ldots \\ a_{n1}, & a_{n2}, & \ldots\ldots, & a_{nn} \end{vmatrix} \not\equiv 0.$$

The set of transformations clearly forms a group whose order is $(p^n - 1)(p^n - p)\ldots\ldots(p^n - p^{n-1})\,p^n$. The sub-group formed by all the transformations

$$y_1 \equiv x_1 + b_1, \quad y_2 \equiv x_2 + b_2, \ \ldots\ldots, \ y_n \equiv x_n + b_n, \quad \pmod{p},$$

is an Abelian group of order p^n and type (1, 1, ... to n units), and it is a self-conjugate sub-group. Moreover, the only operations of the group, which are permutable with every operation of this self-conjugate sub-group, are the operations of the sub-group itself; and, since the order of the group is equal to the order of the holomorph of the Abelian group, it follows that the group of transformations must be simply isomorphic with the holomorph of the Abelian group.

Ex. 1. Shew that a group whose operations except identity are all of order 2 is necessarily an Abelian group.

Ex. 2. Prove that in a group of order 16, whose operations except identity are all of order 2, the 15 operations of order 2 may be divided into 5 sets of 3 each so that each set of 3 with identity forms a sub-group of order 4; and that this division into sets may be carried out in 56 distinct ways.

Ex. 3. If G is an Abelian group and H a sub-group of G, shew that G contains one or more sub-groups simply isomorphic with G/H.

Ex. 4. If the symbols in the successive rows of a determinant of n rows are derived from those of the first row by performing on them the permutations of a regular Abelian group of order n, prove that the determinant is the product of n linear factors.

(*Messenger of Mathematics*, Vol. XXIII. p. 112.)

Ex. 5. Discuss the number of ways in which a set of independent generating operations of an Abelian group of order p^m and given type may be chosen. Shew that, for a group of type $(m_1, m_2, \ldots\ldots, m_s)$, where $m_1 > m_2 > \ldots\ldots > m_s$, the number of ways is of the form $p^a (p-1)^s$; and in particular that for a group of order $p^{\frac{1}{2}n(n+1)}$ and type $(n, n-1, \ldots\ldots, 2, 1)$, the number of ways is $p^\nu (p-1)^n$, where $\nu = \frac{1}{6}n(n+1)(2n+1) - n$.

Ex. 6. Shew that for any Abelian group a set of independent generating operations

$$S_1, S_2, \ldots, S_{r-1}, S_r, \ldots, S_n$$

can be chosen such that, for each value of r, the order of S_r is equal to, or is a factor of, the order of S_{r-1}.

Ex. 7. Prove that an isomorphism, whose order is a power of p, of an Abelian group of order p^m and type (1, 1, ... to m units) must transform into themselves a series of sub-groups of orders $p^{m-1}, p^{m-2}, \ldots, p$, each of which contains the next. Shew that if such an isomorphism leaves just p operations unchanged, it can, by suitably choosing the generating operations, be expressed in the form

$$\begin{pmatrix} P_1, & P_2, & P_3, & \ldots, & P_{m-1}, & P_m \\ P_1P_2, & P_2P_3, & P_3P_4, & \ldots, & P_{m-1}P_m, & P_m \end{pmatrix},$$

and that, if $m \leqslant p$, its order is p.

CHAPTER VIII.

ON GROUPS WHOSE ORDERS ARE THE POWERS OF PRIMES.

91. HAVING in the last chapter dealt in some detail with Abelian groups of order p^m, where p is a prime, we shall now investigate some of the more important properties of groups, which have the power of a prime for their order but are not necessarily Abelian. Besides illustrating and leading to many interesting applications of the earlier results, the discussion of groups, whose order is the power of a prime, will be found in many ways to facilitate the subsequent discussion of other groups, whose order is not thus limited.

92. If G is a group whose order is p^m, where p is a prime, the order of every sub-group of G must also be a power of p; and therefore (§ 25) the number of operations of G which are conjugate with any given operation must be a power of p. The identical operation of G is self-conjugate. Hence the equation of § 26 becomes in this case

$$p^m = 1 + p^{\alpha_2} + p^{\alpha_3} + \ldots\ldots + p^{\alpha_r}.$$

This equation can only be true if $p^s - 1$ of the indices $\alpha_2, \alpha_3, \ldots\ldots$ are zero, s being some integer not less than unity. Therefore G must contain p^s $(s \geqslant 1)$ self-conjugate operations, which form (§ 27) a self-conjugate sub-group*. Hence:—

THEOREM I. *Every group whose order is the power of a prime contains self-conjugate operations, other than the identical operation; and no such group can be simple.*

* Sylow, *Math. Ann.* (1872), p. 588.

93. If H, of order p^s, is the central, i.e. the sub-group formed of the self-conjugate operations, of G, whose order is p^m, then G/H or G' of order p^{m-s} must have a central K'. Let K be the corresponding sub-group, necessarily self-conjugate, of G. Then again G/K, being a group whose order is a power of p, must have a central. This process may be continued till we arrive at a factor-group which is its own central, that is to say, which is Abelian.

Hence G must contain a series of self-conjugate sub-groups,

$$H_1,\ H_2, \ldots,\ H_i, \ldots,\ H_n,\ E,$$

such that, for each i, H_{i-1}/H_i is the central of G/H_i, H_0 being the group G itself and H_{n+1} the identical operation E.

From its formation it is obvious that each of these sub-groups is a characteristic sub-group of G. Each factor-group

$$H_{i-1}/H_i \quad (i = 1, 2, \ldots, n+1)$$

is an Abelian group on whose type in general there is no necessary limitation. The first factor-group G/H_1 however cannot be cyclical*. In fact, if G/H_1 were a cyclical group of order p^a, the operations of G/H_2 could be arranged in the sets

$$H_1/H_2,\ PH_1/H_2,\ P^2H_1/H_2, \ldots,\ P^{p^a-1}H_1/H_2,$$

where P^{p^a} belongs to H_1/H_2. But since the operations of H_1/H_2 are self-conjugate in G/H_2, this involves that G/H_2 is the Abelian group generated by P and H_1/H_2, which by supposition is not the case.

94. Since G/H_1 is Abelian the derived group of G is contained in H_1 (§ 39), and is therefore necessarily distinct from G. Hence:—

THEOREM II. *A group whose order is the power of a prime is necessarily distinct from its derived group; and its series of derived groups terminates with the identical operation.*

Let $$G,\ G_1,\ G_2, \ldots,\ G_\nu,\ E$$

be the series of derived groups of G. Each of these again is obviously, from its mode of formation, a characteristic sub-group

* Young, *American Journal*, vol. xv. (1893), p. 132.

of G; and each of the factor-groups G_{i-1}/G_i is an Abelian group. Moreover, since G_1 is contained in H_1, G/G_1 cannot be a cyclical group. Either of the series of groups

$$G,\ H_1,\ H_2, \ldots,\ H_n,\ E,$$

or

$$G,\ G_1,\ G_2, \ldots,\ G_\nu,\ E,$$

may clearly be used to form a chief-series for G. If p^t is the order of H_{i-1}/H_i, then, since each of these factor-groups is Abelian, a series of $t-1$ groups may be interpolated between H_{i-1} and H_i, say

$$H_{i-1},\ K_1,\ K_2, \ldots,\ K_t,\ H_i,$$

each of which is self-conjugate in G and is contained in the preceding, while K_{j-1}/K_j is of order p. The complete series obtained in this way is clearly a chief-series for G; and a similar series may be obtained from the derived groups.

95. If in the two series of groups

$$G,\ H_1,\ H_2, \ldots,\ H_n,\ E,$$

$$G,\ G_1,\ G_2, \ldots,\ G_\nu,\ E,$$

H_s contains G_s, then, since H_s/H_{s+1} is Abelian, every commutator of G_s must belong to H_{s+1}. Therefore, since the commutators of G_s generate G_{s+1}, G_{s+1} must be contained in H_{s+1}. Hence, as H_1 contains G_1, H_s contains G_s for each s. In particular H_n, an Abelian group, contains G_n. If ν were greater than n, G_n would not be an Abelian group, and therefore

$$\nu \leqslant n.$$

It may be noticed that since no one of the groups G_i/G_{i+1} can be cyclical, the order of a group whose derived series is

$$G,\ G_1,\ G_2, \ldots,\ G_\nu,\ E$$

cannot be less than $p^{2\nu+1}$.

96. Let G_s be any sub-group of G of order p^s, and let H_i be the first of the series of sub-groups

$$H_1,\ H_2, \ldots,\ H_n,\ E,$$

which is contained in G_s. Then G_s/H_i is a sub-group of G/H_i which does not contain all the operations of H_{i-1}/H_i. Every operation of H_{i-1}/H_i is self-conjugate in G/H_i; and therefore

G_s/H_i is self-conjugate in $\{G_s/H_i, H_{i-1}/H_i\}$, a group of order greater than its own. Hence G_s must be contained self-conjugately in some group G_{s+t} of order p^{s+t}, where t is not less than unity. Moreover since G_{s+t}/G_s must contain operations of order p, there must be one or more groups of order p^{s+1} which contain G_s self-conjugately. Hence:—

THEOREM III. *If G_s of order p^s is a sub-group of G, which is of order p^m, then G must contain a sub-group of order p^{s+t}, $t \nless 1$, within which G_s is self-conjugate. In particular, every sub-group of order p^{m-1} of G is a self-conjugate sub-group**.

Suppose now that G_{s+t}, of order p^{s+t}, is the greatest sub-group of G which contains a given sub-group G_s, of order p^s, self-conjugately; so that G_s is one of p^{m-s-t} conjugate sub-groups. Suppose also that G_{s+t+u}, of order p^{s+t+u}, $(u \nless 1)$, is the greatest sub-group of G that contains G_{s+t} self-conjugately. Every operation of G_{s+t+u} transforms G_{s+t} into itself; and no operation of G_{s+t+u} that is not contained in G_{s+t} transforms G_s into itself. Hence, in G_{s+t+u}, G_s is one of p^u conjugate sub-groups and each of these is self-conjugate in G_{s+t}.

The p^{m-s-t} sub-groups conjugate to G_s may therefore be divided into $p^{m-s-t-u}$ sets of p^u each, $(u \nless 1)$, such that any operation of a sub-group belonging to one of the sets transforms each sub-group of that set into itself.

Similarly if G_s, of order p^s, is the greatest sub-group of G that contains a given operation P self-conjugately, and if G_{s+t}, $t \nless 1$, is the greatest sub-group that contains G_s self-conjugately, then G_s must contain self-conjugately p^t operations of the conjugate set to which P belongs, and therefore any two of these p^t operations are permutable. Hence the p^{m-s} conjugate operations of the set to which P belongs can be divided into p^{m-s-t} sets of p^t each, $(t \nless 1)$, such that all the operations of any one set are permutable with each other. In particular, if P is one of a set of p conjugate operations, all the operations of the set are permutable.

* Frobenius, "Ueber endliche Gruppen," *Berliner Sitzungsberichte* (1895), p. 173: Burnside, "Notes on the theory of groups of finite order," *Proc. London Mathematical Society*, Vol. XXVI (1895), p. 209.

97. Let P be an operation of G which belongs to H_i in the series of groups (§ 93)

$$G,\ H_1,\ H_2, \ldots,\ H_n,\ E,$$

and does not belong to H_{i+1}. Then $\{P, H_{i+1}\}$ is a sub-group of H_i; and therefore $\{P, H_{i+1}\}/H_{i+1}$ is a self-conjugate sub-group of G/H_{i+1}. The set of operations PH_{i+1} is therefore transformed into itself by every operation of G; and hence every operation conjugate to P is contained in the set PH_{i+1}. Suppose now, if possible, that every operation conjugate to P were contained in the set PH_{i+2}. Then every operation of G would transform this set into itself; and therefore every operation of $\{P, H_{i+2}\}/H_{i+2}$ would be self-conjugate in G/H_{i+2}. This is not the case, since P does not belong to H_{i+1}. There are therefore operations conjugate to P which belong to PH_{i+1} and do not belong to PH_{i+2}.

Suppose now that S and S' are two operations of G which transform P into operations of the set PH_s, so that

$$S^{-1}PS = PP_s,$$

$$S'^{-1}PS' = PP_s',$$

where P_s and P_s' both belong to H_s. Then

$$\begin{aligned} S'^{-1}S^{-1}PSS' &= P \,.\, P_s' \,.\, S'^{-1}P_sS' \\ &= PP_s'', \end{aligned}$$

where, since H_s is a self-conjugate sub-group, P_s'' belongs to H_s. The operations which transform P into an operation of the set PH_s therefore form a sub-group.

Next let T be an operation of G which transforms P into an operation of the set PH_{s-1}, so that

$$T^{-1}PT = PP_{s-1}.$$

Then $$T^{-1}S^{-1} \,.\, P \,.\, ST = T^{-1}PP_sT,$$

or $$T^{-1}S^{-1}T \,.\, PP_{s-1} \,.\, T^{-1}ST = PP_{s-1}T^{-1}P_sT,$$

and $$\begin{aligned} &T^{-1}S^{-1}T \,.\, P \ \ T^{-1}ST \\ &= P \,.\, P_{s-1}T^{-1}P_sTP_{s-1}^{-1} \,.\, P_{s-1} \,.\, T^{-1}S^{-1}T \,.\, P_{s-1}^{-1} \,.\, T^{-1}ST. \end{aligned}$$

Now $P_{s-1}T^{-1}P_sTP_{s-1}^{-1}$ belongs to H_s, and

$$P_{s-1} \,.\, T^{-1}S^{-1}T \,.\, P_{s-1}^{-1} \,.\, T^{-1}ST,$$

i.e. the product of P_{s-1} and the inverse of one of its conjugates also belong to H_s. Hence

$$T^{-1}S^{-1}T\,.\,P\,.\,T^{-1}ST = P\,.\,P_s''',$$

where P_s''' belongs to H_s. The operations which transform P into operations of the set PH_s therefore constitute a self-conjugate sub-group of those which transform P into operations of the set PH_{s-1}.

If G_P denote the sub-group formed of all the operations permutable with P, and $G_{P^{(s)}}$ the sub-group formed of those operations which transform P into operations of the set PH_s, then in the series of groups

$$G_P,\ G_{P^{(n)}},\ G_{P^{(n-1)}},\ldots,\ G_{P^{(i+1)}},$$

each is a self-conjugate sub-group of the succeeding one, and the last is the group G itself.

Moreover from

$$S^{-1}PS = PP_s,\quad S'^{-1}PS' = PP_s',$$

it follows that

$$S'SS'^{-1}S^{-1}\,.\,P\,.\,SS'S^{-1}S'^{-1}$$
$$= P\,.\,S'P_s'^{-1}S'^{-1}\,.\,S'SP_s^{-1}S^{-1}S'^{-1}\,.\,S'SP_s'S^{-1}S'^{-1}$$
$$.\,S'SS'^{-1}P_sS'S^{-1}S'^{-1} = P\,.\,P_{s+1},$$

where P_{s+1} belong to H_{s+1}. Hence $SS'S^{-1}S'^{-1}$ belongs to $G_{P^{(s+1)}}$, and therefore $G_{P^{(s)}}/G_{P^{(s+1)}}$ is Abelian. The groups of the series are not necessarily all distinct, for it may be the case that there are no conjugates to P which belong to PH_s and do not belong to PH_{s+1}. Since, when P_{s-1} belongs to H_{s-1}, $P^{-1}P^{-1}_{s-1}PP_{s-1}$ belongs to H_s, it follows that $G_{P^{(s)}}$ necessarily contains H_{s-1}.

98. In illustration of the preceding paragraphs we will consider some of the properties of a group G of order p^m containing conjugate sets with as large a number of operations as possible. If P is an operation of G which is not self-conjugate and R a self-conjugate operation, then every operation of $\{P, R\}$ is permutable with P. The order of $\{P, R\}$ cannot be less than p^2, and therefore the number of operations in the conjugate set to which P belongs cannot exceed p^{m-2}. Moreover it cannot be equal to p^{m-2} unless the order of the central of G is p. Let H_n be the central of G, and P' be the operation of G/H_n which corresponds to P. If P' were one of less than p^{m-3} conjugates in G/H_n, P would be one of less than p^{m-2} conjugates in G. But P' cannot be one of p^{m-3} conjugates in G/H_n unless the central of G/H_n is of order p. Hence H_{n-1}, the sub-group of G which corresponds to the central of G/H_n is of order p^2. This reasoning may clearly be repeated, and the orders of the series of groups (§ 93)

$$G,\ \ H_1,\ \ H_2,\ \ \ldots\ldots,\ H_n,\ \ E,$$

are

$$p^m,\ p^{m-2},\ p^{m-3},\ \ldots\ldots,\ p,\ \ \ 1;$$

so that n is $m-2$.

Every operation conjugate to P is contained in the set PH_1, and this set has just p^{m-2} distinct operations. Hence every operation of the set PH_1 is conjugate to P, and every operation of H_1 is a commutator, so that H_1 is the derived group.

If Q is an operation of G which does not belong to

$$H_1,\ PH_1,\ P^2H_1,\ \ldots\ldots,\ \text{or}\ P^{p-1}H_1,$$

and if P_i denotes an operation which belongs to H_i and not to H_{i+1}, the relations

$$\begin{aligned} Q^{-1}PQ &= PP_1,\\ P_1^{-1}PP_1 &= PP_2,\\ &\ldots\ldots\ldots\ldots\ldots\ldots\\ P_{m-3}^{-1}PP_{m-3} &= PP_{m-2},\\ P_{m-2}^{-1}PP_{m-2} &= P, \end{aligned}$$

follow from the fact that PH_1 is the set of operations conjugate to P. The group then can be generated by the two operations P and Q.

Ex. With the above notation shew that if $Q, P, P_1, \ldots, P_{m-2}$ are all of order p, and if $Q, P_1, P_2, \ldots, P_{m-2}$ are independent and permutable, the operations of the group are all of order p when $m \leqslant p$; and that when $m > p$, the group contains operations of order p^2.

99. In further illustration we will consider some of the properties of a group G, of order p^m, in which each operation is either self-conjugate or one of p conjugate operations. If P, Q are two non-permutable operations of such a group,

$$Q,\ P^{-1}QP,\ P^{-2}QP^2,\ \ldots\ldots,\ P^{-p+1}QP^{p-1}$$

form a complete conjugate set of operations.

For if

$$P^{-i}QP^i = P^{-j}QP^j,\ j > i,$$

$$P^{-j+i}QP^{j-i} = Q,$$

so that P^{j-i} and therefore also P would be permutable with Q. It follows that $P^{-p}QP^p$ must be one of the above set. If

$$P^{-p}QP^p = P^{-i}QP^i \quad (i > 0)$$

P would be permutable with Q. Hence

$$P^{-p}QP^p = Q,$$

and the pth power of every operation of G is a self-conjugate operation.

Every operation which is permutable with Q must transform among themselves the p operations which are conjugate to Q, and must therefore be permutable with each of them. Hence every operation of the sub-group G_Q, of order p^{m-1}, which contains Q self-conjugately, is permutable with $Q^{-1}P^{-1}QP$. But P is also permutable with this operation. Hence every operation of $\{P, G_Q\}$, i.e. of G, is permutable with $Q^{-1}P^{-1}QP$; and every commutator is a self-conjugate operation. Hence if H is the central of G, G/H is an Abelian group of type $(1, 1, 1, \ldots\ldots, 1)$.

Ex. 1. Prove that if G is a non-Abelian group of order p^m in which no conjugate set contains more than p operations and if H is the central of G, then G/H must have an even number of generators. Shew also that the order of the derived group of G is p.

Ex. 2. If G is a group in which no conjugate set contains more than p^s operations, the p^sth power of every operation is self-conjugate.

100. If P is an operation of G, of order p^n, which is conjugate to one of its own powers P^α, there must be some other operation Q of G such that

$$Q^{-1}PQ = P^\alpha.$$

From this equation it follows that

$$Q^{-2}PQ^2 = Q^{-1}P^\alpha Q = P^{\alpha^2},$$

and

$$Q^{-\beta}PQ^\beta = P^{\alpha^\beta}.$$

If Q^β is the lowest power of Q which is permutable with P, then in $\{P, Q\}$ P will be one of β conjugate operations, and therefore β must be a power of p, say p^s, less than p^n. Further, if Q^{p^s} is permutable with P,

$$P^{\alpha^{p^s}} = P,$$

and therefore

$$\alpha^{p^s} \equiv 1 \pmod{p^n},$$

while

$$\alpha^{p^{s-1}} \not\equiv 1 \pmod{p^n}.$$

First, we will suppose that p is an odd prime. Then since

$$x^{p^s} \equiv x \pmod{p},$$

whatever integer x may be, we may assume that $\alpha = 1 + kp^t$, where k is not a multiple of p; and then

$$\alpha^{p^s} = 1 + kp^{s+t} + \ldots\ldots$$

$$\alpha^{p^{s-1}} = 1 + kp^{s+t-1} + \ldots\ldots$$

Hence $$s + t = n,$$

and $$\alpha \equiv 1 \pmod{p^{n-s}}.$$

Conversely if P and $P^{1+kp^{n-s}}$ ($k \not\equiv 0 \pmod{p}$) are conjugate operations, there must be an operation Q such that

$$Q^{-1}PQ = P^{1+kp^{n-s}}$$

From this it follows that the lowest power of Q which is permutable with P is the p^sth, so that in $\{Q, P\}$ P is one of p^s conjugate operations. Now $P^{1+kp^{n-s-1}}$ ($k \not\equiv 0 \pmod{p}$) cannot be one of these, for if

$$Q^{-x}PQ^x = P^{1+kp^{n-s-1}},$$

$$Q^{-xp^s}PQ^{xp^s} = P^{(1+kp^{n-s-1})p^s}$$

$$= P^{1+kp^{n-1}},$$

so that Q^{p^s} would not be permutable with P. Hence the p^s operations conjugate to P are $P^{1+kp^{n-s}}$ ($k = 1, 2, \ldots, p^s$).

In particular, we see that no operation of order p can be conjugate to one of its powers. Hence if P and P' are two conjugate operations of order p, $\{P\}$ and $\{P'\}$ have no operation in common except identity. Also, if $\{P\}$ be a self-conjugate sub-group of order p, each of its operations is self-conjugate.

If p is 2, we must take

$$\alpha = \pm 1 + k2^t,$$

where k is odd, and we are led by the same process to the result

$$\alpha \equiv \pm 1 \pmod{2^{n-s}}$$

101. It has been seen in § 96 that every sub-group G' of order p^{m-1} of a group G of order p^m is self-conjugate. Suppose now that G contains two such sub-groups G' and G''. Then since G' and G'' are permutable with each other, while the order of $\{G', G''\}$ is p^m, the order of the greatest group g' common to them must (§ 33) be p^{m-2}; and since g' is the greatest common sub-group of two self-conjugate sub-groups of G, it must itself be a self-conjugate sub-group of G. The factor-group G/g' of order p^2 contains the two distinct sub-groups G'/g' and G''/g', which are of order p and permutable with each other. Hence G/g' must be an Abelian group of type (1, 1) and it therefore contains (§ 84) $p+1$ sub-groups of order p. Hence, besides G', G must contain p other sub-groups of order p^{m-1} which have in common with G' the sub-group g'. If the $p+1$ sub-groups thus obtained do not exhaust the sub-groups of G of order p^{m-1}, let G''' be a new one. Then, as before, G' and G''' must have a common sub-group g'', of order p^{m-2}, which is self-conjugate in G. If g'' were the same as g', G'''/g' would be contained in G/g', which by supposition is not the case. It may now be shewn as above that there are, in addition to G', p sub-groups of order p^{m-1} which have in common with G' the group g''. These are therefore necessarily distinct from those before obtained. This process may clearly be repeated till all the sub-groups of order p^{m-1} are exhausted. Hence finally, if the number of sub-groups of G, of order p^{m-1} be r_{m-1}, we have $r_{m-1} \equiv 1 \pmod{p}$.

102. The self-conjugate operations of a group G of order p^m, whose orders are p, form with identity a self-conjugate sub-group whose order is some power of p; and therefore their number must be congruent to -1, mod. p. On the other hand, if P is any operation of G of order p which is not self-conjugate, the number of operations in the conjugate set to which P belongs is a power of p. Hence the total number of operations of G, of order p, is congruent to -1, mod. p. Now if r_1 is the total number of sub-groups of G of order p, the number of operations of order p is $r_1(p-1)$, since no two of these sub-groups can have a common operation, except identity. It follows that

$$r_1(p-1) \equiv -1, \text{ (mod. } p),$$

and therefore
$$r_1 \equiv 1, \text{ (mod. } p).$$

If now G_s is any sub-group of G of order p^s, and if G_{s+t} is the greatest sub-group of G in which G_s is contained self-conjugately, then every sub-group of G which contains G_s self-conjugately is contained in G_{s+t}. But every sub-group of order p^{s+1}, which contains G_s, contains G_s self-conjugately; and therefore every sub-group of order p^{s+1}, which contains G_s, is itself contained in G_{s+t}. By the preceding result, the number of sub-groups of G_{s+t}/G_s of order p is congruent to unity, mod. p. Hence the number of sub-groups of G of order p^{s+1}, which contain G_s of order p^s, is congruent to unity, mod. p.

103. Let now r_s represent the total number of sub-groups of order p^s contained in a group G of order p^m. If any one of them is contained in a_x sub-groups of order p^{s+1}, and if any one of the sub-groups of order p^{s+1} contains b_y sub-groups of order p^s; then

$$\sum_{x=1}^{x=r_s} a_x = \sum_{y=1}^{y=r_{s+1}} b_y ;$$

for the numbers on either side of this equation are equal to the number of sub-groups of order p^{s+1}, when each of the latter is reckoned once for every sub-group of order p^s that it contains. It has however been shewn, in the two preceding paragraphs, that for all values of x and y

$$a_x \equiv 1, \; b_y \equiv 1 \pmod{p}.$$

Hence $$r_s \equiv r_{s+1} \pmod{p}.$$

Now it has just been proved that

$$r_1 \equiv 1 \text{ and } r_{m-1} \equiv 1 \pmod{p};$$

and therefore finally, for all values of s,

$$r_s \equiv 1 \pmod{p}.$$

We may state the result thus obtained as follows :—

THEOREM IV. *The number of sub-groups of any given order p^s of a group of order p^m is congruent to unity, mod. p**.

Corollary. The number of self-conjugate sub-groups of order p^s of a group of order p^m is congruent to unity, mod. p.

* Frobenius, "Verallgemeinerung des Sylow'schen Satzes," *Berliner Sitzungsberichte* (1895), p. 989.

This is an immediate consequence of the theorem, since the number of sub-groups in any conjugate set is a power of p.

104. Having shewn that the number of sub-groups of G of order p^s is of the form $1 + kp$, we may now discuss under what circumstances it is possible for k to be zero, so that G of order p^m contains only one sub-group G_s of order p^s.

If this is the case, and if P is any operation of G not contained in G_s, the order of P must not be less than p^{s+1}; for if it were less, G would have some sub-group of order p^s containing P and this would necessarily be different from G_s. If the order of P is p^{s+t}, then $\{P^{p^t}\}$ is a cyclical sub-group of order p^s; and it must coincide with G_s. Hence, if G_s is the only sub-group of order p^s, it must be cyclical.

Suppose now that G contains operations of order p^r $(r > s)$, but no operations of order p^{r+1}; and let P be an operation of G of order p^r. Then $\{P\}$ must be contained self-conjugately in a non-cyclical sub-group of order p^{r+1}.

We will take first the case in which p is an odd prime. Then (§ 100) G must contain an operation P' which does not belong to $\{P\}$, such that

$$P'^{-1}PP' = P^{\alpha}, \quad P'^{p} = P^{\beta}.$$

If α were unity, $\{P, P'\}$ would be an Abelian group of order p^{r+1} containing no operation of order p^{r+1}. Its type would therefore be $(r, 1)$, and it would necessarily contain an operation of order p not occurring in $\{P\}$. It has been shewn that this is impossible if G_s is the only sub-group of order p^s, and therefore α cannot be unity.

We may then without loss of generality (§ 100) assume that

$$\alpha = 1 + p^{r-1}.$$

Moreover if β were not divisible by p, the order of P' would be p^{r+1}, contrary to supposition. Hence we must have the relations

$$P'^{-1}PP' = P^{1+p^{r-1}}, \quad P'^{p} = P^{\gamma p}.$$

By successive applications of the first of these equations, we get

$$P'^{-y}P^{x}P'^{y} = P^{x(1+yp^{r-1})},$$

for all values of x and y; and from this it immediately follows that

$$(P^x P')^p = P'^p P^{x\{p+\frac{1}{2}p(p+1)p^{r-1}\}}$$
$$= P^{(x+\gamma)p}.$$

Hence the order of $P^{-\gamma}P'$, an operation not contained in $\{P\}$, is p. This is impossible if G_s is the only sub-group of order p^s. If then $r < m$, G must contain operations of order greater than p^r; and G is therefore a cyclical group. Hence :—

THEOREM V. *If G, of order p^m, where p is an odd prime, contains only one sub-group of order p^s, G must be cyclical.*

105. When $p = 2$, the result is not so simple.

Let $\{P, Q\}$ be a non-cyclical sub-group of order 2^{r+1}, which contains the cyclical sub-group $\{P\}$ self-conjugately: and suppose Q chosen so that its order is as small as possible. It must not be less than 2^{s+1}, and not greater than 2^r. Hence

$$Q^2 = P^{2^t}, \quad 1 \leqslant t \leqslant r - s,$$

while (§ 100)

$$Q^{-1}PQ = P^{\alpha}, \quad \alpha = \pm 1 + 2^{r-1} \text{ or } -1.$$

If $\alpha = 1 + 2^{r-1}$, $(P^x Q)^2 = P^{x(2+2^{r-1})+2^t}$.

Hence if x is chosen so that $x(1 + 2^{r-2}) + 2^{t-1}$ is a multiple of 2^{r-1}, $P^x Q$ is an operation of order 2 not contained in $\{P\}$. This case therefore cannot occur.

If $\alpha = -1 + 2^{r-1}$, $\quad (P^x Q)^2 = P^{x2^{r-1}+2^t}$,

while $\quad Q^{-1}P^{2^t}Q = P^{-2^t}$,

and $\quad Q^{-1}P^{2^t}Q = P^{2^t}$.

Hence $P^{2^{t+1}} = E$, and either Q or PQ is an operation of order 2. This case again cannot occur.

If $\alpha = -1$, $\quad (P^x Q)^2 = P^{2^t}$,

and $\quad P^{2^{t+1}} = E$.

In this case, if $t = r - 1$, every operation of $\{P, Q\}$ which is not contained in $\{P\}$ is of order 4, and $\{P, Q\}$ contains a single sub-group of order 2, viz. $\{P^{2^{r-1}}\}$, so that s must be unity.

If the order of the group were greater than 2^{r+1}, $\{P, Q\}$ would be contained self-conjugately in a group of order 2^{r+2}. Let Q' be an operation of this group which does not belong to $\{P, Q\}$. Then since $\{P\}$ is the only cyclical group of order 2^r contained in $\{P, Q\}$, Q' must transform $\{P\}$ into itself. If Q'^2 is contained in $\{P\}$, the above discussion shews that

$$Q'^{-1}PQ' = P^{-1},$$

and therefore

$$Q^{-1}Q'^{-1}PQ'Q = P.$$

In this case $\{P, Q'Q\}$ is a non-cyclical Abelian group containing three sub-groups of order 2. If, on the other hand, Q'^4 is the lowest power of Q' contained in $\{P\}$, then

$$Q'^{-1}PQ' = P^{\beta}, \quad \beta = \pm 1 + 2^{r-2} \text{ or } -1,$$

and

$$Q'^4 = P^{4\gamma}.$$

Hence

$$Q'^{-2}PQ'^2 = P \text{ or } P^{1+2^{r-1}},$$

and $\{P, Q'^2\}$ contains more than one sub-group of order 2. Finally, then, any group of order 2^{r+2} which contains $\{P, Q\}$ self-conjugately has more than one sub-group of order 2. The result may therefore be summed up as follows:—

THEOREM VI. *If a group G, of order 2^m, has a single sub-group of order 2^s, $(s > 1)$, it must be cyclical; if it has a single sub-group of order 2, it is either cyclical or of the type defined by*

$$P^{2^{m-1}} = E, \quad Q^2 = P^{2^{m-2}}, \quad Q^{-1}PQ = P^{-1}, \quad (m > 2).$$

106. When $m = 3$, the group defined by these relations is known as the *quaternion-group*. In this case the defining relations become

$$P^4 = E, \quad Q^2 = P^2, \quad Q^{-1}PQ = P^{-1}.$$

The operations of the group are

$$E, \quad P^2, \quad P, \quad P^3, \quad Q, \quad QP^2, \quad PQ, \quad QP;$$

where P and P^3, Q and QP^2, PQ and QP are pairs of inverse and conjugate operations of order 4. The group has three cyclical sub-groups of order 4, and admits an outer isomorphism which permutes these three sub-groups, so that each of them bears the same relation to the group. In fact, if

$$C^3 = E, \quad C^{-1}PC = Q, \quad C^{-1}QP = PQ,$$

then

$$C^{-1}PQC = P,$$

and in $\{C, P, Q\}$, which contains $\{P, Q\}$ self-conjugately, P, Q and PQ form a conjugate set.

Further if three symbols i, j, k be defined by the relations

$$i(E-P^2)=(E-P^2)\,i=P-P^3,$$
$$j(E-P^2)=(E-P^2)\,j=Q-QP^2,$$
$$k(E-P^2)=(E-P^2)\,k=PQ-QP,$$

and the multiplication-table of the group be taken account of, it will be found that i, j, k combine according to the laws,

$$i^2=j^2=k^2=-1,$$
$$ij=-ji=k, \quad jk=-kj=i, \quad ki=-ik=j,$$

which are identical with the laws obeyed by Hamilton's celebrated symbols denoted by the same letters.

An alternative form of statement is that, E, P^2, P, Q, PQ combine by multiplication according to the same laws as $1, -1, i, j, k$.

When $m>3$, the group contains $2^{m-2}+1$ cyclical sub-groups of order 4, of which one is self-conjugate while the remainder form two conjugate sets of 2^{m-3} each. The sub-groups of order 4 no longer all bear the same relation to the group, and there is no isomorphism whose order is divisible by an odd prime.

Ex. Shew that the group of isomorphisms of the group defined by

$$P^{2^{m-1}}=E, \quad Q^2=P^{2^{m-2}}, \quad Q^{-1}PQ=P^{-1}, \quad (m>3),$$

has 2^{2m-3} for its order.

107. It has been seen (§ 81) that the distinct operations which arise when every operation of an Abelian group is raised to the power p^μ constitute a sub-group. This is not in general true for a non-Abelian group of order p^m; but it may be shewn that the p^μth powers of the operations of such a group generate a sub-group for whose order an upper limit can be obtained.

Let G be a group of order p^m, and suppose the type of G/G_1 to be $(m_1, m_2, \ldots, m_s)$. The sub-group constituted by the distinct pth powers of the operations of G/G_1 is of order $p^{m_1+m_2+\ldots+m_s-s}$ (§ 81); and the corresponding sub-group of G is of order p^{m-s}. The pth power of every operation of G must belong to this sub-group. For to the pth power of any operation of G which is not contained in G_1 there corresponds the pth power of an operation of G/G_1; while the pth power of every operation of G_1 is contained in G_1. Hence the group generated by the pth powers of the operations of G is contained in the above determined sub-group of order p^{m-s}. If this sub-group is called G' and if G_1' is its derived group, then s' being the number of independent generators of G'/G_1', the sub-group generated by the pth powers of the operations of G' will have order not exceeding $p^{m-s-s'}$. This group obviously contains the group generated by the p^2th powers of the operations of G. The process may be continued and each succeeding s is equal to or greater than 2 until a cyclical group is reached. It is clear that the group generated by the p^μth powers of the operations of G is a characteristic sub-group.

108. We shall now proceed to discuss, in application of the foregoing theorems and for the importance of the results themselves, the various types of groups of order p^m which contain self-conjugate cyclical sub-groups of orders p^{m-1} and p^{m-2} respectively*. It is clear from Theorem VI that the case $p = 2$ requires independent investigation; we shall only deal in detail with the case in which p is an odd prime, and shall state the results for the case when $p = 2$.

The types of Abelian groups of order p^m which contain operations of order p^{m-2} are those corresponding to the symbols (m), $(m-1, 1)$, $(m-2, 2)$, and $(m-2, 1, 1)$. We will assume that the groups which we consider in the following paragraphs are not Abelian.

109. We will first consider a group G, of order p^m, which contains an operation P of order p^{m-1}. The cyclical sub-group $\{P\}$ is self-conjugate and contains a single sub-group $\{P^{p^{m-2}}\}$ of order p. By Theorem V, since G is not cyclical, it must contain an operation Q', of order p, which does not occur in $\{P\}$. Since $\{P\}$ is self-conjugate and the group is not Abelian, Q' must transform P into one of its own powers. Hence

$$Q'^{-1}PQ' = P^\alpha,$$

and since Q'^p is permutable with P it follows, from § 100, that

$$\alpha = 1 + kp^{m-2}.$$

* Groups of order p^m which contain operations of order p^{m-2} are discussed by Miller, *Transactions of the American Mathematical Society* (1902), pp. 383–387.

Since the group is not Abelian, k cannot be zero; but it may have any value from 1 to $p-1$. If now

$$kx \equiv 1 \ (\text{mod. } p),$$

then
$$Q'^{-x}PQ'^{x} = P^{1+p^{m-2}};$$

and therefore, writing Q for Q'^{x}, the group is defined by

$$P^{p^{m-1}} = E, \qquad Q^p = E, \qquad Q^{-1}PQ = P^{1+p^{m-2}}.$$

These relations are clearly self-consistent, and they define a group of order p^m.

There is therefore a single type of non-Abelian group of order p^m which contains operations of order p^{m-1}, because, for any such group, a pair of generating operations may be chosen which satisfy the above relations.

From the relation $Q^{-1}PQ = P^{1+p^{m-2}}$,

it follows by repetition and multiplication that

$$Q^{-y}P^xQ^y = P^{x(1+yp^{m-2})},$$

and therefore that

$$(Q^yP^x)^z = Q^{yz}P^{xz(1+\frac{1}{2}(z-1)yp^{m-2})},$$

and
$$(Q^yP^x)^p = P^{xp}.$$

Hence G contains p cyclical sub-groups of order p^{m-1}, of which P and Q^yP ($y = 1, 2, \ldots\ldots, p-1$) may be taken as the generating operations. Since Q and P^p are permutable, G also contains an Abelian non-cyclical sub-group $\{Q, P^p\}$ of order p^{m-1}. It is easy to verify that the $1+p$ sub-groups thus obtained exhaust the sub-groups of order p^{m-1}; and that, for any other order p^s, there are also exactly $p+1$ sub-groups of which p are cyclical and one is Abelian of type $(s-1, 1)$.

The reader will find it an instructive exercise to verify the results of the corresponding case where p is 2; they may be stated thus. There are four distinct types of non-Abelian group of order 2^m, which contain operations of order 2^{m-1}, when $m > 3$. Of these, one is the type given in Theorem VI, and the remaining three are defined by

$$P^{2^{m-1}} = E, \quad Q^2 = E, \quad QPQ = P^{1+2^{m-2}};$$

$$P^{2^{m-1}} = E, \quad Q^2 = E, \quad QPQ = P^{-1+2^{m-2}};$$

$$P^{2^{m-1}} = E, \quad Q^2 = E, \quad QPQ = P^{-1}.$$

When $m = 3$, there are only two distinct types. In this case, the second and the fourth of the above groups are identical, and the third is Abelian.

110. Suppose next that G, a group of order p^m, has a self-conjugate cyclical sub-group $\{P\}$ of order p^{m-2}, and that no operation of G is of higher order than p^{m-2}. We may at once distinguish three cases for separate discussion, according as P is self-conjugate, one of p, or one of p^2 conjugate operations.

Taking the first case, there can be no operation Q' in G such that Q'^{p^2} is the lowest power of Q' contained in $\{P\}$, for if there were, $\{Q', P\}$ would be Abelian and, its order being p^m, it would necessarily coincide with G. Hence any operation Q', not contained in $\{P\}$, generates with P an Abelian group of type $(m-2, 1)$, and we may choose P and Q as independent generators of this sub-group, the order of Q being p. If now R' is any operation of G not contained in $\{Q, P\}$, then $\{R', P\}$ is again an Abelian group of type $(m-2, 1)$. If P and R are independent generators of this group, the latter cannot occur in $\{Q, P\}$. Now since Q is not self-conjugate,

$$R^{-1}QR = QP^{\beta};$$

and since R^p, or E, is permutable with Q

$$P^{p\beta} = E,$$

so that $$\beta \equiv 0 \pmod{p^{m-3}}.$$

Hence $$R^{-1}QR = QP^{kp^{m-3}},$$

where k is not a multiple of p. If finally, P^k be taken as a generating operation in the place of P, the group is defined by

$$P^{p^{m-2}} = E, \quad Q^p = E, \quad R^p = E, \quad R^{-1}QR = QP^{p^{m-3}},$$
$$PQ = QP, \quad PR = RP.$$

There is therefore a single type of group of order p^m, which contains a self-conjugate operation of order p^{m-2}, and no operation of order p^{m-1}.

111. Next let P be one of p conjugate operations. These (§ 100) must be $P^{1+kp^{m-3}}$ $(k = 1, 2, \ldots, p)$.

If $G/\{P\}$ is cyclical, let Q' be an operation, the lowest power of which in $\{P\}$ is Q'^{p^2}.

If Q' were permutable with P, G would be Abelian. Hence we may take

$$Q'^{-1}PQ' = P^{1+p^{m-3}},$$

while $$Q'^{p^2} = P^{kp^2}.$$

These relations give

$$(Q'P^x)^{p^2} = P^{(x+k)p^2}.$$

Hence if $Q'P^{-k} = Q$, the group is defined by

$$P^{p^{m-2}} = E, \qquad Q^{p^2} = E, \qquad Q^{-1}PQ = P^{1+p^{m-3}},$$

and there is a single type.

If $G/\{P\}$ is non-cyclical, G must contain a sub-group of order p^{m-1} in which P is self-conjugate and another in which P is one of p conjugate operations. The former is an Abelian group of type $(m-2, 1)$, of which P and R may be taken as independent generating operations. The latter is a group of the type considered in § 109 (with $m-1$ for m) defined by

$$P^{p^{m-2}} = E, \qquad Q^p = E, \qquad Q^{-1}PQ = P^{1+p^{m-3}}$$

With this group R is permutable, and therefore

$$R^{-1}QR = Q^{\alpha}P^{\beta p^{m-3}},$$

since the only operations of order p in $\{P, Q\}$ are of this form (§ 109).

Now $$R^{-1}Q^{-1}PQR = P^{1+p^{m-3}},$$

or $$Q^{-\alpha}PQ^{\alpha} = P^{1+p^{m-3}},$$

and therefore $$\alpha = 1.$$

Also $$P^{-1}QP = QP^{-p^{m-3}},$$

hence $$P^{-\beta}R^{-1}QRP^{\beta} = Q,$$

and RP^{β} is a self-conjugate operation. If β is not a multiple of p, RP^{β} is an operation of order p^{m-2}, and by supposition the group has no self-conjugate operation of order p^{m-2}. Hence β must be a multiple of p, and R is a self-conjugate operation Again then there is one type defined by

$$P^{p^{m-2}} = E, \quad Q^p = E, \quad R^p = E, \quad Q^{-1}PQ = P^{1+p^{m-3}},$$
$$R^{-1}PR = P, \qquad R^{-1}QR = Q.$$

It is the direct product of $\{R\}$ and $\{P, Q\}$.

Lastly let P be one of p^2 conjugate operations. These (§ 100) must be $P^{1+kp^{m-4}}$ $(k = 1, 2, \ldots, p^2)$; and this case can only occur if $m > 4$. The order of an operation which transforms P into $P^{1+p^{m-4}}$ must be equal to or a multiple of p^2. If there were no operation of order p^2 effecting the transformation, every operation of the group not belonging to $\{P\}$ would be of order p^2 or greater, and the group would only have one sub-group of order p. Hence there must be an operation of order p^2 transforming P into $P^{1+p^{m-4}}$. Denoting this operation by Q, there is again a single type * defined by

$$P^{p^{m-2}} = E, \qquad Q^{p^2} = E, \qquad Q^{-1}PQ = P^{1+p^{m-4}}.$$

It is to be expected, from the result of the corresponding case at the end of § 109, that the number of distinct types when $p = 2$ is much greater than when p is an odd prime. There are, in fact, when $m > 5$, fourteen distinct types of non-Abelian groups of order 2^m, which contain a self-conjugate cyclical sub-group of order 2^{m-2} and no operation of order 2^{m-1}. They may be classified as follows.

Suppose first that the group has a self-conjugate operation A of order 2^{m-2}. There is then a single type defined by the relations

$$\text{(i)} \quad A^{2^{m-2}} = E, \quad B^2 = E, \quad C^2 = E, \quad CBC = BA^{2^{m-3}}.$$

Suppose next that the group G has no self-conjugate operation of order 2^{m-2}, and let $\{A\}$ be a self-conjugate cyclical sub-group of order 2^{m-2}. If $G/\{A\}$ is cyclical, there are, when $m > 5$, five distinct types. The common defining relations of these are

$$A^{2^{m-2}} = E, \quad B^4 = E, \quad B^{-1}AB = A^{\alpha};$$

* In each of the cases to which we have been led in the discussion contained in §§ 109–111, and in previous discussions of special types of group, we have arrived at a set of defining relations, containing no indeterminate symbols, such that in each case a set of generating operations can be chosen to satisfy these relations. To justify the statement, in each particular case, that such a set of relations gives a distinct type of group, it is finally necessary to verify that the relations actually define a group of order p^m. In the cases dealt with in the text, this verification is implicitly contained in the process by which the relations have been arrived at. We have therefore omitted the direct verification, which moreover is extremely simple. We shall similarly omit the corresponding verifications in the discussion of groups of orders p^3 and p^4, as in none of these cases does it present any difficulty.

To illustrate the necessity of such a verification in general, we may consider a simple case. The relations

$$P^3 = E, \quad Q^9 = E, \quad P^{-1}QP = Q^{\alpha},$$

where α is any given integer, certainly define a group whose order is equal to or is a factor of 27, since they indicate that $\{P\}$ and $\{Q\}$ are permutable. They will not however give a type of group of order 27, unless α is 1, 4 or 7. For instance, if $\alpha = 5$, the relations involve

$$Q = P^{-3}QP^3 = Q^8, \text{ or } Q^7 = E.$$

Hence
$$Q = Q^{4\cdot7-3\cdot9} = E,$$

and the relations hold only for a group of order 3.

Again, if $\alpha = 3$, the relations give

$$P^{-1}Q^3P = Q^9 = E, \text{ or } Q^3 = E, \text{ whence } Q = E,$$

and as before they define a group of order 3.

and the five distinct types are

$$\text{(ii) } \alpha = -1, \quad \text{(iii) } \alpha = 1 + 2^{m-3}, \quad \text{(iv) } \alpha = -1 + 2^{m-3},$$

$$\text{(v) } \alpha = 1 + 2^{m-4}, \quad \text{(vi) } \alpha = -1 + 2^{m-4}.$$

If $m = 5$, then (iv) and (v) are identical, and (vi) is Abelian; so that there are only three distinct types. If $m = 4$, there is a single type; it is given by (ii).

When $G/\{A\}$ is not cyclical, the square of every operation of G is contained in $\{A\}$. If all the self-conjugate operations of G are not contained in $\{A\}$, there must be a self-conjugate operation B, of order 2, which does not occur in $\{A\}$. If C is any operation of G, not contained in $\{A, B\}$, then $\{A, C\}$ is a self-conjugate sub-group of order 2^{m-1}, which has no operation except identity in common with $\{B\}$. Hence G is a direct product of a group of order 2 and a group of order 2^{m-1}. There are therefore, for this case, four types (vii), (viii), (ix), (x), when $m > 4$, corresponding to the four groups of order 2^{m-1} of § 109. If $m = 4$, there are two types.

Next, let all the self-conjugate operations of G be contained in $\{A\}$; and suppose that A is one of two conjugate operations. Then G must contain an Abelian sub-group of type $(m-2, 1)$, in which A occurs; and it may be shewn that, when $m > 4$, there are two types defined by the relations

$$A^{2^{m-2}} = E, \quad B^2 = E, \quad BAB = A, \quad C^2 = E,$$

(xi) and (xii)

$$CBC = BA^{2^{m-3}}, \quad CAC = A^{-1} \text{ or } A^{-1+2^{m-3}}.$$

When $m = 4$, there is, for this case, no type.

Lastly, suppose that A is one of four conjugate operations. Then G must contain sub-groups of order 2^{m-1}, of the second and the third types of § 109, and a sub-group of order 2^{m-1} of either the first or fourth type (*l.c.*). In this last case, there are two distinct types defined by

$$A^{2^{m-2}} = E, \quad B^2 = E, \quad BAB = A^{1+2^{m-3}},$$

(xiii) and (xiv)

$$C^2 = E, \quad CAC = A^{-1+2^{m-3}}, \quad CBC = B \text{ or } BA^{2^{m-3}}.$$

These two types exist only when $m > 4$.

112. We shall now, as a final illustration, determine and tabulate all types of groups of orders p^2, p^3 and p^4. It has been already seen that when $p = 2$ the discussion must, in part at least, be distinct from that for an odd prime; for the sake of brevity we shall not deal in detail with this case, but shall state the results only and leave their verification as an exercise to the reader.

It has been shewn (§ 36) that all groups of order p^2 are Abelian; and hence the only distinct types are those represented by (2) and (1, 1).

For Abelian groups of order p^3, the distinct types are (3), (2, 1) and (1, 1, 1).

If a non-Abelian group of order p^3 contains an operation of order p^2, the sub-group it generates is self-conjugate; hence (§ 109) in this case there is a single type of group defined by

$$P^{p^2} = E, \quad Q^p = E, \quad Q^{-1}PQ = P^{1+p}.$$

If there is no operation of order p^2, then since there must be a self-conjugate operation of order p, the group comes under the head discussed in § 110; there is again a single type of group defined by

$$P^p = E, \quad Q^p = E, \quad R^p = E, \quad R^{-1}QR = QP,$$
$$R^{-1}PR = P, \quad Q^{-1}PQ = P.$$

These two types exhaust all the possibilities for non-Abelian groups of order p^3.

113. For Abelian groups of order p^4, the possible distinct types are (4), (3, 1), (2, 2), (2, 1, 1) and (1, 1, 1, 1).

For non-Abelian groups of order p^4 which contain operations of order p^3 there is a single type, namely that given in § 109 when m is put equal to 4.

For non-Abelian groups which contain a self-conjugate cyclical sub-group of order p^2 and no operation of order p^3, there are three distinct types, obtained by writing 4 for m in the group of § 110 and in the first and the last groups of § 111. The defining relations of these need not be here repeated, as they will be given in the summarizing table (§ 117).

It remains now to determine all distinct types of groups of order p^4, which contain no operation of order p^3 and no self-conjugate cyclical sub-group of order p^2. We shall first deal with groups which contain operations of order p^2.

Let S be an operation of order p^2 in a group G of order p^4. The cyclical sub-group $\{S\}$ must be self-conjugate in a non-cyclical sub-group $\{S, T\}$ of order p^3, defined by

$$S^{p^2} = E, \quad T^p = E, \quad T^{-1}ST = S^{1+kp}.$$

If R is any operation of G, not contained in $\{S, T\}$, then since $\{S\}$ is not self-conjugate, we must have (§ 97)

$$R^{-1}SR = S^{1+\alpha p}T^{\beta},$$

and therefore $$R^{-1}S^pR = S^p.$$

Now $$T^{-1}S^pT = S^p,$$

and therefore the pth power of every operation of order p^2 in G is a self-conjugate operation.

First let us suppose that G contains other self-conjugate operations besides those of $\{S^p\}$. Every such operation must occur in the group that contains $\{S\}$ self-conjugately; hence in this case T must be self-conjugate.

We now therefore have

$$S^{p^2} = E, \quad T^p = E, \quad T^{-1}ST = S,$$

$$R^{-1}SR = S^{1+\alpha p}T^\beta, \quad R^{-1}TR = T,$$

$$R^p = S^{\gamma p}T^\delta.$$

These equations give

$$(S^x R)^p = R^p S^{xp} = S^{(x+\gamma)p}T^\delta.$$

Hence, if $\delta = 0$, $S^{-\gamma}R$ is an operation of order p. Denoting this by R' and $S^{\alpha p}T^\beta$ by T', the group is defined by

$$S^{p^2} = E, \quad T'^p = E, \quad R'^p = E, \quad R'^{-1}SR' = ST',$$

$$T'^{-1}ST' = S, \quad R'^{-1}T'R' = T'.$$

On the other hand, if δ is not zero, $S^{\frac{\delta\alpha}{\beta}-\gamma}R$ is an operation of order p^2 such that R transforms it into a power of itself. This is contrary to the supposition that the group contains no cyclical self-conjugate sub-group of order p^2. Hence δ cannot be different from zero: we therefore have only one type of group.

114. Next, let $\{S^p\}$ contain all the self-conjugate operations of G; and as before, let $\{S, T\}$ be the group that contains $\{S\}$ self-conjugately. If G contains an operation S' of order p^2 which does not occur in $\{S, T\}$, there must also be a non-cyclical sub-group $\{S', T'\}$ of order p^3 which contains $\{S'\}$ self-conjugately. Now $\{S, T\}$ and $\{S', T'\}$ must have a common sub-group of order p^2; since this is self-conjugate in G, it cannot be cyclical. The only non-cyclical sub-groups of orders p^2 that $\{S, T\}$ and $\{S', T'\}$ contain are $\{S^p, T\}$ and $\{S'^p, T'\}$. Hence these must be identical, and therefore T must occur in $\{S', T'\}$. If now $\{S, T\}$ and $\{S', T'\}$ were both Abelian, T would be permutable both with S and with S', and would therefore, contrary to supposition, be a self-conjugate operation. Hence either (i) G must contain a non-Abelian group $\{S, T\}$ of order p^3, in which S is an operation of order p^2; or (ii) the Abelian group $\{S, T\}$, in which S is an operation of order p^2, must contain all the operations of G of order p^2.

In the case (i), the group is defined by

$$S^{p^2}=E,\quad T^p=E,\quad T^{-1}ST=S^{1+p},$$
$$R^{-1}SR=S^{1+\alpha p}T^{\beta},\quad R^{-1}TR=S^{\gamma p}T,$$
$$R^p=S^{\delta p}.$$

If
$$R'=RS^{\gamma}T^{\beta\gamma-\alpha},$$
it is found that

$$R'^{-1}SR'=ST^{\beta},\quad R'^{-1}TR'=T;$$

and if $R''=R'^{\beta'}$, where $\beta\beta'\equiv 1 \pmod{p}$, then

$$R''^{-1}SR''=ST,\quad R''^{-1}TR''=T.$$

Hence dropping accents, the group is defined by

$$S^{p^2}=E,\quad T^p=E,\quad T^{-1}ST=S^{1+p},$$
$$R^{-1}SR=ST,\quad R^{-1}TR=T,$$
$$R^p=S^{\alpha p}.$$

Write now

$$S_1=S^x,\quad T_1=TS^{-\frac{1}{2}(x-1)p},\quad R_1=R^{x'},$$

where $xx'\equiv 1 \pmod{p}$.

It is then found that the defining relations are reproduced, except that the last becomes

$$R_1{}^p=S_1{}^{\alpha x'^2 p}.$$

There are therefore not more than three types corresponding to 0, 1 and any non-residue as values of α. That the type corresponding to $\alpha=0$ is distinct from the other two is obvious on consideration of the sub-group that contains T self-conjugately. That the other two are distinct is left as an exercise for the reader.

In case (ii), the group is defined by

$$S^{p^2}=E,\quad T^p=E,\quad T^{-1}ST=S,$$
$$R^{-1}SR=S^{1+\alpha p}T^{\beta},\quad R^{-1}TR=S^{\gamma p}T,$$
$$R^p=E;$$

with the condition that all operations of G, not contained in $\{S, T\}$, are of order p.

The formulæ for $R^{-x}SR^x$ and $R^{-x}TR^x$ enable us to calculate directly the power of any given operation of G. Thus they give

$$(S^xR)^p=S^{px\{1+\frac{1}{6}\beta\gamma(p+1)p(p-1)+\frac{1}{2}\alpha p(p+1)\}}.$$

If $p > 3$, this gives

$$(S^x R)^p = S^{px},$$

so that, if x is not a multiple of p, the order of $S^x R$ is p^2. Hence the type of group under consideration can only occur when $p = 3$.

In this case $$(S^x R)^3 = S^{3x(1+\beta\gamma)}.$$

Hence if $p = 3$ and $\beta\gamma \equiv -1$ (mod. 3), we obtain a new type. A reduction similar to that in the previous case may now be effected; and taking unity for x, the group is defined by

$$S^9 = E, \quad T^3 = E, \quad R^3 = E, \quad T^{-1}ST = S,$$
$$R^{-1}SR = ST, \quad R^{-1}TR = S^{-3}T.$$

115. It only remains to determine the distinct types which contain no operation of order p^2.

Suppose first that the self-conjugate operations of G form a group of order p^2. This must be generated by two independent operations P and Q of order p.

If now R is any other operation of the group, $\{P, Q, R\}$ must be an Abelian group of type (1, 1, 1). If again S is any operation not contained in $\{P, Q, R\}$, it cannot be permutable with R; for if it were, R would be self-conjugate. There must therefore be a relation of the form (§ 97)

$$S^{-1}RS = RP^\alpha Q^\beta.$$

Since any operation of $\{P, Q\}$ may be taken for one of its generating operations, we may take $P^\alpha Q^\beta$ or P' for one. If then Q' is an independent operation of $\{P, Q\}$, G will be defined by

$$P'^p = E, \quad Q'^p = E, \quad R^p = E, \quad S^p = E, \quad S^{-1}RS = RP',$$

in addition to the relations expressing that P' and Q' are self-conjugate. There is then in this case a single type. That all the operations of G in this case are actually of order p follows from the fact that the group is the direct product of $\{Q'\}$ and $\{S, R\}$, the latter being of the second type of non-Abelian group of order p^3.

116. Suppose, secondly, that the self-conjugate operations of G form a sub-group of order p, generated by P. There must then be some operation Q which belongs to a set of p conjugate operations; for if every operation of G which is not self-conjugate were one of a set of p^2 conjugate operations, the total number of operations in the group would be congruent to p (mod. p^2). It follows that Q must be self-conjugate in a group of order p^3; and since P is also self-conjugate in this group, it must be Abelian. Let P, Q, R be generators of this group and S any operation of G not contained in it. We may now assume that Q belongs to the sub-group H_2 (§ 93), and therefore that

$$S^{-1}QS = QP^{\alpha},$$

while $$S^{-1}RS = RQ^{\beta}P^{\gamma}.$$

If β were zero, $Q^{\frac{1}{\alpha}}R^{-\frac{1}{\gamma}}$ would be a self-conjugate operation not contained in $\{P\}$; and therefore β must be different from zero. We may now put

$$Q^{\beta}P^{\gamma} = Q', \quad P^{\alpha\beta} = P';$$

and the group is then defined by the relations

$$P'^p = E,\ \ Q'^p = E,\ \ R^p = E,\ \ S^p = E,\ \ S^{-1}RS = RQ',\ \ S^{-1}Q'S = Q'P',$$

together with the relations expressing that P' is self-conjugate, and $\{P', Q', R\}$ Abelian. There is thus again in this case, at most, a single type. It remains to determine whether the operations are all actually of order p.

Dropping accents the defining relations give

$$S^{-1}P^{\alpha_x}Q^{\beta_x}R^{\gamma_x}S = P^{\alpha_{x+1}}Q^{\beta_{x+1}}R^{\gamma_{x+1}},$$

where $$\alpha_{x+1} = \alpha_x + \beta_x,\quad \beta_{x+1} = \beta_x + \gamma_x,\quad \gamma_{x+1} = \gamma_x;$$

and therefore $$S^{-x}P^{\alpha}Q^{\beta}R^{\gamma}S^{x} = P^{\alpha_x}Q^{\beta_x}R^{\gamma_x},$$

where $$\alpha_x = \alpha + x\beta + \tfrac{1}{2}x(x-1)\gamma,\quad \beta_x = \beta + x\gamma,\quad \gamma_x = \gamma.$$

Hence

$$\begin{aligned}(P^{\alpha}Q^{\beta}R^{\gamma}S)^p &= P^{\sum_1^p \alpha_x}Q^{\sum_1^p \beta_x}R^{\sum_1^p \gamma_x}\\ &= P^{p\alpha+\frac{1}{2}p(p-1)\beta+\frac{1}{6}(p+1)p(p-1)\gamma}\,Q^{p\beta+\frac{1}{2}p(p-1)\gamma}\,R^{p\gamma}.\end{aligned}$$

If p is a greater prime than 3, the indices of P, Q, R are all multiples of p; hence $P^{\alpha}Q^{\beta}R^{\gamma}S$ is of order p, S being any operation not contained in G. If however $p = 3$, then

$$(P^{\alpha}Q^{\beta}R^{\gamma}S)^3 = P^{\gamma},$$

so that, if γ is not a multiple of 3, $P^{\alpha}Q^{\beta}R^{\gamma}S$ is an operation of order 9. Hence this last type of group exists as a distinct type for all primes greater than 3; but for $p = 3$, it is not distinct from one of the previous types containing operations of order 9.

117. In tabulating, as follows, the types of group thus obtained, we give with each group G a symbol of the form

$$(a, b, \ldots\ldots)(a', b', \ldots\ldots)(a'', b'', \ldots\ldots)\ldots\ldots,$$

indicating the types of H_n, H_{n-1}/H_n, H_{n-2}/H_{n-1}, ... where

$$G,\ H_1,\ H_2,\ \ldots,\ H_n,$$

is the series of self-conjugate sub-groups defined in § 93. This symbol is to be read from the left so that $(a, b, \ldots\ldots)$ is the type of H_n.

Moreover in each group there is no operation of higher order than that denoted by P.

Table of groups of order p^n, p an odd prime.*

I. $n = 2$, two types.

(i) (2); (ii) (1, 1)

II. $n = 3$, five types.

(i) (3); (ii) (2, 1); (iii) (1, 1, 1);

(iv) $P^{p^2} = E,\ Q^p = E,\ Q^{-1}PQ = P^{1+p}$, (1) (11);

(v) $P^p = E,\ Q^p = E,\ R^p = E,\ R^{-1}QR = QP,$

$R^{-1}PR = P,\quad Q^{-1}PQ = P$, (1) (11)

III. $n = 4$, fifteen types.

(i) (4); (ii) (3, 1); (iii) (2, 2); (iv) (2, 1, 1);

(v) (1, 1, 1, 1);

(vi) $P^{p^3} = E,\ Q^p = E,\ Q^{-1}PQ = P^{1+p^2}$, (2) (11);

(vii) $P^{p^2} = E,\ Q^p = E,\ R^p = E,\ R^{-1}QR = QP^p,\ Q^{-1}PQ = P,$

$R^{-1}PR = P$, (2) (11);

(viii) $P^{p^2} = E,\ Q^{p^2} = E,\ Q^{-1}PQ = P^{1+p}$, (11) (11);

(ix) $P^{p^2} = E,\ Q^p = E,\ R^p = E,\ R^{-1}PR = P^{1+p},\ P^{-1}QP = Q,$

$R^{-1}QR = Q$, (11) (11),

this group (ix) being the direct product of $\{Q\}$ and $\{P, R\}$;

(x) $P^{p^2} = E,\ Q^p = E,\ R^p = E,\ R^{-1}PR = PQ,\ Q^{-1}PQ = P,$

$R^{-1}QR = Q$, (11) (11);

(xi), (xii), and (xiii),

$P^{p^2} = E,\ Q^p = E,\ Q^{-1}PQ = P^{1+p},\ R^{-1}PR = PQ,$

$R^{-1}QR = Q,\ R^p = P^{\alpha p}$, (1) (1) (11),

* On groups of orders p^3 and p^4, the reader may consult, in addition to Young's memoir already referred to, Hölder, "Die Gruppen der Ordnungen p^3, pq^2, pqr, p^4," *Math. Ann.* XLIII (1893), in particular, pp. 371—410.

where for (xi) $\alpha = 0$, for (xii) $\alpha = 1$, for (xiii) $\alpha =$ any non-residue, (mod. p);

$$\text{(xiv)}\ P^p = E,\ Q^p = E,\ R^p = E,\ S^p = E,\ S^{-1}RS = RP,$$
$$S^{-1}QS = Q,\ S^{-1}PS = P,\ R^{-1}QR = Q,\ R^{-1}PR = P,$$
$$Q^{-1}PQ = P,\ (11)\,(11),$$

this group (xiv) being the direct product of $\{Q\}$ and $\{P, R, S\}$;

(xv) $p > 3$,

$$P^p = E,\ Q^p = E,\ R^p = E,\ S^p = E,\ S^{-1}RS = RQ,\ S^{-1}QS = QP,$$
$$S^{-1}PS = P,\ R^{-1}QR = Q,\ R^{-1}PR = P,$$
$$Q^{-1}PQ = P,\ (1)\,(1)\,(11);$$

(xv) $p = 3$,

$$P^9 = E,\ Q^3 = E,\ R^3 = E,\ Q^{-1}PQ = P,\ R^{-1}PR = PQ,$$
$$R^{-1}QR = P^{-3}Q,\ (1)\,(1)\,(11).$$

118. To complete the list, we add, as was promised in § 112, the types of non-Abelian groups of orders 2^3 and 2^4; the possible types of Abelian groups being the same as for an odd prime.

Non-Abelian groups of order 2^3; two types.

(i) identical with II (iv), writing 2 for p;

(ii) $P^4 = E,\ Q^4 = E,\ Q^{-1}PQ = P^{-1},\ Q^2 = P^2,\ (1)\,(11)$.

Non-Abelian groups of order 2^4; nine types.

(i), (ii), (iii), (iv) and (v) identical with III (vi), (vii), (viii), (ix) and (x), writing 2 for p;

$$\text{(vi)}\ P^4 = E,\ Q^4 = E,\ R^2 = E,\ Q^{-1}PQ = P^{-1},\ Q^2 = P^2,$$
$$R^{-1}QR = Q,\ R^{-1}PR = P,\ (11)\,(11),$$

this group (vi) being the direct product of $\{R\}$ and $\{P, Q\}$;

(vii) $P^8 = E,\ Q^2 = E,\ Q^{-1}PQ = P^{-1},\ (1)\,(1)\,(11)$;

(viii) $P^8 = E,\ Q^2 = E,\ Q^{-1}PQ = P^3,\ (1)\,(1)\,(11)$;

(ix) $P^8 = E,\ Q^4 = E,\ Q^{-1}PQ = P^{-1},\ Q^2 = P^4,\ (1)\,(1)\,(11)$.

119. Ex. 1. If G, of order p^m, is not Abelian, and if every sub-group of G is self-conjugate, shew that p must be 2. (Dedekind.)

Ex. 2. Shew that a non-Abelian group of order p^4 contains $2p^2 - 1$ conjugate sets of operations, if the central is of order p; and $p^3 + p^2 - p$ conjugate sets if the central is of order p^2.

Ex. 3. Prove that a group whose order is a power of a prime cannot be generated by two operations which are conjugate within it.

Ex. 4. Prove that a group of order p^a necessarily contains an Abelian group of order p^A, where $A(A+1) \geqslant 2a$.

(Miller, *Messenger of Mathematics*, Vol. 27, p. 119.)

Ex. 5. If G is of order p^m, and H_1 is an Abelian group of type (1, 1,...... with $m-2$ units), and if $m>5$, G is the direct product of two groups. If $m=5$, there is one type for which G is not a direct product, viz.

$$Q_1^{p^2}=E,\quad Q_2^{p^2}=E,\quad P^p=E,\quad Q_2^{-1}Q_1Q_2=Q_1P,$$
$$Q_1^{-1}PQ_1=P,\quad Q_2^{-1}PQ_2=P.$$

Ex. 6. Discuss the groups of order p^{m+2} which contain two cyclical sub-groups of orders p^m and p^2 with no common operation except E. Shew that if P and Q generate these sub-groups, so that

$$P^{p^m}=E,\quad Q^{p^2}=E,$$

the further defining relations are of the following forms:

$$\text{(i)}\quad Q^{-1}PQ=P^{1+p^{m-1}};\quad \text{(ii)}\quad Q^{-1}PQ=P^{1+p^{m-2}};$$
$$\text{(iii)}\quad Q^{-1}PQ=PQ^p;$$
$$\text{(iv)}\quad Q^{-p}PQ^p=P^{1+p^{m-1}},\quad Q^{-1}PQ=P^{1+p^{m-2}}Q^{\alpha p}.$$

How many types come under the last head?

Ex. 7. Prove that the relations

$$A_i^2=E,\quad (i=1,2,\ldots,4n),\quad C^2=E,$$
$$A_iA_jA_iA_j=C,\quad (i\neq j)$$

define a group of order 2^{4n+1}, of which E and C are the only self-conjugate operations. Shew also that the group contains

$$2^{4n}+(-1)^{n+1}2^{2n}$$

operations of order 4, and $2^{4n}-(-1)^{n+1}2^{2n}-1$ operations of order 2.

Ex. 8. Shew that, when $n=1$, the group of the previous example can be expressed in the form in which A_1, A_2, A_3, A_4 are the substitutions,

$$x_1'=x_2,\quad x_2'=x_1,\quad x_3'=x_4,\quad x_4'=x_3;$$
$$x_1'=x_1,\quad x_2'=-x_2,\quad x_3'=-x_3,\quad x_4'=x_4;$$
$$x_1'=ix_2,\quad x_2'=-ix_1,\quad x_3'=ix_4,\quad x_4'=-ix_3;$$
$$x_1'=ix_3,\quad x_2'=-ix_4,\quad x_3'=-ix_1,\quad x_4'=ix_2;$$
$$i^2=-1.$$

(This, in fact, gives the most general group of space-collineations which are all of order 2. The reader should verify that it can be expressed in a real form.)

Ex. 9. If the order of every operation of a group, except identity, is 3, prove that any two conjugate operations are permutable. Shew also that if the group be generated by n independent operations, its order is equal to or is a factor of 3^{2^n-1}.

(*Quarterly Journal of Pure and Applied Mathematics*, 1902.)

Ex. 10. Discuss the group generated by A and B, where

$$A^2 = B^2, \quad S^{2^n} = E,$$

S being any operation of the group. In particular prove that the order of the group is 2^{2n}, the order of its central is 2^n, and the order of $A^{-1}B^{-1}AB$ is 2^{n-1}. Shew also that $\{A^2, A^{-1}B^{-1}AB\}$ is an Abelian self-conjugate sub-group of type $(n-1, n-1)$, and that every operation of the group not contained in this sub-group is of order 2^n.

Ex. 11. Prove that the relations

$$P_2^{-1}P_3^{-1}P_2P_3 = Q_1, \quad P_3^{-1}P_1^{-1}P_3P_1 = Q_2, \quad P_1^{-1}P_2^{-1}P_1P_2 = Q_3,$$

$$P_1^p = P_2^p = P_3^p = Q_1^p = Q_2^p = Q_3^p = E,$$

while Q_1, Q_2, Q_3 are self-conjugate operations, p being an odd prime, define a group of order p^6, all of whose operations are of order p; and shew that in this group every operation is either self-conjugate or one of a set of p^2 conjugate operations.

Ex. 12. Prove that a group, the order of whose central is p, cannot be the derived group of any group whose order is a power of p. Hence shew that all groups of order p^5 are metabelian.

CHAPTER IX.

ON SYLOW'S THEOREM.

120. We have seen in § 35 that if p^m divides the order of a group, p being a prime, there is at least one sub-group of order p^m. If p^α is the highest power of p which divides the order, the group can contain no sub-group of order $p^{\alpha+1}$, since this number is not a factor of the order of the group. That the group actually contains sub-groups of order p^α, that these sub-groups form a single conjugate set and that their number is congruent to unity, mod. p, was first established by Sylow*.

We shall devote the present chapter to the proof of Sylow's theorem; and a consideration of some of its more immediate consequences. These constitute, as will be seen later on, a most important set of results.

THEOREM I. *If p^α is the highest power of a prime p which divides the order of a group G, the sub-groups of G of order p^α form a single conjugate set, and their number is congruent to unity, mod. p.*

That G has at least one sub-group of order p^α has been proved in § 35.

If H is a sub-group of G of order p^α the only operations of G, which are permutable with H and have powers of p for their orders, are the operations of H itself. For if P is an operation of order p^r, permutable with H, and if p^s is the order of the greatest group common to $\{P\}$ and H, the order of $\{H, P\}$ is $p^{\alpha+r-s}$. But G can have no such sub-group unless $s = r$, in which case P belongs to H.

* Sylow, Théorèmes sur les groupes de substitutions, *Math. Ann.* v (1872), pp. 584 et seq. Compare also Frobenius, Neuer Beweis des Sylow'schen Satzes, *Crelle*, c (1886), p. 179.

Suppose now that H' is any sub-group conjugate to H; and let p^β be the order of the group h common to H and H', when H' is transformed by all the operations of H, the operations of h are the only ones which transform H' into itself. Hence the operations of H can be divided into $p^{\alpha-\beta}$ sets of p^β each, such that the operations of each set transform H' into a distinct sub-group. In this way, $p^{\alpha-\beta}$ sub-groups are obtained distinct from each other and from H and conjugate to H. If these sub-groups do not exhaust the set of sub-groups conjugate to H, let H'' be a new one. From H'' another set of $p^{\alpha-\beta'}$ sub-groups can be formed, distinct from each other and from H and conjugate to H. Moreover no sub-group of this latter set can coincide with one of the previous set. For if

$$P_1^{-1}H''P_1 = P_2^{-1}H'P_2,$$

where P_1 and P_2 are operations of H, then

$$H'' = P_3^{-1}H'P_3,$$

where $P_3 (= P_2P_1^{-1})$ is an operation of H; and this is contrary to the supposition that H'' is different from each group of the previous set. By continuing this process, it may be shewn that the number of sub-groups in the conjugate set containing H is

$$1 + p^{\alpha-\beta} + p^{\alpha-\beta'} + \ldots\ldots,$$

where no one of the indices $\alpha - \beta$, $\alpha - \beta'$, ... can be less than unity. The number of sub-groups in the conjugate set containing H is therefore congruent to unity, mod. p.

If now G contains another sub-group H_1 of order p^α, it must belong to a different conjugate set. The number of sub-groups in the new set may be shewn, as above, to be congruent to unity, mod. p. But on transforming H_1 by the operations of H, a set of $p^{\alpha-\gamma}$ conjugate sub-groups is obtained where p^γ is the order of the sub-group common to H and H_1. A further sub-group of the set, if it exists, gives rise to $p^{\alpha-\gamma'}$ additional conjugate sub-groups, distinct from each other and from the previous $p^{\alpha-\gamma}$. Proceeding thus we shew that the number of sub-groups in the conjugate set is a multiple of p; and as it cannot be at once a multiple of p and congruent to unity, mod. p, the set does not exist. The sub-groups of order p^α therefore form a single conjugate set and their number is congruent to unity, mod. p.

Corollary I. If $p^\alpha m$ is the order of the greatest group I, within which the group H of order p^α is contained self-conjugately, the order of the group G must be of the form

$$p^\alpha m(1+kp).$$

Corollary II. The number of groups of order p^α contained in G, i.e. the factor $1+kp$ in the preceding expression for the order of the group, can be expressed in the form

$$1+k_1p+k_2p^2+\dots+k_\alpha p^\alpha,$$

where k_rp^r is the number of groups having, with a given group H of the set, greatest common sub-groups of order $p^{\alpha-r}$.

This follows immediately from the arrangement of the set of groups given in the proof of the theorem. Thus each of the $p^{\alpha-\beta}$ groups, obtained on transforming H' by the operations of H, has in common with H a greatest common sub-group of order p^β. It may of course happen that any one or more of the numbers $k_1, k_2, \dots, k_\alpha$ is zero. If no two sub-groups of the set have a common sub-group whose order is greater than p^r, then $k_1, k_2, \dots, k_{\alpha-r-1}$ all vanish; and the number of sub-groups in the set is congruent to unity, mod. $p^{\alpha-r}$. Conversely, if p^s is the highest power of p that divides kp, some two sub-groups of the set must have a common sub-group whose order is not less than $p^{\alpha-s}$; for if there were no such common sub-groups, the number of sub-groups in the set would be congruent to unity, mod. p^{s+1}.

Corollary III. Every sub-group of G whose order is p^β, $(\beta<\alpha)$, must be contained in one or more sub-groups of order p^α.

For if the sub-group of order p^β is contained in no sub-group of order $p^{\beta+1}$, the only operations whose orders are powers of p that transform it into itself are its own. In this case, the preceding method may be used to shew that the number of sub-groups in the conjugate set to which the given sub-group belongs must be congruent to unity, mod. p. But this is impossible, as the number of such sub-groups must, on the assumption made be a multiple of $p^{\alpha-\beta}$. The sub-group of order p^β is therefore contained in one of order $p^{\beta+1}$, and hence repeating the same reasoning in one of order p^α.

121. We shall refer to Theorem I as Sylow's theorem. In discussing in this and the following paragraphs some of the results that follow from Sylow's theorem, we shall adhere to the notation that has been used in establishing the theorem itself. Thus p^α will always denote the highest power of a prime p which divides the order of G; the sub-groups of G of order p^α will be denoted by $H, H_1, \ldots$, and the greatest sub-groups of G that contain these self-conjugately by $I, I_1, \ldots$. These latter form a single conjugate set of sub-groups of G, whose orders are $p^\alpha m$, the order of G itself being $p^\alpha m\,(1+kp)$. Moreover the number of groups in this conjugate set is $1+kp$.

Suppose now that S is any operation of G whose order is a power of p. When the $1+kp$ sub-groups

$$H, H_1, H_2, \ldots, H_{kp}$$

are transformed by S, each one that contains S is transformed into itself, while the remainder are interchanged in sets, the number in any set being a power of p. Hence the number of these groups which contain S must be congruent to unity, mod. p. In precisely the same way, it may be shewn that the number of sub-groups of order p^α, which contain a given sub-group of order p^β, is congruent to unity, mod. p.

If $g_1, g_2, \ldots, g_x$ are the different sub-groups of order p^β contained in G, and if g_i enters in $1+l_ip$ sub-groups of order p^α, then $\sum_{i=1}^{i=x}(1+l_ip)$ is the number of sub-groups of order p^β when each is reckoned once for each sub-group of order p^α in which it enters. Now it has been seen in § 103 that a group of order p^α has $1+lp$ sub-groups of order p^β; and since the $1+kp$ sub-groups of order p^α in G are all conjugate, they each contain the same number of sub-groups of order p^β. Hence

$$\sum_1^x (1+l_ip)=(1+lp)(1+kp),$$

or

$$x\equiv 1 \pmod{p}.$$

THEOREM II. *If p^β divides the order of a group, the number of sub-groups of order p^β is congruent to unity, mod. p**.

When $\beta<\alpha$ this set of sub-groups will obviously, in general, not form a conjugate set.

* Frobenius, *Berliner Sitzungsberichte* (1895), p. 998.

122. THEOREM III. *Let p^α be the highest power of a prime p which divides the order of a group G, and let H be a sub-group of G of order p^α. Let h be a sub-group common to H and some other sub-group of order p^α, such that no sub-group, which contains h and is of greater order, is common to any two sub-groups of order p^α. Then there must be some operation of G, of order prime to p, which is permutable with h and not with H*.*

Suppose that H and H' are two groups of order p^α to which h is common; and let h_1 and h_1' be sub-groups of H and H', of greater order than h, in which h is self-conjugate. If h_1 and h_1' generate a group whose order is a power of p, it must occur in some group H'' of order p^α; and then H and H'' have a common group h_1, which contains h and is of greater order. This is contrary to supposition, and therefore the order of the group generated by h_1 and h_1' is not a power of p. Hence h is permutable with some operation whose order is prime to p.

Let p^r be the order of h, and $p^{r+s}n$ be the order of the greatest sub-group i of G that contains h self-conjugately. If i contained a self-conjugate sub-group of order p^{r+s}, h_1 and h_1' would be sub-groups of it and they would generate a group whose order is a power of p which is not the case. If two sub-groups of i of order p^{r+s} had a common sub-group of order p^{r+1}, then two sub-groups of G of order p^α would have a common sub-group containing h and of greater order, which again is not the case. Hence i must contain $1 + k'p^s$ sub-groups of order p^{r+s}, and $n = m'(1 + k'p^s)$; so that in i a sub-group of order p^{r+s} is self-conjugate in a sub-group of order $p^{r+s}m'$. No sub-group of i of order p^{r+t} $(t > 0)$ can occur in more than one sub-group of order p^α; and the $1 + k'p^s$ sub-groups of i of order p^{r+s} belong therefore to $1 + k'p^s$ distinct sub-groups of order p^α. Moreover h occurs in no sub-groups of order p^α other than these $1 + k'p^s$. For if h occurred in another sub-group H_1, it would in this sub-group be self-conjugate in a group of order $p^{r+s'}$ $(s' > 0)$; and this group would occur in i. This group would then be common to two sub-groups of order p^α, contrary to supposition.

* Frobenius, "Ueber endliche Gruppen," *Berliner Sitzungsberichte* (1895), p. 176: and Burnside, "Notes on the theory of groups of finite order," *Proc. London Mathematical Society*, Vol. XXVI (1895), p. 209.

An operation of i, which transforms one of its sub-groups of order p^{r+s} into another, must transform the sub-group of order p^{α} containing the one into that containing the other. Hence i must contain operations which are not permutable with H. The greatest common sub-group of i and I is that sub-group of i of order $p^{r+s}m'$ which contains the sub-group of order p^{r+s} belonging to H self-conjugately. For every operation, that transforms this sub-group of order p^{r+s} into itself, must transform H into itself; and no operation of i can transform H into itself which transforms this sub-group of order p^{r+s} into another.

The sub-group h of order p^r here considered may be called a maximum common sub-group of two sub-groups of order p^{α}. It is not necessarily a sub-group of the greatest possible order common to two sub-groups of order p^{α}; but no sub-group containing it and of greater order is common to two such sub-groups.

When H is Abelian a corresponding theorem holds for the common sub-group of any pair of sub-groups of order p^{α}. Let h be the common sub-group of H and H'. Then every operation of h is a self-conjugate operation in $\{H, H'\}$. If then K is the greatest sub-group of G in which every operation of h is self-conjugate, K containing two must contain $1 + k'p$ sub-groups of order p^{α}; and its order must be $p^{\alpha}m'(1 + k'p)$, where $p^{\alpha}m'$ is the order of the greatest sub-group of I in which every operation of h is self-conjugate. In this case every operation common to two sub-groups of order p^{α} is permutable with some operation whose order is relatively prime to p.

123. Let P be an operation, or sub-group, which is self-conjugate in H; and let Q be another operation, or sub-group, of H, which is conjugate to P in G, but not conjugate to P in I. Suppose first that, if possible, Q is self-conjugate in H. There must be an operation S which transforms P into Q and H into some other sub-group H', so that

$$S^{-1}PS = Q,$$

$$S^{-1}HS = H'.$$

Now in the sub-group which contains Q self-conjugately, the sub-groups of order p^{α} form a single conjugate set, and

H must occur among them. Hence this sub-group must contain an operation T such that

$$T^{-1}QT = Q,$$

and $$T^{-1}H'T = H.$$

It follows that

$$T^{-1}S^{-1}PST = Q,$$
$$T^{-1}S^{-1}HST = H,$$

or that, contrary to supposition, P and Q are conjugate in I. Hence:—

THEOREM IV. *Let G and H be defined as in the previous theorem, and let I be the greatest sub-group of G which contains H self-conjugately. Then if P and Q are two self-conjugate operations or sub-groups of H, which are not conjugate in I, they are not conjugate in G.*

Corollary. If H is Abelian, no two operations of H which are not conjugate in I can be conjugate in G. Hence the number of distinct sets of conjugate operations in G, which have powers of p for their orders, is the same as the number of such sets in I.

124. Suppose next that Q is not self-conjugate in H. Then every operation that transforms Q into P must transform H into a sub-group of order p^a in which P is not self-conjugate. Of the sub-groups of order p^a, to which P belongs and in which P is not self-conjugate, choose H' so that, in H', P forms one of as small a number of conjugate operations or sub-groups as possible. Let g be the greatest sub-group of H' that contains P self-conjugately. Among the sub-groups of order p^a that contain P self-conjugately, there must be one or more to which g belongs. Let H be one of these; and suppose that h and h' are the greatest sub-groups of H and H respectively that contain g self-conjugately. The orders of both h and h' must (Theorem III, § 96) be greater than the order of g; and in consequence of the assumption made with respect to H', every sub-group, having a power of p for its order and containing h, must contain P self-conjugately.

Now consider the sub-group $\{h, h'\}$. Since it does not contain P self-conjugately, its order cannot be a power of p.

Also if p^β is the highest power of p that divides its order, it must contain more than one sub-group of order p^β. For any sub-group of order p^β, to which h belongs, contains P self-conjugately; and any sub-group of order p^β, to which h' belongs, does not. Suppose now that S is an operation of $\{h, h'\}$, having its order prime to p and transforming a sub-group of $\{h, h'\}$ of order p^β, to which h belongs, into one to which h' belongs. Then S cannot be permutable with P; for if it were, P would be self-conjugate in each of these sub-groups of order p^β. When P is an operation, we may reason in the same way with respect to $\{P\}$. Since g is self-conjugate in both h and h', S must transform g into itself. Now P is self-conjugate in g, and therefore $S^{-r}PS^r$ is also self-conjugate in g for all values of r. If then S^t is the first power of S which is permutable with P, the series of groups $P, S^{-1}PS, \ldots\ldots, S^{-t+1}PS^{t-1}$ are all distinct and each is a self-conjugate sub-group of g. Every group in this series is therefore permutable with every other. Hence:—

THEOREM V. *If G and H are defined as in the two preceding theorems, and if P is a self-conjugate sub-group or operation of H, then either* (i) *P must be self-conjugate in every sub-group of G, of order p^α, in which it enters, or* (ii) *there must be an operation S, of order q prime to p, such that the set of sub-groups $S^{-r}\{P\}S^r$ $(r=0, 1, \ldots\ldots, q-1)$ are all distinct and permutable with each other.*

125. If K is a characteristic sub-group of H, a sub-group of order p^α of G, it is necessarily a self-conjugate sub-group of I. The greatest sub-group J in which K is self-conjugate must contain $1 + k'p$ $(k' \geqslant 0)$ sub-groups of order p^α, which in J form a single conjugate set, and its order will be $p^\alpha m(1 + k'p)$. It will be one of a set of $1 + k''p$ conjugate sub-groups, where

$$(1 + k'p)(1 + k''p) = 1 + kp.$$

Since this set of conjugate sub-groups contains all the sub-groups of order p^α, each of the latter will enter in one only of the former.

If H contains a second sub-group K', of the conjugate set to which K belongs, then K' cannot be self-conjugate in H; for if it were H would occur in two distinct sub-groups of the set to which J belongs.

Now h, the central of H, is a characteristic sub-group; and if h is the common sub-group of H and H', every operation of h is permutable with every operation of $\{h, h'\}$. With respect to the latter group there are three possibilities.

First, h and h' may be identical with each other. In this case h must be one of $1 + k''p\,(0 < k'' \leqslant k)$ conjugate sub-groups.

Secondly, h and h' being distinct, the order of $\{h, h'\}$ may be a power of p. When this is so there must be a sub-group H'', of order p^α, containing $\{h, h'\}$; and in H'' either h or h', say h, is not the central. Then h is not self-conjugate in H'', and therefore by Theorem V there must be an operation S, of order q prime to p, such that $h, S^{-1}hS, \ldots, S^{-q+1}hS^{q-1}$ are distinct and permutable with each other.

Lastly, if the order of $\{h, h'\}$ is not a power of p, there must be an operation, of order prime to p, permutable with every operation of h. Hence:—

THEOREM VI. *If p^α is the highest power of p dividing the order of G and if G contains more than one sub-group of order p^α, then either* (i) *every operation belonging to two sub-groups of order p^α must be permutable with some operation whose order is prime to p, or* (ii) *two or more sub-groups of order p^α must have the same central, or* (iii) *there must be q, prime to p, sub-groups of order p^α, whose centrals are distinct and permutable with each other, and are permuted cyclically on transformation by an operation of order q.*

126. In illustration of Sylow's Theorem and its consequences we will deal with the problem of determining all distinct types of group of order 24.

A group of order 24 must contain either 1 or 3 sub-groups of order 8, and either 1 or 4 sub-groups of order 3. If it has one sub-group of order 8 and one sub-group of order 3, the group must, since each of these sub-groups is self-conjugate, be their direct product. We have seen (§ 118) that there are five distinct types of group of order 8; there are therefore five distinct types of group of order 24, which are obtained by taking the direct product of any group of order 8 and a group of order 3.

If there are 3 groups of order 8, some two of them must (Theorem I, Cor. II, § 120) have a common sub-group of order 4; and (Theorem III, § 122) this common sub-group must be a self-conjugate sub-group of the group of order 24. Moreover if, in this case, a sub-group of order 8 is Abelian, each operation of the self-conjugate sub-group of order 4 must (§ 122) be a self-conjugate operation of the group of order 24.

With the aid of these general considerations, it now is easy to determine for each type of group of order 8, the possible types of group of order 24, in addition to the five types already obtained.

(i) Suppose a group of order 8 to be cyclical, and let A be an operation that generates it. If $\{A\}$ is self-conjugate and B is an operation of order 3, then

$$B^{-1}AB = A^{\alpha},$$

and therefore $$B^{-3}AB^3 = A^{\alpha^3},$$

Hence $$\alpha^3 \equiv 1 \pmod{8},$$

and therefore $$\alpha \equiv 1 \pmod{8};$$

so that A and B are permutable. This is one of the types already obtained. Hence for a new type, $\{A\}$ cannot be self-conjugate, and A^2 must be a self-conjugate operation; B is therefore one of two conjugate operations, while $\{B\}$ is self-conjugate. Hence the only possible new type in this case is given by

$$A^{-1}BA = B^{-1}.$$

(ii) Next, let a group of order 8 be an Abelian group defined by

$$A^4 = E, \quad B^2 = E, \quad AB = BA.$$

If this is self-conjugate, then, by considerations similar to those of the preceding case, we infer that the group is the direct product of groups of orders 8 and 3. Hence there is not in this case a new type.

If the group of order 8 is not self-conjugate, the self-conjugate group of order 4 may be either $\{A\}$ or $\{A^2, B\}$. In either case, if C is an operation of order 3, it must be one of two conjugate operations while $\{C\}$ is self-conjugate. Hence there are two new types respectively given by

$$C^3 = E, \quad BCB = C^{-1}, \quad A^{-1}CA = C;$$

and $$C^3 = E, \quad A^{-1}CA = C^{-1}, \quad BCB = C.$$

(iii) Let a group of order 8 be an Abelian group defined by

$$A^2 = E, \quad B^2 = E, \quad C^2 = E, \quad AB = BA, \quad BC = CB, \quad CA = AB.$$

If it is self-conjugate, and if the group of order 24 is not the direct product of groups of orders 8 and 3, an operation D of order 3 must transform the 7 operations of order 2 among themselves; and it must therefore be permutable with one of them. Now the relations

$$D^{-1}AD = A, \quad D^{-1}BD = AB,$$

are not self-consistent, because they give

$$D^{-2}BD^2 = B.$$

Hence, since the group of order 8 is generated by A, B and any other operation of order 2 except AB, we may assume, without loss of generality, that

$$D^{-1}AD = A, \quad D^{-1}BD = C, \quad D^{-1}CD = A^xB^yC^z.$$

These relations give

$$B = D^{-3}BD^3 = D^{-1}A^xB^yC^zD = A^{x(1+z)}B^{yz}C^{y+z^2},$$

and therefore $$y = z = 1.$$

Now if $$D^{-1}CD = ABC,$$

and if $$AB = B', \quad AC = C',$$

then $$D^{-1}B'D = C', \quad D^{-1}C'D = B'C';$$

so that the two alternatives $x = 0$ and $x = 1$ lead to simply isomorphic groups.

Hence there is in this case a single type. It is the direct product of $\{A\}$ and $\{D, B, C\}$, where

$$D^{-1}BD = C, \quad D^{-1}CD = BC.$$

If the group of order 8 is not self-conjugate, the self-conjugate group of order 4 may be taken to be $\{A, B\}$; and D being an operation of order 3, there is a single new type given by

$$D^3 = E, \quad CDC = D^{-1}, \quad ADA = D, \quad BDB = D.$$

(iv) Let a group of order 8 be a non-Abelian group defined by

$$A^4 = E, \quad B^4 = E, \quad A^2 = B^2, \quad B^{-1}AB = A^{-1};$$

and let C be an operation of order 3. If the group of order 8 is self-conjugate, and the group of order 24 is not a direct product of groups of orders 8 and 3, C must transform the 3 sub-groups of order 4, $\{A\}$, $\{B\}$ and $\{AB\}$, among themselves. Hence we may take

$$C^{-1}AC = B,$$

and $$C^{-1}BC = AB \text{ or } (AB)^3.$$

The supposition that C transforms B into $(AB)^3$ leads to a contradiction. Hence in this case there is only one new type, given by

$$C^3 = E, \; C^{-1}AC = B, \; C^{-1}BC = AB.$$

If the sub-group of order 8 is not self-conjugate, the self-conjugate sub-group of order 4 is cyclical, and each of its operations must be permutable with C. Hence again we get a single new type, given by

$$C^3 = E, \quad A^{-1}CA = C, \quad B^{-1}CB = C^{-1}.$$

(v) Lastly, let a sub-group of order 8 be a non-Abelian group defined by

$$A^4 = E, \quad B^2 = E, \quad BAB = A^{-1}.$$

This contains one cyclical and two non-cyclical sub-groups of order 4. If it is self-conjugate, the group of order 24 must therefore be the direct product of groups of orders 8 and 3; and there is no new type.

If the sub-group of order 8 is not self-conjugate, and the self-conjugate sub-group of order 4 is the cyclical group $\{A\}$, then A must be permutable with an operation C of order 3, and there is a single new type given by

$$C^3 = E, \quad A^{-1}CA = C, \quad BCB = C^{-1}.$$

If the self-conjugate sub-group of order 4 is not cyclical, it may be taken to be $\{E, A^2, B, A^2B\}$. If C is permutable with each operation of this sub-group, there is a single type given by

$$C^3 = E, \quad A^{-1}CA = C^{-1}, \quad BCB = C.$$

If C is not permutable with every operation of the self-conjugate sub-group, it must transform A^2, B, A^2B among themselves and we may take

$$C^{-1}A^2C = B, \quad C^{-1}BC = A^2B.$$

Now $\{C, A^2, B\}$ is self-conjugate, and therefore A must transform C into another operation of order 3 contained in this sub-group. Hence

$$A^{-1}CA = C^x A^{2y} B^z.$$

The only values of x, y, z which are consistent with the previous relation

$$A^2CA^2 = CA^2B,$$

are $\quad x = 2, \quad y = z = 1; \text{ or } x = 2, \quad y = 1, \quad z = 0.$

Either set of values lead to the same type defined by

$$A^4 = E, \quad B^2 = E, \quad BAB = A^{-1},$$
$$C^3 = E, \quad C^{-1}A^2C = B, \quad C^{-1}BC = A^2B,$$
$$A^{-1}CA = C^2A^2B.$$

When B is eliminated between these relations, it will be found that the only independent relations remaining are

$$A^4 = E, \quad C^3 = E, \quad (AC)^2 = E.$$

It is a good exercise to verify that these form a complete set of defining relations for the group. (Compare Ex. 1, § 34.)

There are therefore, in all, fifteen distinct types of group of order 24. The last of these is the only type, which has neither a self-conjugate sub-group of order 8, nor one of order 3. The reader should satisfy himself, as an exercise, that, in the ten cases where the group is not a direct product of groups of orders 8 and 3, the defining relations which we have given are self-consistent. This is of course an essential part of the investigation, and we have omitted it for the sake of brevity.

It is to be noticed that the last type obtained gives an example, and indeed the simplest possible, of Theorem V, § 124. Thus in $\{A, B\}$ of order 8, A^2 is a self-conjugate operation and B is not. In the group of order 24, the operations A^2 and B are conjugate; and C is an operation, of order prime to 2, such that A^2, $C^{-1}A^2C$, $C^{-2}A^2C^2$ generate three mutually permutable sub-groups.

A discussion similar to that of the present section (but simpler, since in each case the number of types is smaller), will verify the following table*:—

Order......	6	10	12	14	15	18	20	21	22	24	26	28	30
Number...	2	2	5	2	1	5	5	2	2	15	2	4	4

This table, taken with the results of Chapter VIII, gives the number of distinct types of groups for all orders less than 32.

127. As a second example, we will discuss the groups of order 60 which have no self-conjugate sub-group of order 5. (The reader will find it a good exercise to verify that there are 12 distinct types of group of order 60 with a self-conjugate sub-group of order 5.)

A group G of order 60 must, by Sylow's theorem, contain either 1 or 6 cyclical sub-groups of order 5. If it contains 6, no operation of order 3 can be permutable with an operation of order 5, and therefore by Sylow's theorem there must be 10 conjugate sub-groups of order 3. Hence G contains 24 operations of order 5 and 20 operations of order 3. If any operation of order 5 were permutable with an operation of order 2, all its powers would be permutable with the same operation, and therefore, since the sub-groups of order 5 form a single conjugate set, every operation of order 5 would be permutable with an operation of order 2. The group would then contain at least 24 operations of order 10. This is clearly impossible, since the sum of the numbers of operations of orders 3, 5 and 10 would be greater than the order of the group. Hence the sub-group of order 10, which contains self-conjugately a sub-group of order 5, must be of the type

$$A^2 = E, \quad S^5 = E, \quad ASA = S^{-1}.$$

* Miller, *Comptes Rendus*, CXXII (1896), p. 370.

In a similar way, we shew that a sub-group of order 6, which contains self-conjugately a sub-group of order 3, is of the type

$$A^2 = E, \quad B^3 = E, \quad ABA = B^{-1}.$$

Since no operation of order 3 or 5 is permutable with an operation of order 2, it follows (Theorem III, § 122) that no two sub-groups of order 4 can have a common operation other than identity. Hence there must be 5 sub-groups of order 4; for if there were 3 or 15, some of them would necessarily have common operations. Each sub-group of order 4 is therefore contained self-conjugately in a sub-group of order 12. Such a sub-group of order 12 can contain no self-conjugate operation of order 2, since G contains no operation of order 6. Hence the sub-groups of order 4 are non-cyclical, and the 3 operations of order 2 in any sub-group of order 4 are conjugate operations in the sub-group of order 12 containing it. This sub-group must therefore be of the type

$$B^3 = E, \quad B^{-1}A_1B = A_2, \quad B^{-1}A_2B = A_1A_2,$$

where A_1 and A_2 are permutable operations of order 2.

The 5 sub-groups of order 4 contain therefore 15 distinct operations of order 2; and these form a conjugate set. We have already seen that the 20 operations of order 3 form a conjugate set, and that the 24 operations of order 5 form two conjugate sets of 12 each. Hence the 60 operations of the group are distributed in 5 conjugate sets, containing respectively 1, 12, 12, 15 and 20 operations. It follows at once (§ 27) that the group, if it exists, is simple.

A sub-group of order 12, the existence of which has been proved, must be one of 5 conjugate sub-groups; and, since the group is simple, no operation can transform each of these into itself. Hence if the 5 conjugate sub-groups

$$H_1, \quad H_2, \quad H_3, \quad H_4, \quad H_5$$

are transformed by any operation of the group into

$$H_1', \quad H_2', \quad H_3', \quad H_4', \quad H_5',$$

and if we regard

$$\begin{pmatrix} H_1, & H_2, & H_3, & H_4, & H_5 \\ H_1', & H_2', & H_3', & H_4', & H_5' \end{pmatrix}$$

as a permutation performed on 5 symbols, the group is simply isomorphic with a permutation-group of 5 symbols. In other words, the group can be represented as a group of permutations of 5 symbols. Now there are just 60 even permutations of 5 symbols; and it is easy to verify that the group they form satisfy all the conditions above determined. Moreover it will be formally proved in Chapter X, and it is indeed almost obvious, that no group of permutations can be simple if it contains odd permutations. Hence finally, there is one and only one type of group of order 60 which contains 6 sub-groups of order 5.

Ex. 1. Shew that there is a single type of group of order 84 which contains 28 sub-groups of order 3; and determine its defining relations.

Ex. 2. Discuss the different types of group whose order is $3^4 . 13$.

Ex. 3. If p^a $(a>1)$ is the highest power of p which divides the order of G, and if $1+kp$ be the number of sub-groups of G of order p^a, shew that (i) if $1+kp<p^2$, or (ii) if a group of order p^a is cyclical and $1+kp<p^a$, G is composite.

(Maillet, *Comptes Rendus*, CXVIII (1894), p. 1188.)

128. We shall now consider the particular case in which the Sylow sub-groups, i.e. the sub-groups whose orders are the highest powers of primes dividing the order of the group, are all cyclical.

Let the order N of G be $p_1^{a_1}p_2^{a_2}\dots p_n^{a_n}$, where $p_1<p_2<\dots<p_n$ are primes. Since G contains operations whose orders divide N and do not divide N/p_1, the number of operations whose orders divide N/p_1 must be $\lambda N/p_1$, where $\lambda<p_1$. If P_1 is any operation of G of order $p_1^{a_1}$, the cyclical sub-group $\{P_1\}$ contains $p_1^{a_1}-p_1^{a_1-1}$ operations of order $p_1^{a_1}$, each of which is permutable with the same number of operations whose orders are prime to p_1. Hence, since no two distinct sub-groups of order $p_1^{a_1}$ contain a common operation of order $p_1^{a_1}$, while an operation of the group whose order is divisible by $p_1^{a_1}$ can be represented in one way only in the form PS, where P and S are permutable and of order $p_1^{a_1}$ and s (prime to p_1), the number of operations whose orders are divisible by $p_1^{a_1}$ is a multiple of p_1-1. Now this number is $(p_1-\lambda)N/p_1$; and as p_1 is the smallest prime factor of N, p_1-1 cannot divide N/p_1. Therefore p_1-1 divides $p_1-\lambda$, or $\lambda=1$.

The number of operations of the group whose orders divide N/p_1 is therefore equal to N/p_1. This reasoning may be repeated to shew that the number of operations which divide N/p_1^a $(a=1, 2, \dots a_1)$ is equal to N/p_1^a. Moreover the same reasoning, since the group contains operations of order $p_2^{a_2}$, may be applied to shew that the number of operations whose orders divide $N/p_1^{a_1}p_2^b$ $(b=1, 2, \dots a_2)$ is equal to $N/p_1^{a_1}p_2^b$. Hence if $0\leqslant a_i\leqslant a_i$, the number of operations of the group whose orders divide $p_i^{a_i}p_{i+1}^{a_{i+1}}\dots p_n^{a_n}$ is equal to this number, for all values of

i from 1 to n. In particular the number of operations of the group satisfying

$$S^{p_n^{\alpha_n}} = E$$

is $p_n^{\alpha_n}$. The group therefore has a single sub-group of order $p_n^{\alpha_n}$, which is necessarily self-conjugate. Let G_n be this sub-group, and H_{n-1} any sub-group of G of order $p_{n-1}^{\alpha_{n-1}}$. Then since G_n is self-conjugate, G_n and H_{n-1} are permutable; while since their orders are relatively prime, they have no common operation except E. Hence the order of $\{H_{n-1}, G_n\}$, or G_{n-1}, is $p_{n-1}^{\alpha_{n-1}} p_n^{\alpha_n}$. Now G contains just $p_{n-1}^{\alpha_{n-1}} p_n^{\alpha_n}$ operations whose orders divide this number. Hence G_{n-1} consisting of these operations is the only sub-group of G of order $p_{n-1}^{\alpha_{n-1}} p_n^{\alpha_n}$, and is therefore self-conjugate. Similarly it may be shewn that, for each i, G contains a single sub-group, necessarily self-conjugate, of order $p_i^{\alpha_i} p_{i+1}^{\alpha_{i+1}} \dots p_n^{\alpha_n}$. Moreover if H is a sub-group of G_i of order $p_i^{a_i}$ $(0 < a_i < \alpha_i)$, $\{H, G_{i+1}\}$ is a sub-group of order $p_i^{a_i} p_{i+1}^{\alpha_{i+1}} \dots p_n^{\alpha_n}$ of G; and therefore from what has been proved above is the only sub-group of G of this order.

Since G_j is a self-conjugate sub-group of G, it must contain all the sub-groups of order $p_j^{\alpha_j}$. If there are $1 + kp_j$ of these sub-groups, $1 + kp_j$ must be a factor of $p_{j+1}^{\alpha_{j+1}} \dots p_n^{\alpha_n}$; and a sub-group of order $p_j^{\alpha_j}$ is contained self-conjugately in a sub-group of order $N/(1 + kp_j)$. If $i < j$, this number is divisible by $p_i^{\alpha_i}$, and therefore G contains sub-groups of order $p_i^{\alpha_i} p_j^{\alpha_j}$. This process may clearly be used to shew that if N_1, a factor of N, and N/N_1 are relatively prime, G contains sub-groups of order N_1. Since G_2 is a self-conjugate sub-group and G/G_2 is Abelian, the derived group of G is contained in G_2. Similarly the derived group of G_2 is contained in G_3 and so on. The group G is therefore a soluble group.

It is to be noticed that the only part of the preceding investigation which depends on the group of order $p_n^{\alpha_n}$ being cyclical is the statement that the number of operations of G whose orders divide $p_n^{a_n}$ $(a_n < \alpha_n)$ is equal to $p_n^{a_n}$. If this statement be omitted, the remaining results hold good whatever the type of the group of order $p_n^{\alpha_n}$ may be.

129. Let $P_1, P_2, \ldots, P_n$ be operations of G of orders

$$p_1^{a_1},\ p_2^{a_2},\ \ldots,\ p_n^{a_n}.$$

If $P_{n-1}^{p_{n-1}^{a_{n-1}-\alpha_{n-1}}}$ is the lowest power of P_{n-1} which is permutable with P_n, then G_{n-1} (and therefore G) contains a single cyclical sub-group of order $p_{n-1}^{\alpha_{n-1}}p_n^{\alpha_n}$ and no cyclical sub-group of order $p_{n-1}^{\alpha_{n-1}+1}p_n^{\alpha_n}$. It is generated by

$$P_{n-1}^{p_{n-1}^{a_{n-1}-\alpha_{n-1}}} P_n, \text{ or } Q_{n-1}.$$

If $P_{n-2}^{p_{n-2}^{a_{n-2}-\alpha_{n-2}}}$ is the lowest power of P_{n-2} which is permutable with Q_{n-1}, then G_{n-2} (and therefore G) contains a single cyclical sub-group of order $p_{n-2}^{\alpha_{n-2}}p_{n-1}^{\alpha_{n-1}}p_n^{\alpha_n}$ and no cyclical sub-group whose order is a multiple of this. It is generated by

$$P_{n-2}^{p_{n-2}^{a_{n-2}-\alpha_{n-2}}} Q_{n-1} \text{ or } Q_{n-2}.$$

Continuing thus G contains a single cyclical sub-group of order $p_1^{\alpha_1}p_2^{\alpha_2}\ldots p_{n-1}^{\alpha_{n-1}}p_n^{\alpha_n}$ and no cyclical sub-group whose order is a multiple of this. It is generated by

$$P_1^{p_1^{a_1-\alpha_1}} P_2^{p_2^{a_2-\alpha_2}} \ldots P_{n-1}^{p_{n-1}^{a_{n-1}-\alpha_{n-1}}} P_n \text{ or } Q.$$

No operation of G which is not contained in $\{Q\}$ can be permutable with Q. For if S were such an operation $\{S, Q\}$ would be an Abelian group, necessarily cyclical, whose order would be a multiple of $p_1^{\alpha_1}p_2^{\alpha_2}\ldots p_n^{\alpha_n}$; and no such group exists. If S, T are any two operations of G which are not contained in $\{Q\}$, and if

$$S^{-1}QS = Q^{\alpha},\quad T^{-1}QT = Q^{\beta},$$

then

$$T^{-1}S^{-1}QST = T^{-1}Q^{\alpha}T = Q^{\alpha\beta},$$

$$ST^{-1}S^{-1}QSTS^{-1} = SQ^{\alpha\beta}S^{-1} = Q^{\beta},$$

$$TST^{-1}S^{-1}QSTS^{-1}T^{-1} = TQ^{\beta}T^{-1} = Q,$$

and therefore $STS^{-1}T^{-1}$ is contained in $\{Q\}$. Hence $G/\{Q\}$ is Abelian, and therefore necessarily cyclical. Let R be an operation of G which corresponds to a generating operation of $G/\{Q\}$. Then if

$$p_1^{\alpha_1}p_2^{\alpha_2}\ldots p_n^{\alpha_n} = \mu, \text{ and } N = \mu\nu,$$

$$Q^{\mu} = E,\quad R^{\nu} = Q^{t},\quad R^{-1}QR = Q^{\alpha},$$

where α belongs to index ν, mod. μ are the generating relations of G.

In the particular case* in which N contains no repeated prime factor, G has a sub-group of order ν, and the relation

$$R^\nu = Q^t$$

is replaced by the simpler one

$$R^\nu = E.$$

In the general case

$$Q^{-1}RQ = RQ^{1-\alpha},$$

and therefore t is subject to the condition $(\alpha - 1)t \equiv 0 \pmod{\mu}$†.

130. We shall conclude the present chapter by shewing that any group which has a series of self-conjugate sub-groups similar to those of § 93 is the direct product of its Sylow sub-groups.

THEOREM VII. *If a group G, of order $p^\alpha q^\beta \dots r^\gamma$, where $p, q, \dots, r$ are distinct primes, has a series of self-conjugate sub-groups*

$$G, H_1, H_2, \dots, H_n, E,$$

such that in G/H_s every operation of H_{s-1}/H_s is self-conjugate, then G is the direct product of groups of orders $p^\alpha, q^\beta, \dots, r^\gamma$.

Suppose, if possible, that p divides the order of H_{n-1} and does not divide the order of H_n. If P is an operation of order p contained in H_{n-1}, $\{P, H_n\}$ is a self-conjugate sub-group of G; and every operation conjugate to P is contained in the set PH_n. But the only operation of this set, whose order is p, is P. Hence P must be a self-conjugate operation, contrary to the supposition that has been made. Hence if the order of H_n is not divisible by p, neither is the order of H_{n-1}. Suppose, next, that p^x is the highest power of p that divides the orders of both H_s and H_{s+1}. Then the order of the sub-group H_s/H_{s+1} of G/H_{s+1}, formed of the self-conjugate operations of the latter, is not divisible by p; and therefore the order of H_{s-1}/H_{s+1} is not divisible by p. Hence p^x is the highest power of p that divides the order of H_{s-1}. This reasoning may be repeated to shew that p^x is the highest power of p that divides the order of each

* Hölder, "Die Gruppen mit quadratfreien Ordnungszahl," *Göttingen Nachrichten*, 1895, pp. 211—229.

† Burnside, "On finite groups in which all the Sylow sub-groups are cyclical," *Messenger of Mathematics*, Vol. XXXV (1905), pp. 46—50.

of the groups H_{s-2}, H_{s-3}, ... Hence x must be equal to α; and therefore the order of H_n must be divisible by each of the primes $p, q, \ldots, r$.

Suppose now that, for each prime p which divides the order of G, every operation of H_s, whose order is a power of p, is permutable with every operation of G whose order is relatively prime to p, so that H_s is the direct product of its Sylow sub-groups $g_p, g_q, \ldots, g_r$. Let P be any operation, whose order is a power of p, belonging to H_{s-1} and not to H_s; and let Q be any operation of G whose order is relatively prime to p. The sub-group g_p is contained self-conjugately in $\{P, g_p\}$, and therefore every operation of this sub-group is a power of p. If Q is not permutable with P, then

$$Q^{-1}PQ = Ph_s,$$

where h_s is some operation of H_s. The order of h_s must be a power of p. For let $h_s = h_s'h_s''$, where the order of h_s' is a power of p and the order of h_s'' is relatively prime to p. Then, from the supposition made with regard to the sub-group H_s, the operation Ph_s is the product of the permutable operations Ph_s' and h_s''. But, since the orders of Ph_s and Ph_s' are powers of p, this is impossible unless h_s'' is identity. If the order of h_s is p^β, then

$$Q^{-p^\beta} PQ^{p^\beta} = Ph_s^{p^\beta} = P;$$

and this equation implies that Q is permutable with P, since p^β and the order of Q are relatively prime. Hence if the supposition that has been made holds for H_s, it also holds for H_{s-1}. But it certainly holds for H_n, and therefore it is true for G. Hence every operation of G whose order is a power of p is permutable with every operation of G whose order is relatively prime to p. The group therefore contains self-conjugate sub-groups of each of the orders $p^\alpha, q^\beta, \ldots, r^\gamma$; and it follows, from the definition of § 31, that G is the direct product of these groups.

We add here three examples in further illustration of the applications of Sylow's theorem.

Ex. 1. If p is a prime, greater than 3, shew that the number of distinct types of group of order $6p$ is 6 or 4, according as p is congruent to 1 or 5, mod. 6.

Ex. 2. If p is a prime, greater than 5, shew that the number of distinct types of group of order $12p$ is 18, 12, 15 or 10, according as p is congruent to 1, 5, 7 or 11, mod. 12.

Ex. 3. Shew that there are 7 distinct types of group of order 903.

CHAPTER X.

ON PERMUTATION-GROUPS: TRANSITIVE AND INTRANSITIVE GROUPS: PRIMITIVE AND IMPRIMITIVE GROUPS.

131. It has been proved, in the theorem in § 20, that every group is capable of being represented as a group of permutations performed on a number of symbols equal to the order of the group. For applications to Algebra, and in particular to the Theory of Equations, the presentation of a group as a group of permutations is of special importance; and we shall now proceed to consider the more important properties of this special mode of representing groups*.

Definition. When a group is represented by means of permutations performed on a finite set of n distinct symbols, the integer n is called the *degree* of the group.

It is obvious, by a consideration of simple cases, that a group can always be represented in different forms as a group of permutations, the number of symbols which are permuted in two forms not being necessarily the same; examples have already been given in Chapter II. The "degree of a group" is therefore only an abbreviation of "the degree of a special representation of the group as a permutation-group."

The $n!$ permutations, including the identical permutation, that can be performed upon n distinct symbols, clearly form a group; for they satisfy the conditions of the definition (§ 12). Moreover they form the greatest group of permutations that can be performed on the n symbols, because every possible permutation occurs among them. When a group then is spoken of as of

* When it is necessary to call attention directly to the fact that the group we are dealing with is supposed to be presented as a group of permutations, the group will be spoken of as a *permutation-group*.

degree n, it is implicitly being regarded as a sub-group of this most general group of order $n!$ which can be represented by permutations of the n symbols; and therefore (Theorem I, § 22) the order of a permutation-group of degree n must be a factor of $n!$

132. It has been seen in § 11 that any permutation performed on n symbols can be represented in various ways as the product of transpositions; but that the number of transpositions entering in any such representation of the permutation is either always even or always odd. In particular, the identical permutation can only be represented by an even number of transpositions. Hence if S and S' are any two even (§ 11) permutations of n symbols, and T any permutation at all of n symbols, then SS' and $T^{-1}ST$ are even permutations. The even permutations therefore form a self-conjugate sub-group H of the group G of all permutations.

If now T is any odd permutation, the set of permutations TH are all odd and all distinct. Moreover they give all the odd permutations; for if T' is any odd permutation distinct from T, then $T^{-1}T'$ is an even permutation and must be contained in H. Hence the number of even permutations is equal to the number of odd permutations: and the order of G is twice that of H.

Definitions. The group of order $n!$ which consists of all the permutations that can be performed on n symbols is called the *symmetric* group of degree n.

The group of order $\frac{1}{2}n!$ which consists of all the even permutations of n symbols is called the *alternating** group of degree n.

If the permutations of a group of degree n are not all even, the preceding reasoning may be repeated to shew that its even permutations form a self-conjugate sub-group whose order is half the order of the group; and this sub-group is a sub-group of the alternating group of the n symbols.

* The symmetric group has been so called because the only functions of the n symbols which are unaltered by all the permutations of the group are the symmetric functions.

All the permutations of the alternating group leave the square root of the discriminant unaltered (§ 11).

133. Definition. A permutation-group is called *transitive* when, by means of its permutations, a given symbol a_1 can be changed into every other symbol $a_2, a_3, \ldots, a_n$ operated on by the group. When it has not this property, the group is called *intransitive.*

A transitive group contains permutations changing any one symbol into any other. For if S and T respectively change a_1 into a_s and a_t, then $S^{-1}T$ changes a_s into a_t.

THEOREM I. *The permutations of a transitive group G, which leave a given symbol a_1 unchanged, form a sub-group; and the number of permutations, which change a_1 into any other symbol a_r, is equal to the order of this sub-group.*

The permutations which leave a_1 unchanged must form a sub-group H of G; for if S and S' both leave a_1 unchanged, so also does SS'.

Let the operations of G be divided into the sets

$$H, HS_1, HS_2, \ldots, HS_{m-1}.$$

No operation of the set HS_p leaves a_1 unchanged; and each operation of the set HS_p changes a_1 into a_p, if S_p does so. If the operations of any other set HS_q also changed a_1 into a_p, then $S_pS_q^{-1}$ would leave a_1 unchanged and would belong to H, which it does not. Hence each set changes a_1 into a distinct symbol. The number of sets must therefore be equal to the number of symbols, while from their formation each set contains the same number of permutations. If N is the order and n the degree of the transitive group G, then N/n is the order of the sub-group that leaves any symbol a_1 unchanged; and there are N/n permutations changing a_1 into any other given symbol a_p.

Corollary. The order of a transitive group must be divisible by its degree.

Every group conjugate to H leaves one symbol unchanged. For if S changes a_1 into a_p, then $S^{-1}HS$ leaves a_p unchanged. The sub-groups which leave the different symbols unchanged form therefore a conjugate set.

A transitive group of degree n and order mn has, as we have just seen, $m-1$ permutations other than identity which leave a given symbol a_1 unchanged. Hence there must be at least $mn-1-n(m-1)$, i.e. $n-1$, permutations in the group that displace every symbol. If the $m-1$ permutations, other than identity, that leave a_1 unchanged are all distinct from the $m-1$ that leave a_p unchanged, whatever other symbol a_p may be, $n-1$ will be the actual number of permutations that displace all the symbols; and no operation other than identity will displace less than $n-1$ symbols. If however the sub-groups that leave a_1 and a_p unchanged have other permutations besides identity in common, these permutations must displace less than $n-1$ symbols; and there will be more than $n-1$ permutations which displace all the symbols.

Ex. 1. If the permutations of two transitive groups of degree n which displace all the symbols are the same, the groups can only differ in the permutations that keep just one symbol unchanged.

(Netto.)

Ex. 2. If the permutations, except identity, of a transitive group displace all or all but two of the symbols, shew that the number which displace all the symbols is greater than half and less than three-quarters of the total number.

134. We have seen that every group can be represented as a permutation-group whose degree is equal to its order. A reference to the proof of this theorem (§ 20) will shew that such a permutation-group is transitive, and that the identical permutation is the only one which leaves any symbol unchanged.

We will now consider some of the properties of a transitive group of degree n, whose operations, except identity, displace all or all but one of the n symbols. It has just been seen that such a group has exactly $n-1$ operations which displace all the n symbols. If these $n-1$ operations, with identity, form a sub-group, the sub-group must clearly be self-conjugate.

Suppose now that nm is the order of the group. Then the order of the sub-group, that leaves one symbol a_1 unchanged, is m.

Since no operation leaves two symbols unchanged, this sub-group must permute the remaining $n-1$ symbols in set of m, so that m is a factor of $n-1$, and is relatively prime to n. The orders of the operations which leave one symbol unchanged are factors of m. Hence the $n-1$ operations which displace all the symbols and the identical operation are the only ones satisfying

$$S^n = E.$$

No operation which leaves one symbol unchanged can be permutable with any operation which displaces all the symbols, and therefore the number of these which belong to any conjugate set is a multiple of m.

Let p^α be the highest power of a prime p which divides n. The number of operations whose orders divide n/p^α is a multiple of this number, say $k_p n/p^\alpha$; and the number of operations whose orders are multiples of p is therefore $n - k_p n/p^\alpha$. This number then is a multiple of m, and therefore since n and m are relatively prime, m must be a factor of $p^\alpha - k_p$. If $n = p^\alpha q^\beta \dots r^\gamma$ and $k_q, \dots, k_r$, bear the same relation to $q, \dots, r$ that k_p bears to p, m is a factor of each of the numbers $p^\alpha - k_p$, $q^\beta - k_q$, ..., $r^\gamma - k_r$.

Certain particular cases may be specially noticed. First, a group of degree n and order $n(n-1)$, whose operations other than identity displace all or all but one of the symbols, can exist only when n is the power of a prime*. Groups which satisfy these conditions will be discussed in § 140.

Similarly, a group of degree n and order nm, where m is not less than $\sqrt{n}$, whose operations other than identity displace all or all but one of the symbols, can only exist when n is the power of a prime.

If n is equal to twice an odd number, a transitive group of degree n, none of whose operations except identity leave two symbols unchanged, must be of order n.

Lastly we may shew that, if m is even, a group of degree n and order nm, none of whose operations except identity leave two symbols unchanged, must contain a self-conjugate Abelian sub-group of order and degree n.

A sub-group that keeps one symbol fixed must, if m is even, contain an operation of order 2. If it contained r such operations, the group would contain nr; and each of these could be expressed as the product of $\frac{1}{2}(n-1)$ independent transpositions. Now from n symbols $\frac{1}{2}n(n-1)$ transpositions can be formed. If then r were greater than 1, among the operations of order 2 that keep one symbol fixed there would be pairs of operations with a common transposition; and the product of two such operations would be an operation, distinct from identity, which would keep two symbols at least fixed. This is impossible; therefore r must be unity. Now let

$$A_1,\ A_2,\ \dots,\ A_n$$

be the n operations of order 2 belonging to the group. Since no two of these operations contain a common transposition,

$$A_1A_r,\ A_2A_r,\ \dots,\ A_{r-1}A_r,\ A_{r+1}A_r,\ \dots,\ A_nA_r$$

are the $n-1$ operations which displace all the symbols. These operations may also be expressed in the form

$$A_rA_1,\ A_rA_2,\ \dots,\ A_rA_{r-1},\ A_rA_{r+1},\ \dots,\ A_rA_n;$$

* Jordan, "Récherches sur les substitutions," *Liouville's Journal*, 2me sér. Vol. XVII (1872), p. 355.

and since

$$A_p A_r \,.\, A_r A_q = A_p A_q,$$

the product of any two of these operations is either identity or another operation which displaces all the symbols. Hence the $n-1$ operations which displace all the symbols, with identity, form a self-conjugate sub-group. Now

$$A_r \,.\, A_p A_r \,.\, A_r = A_r A_p,$$

so that A_r transforms every operation of this sub-group into its inverse. Hence

$$A_r A_p \,.\, A_q A_r = A_q A_p = A_q A_r \,.\, A_r A_q\,;$$

i.e. every two operations of this sub-group are permutable, and the sub-group is therefore Abelian.

Herr Frobenius has shewn* that the $n-1$ permutations which displace all the symbols, together with identity, always form a self-conjugate sub-group.

135. If $S=(a_1a_2\ldots\ldots a_i)(a_{i+1}a_{i+2}\ldots\ldots a_j)\ldots\ldots,$

and $$T=\begin{pmatrix} a_1, a_2, \ldots\ldots, a_n \\ b_1, b_2, \ldots\ldots, b_n \end{pmatrix},$$

are any two permutations of a group, then (§ 10)

$$T^{-1}ST=(b_1b_2\ldots\ldots b_i)(b_{i+1}b_{i+2}\ldots\ldots b_j)\ldots\ldots$$

Hence every permutation of the group, which is conjugate to S, is also similar to S. It does not necessarily or generally follow that two similar permutations of a group are conjugate. That this is true however of the symmetric group is obvious, for then the permutation T may be chosen so as to permute n symbols in any way.

A self-conjugate permutation of a transitive group of degree n must be a regular permutation (§ 9) changing all the n symbols. For if it did not change all the n symbols, it would belong to one of the sub-groups that keep a symbol unchanged. Hence, since it is a self-conjugate permutation, it would belong to each sub-group that keeps a symbol unchanged, which is impossible unless it is the identical permutation. Again, if it were not regular, one of its powers would keep two or more symbols unchanged, and this cannot be the case since every power of a self-conjugate permutation must be self-conjugate. On the

* "Ueber auflösbare Gruppen IV," *Berliner Sitzungsberichte* (1901), p. 1225. See also Chapter XVI.

other hand, a self-conjugate sub-group of a transitive group need not contain any permutation which displaces all the symbols. Thus if

$$S=(12)(34),$$

$$T=(135)(246),$$

then $\{S, T\}$ is a transitive group of degree 6. The only permutations conjugate to S are

$$T^{-1}ST=(34)(56) \text{ and } TST^{-1}=(12)(56);$$

and these, with S and identity, form a self-conjugate sub-group of order 4, none of whose permutations displace more than 4 symbols. The form of a self-conjugate sub-group of a transitive group will be considered in greater detail in § 149.

136. Since a self-conjugate permutation of a transitive permutation-group G of degree n must be a regular permutation which displaces all the symbols, the self-conjugate sub-group H of G which consists of all its self-conjugate operations must have n or some submultiple of n for its order. For if S and S' are two self-conjugate permutations of G, so also is $S^{-1}S'$; and therefore S and S' cannot both change a into b. The order of H therefore cannot exceed n; and if the order is n', the permutations of H must interchange the n symbols in sets of n', so that n' is a factor of n. Let now S, some permutation performed on the n symbols of the transitive permutation-group G of degree n, be permutable with every permutation of G. Then S is a self-conjugate operation of the transitive permutation-group $\{S, G\}$ of degree n, and it is therefore a regular permutation in all the n symbols. The totality of the permutations S, which are permutable with every permutation of G, form a group (not necessarily Abelian); and the order of this group is n or a factor of n.

The special case, in which G is a transitive group whose order N is equal to its degree, has already been considered in § 20. The results there obtained may be expressed in the form of the following:

THEOREM II. *Those permutations of N symbols which are permutable with every permutation of a permutation-group G of* *order N, transitive in the N symbols, form a transitive group G' of order and degree N, simply isomorphic with G**.

If, with the notation there used, S_x is a self-conjugate permutation of G, the permutations

$$\begin{pmatrix} S_1, \ldots\ldots, S_N \\ S_1S_x, \ldots\ldots, S_NS_x \end{pmatrix} \text{ and } \begin{pmatrix} S_1, \ldots\ldots, S_N \\ S_xS_1, \ldots\ldots, S_xS_N \end{pmatrix}$$

are the same. Hence G and G' have for their greatest common sub-group, that which is constituted by the self-conjugate permutations of either; and if N' is the order of this sub-group, the order of $\{G, G'\}$ is N^2/N'. In particular, if G is Abelian, G and G' coincide; and if G has no self-conjugate operation except identity, $\{G, G'\}$ is the direct product of G and G'.

The sub-group of $\{G, G'\}$ which leaves one symbol, say S_1, unchanged, is formed of the distinct permutations of the set

$$\begin{pmatrix} S_1, & S_2, & \ldots\ldots, & S_N \\ S_x^{-1}S_1S_x, & S_x^{-1}S_2S_x, & \ldots\ldots, & S_x^{-1}S_NS_x \end{pmatrix}, \quad (x = 1, 2, \ldots\ldots, N).$$

This sub-group will change S_i into S_j if, and only if, S_i and S_j are conjugate operations in G. Hence the number of transitive sets in which it permutes the N symbols is equal to the number of sets of conjugate operations in G.

When G has no self-conjugate operation except identity, the order of this sub-group is N, and it is simply isomorphic with G. In fact, in this case the order of $\{G, G'\}$, a transitive group of degree N, is N^2, and therefore the order of a sub-group that keeps one symbol unchanged is N. Again

$$\begin{pmatrix} S_1, & S_2, & \ldots\ldots, & S_N \\ S_x^{-1}S_1S_x, & S_x^{-1}S_2S_x, & \ldots\ldots, & S_x^{-1}S_NS_x \end{pmatrix}$$

$$\begin{pmatrix} S_1, & S_2, & \ldots\ldots, & S_N \\ S_y^{-1}S_1S_y, & S_y^{-1}S_2S_y, & \ldots\ldots, & S_y^{-1}S_NS_y \end{pmatrix}$$

$$= \begin{pmatrix} S_1, & S_2, & \ldots\ldots, & S_N \\ S_x^{-1}S_1S_x, & S_x^{-1}S_2S_x, & \ldots\ldots, & S_x^{-1}S_NS_x \end{pmatrix}$$

$$\begin{pmatrix} S_x^{-1}S_1S_x, & S_x^{-1}S_2S_x, & \ldots\ldots, & S_x^{-1}S_NS_x \\ S_y^{-1}S_x^{-1}S_1S_xS_y, & S_y^{-1}S_x^{-1}S_2S_xS_y, & \ldots\ldots, & S_y^{-1}S_x^{-1}S_NS_xS_y \end{pmatrix}$$

$$= \begin{pmatrix} S_1, & S_2, & \ldots\ldots, & S_N \\ S_y^{-1}S_x^{-1}S_1S_xS_y, & S_y^{-1}S_x^{-1}S_2S_xS_y, & \ldots\ldots, & S_y^{-1}S_x^{-1}S_NS_xS_y \end{pmatrix};$$

* Jordan, *Traité des Substitutions* (1870), p. 60.

thus giving a direct verification that the sub-group is isomorphic with G. When G contains self-conjugate operations, it will be multiply isomorphic with the sub-group K_1 of $\{G, G'\}$ which keeps the symbol S_1 fixed; and if g is the group constituted by the self-conjugate operations of G (or G'), then K_1 is simply isomorphic with G/g.

If K_1 is not a maximum sub-group of $\{G, G'\}$, let I be a greater sub-group containing K_1. Then I and G' (or G) must contain common permutations. For every permutation of $\{G, G'\}$ is of the form

$$\begin{pmatrix} S_1, & S_2, \ldots\ldots, & S_N \\ S_yS_1S_x, & S_yS_2S_x, \ldots\ldots, & S_yS_NS_x \end{pmatrix};$$

and if this permutation belongs to I, then

$$\begin{pmatrix} S_1, & S_2, \ldots\ldots, & S_N \\ S_yS_1S_x, & S_yS_2S_x, \ldots\ldots, & S_yS_NS_x \end{pmatrix} \begin{pmatrix} S_1, & S_2, \ldots\ldots, & S_N \\ S_xS_1S_x^{-1}, & S_xS_2S_x^{-1}, \ldots\ldots, & S_xS_NS_x^{-1} \end{pmatrix},$$

or

$$\begin{pmatrix} S_1, & S_2, \ldots\ldots, & S_N \\ S_xS_yS_1, & S_xS_yS_2, \ldots\ldots, & S_xS_yS_N \end{pmatrix},$$

is a permutation of G' which belongs to I. Moreover, since G' is a self-conjugate sub-group of $\{G, G'\}$, the permutations of G' which belong to I form a self-conjugate sub-group of I: this sub-group we will call H'.

Now every permutation of the group can be represented as the product of a permutation of K_1 by a permutation of G: and therefore all the sub-groups conjugate to I will be obtained on transforming I by the operations of G. Hence, because every permutation of G transforms H' into itself, H' is common to the complete set of conjugate sub-groups to which I belongs; and H' is therefore a self-conjugate sub-group of $\{G, G'\}$. Finally then, K_1 is a maximum sub-group of $\{G, G'\}$, if and only if G is a simple group.

137. Definition. A permutation-group, that contains one or more permutations changing k given symbols $a_1, a_2, \ldots, a_k$ into any other k symbols, is called *k-ply transitive*.

Such a group clearly contains permutations changing any

set of k symbols into any other set of k; and the order of the sub-group keeping any j ($\not> k$) symbols unchanged is independent of the particular j symbols chosen.

THEOREM III. *The order of a k-ply transitive group of degree n is* $n(n-1)......(n-k+1)m$, *where m is the order of the sub-group that leaves any k symbols unchanged. This sub-group is contained self-conjugately in a sub-group of order* $k!m$.

If N is the order of the group, the order of the sub-group which keeps one symbol fixed is N/n, by Theorem I (§ 133). Now this sub-group is a transitive group of degree $n-1$; and therefore the order of the sub-group that keeps two symbols unchanged is $N/n(n-1)$. If $k > 2$, this sub-group again is a transitive group of degree $n-2$; and so on. Proceeding thus, the order of the sub-group which keeps k symbols unchanged is seen to be

$$\frac{N}{n(n-1)......(n-k+1)},$$

which proves the first part of the theorem.

Let $a_1, a_2, ..., a_k$ be the k symbols which are left unchanged by a sub-group H of order m. Since the group is k-ply transitive, it must contain permutations of the form

$$\begin{pmatrix} a_1, a_2, ..., a_k, b, c, ... \\ a_1', a_2', ..., a_k', b', c', ... \end{pmatrix},$$

where $a_1', a_2', ..., a_k'$ are the same k symbols as $a_1, a_2, ..., a_k$ arranged in any other sequence. Also every permutation of this form is permutable with H, since it interchanges among themselves the symbols left unchanged by H. Further, if S_1 and S_2 are any two permutations of this form, $S_1^{-1}S_2$ will belong to H if, and only if, S_1 and S_2 give the same permutation of the symbols $a_1, a_2, ..., a_k$. Hence finally, since $k!$ distinct permutations can be performed on the k symbols, the order of the sub-group that contains H self-conjugately is $k!m$.

If m is unity, the identical permutation is the only one that keeps any k symbols fixed, and there is just one permutation that changes k symbols into any other k. In the same case, the group contains permutations which displace $n-k+1$ symbols only, and there are none, except the identical permutation, which displace fewer.

If $m > 1$, the group will contain $m - 1$ permutations besides identity, which leave unchanged any k given symbols, and therefore displace $n - k$ symbols at most.

It follows from § 134 that a k-ply transitive group of degree n and order $n(n-1)\ldots\ldots(n-k+1)$ can exist only if $n-k+2$ is the power of a prime. For such a group must contain sub-groups of order $(n-k+2)(n-k+1)$, which keep $k-2$ symbols unchanged and are doubly transitive in the remaining $n-k+2$. When k is n, the group is the symmetric group; and when k is $n-2$, we shall see (in § 138) that the group is the alternating group. If k is less than $n-2$, M. Jordan* has shewn that, with two exceptions for $n=11$ and $n=12$, the value of k cannot exceed 3. The actual existence of triply transitive groups of degree p^n+1 and order $(p^n+1)p^n(p^n-1)$, for all prime values of p, will be established in § 141.

138. Let

$$S=(a_1a_2\ldots\ldots a_i)\ldots\ldots(\ldots\ldots a_{j-1}a_j)(a_{j+1}\ldots\ldots a_{k-1}a_k\ldots\ldots)\ldots\ldots$$

be a permutation of a k-ply transitive group displacing $s\,(>k)$ symbols. If $j<k-1$, take

$$T=\begin{pmatrix}a_1, & a_2, & \ldots\ldots, & a_{k-1}, & a_k, & \ldots\ldots \\ a_1, & a_2, & \ldots\ldots, & a_{k-1}, & b_k, & \ldots\ldots\end{pmatrix},$$

where b_k is some other symbol occurring in S. Since the group is k-ply transitive, it must contain a permutation such as T. Now

$$T^{-1}ST=(a_1a_2\ldots\ldots a_i)\ldots\ldots(\ldots\ldots a_{j-1}a_j)(a_{j+1}\ldots\ldots a_{k-1}b_k\ldots\ldots)\ldots\ldots;$$

and this is certainly not identical with S, so that $T^{-1}STS^{-1}$ cannot be the identical permutation. Moreover $a_1, a_2, \ldots\ldots, a_{k-2}$ are not affected by $T^{-1}STS^{-1}$; and therefore this permutation will displace at most $2s-2k+2$ symbols.

If $j=k-1$, take

$$T=\begin{pmatrix}a_1, & a_2, & \ldots\ldots, & a_{k-1}, & a_k, & \ldots\ldots \\ a_1, & a_2, & \ldots\ldots, & a_{k-1}, & c_k, & \ldots\ldots\end{pmatrix},$$

* "Récherches sur les substitutions," *Liouville's Journal*, 2me sér. Vol. XVII (1872), pp. 357—363.

where c_k is a symbol that does not occur in S. Then

$$T^{-1}ST = (a_1 a_2 \ldots\ldots a_i) \ldots\ldots (\ldots\ldots a_{k-2} a_{k-1}) (c_k \ldots\ldots),$$

and this cannot coincide with S. Now in this case, $a_1, a_2, \ldots\ldots, a_{k-1}$ are not affected by $T^{-1}STS^{-1}$; and therefore this operation will again displace at most $2s - 2k + 2$ symbols.

If then
$$2s - 2k + 2 < s,$$
or
$$s < 2k - 2,$$

the group must contain a permutation affecting fewer symbols than S. This process may be repeated till we arrive at a permutation

$$\Sigma = (\alpha_1 \alpha_2 \ldots\ldots \alpha_i)(\alpha_{i+1} \ldots\ldots \alpha_j) \ldots\ldots (\alpha_{j+1} \ldots\ldots \alpha_k),$$

which affects exactly k symbols; and if this permutation be transformed by

$$T = \begin{pmatrix} \alpha_1, & \alpha_2, & \ldots\ldots, & \alpha_{k-1}, & \alpha_k, & \ldots\ldots \\ \alpha_1, & \alpha_2, & \ldots\ldots, & \alpha_{k-1}, & \beta_k, & \ldots\ldots \end{pmatrix},$$

then

$$T^{-1}\Sigma T = (\alpha_1 \alpha_2 \ldots\ldots \alpha_i)(\alpha_{i+1} \ldots\ldots \alpha_j) \ldots\ldots (\alpha_{j+1} \ldots\ldots \alpha_{k-1} \beta_k),$$

and
$$\Sigma^{-1} T^{-1} \Sigma T = (\alpha_k \beta_k \alpha_{j+1}).$$

Thus in the case under consideration the group contains one, and therefore every, circular permutation of three symbols; and hence (§ 11) it must contain every even permutation. It is therefore either the alternating or the symmetric group. If then a k-ply transitive group of degree n does not contain the alternating group of n symbols, no one of its permutations, except identity, must displace fewer than $2k - 2$ symbols. It has been shewn that such a group contains permutations displacing not more than $n - k + 1$ symbols; and therefore, for a k-ply transitive group of degree n, other than the alternating or the symmetric group, the inequality

$$n - k + 1 \nless 2k - 2,$$

or

$$k \ngtr \tfrac{1}{3}n + 1,$$

must hold. Hence :—

THEOREM IV. *A group of degree n, which does not contain the alternating group of n symbols, cannot be more than $(\frac{1}{3}n + 1)$-ply transitive.*

The symmetric group is n-ply transitive; and, since of the two permutations

$$\begin{pmatrix} a_1, a_2, \ldots\ldots, a_{n-2}, a_{n-1}, a_n \\ b_1, b_2, \ldots\ldots, b_{n-2}, b_{n-1}, b_n \end{pmatrix} \text{ and } \begin{pmatrix} a_1, a_2, \ldots\ldots, a_{n-2}, a_{n-1}, a_n \\ b_1, b_2, \ldots\ldots, b_{n-2}, b_n, b_{n-1} \end{pmatrix},$$

one is evidently even and the other odd, the alternating group is $(n-2)$-ply transitive. The discussion just given shews that no other group of degree n can be more than $(\frac{1}{3}n+1)$-ply transitive*.

139. The process used in the preceding paragraph may be applied to shew that, unless $n = 4$, the alternating group of n symbols is simple. It has just been shewn that the alternating group is $(n-2)$-ply transitive. Therefore, if S is a permutation of the alternating group displacing fewer than $n-1$ symbols, a permutation $T^{-1}ST$ can certainly be found such that $S^{-1}T^{-1}ST$ is a circular permutation of three symbols. In this case, the self-conjugate group generated by S and its conjugate permutations contains all the circular permutations of three symbols, and therefore it coincides with the alternating group itself. If S displaces $n-1$ symbols, then $T^{-1}ST$ can be taken so that $S^{-1}T^{-1}ST$ displaces not more than $2(n-1)-2(n-2)+2$, or 4 symbols; and if S displaces n symbols, $S^{-1}T^{-1}ST$ can be found to displace not more than $2n-2(n-2)+2$, or 6 symbols.

It is therefore only necessary to consider the case $n = 5$, when S displaces $n-1$ symbols; and the cases $n = 4, 5, 6$, when S displaces n symbols; in all other cases, the group generated by S and its conjugate permutations must contain circular permutations of 3 symbols.

When $n = 5$, and S is an even permutation displacing 4 symbols, we may take

$$S = (12)(34).$$

If
$$T = (12)(35),$$

then
$$T^{-1}ST = (12)(45),$$

and
$$S^{-1}T^{-1}ST = (345).$$

* For a further discussion of the limits of transitivity of a permutation-group, compare Jordan, *Traité des Substitutions*, pp. 76—87; and Bochert, *Math. Ann.* XXIX (1886), pp. 27—49; XXXIII (1888), pp. 573—583.

Hence, in this case again, we are led to the alternating group itself.

When $n = 6$, and S is an even permutation displacing all the symbols, we may take

$$S = (12)(3456),$$

or

$$S' = (123)(456).$$

If now

$$T = (12)(3645),$$

then

$$S^{-1}T^{-1}ST = (356),$$

and

$$S'^{-1}T^{-1}S'T = (14263);$$

and, in either case, we are led to the alternating group.

When $n = 5$, and S is an even permutation displacing all the symbols, we may put

$$S = (12345).$$

If

$$T = (345),$$

then

$$S^{-1}T^{-1}ST = (134);$$

and again the alternating group is generated.

When $n = 4$, and S is an even permutation displacing all the symbols, we may take

$$S = (12)(34).$$

Here the only two permutations conjugate to S are clearly $(13)(24)$ and $(14)(23)$, which are permutable with each other and with S. Hence the alternating group of 4 symbols, which is of order 12, has a self-conjugate sub-group of order 4.

Finally when $n = 3$, the alternating group, being the group $\{(123)\}$, is a simple cyclical group of order 3. Hence:—

THEOREM V. *The alternating group of n symbols is a simple group except when $n = 4$.*

140. It has been seen in § 137 that the order of a doubly transitive group of degree n is equal to or is a multiple of $n(n-1)$. If it is equal to this number, every permutation of the group, except identity, must displace either all or all but one of the symbols; for a sub-group of order $n-1$ which keeps one symbol fixed is transitive in the remaining $n-1$ symbols, and therefore all its permutations, except identity, displace all the $n-1$ symbols.

Now it has been shewn in § 134 that a transitive group of degree n and order $n(n-1)$, whose operations displace all or all but one of the symbols, can exist only if n is the power of a prime p. The $n-1$ operations displacing all the symbols are the only operations of the group whose orders are powers of p; and therefore with identity they form a self-conjugate sub-group of order n. Moreover it also follows from § 134 that the $n-1$ operations of this sub-group other than identity form a single conjugate set. Hence this sub-group must be Abelian, and all its operations are of order p.

Suppose first that n is a prime p, and that P is any operation of the group of order p. If a is a primitive root of p, the existence of a group of order $p(p-1)$ defined by

$$P^p = E, \quad S^{p-1} = E, \quad S^{-1}PS = P^a,$$

has been proved in § 88.

It is an immediate result of a theorem, which will be proved in chapter XII, that this group can be actually represented as a transitive permutation-group of degree p; this may be also verified directly as follows.

Let $$P = (a_1 a_2 \dots a_p),$$

so that $$P^a = (a_1 a_{a+1} a_{2a+1} \dots a_{(p-1)a+1}),$$

where the suffixes are to be reduced (mod. p); and suppose that S is a permutation that keeps a_1 unchanged. Then since

$$S^{-1}PS = P^a,$$

S must change a_2 into a_{a+1}, a_3 into a_{2a+1}, and generally, a_r into $a_{(r-1)a+1}$. Hence

$$S = (a_2 a_{a+1} a_{a^2+1} \dots) \dots;$$

and since a is a primitive root of p, there is only a single cycle; so that

$$S = (a_2 a_{a+1} a_{a^2+1} \dots a_{a^{p-2}+1}).$$

The permutations P and S thus constructed actually generate a doubly transitive permutation-group of degree p and order $p(p-1)$.

That for every value of p^m where p is a prime there is a doubly transitive group* of degree p^m and order $p^m(p^m-1)$, in which a sub-group of order p^m-1 is cyclical, contained in a triply transitive group of degree p^m+1 and order $(p^m+1)p^m(p^m-1)$ may be shewn as follows.

Let i be a primitive root of the congruence

$$i^{p^m-1} \equiv 1 \text{ (mod. } p),$$

so that the distinct roots of the congruence are

$$i, \; i^2, \; i^3, \dots\dots, \; i^{p^m-1}.$$

* On the subject of this and the following paragraph, the reader should consult the memoirs by Mathieu, *Liouville's Journal*, 2me Sér. t. v (1860), pp. 9—42; *ib.* t. VI (1861), pp. 241—323; where the groups here considered were first shewn to exist.

Every rational function of i with real integral coefficients satisfies the same congruence; and therefore every such function is congruent (mod. p) to some power of i not exceeding the $(p^m - 1)$th.

Consider now a set of transformations of the form

$$x' \equiv \alpha x + \beta \text{ (mod. } p),$$

where α is a power of i, and β is either a power of i or zero. Two such transformations, performed successively, give another transformation of the same form; and since α cannot be zero, the inverse of each transformation is another definite transformation; so that the totality of transformations of this form constitute a group. Moreover

$$\left.\begin{aligned} x' &\equiv \alpha x + \beta, \\ \text{and} \quad x' &\equiv \alpha' x + \beta', \end{aligned}\right\} \text{(mod. } p),$$

are not the same transformation unless

$$\alpha \equiv \alpha' \text{ and } \beta \equiv \beta' \text{ (mod. } p).$$

Hence, since α can take $p^m - 1$ distinct values and β can take p^m distinct values, the order of the group, formed of the totality of these transformations, is $p^m(p^m - 1)$.

The transformations for which α is unity clearly form a sub-group. If S and T represent

$$x' \equiv \alpha x + \beta \text{ and } x' \equiv x + \gamma$$

respectively, $S^{-1}TS$ represents

$$x' \equiv x + \alpha\gamma.$$

Hence the transformations for which α is unity form a self-conjugate sub-group whose order is p^m. Every two transformations of this sub-group are clearly permutable; and the order of each of them except identity is p.

Again, the transformations for which β is zero form a sub-group. Since every one of them is a power of the transformation

$$x' \equiv ix,$$

this sub-group is a cyclical sub-group of order $p^m - 1$. If the transformation just written be denoted by I, then $S^{-1}IS$ is

$$x' \equiv ix + \beta(1 - i).$$

Hence the only operations permutable with $\{I\}$ are its own operations, and therefore $\{I\}$ is one of p^m conjugate sub-groups.

The set of transformations

$$x' \equiv \alpha x + \beta$$

therefore forms a group of order $p^m(p^m - 1)$. This group contains a self-conjugate Abelian sub-group of order p^m and type $(1, 1, \ldots, 1)$, and p^m conjugate cyclical sub-groups of order p^m-1, none of whose operations are permutable with any of the operations of the self-conjugate sub-group.

Now if the operation

$$x' \equiv \alpha x + \beta$$

be performed on each term of the series

$$0, i, i^2, \ldots\ldots, i^{p^m-1},$$

it will, since every rational integral function of i with real integral coefficients is congruent (mod. p) to some power of i, change the term into another of the same series; and since the congruence

$$\alpha i^x + \beta \equiv \alpha i^y + \beta \pmod{p}$$

gives

$$x \equiv y \pmod{p^m-1},$$

no two terms of the series can thus be transformed into the same term. Moreover the only operation that leaves every term of the series unchanged is clearly the identical operation.

To each operation of the form

$$x' \equiv \alpha x + \beta$$

therefore will correspond a single permutation performed on the p^m symbols just written, so that to the product of two operations will correspond the product of the two homologous permutations. The group is therefore simply isomorphic with a permutation-group of degree p^m. Moreover since the linear congruence

$$x \equiv \alpha x + \beta \pmod{p}$$

has only a single solution when α is different from unity, and none when α is unity, every permutation except identity must displace all or all but one of the symbols. The permutation-group is therefore doubly transitive*.

Ex. 1. Apply the method just explained to the actual construction of a doubly transitive group of degree 8 and order 56.

Ex. 2. Shew that the equations

$$A^2 = E, \qquad S^{2^m-1} = E, \qquad AS^{-1}AS = S^{-n}AS^n,$$

where n is such that a primitive root of the congruence,

$$i^{2^m-1} - 1 \equiv 0 \pmod{2},$$

satisfies the congruence

$$i^n + i + 1 \equiv 0 \pmod{2},$$

* The author has shewn (*Messenger of Mathematics*, Vol. xxv (1896), pp. 147—153) that the type of group considered in the text is the only type of doubly transitive group of degree p^m and order $p^m(p^m-1)$ when $m=3$; and that, when $m=2$ and $p>3$, the same is true. When $m=2$ and $p=3$, there is one other type.

suffice to define a group which can be expressed as a doubly transitive group of degree 2^m and order $2^m(2^m - 1)$.

(*Messenger of Mathematics*, Vol. xxv, p. 189.)

141. In the place of the operations of the last paragraph, we now consider those of the form

$$x' \equiv \frac{\alpha x + \beta}{\gamma x + \delta} \pmod{p},$$

where again $\alpha, \beta, \gamma, \delta$ are powers of i, limited now by the condition that $\alpha\delta - \beta\gamma$ is not congruent to zero (mod. p). When this relation is satisfied, the set of operations again clearly form a group. Moreover if we represent $\frac{i^x}{0}$ by ∞ for all values of x, any operation of this group, when carried out on the set of quantities

$$\infty, \quad 0, \quad i, \quad i^2, \ldots\ldots, i^{p^m - 1},$$

will change each of them into another of the set; while no operation except identity will leave each symbol of the set unchanged. Hence the group can be represented as a permutation-group of degree $p^m + 1$.

Now $$\frac{x' - i^{a'}}{x' - i^{b'}} \frac{i^{c'} - i^{b'}}{i^{c'} - i^{a'}} \equiv \frac{x - i^a}{x - i^b} \frac{i^c - i^b}{i^c - i^a} \pmod{p}$$

is an operation of the above form, which changes the three symbols i^a, i^b, i^c into $i^{a'}, i^{b'}, i^{c'}$ respectively; and it is easy to modify this form so that it holds when 0 or ∞ occurs in the place of i^a, etc. Hence the permutation-group is triply transitive, since it contains an operation transforming any three of the $p^m + 1$ symbols into any other three.

On the other hand, if the typical operation keeps the symbol x unchanged, then

$$\gamma x^2 + (\delta - \alpha)x - \beta \equiv 0 \pmod{p},$$

and this congruence cannot have more than two roots among the set of $p^m + 1$ symbols. Hence no permutation of the group, except identity, keeps more than two symbols fixed.

Finally then, since the group is triply transitive and since it contains no operation, except identity, that keeps more than two symbols fixed, its order must (§ 137) be $(p^m + 1)p^m(p^m - 1)$.

It obviously contains as a sub-group the group of the previous paragraph.

142. An intransitive permutation-group, as defined in § 133, is one which does not contain permutations changing a_1 into each of the other symbols $a_2, a_3, \ldots\ldots, a_n$ operated on by the group. Let us suppose that the permutations of such a group change a_1 into $a_2, a_3, \ldots\ldots, a_k$ only. Then all the permutations of the group must interchange these k symbols among themselves; for if the group contained a permutation changing a_2 into a_{k+1}, then the product of any permutation changing a_1 into a_2 by this latter permutation would change a_1 into a_{k+1}. Hence the n symbols operated on by the group can be divided into a number of sets, such that the permutations of the group change the symbols of any one set transitively among themselves, but do not interchange the symbols of two distinct sets. It follows immediately that the order of the group must be a common multiple of the numbers of symbols in the different sets.

Suppose now that $a_1, a_2, \ldots\ldots, a_k$ is a set of symbols which are interchanged transitively by all the permutations of a group G of degree n. If for a time we neglect the effect of the permutations of G on the remaining $n-k$ symbols, the group G will reduce to a transitive group H* of degree k. The group G is isomorphic with the group H; for if we take as the permutation of H, that corresponds to a given permutation of G, that which produces the same permutation of the symbols $a_1, a_2, \ldots\ldots, a_k$, then to the product of any two permutations of G will correspond the product of the corresponding two permutations of H. The isomorphism thus shewn to exist may be simple or multiple. In the former case, the order of H is the same as that of G; in the latter case, the permutations of G which correspond to the identical permutation of H, i.e. those permutations of G which change none of the symbols $a_1, a_2, \ldots\ldots, a_k$, form a self-conjugate sub-group.

We will consider in particular an intransitive group G which interchanges the symbols in *two* transitive sets; these we will refer to as the α's and the β's. Let G_α and G_β be the two groups transitive in the α's and β's respectively, to which G reduces when we alternately leave out of account the effect of the permutations on the β's and the α's. Also let g_α and g_β be the self-conjugate sub-groups of G, which keep respectively all the β's and all the α's unchanged; and denote the group $\{g_\alpha, g_\beta\}$ by g. This last group g, which is the direct product of g_α and g_β, is self-conjugate in G, since it is generated by the

* H is called a transitive *constituent* of G.

two self-conjugate groups g_α and g_β. Now g_α is self-conjugate not only in G but also in G_α; for G_α permutes the α's in the same way that G does, while any permutation of g_α, not affecting the β's, is necessarily permutable with every permutation performed on the β's. The group G_α is simply isomorphic with the group G/g_β, and G_β with G/g_α; hence, using n_H to denote the order of a group H,

$$n_G = n_{G_\alpha} n_{g_\beta} = n_{G_\beta} n_{g_\alpha}.$$

Let the permutations of G be now divided into sets in respect of the self-conjugate sub-group g, so that

$$G = g,\ Sg,\ Tg, \ldots\ldots$$

If we neglect the effect of the permutations on the symbols β, the group G reduces to G_α and g reduces to g_α, and hence

$$G_\alpha = g_\alpha,\ S_\alpha g_\alpha,\ T_\alpha g_\alpha, \ldots\ldots,$$

where S_α, T_α, ... represent the permutations S, T, ..., so far as they affect the α's. Moreover the permutations in the different sets into which G_α is thus divided must be all distinct since, by the preceding relations between the orders of the groups, their number is just equal to the order of G_α. Hence G_α/g_α is defined by the laws according to which these sets of permutations combine. But if

$$Sg \,.\, Tg = Ug,$$

then necessarily $$S_\alpha g_\alpha \,.\, T_\alpha g_\alpha = U_\alpha g_\alpha,$$

and therefore, finally, the three groups G/g, G_α/g_α, and G_β/g_β are simply isomorphic.

143. The relation of simple isomorphism between G_α/g_α and G_β/g_β thus arrived at establishes between the groups G_α and G_β an isomorphism of the most general kind (§ 32).

To every operation of G_α correspond n_{g_β} operations of G_β, and to every operation of G_β correspond n_{g_α} operations of G_α; so that to the product of any two operations of G_α (or G_β) there corresponds a definite set of n_{g_β} operations of G_β (or n_{g_α} operations of G_α).

Returning now to the intransitive group G, its genesis from the two transitive groups G_α and G_β, with which it is isomorphic, may be represented as follows. The n_{g_α} to n_{g_β} correspondence, such as has just been described, having been established between the groups G_α and G_β, each permutation of G_α is multiplied by the n_{g_β} permutations that correspond to it in G_β. The set of $n_{G_\alpha} n_{g_\beta}$ permutations so obtained form a group, for

$$S_\alpha S_\beta \,.\, S_\alpha' S_\beta' = S_\alpha S_\alpha' \,.\, S_\beta S_\beta' = S_\alpha'' S_\beta'',$$

where, if S_β, S_β' are permutations corresponding to S_α, S_α', then S_β'' is a permutation corresponding to S_α''. Moreover, this group may be equally well generated by multiplying every one of the permutations of G_β by the n_{g_α} corresponding permutations of G_α; and by a reference to the representations of G, G_α, and G_β, as divided into sets of permutations given above, it is immediately obvious that all these permutations occur in G. Hence, as their number is equal to the order of G, the group thus formed coincides with G.

144. The general result for any intransitive group, the simplest case of which has been considered in the two last paragraphs, may be stated in the following form:—

THEOREM VI. *If G is an intransitive group of degree n which permutes the n symbols in s transitive sets, and if* (i) *G_r is what G becomes when the permutations of G are performed on the rth set of symbols only,* (ii) *Γ_r is what G becomes when the permutations of G are performed on all the sets except the rth,* (iii) *g_r is that sub-group of G which changes the symbols of the rth set only,* (iv) *γ_r is that sub-group of G which keeps all the symbols of the rth set unchanged: then the groups G_r/g_r and Γ_r/γ_r are simply isomorphic, and n_r, ν_r being the orders of g_r, γ_r, an n_r to ν_r correspondence is thus established between the permutations of the groups G_r and Γ_r. Moreover, the permutations of G are given, each once and once only, by multiplying each permutation of G_r by the ν_r permutations of Γ_r that correspond to it*.*

It is not necessary to give an independent proof of this theorem, since if, in the discussion of the two preceding paragraphs, G_α, G_β, g_a, g_b, g be replaced by G_r, Γ_r, g_r, γ_r, $\{g_r, \gamma_r\}$, it

* On intransitive groups, reference may be made to Bolza, "On the construction of intransitive groups," *Amer. Journal*, Vol. XI (1889), pp. 195—214. The general isomorphism which underlies the construction of these groups is considered by Klein and Fricke, *Vorlesungen über die Theorie der elliptischen Modulfunctionen*, Vol. I (1890), pp. 402—406.

will be found each step of the process there carried out may be repeated without alteration.

If we regard G_α and G_β as two given transitive groups in distinct sets of symbols, the determination of all the intransitive groups in the combined symbols, which reduce to G_α or G_β when the symbols of the second or first set are neglected, involves a knowledge of the composition of the two groups. To each distinct m to n isomorphism, that can be established between the two groups, there will correspond a distinct intransitive group. If G_α is a simple group, containing therefore only itself and identity self-conjugately, then to each permutation of G_β there must correspond either one or all of the permutations of G_α; and the former can be the case only when G_β contains a self-conjugate sub-group H, such that G_β/H is simply isomorphic with G_α. Hence, if the order of G_β is less than twice the order of G_α, the only possible intransitive group is the direct product of G_α and G_β, unless G_β is simply isomorphic with G_α.

Ex. Prove that $\{(123)(456), (1346)\}$, $\{(1234)(56), (123)\}$, and $\{(1234)(56), (123)(567)\}$ are respectively a transitive group of degree 6, an intransitive group of degree 6 and an intransitive group of degree 7, all of which are simply isomorphic with the symmetric group of 4 symbols.

145. Let $\nu_r\,(r=0, 1, 2, \ldots\ldots, n)$ be the number of permutations of a group of degree n and order N which leave exactly r symbols unchanged, so that

$$N = \sum_{r=0}^{r=n} \nu_r.$$

Suppose first that the group is transitive; and in a sub-group, which keeps one symbol unchanged, let $\nu_r'\,(r=1, 2, \ldots\ldots, n)$ be the number of permutations that leave exactly r symbols unchanged, so that

$$\frac{N}{n} = \sum_{r=1}^{r=n} \nu_r'.$$

Each of the n sub-groups, which leave a single symbol unchanged, have ν_r' permutations which leave exactly r symbols unchanged; and each of these permutations belong to r sub-groups which leave one symbol unchanged. Hence

$$n\nu_r' = r\nu_r,$$

and therefore $$N = \sum_{r=1}^{r=n} r\nu_r;$$
or the number of unchanged symbols in all the permutations of a transitive group is equal to the order of the group.

Suppose, next, that the group is intransitive; and consider a set of s symbols among the n, which are permuted transitively among themselves by the operations of the group. Let N_1 be the order of the self-conjugate sub-group H_1, which leaves unchanged each of this set of s symbols. Then if we consider the effect of the permutations on this set of s symbols only, the group reduces to a transitive group of order N/N_1 with which the original group is multiply isomorphic. If S' is any permutation of this group of order N/N_1, and if SH_1 denote the corresponding N_1 operations of the original group, then every permutation of the set SH_1 produces the same effect on the s symbols that S' produces. Now the number of unchanged symbols in all the permutations of the transitive group of degree s and order N/N_1 is N/N_1; therefore, in all the permutations of the original group, the number of symbols of the set of s that remain unchanged is N. The same reasoning applies to each separate set of the n symbols, which are permuted transitively among themselves by the operations of the group. Hence if there are t such transitive sets, the total number of symbols which remain unchanged in all the permutations of the group is Nt; or

$$Nt = \sum_{r=1}^{r=n} r\nu_r.$$

Returning now to the case in which the group is transitive, let G_1 be a sub-group of order N/n of G which leaves one symbol unchanged, and let the n symbols be permuted by G_1 in s transitive sets, containing

$$m_1\,(=1),\ m_2,\ \ldots,\ m_s$$

symbols. The immediately preceding result shews that

$$\sum_1^n r\nu_r' = Ns/n,$$

and therefore, since

$$n\nu_r' = r\nu_r,$$

$$Ns = \sum_1^n r^2\nu_r.$$

Hence:—

THEOREM VII. *The sum of the numbers of symbols left unchanged by each of the permutations of a permutation-group of order N is tN, where t is the number of transitive sets in which the group permutes the symbols. The sum of the squares of the numbers of symbols left unchanged by each of the permutations of a transitive group of order N is sN, where s is the number of transitive sets in which a sub-group leaving one symbol unchanged permutes the symbols.*

Ex. Prove that, for a triply transitive group of order N,

$$\sum_1^n r^3 \nu_r = 5N.$$

146. We have just seen that the symbols permuted by the operations of an intransitive permutation-group may be divided into sets, such that every permutation of the group permutes the symbols of each set among themselves. For a transitive group the symbols must, from this point of view, be regarded as forming a single set. It may however in particular cases be possible to divide the symbols permuted by a transitive group into sets in such a way, that every permutation of the group either interchanges the symbols of any set among themselves or else changes them all into the symbols of some other set. That this may be possible, it is clearly necessary that each set shall contain the same number of symbols.

Definition. When the symbols operated on by a transitive permutation-group can be divided into sets, each set containing the same number of distinct symbols and no symbol occurring in two different sets, and when the sets are such that all the symbols of any set are either interchanged among themselves or changed into the symbols of another set by every permutation of the group, the group is called *imprimitive*. When no such division into sets is possible, the group is called *primitive*. The sets of symbols which are interchanged by an imprimitive group are called *imprimitive systems*.

A simple example of an imprimitive group is given by group VII of § 17. An examination of the permutations of this group will shew that they all either transform the systems of symbols *xyz* and *abc* into themselves or else interchange them, and that the same is true of the systems *xa*, *yb*, *zc*; so that, in this case, the symbols may be divided into two distinct sets of imprimitive systems.

It follows at once, from the definition, that an imprimitive group cannot be more than simply transitive. For if it were doubly transitive, it would contain permutations changing any two symbols into any other two, and of these the first pair might be chosen from the same imprimitive system and the second pair from distinct systems.

It is also obvious that those permutations of the group, which interchange among themselves the symbols of each imprimitive system, constitute a self-conjugate sub-group.

147. An actual test to determine whether any transitive group is primitive or imprimitive may be applied as follows. Consider the effect of the permutations of the group G on r of the symbols which are permuted transitively by it. Those permutations, which permute the r symbols, say

$$a_1, a_2, \ldots\ldots, a_r$$

among themselves, form a sub-group H. Now suppose that every permutation, which changes a_1 into one of the r symbols, belongs to H. Then if S is a permutation, which does not permute the r symbols among themselves, it must change them into a new set

$$b_1, b_2, \ldots\ldots, b_r,$$

which has no symbol in common with the previous set; and every operation of the set HS changes all the a's into b's. Moreover, since G is transitive, H must permute the a's transitively; and therefore the set HS must contain permutations changing a_1 into each one of the b's.

Suppose now, if possible, that the group contains a permutation S', which changes some of the a's into b's, and the remainder into new symbols. We may assume that S' changes a_1 into b_1, and a_2 into a new symbol c_2. Among the set HS there is at least one permutation, T, which changes a_1 into b_1. Hence $S'T^{-1}$ changes a_1 into itself and a_2 into some new symbol. This however contradicts the supposition that every permutation, which changes a_1 into one of the set of a's, belongs to H. Hence no permutation such as S' can belong to G; and every permutation, which changes one of the a's into one of the b's, must change all the a's into b's.

If the permutations of the group are not thus exhausted, there must be another set of r symbols

$$c_1, c_2, \ldots\ldots, c_r,$$

which are all distinct from the previous sets, such that some permutation changes all the a's into c's. We may now repeat the previous reasoning to shew that every permutation, which changes an a into a c, must change all the a's into c's. By continuing this process, we finally divide the symbols into a number of distinct sets of r each, such that every permutation of the group must change the a's either into themselves or into some other set: and therefore also must change every set either into itself or into some other set. The group must therefore be imprimitive. Hence :—

THEOREM VIII. *If, among the symbols permuted by a transitive group, it is possible to choose a set such that every permutation of the group, which changes a chosen symbol of the set either into itself or into another of the set, permutes all the symbols of the set among themselves; then the group is imprimitive, and the set of symbols forms an imprimitive system.*

Corollary I. If $a_1, a_2, \ldots\ldots, a_r$ are a part of the symbols permuted by a primitive group, there must be permutations of the group, which replace some of this set of symbols by others of the set, and the remainder by symbols not belonging to the set.

Corollary II. A sub-group of a primitive group, which keeps one symbol unchanged, must contain permutations which displace any other symbol.

If the sub-group H, that leaves a_1 unchanged, leaves every symbol of the set $a_1, a_2, \ldots\ldots, a_r$ unchanged, then H must be transformed into itself by every permutation which changes any one of these symbols into any other. Every permutation, which changes one of the set into another, must therefore permute the set among themselves; and the group, contrary to supposition, is imprimitive.

148. It may be possible to distribute the symbols, which are permuted by an imprimitive group, into imprimitive systems in more than one way. When this is possible, suppose that two systems which contain a_1 are

$$a_1, a_2, \ldots\ldots, a_r, a_{r+1}, \ldots\ldots, a_m,$$

and
$$a_1, a_2, \ldots\ldots, a_r, a'_{r+1}, \ldots\ldots\ldots\ldots, a_n';$$

and that the symbols common to the two systems are

$$a_1, a_2, \ldots\ldots, a_r.$$

A permutation of the group, which changes a_1 into a'_{r+1}, must change $a_1, a_2, \ldots\ldots, a_r$ into r symbols of that system of the first set which contains a'_{r+1}, while it changes the system of the second set that contains a_1 into itself. Hence the latter system contains at least r symbols of that system of the first set in which a'_{r+1} occurs. By considering the effect of the inverse permutation, it is clear that the system

$$a_1, a_2, \ldots\ldots, a_r, a'_{r+1}, \ldots\ldots, a_n'$$

cannot have more than r symbols in common with the system of the first set that contains a'_{r+1}. Hence the n symbols of this system can be divided into sets of r, such that each set is contained in some system of the first set. It follows that n, and therefore also m, must be divisible by r.

Suppose now that b_1 is any symbol which is not contained in either of the above systems. A permutation that changes a_1 into b_1 must change the two systems into two others, which have r symbols

$$b_1, b_2, \ldots\ldots, b_r$$

in common; and since no two systems of either set have a common symbol, these r symbols must be distinct from

$$a_1, a_2, \ldots\ldots, a_r.$$

Further, from the mode in which the set $b_1, b_2, \ldots\ldots, b_r$ has been obtained, any operation, which changes one of the symbols $a_1, a_2, \ldots\ldots, a_r$ into one of the symbols $b_1, b_2, \ldots\ldots, b_r$, must change all the symbols of the first set into those of the second. Hence the symbols operated on by the group can be divided into systems of r each, by taking together the sets of r symbols which are common to the various pairs of the two given sets of imprimitive systems; and the group is imprimitive in regard to this new set of systems of r symbols each. Hence :—

THEOREM IX. *If the symbols permuted by a transitive group can be divided into imprimitive systems in two distinct ways, m being the number of symbols in each system of one set and n in each system of the other; and if some system of the first set has r symbols in common with some system of the second set; then* (i) *r is a factor of both m and n, and* (ii) *the symbols can be divided into a set of systems of r each, in respect of which the group is imprimitive.*

It might be expected that, just as we can form a new set of imprimitive systems by taking together the symbols which are common to pairs of systems of two given sets, so we might form another new set of systems by combining all the systems of one set which have any symbols in common with a single system of the other set. A very cursory consideration will shew however that this is not in general the case. In fact, it is sufficient to point out that, with the notation already used, the number of symbols in such a new system would be mn/r; and this number is not necessarily a factor of the degree of the group. Also, even if this number is a factor of the degree of the group, it will not in general be the case that the symbols so grouped together form an imprimitive system.

149. We may now discuss, more fully than was possible in § 135, the form of a self-conjugate sub-group of a given transitive group. Such a sub-group must clearly contain one or more operations displacing any symbol operated on by the group. For if every operation of the sub-group keeps the symbol a_1 unchanged, then since it is self-conjugate, every operation will keep $a_2, a_3, \ldots\ldots,$ unchanged: and the sub-group must reduce to the identical operation only.

Suppose now, if possible, that H is an intransitive self-conjugate sub-group of a transitive group G; and that H permutes the n symbols of G in the separate transitive sets $a_1, a_2, \ldots\ldots, a_{n_1}$; $b_1, b_2, \ldots\ldots, b_{n_2}$; ...... If S is any operation of G which changes a_1 into b_1, then, since

$$S^{-1}HS = H,$$

it must change all the a's into b's; and since

$$SHS^{-1} = H,$$

S^{-1} must change all the b's into a's. Hence the number of symbols in the two sets, and therefore the number of symbols in each of the sets, must be the same.

Moreover every operation of G, since it transforms H into itself, must either permute the symbols of any set among themselves, or it must change them all into the symbols of some other set. Hence G must be imprimitive, and H must consist of those operations of G which permute the symbols of each imprimitive system among themselves.

Conversely, when G is imprimitive, it is immediately obvious that those operations of G, if any such exist, which permute the symbols of each of a set of imprimitive systems among themselves, form a self-conjugate sub-group. Hence:—

THEOREM X. *A self-conjugate sub-group of a primitive group must be transitive; and if an imprimitive group has an intransitive self-conjugate sub-group, it must consist of the operations which permute among themselves the symbols of each of a set of imprimitive systems.*

If G is an imprimitive group of degree mn, and if there are n imprimitive systems of m symbols each, then by considering the effect of G on the systems it is clear that G is isomorphic with a group G' of degree n. In particular instances, it may at once be evident, from the order of G, that this isomorphism cannot be simple. For example, if the order of G has a factor which does not divide $n!$, this is certainly the case: and more generally, if it is known independently that G is not simply isomorphic with any transitive group of degree n, then G must certainly be multiply isomorphic with G'. In such instances the self-conjugate sub-group of G, which corresponds to the identical operation of G', is that intransitive self-conjugate sub-group, which interchanges among themselves the symbols of each imprimitive system.

If G is soluble, a minimum self-conjugate sub-group of G must have for its order a power of a prime. Also, if G has an intransitive self-conjugate sub-group, it must have an intransitive minimum self-conjugate sub-group. Hence if G is soluble and has intransitive self-conjugate sub-groups, the symbols permuted by G must be capable of division into imprimitive systems, such that the number in each system is the power of a prime.

150. Let G be a k-ply transitive group of degree $n\,(k > 2)$, and let G_r be that sub-group of G which keeps $r\,(< k)$ given symbols unchanged, so that G_r is $(k-r)$-ply transitive in the remaining $n-r$ symbols. Also, let H be a self-conjugate sub-group of G, and let H_r be that sub-group of H which keeps the same r symbols unchanged; so that H_r is the common sub-group of H and G_r. Since every operation of G_r transforms both H and G_r into themselves, every operation of G_r must be permutable with H_r; i.e. H_r is a self-conjugate sub-group of G_r. Now, if $r = k-2$, G_{k-2} is doubly transitive in the $n-k+2$ symbols on which it operates; it is therefore primitive. Hence, unless H_{k-2} consists of the identical operation only, it must be transitive in the $n-k+2$ symbols. If H_{k-2} is the identical operation, H contains no operation, except identity, which displaces less than $n-k+3$ symbols.

Suppose, first, that H contains operations, other than identity, which leave one or more symbols unchanged. Then, since H is a self-conjugate sub-group and G is k-ply transitive, it may be shewn, exactly as in § 138, that H must contain operations displacing not more than $2k-2$ symbols. Hence H_{k-2} can consist of the identical operation alone, only if

$$n-k+3 \not> 2k-2,$$

or

$$k \not< \tfrac{1}{3}n + \tfrac{5}{3}.$$

When this inequality holds, we have seen (§ 138) that G contains the alternating group. Hence in this case, if G does not contain the alternating group, it follows that H_{k-2} is transitive in the $n-k+2$ symbols on which it operates.

Since H is self-conjugate and G is k-ply transitive, H must contain a sub-group conjugate to H_{k-2} which keeps any other $k-2$ symbols unchanged. Hence H_{k-3} must be doubly transitive in the $n-k+3$ symbols on which it operates; and so on. Finally, if G is not the symmetric group (the alternating group, being simple, contains no self-conjugate sub-group) H must be $(k-1)$-ply transitive.

Suppose, next, that H contains no operation, except identity, which leaves any symbol unchanged. Then if, with the notation of § 138, $j = k - 1$ for every operation of H, the argument there used does not apply. For it is impossible to choose the operation T so that c_k is a symbol which does not occur in S.

The self-conjugate sub-group H contains a single operation changing a given symbol a_1 into any other symbol a_r. Also G contains operations which leave a_1 unchanged and change a_r into any other symbol a_s. Hence the operations of H, other than identity, form a single conjugate set in G; and therefore H must be an Abelian group of order p^m and type (1, 1, ..., to m units); p being a prime. Further, since G is by supposition at least triply transitive, it must contain operations which transform any two operations of H, other than identity, into any other two. If p were an odd prime, and P_1 and P_2 were two of the generating operations of H, it follows that G would have an operation S such that

$$S^{-1}P_1S = P_1, \quad S^{-1}P_2S = P_1^{a};$$

and this is impossible. Hence p must be 2. Further if G were more than triply transitive, and if A, B, C were three independent generating operations of H, then G would have an operation Σ such that

$$\Sigma^{-1}A\Sigma = A, \quad \Sigma^{-1}B\Sigma = B, \quad \Sigma^{-1}C\Sigma = AB.$$

This again is impossible, and therefore k must be 3. Hence:—

THEOREM XI. *A self-conjugate sub-group of a k-ply transitive group of degree n ($2 < k < n$), is in general at least ($k - 1$)-ply transitive*. The only exception is that a triply transitive group of degree 2^m may have a self-conjugate sub-group of order 2^m.*

151. We will now consider, from a rather different point of view, the possibility of an imprimitive self-conjugate sub-group in a doubly transitive group. Let G be a doubly transitive group of degree mn, and let H be an imprimitive self-conjugate sub-group of G. Suppose that m is the smallest number, other than unity, of symbols which occur in an imprimitive system; and let

$$a_1, a_2, \ldots\ldots, a_m$$

* Jordan, *Traité des Substitutions*, p. 65.

form an imprimitive system. Since G is doubly transitive, it must contain a permutation S, which leaves a_1 unchanged and changes a_2 into a_{m+1}, a symbol not contained in the given set. If S changes the given set into

$$a_1, a_{m+1}, \ldots\ldots, a_{2m-1},$$

then, since

$$S^{-1}HS = H,$$

this new set must form an imprimitive system for H. Also, since m is the smallest number of symbols that can occur in an imprimitive system, the two sets have no symbol in common except a_1.

Now a_{m+1} may be any symbol not contained in the original system. Hence it must be possible to distribute the mn symbols into sets of imprimitive systems of m each, such that every pair of symbols occurs in one system and no pair in more than one system. This implies that $mn-1$ is divisible by $m-1$, or that $n-1$ is divisible by $m-1$.

Consider now a permutation of H which leaves a_1 unchanged. It must permute among themselves the remaining $m-1$ symbols of each of the $(mn-1)/(m-1)$ systems in which a_1 occurs. If a_r is any other symbol, a similar statement applies to it. Now no two systems have more than one symbol in common. Hence every permutation of H, which leaves both a_1 and a_r unchanged, must leave all the symbols unchanged. The sub-group H is therefore such that each of its permutations displaces all or all but one of the symbols. Moreover the permutations, which leave a_1 unchanged, permute among themselves the remaining symbols of each system in which a_1 occurs; therefore the order of H must be $mn\mu$, where μ is a factor of $m-1$.

Now (§ 134, footnote) the $mn-1$ operations of H, which permute all the symbols, form with identity a characteristic sub-group H_1 of H, which is a regular permutation-group in the mn symbols. This is necessarily a self-conjugate sub-group of G; and by the preceding paragraph all of its operations, except identity, are conjugate in G and are therefore of prime order. Hence if a doubly transitive group has an imprimitive self-conjugate sub-group, its degree must be the power, p^m, of a prime; and it must also contain a regular Abelian group of order p^m and type $(1, 1, \ldots, 1)$ as a self-conjugate sub-group.

152. For the further discussion of the self-conjugate sub-groups of a primitive group, it is necessary to consider in what forms the direct product of two groups can be represented as a transitive group.

Let G be the direct product of two groups H_1 and H_2, and suppose that G can be represented as a transitive group of degree n. When G is thus represented, we will suppose that H_1 is transitive in the n symbols that G permutes. We have seen in § 136 that every permutation of n symbols, which is permutable with each of the permutations of a group transitive in the n symbols, must displace all the n symbols. It follows that every permutation of H_2 must displace all the n symbols on which G operates; and that the order of H_2 is equal to or is a factor of n.

If the order of H_2 is equal to n, then H_2 is transitive in the n symbols, so that the order of H_1 cannot be greater than n. In this case, H_1 and H_2 must (§ 136) be two simply isomorphic groups of order n, which have no self-conjugate operations except identity. Further, if H_1 and H_2 in this case are not simple groups, let K be a self-conjugate sub-group of H_1. Since every operation of H_2 is permutable with every operation of H_1, K is a self-conjugate sub-group of G. Now the order of K is less than n, the degree of G; therefore K is intransitive and G is imprimitive. On the other hand, we have seen (*loc. cit.*) that, if H_1 and H_2 are simple, the sub-group of G that keeps one symbol fixed is a maximum sub-group: and then G is primitive. Hence:—

THEOREM XII. *If the direct product* Γ *of* H_1 *and* H_2 *can be represented as a transitive group of degree* n, *in such a way that* H_1 *and* H_2 *are transitive sub-groups of* Γ, *then* H_1 *and* H_2 *must be simply isomorphic groups of order* n, *which have no self-conjugate operations except identity. When this condition is satisfied,* Γ *will be primitive if, and only if,* H_1 *and* H_2 *are simple.*

153. Suppose now that a primitive group G, of degree n, has two distinct minimum self-conjugate sub-groups H_1 and H_2. Then every operation of H_1 (or H_2) is permutable with

H_2 (or H_1), and H_1, H_2 have no common operation except identity. Hence (§ 34) the group $\{H_1, H_2\}$, which we will call Γ, is the direct product of H_1 and H_2. Now Γ is a self-conjugate sub-group of G: it is therefore transitive in the n symbols which G permutes. Also H_1 and H_2, being self-conjugate sub-groups of G, are transitive. Hence, by Theorem XII (§ 152), H_1 and H_2 are simply isomorphic, and n is equal to the order of H_1. Moreover, since H_1 is a minimum self-conjugate sub-group of G which contains no self-conjugate operations except identity, it must (Theorem IV, § 53) be either a simple group of composite order, or the direct product of several simply isomorphic simple groups of composite order. It follows that G cannot have two distinct minimum self-conjugate sub-groups unless the degree of G is equal to or is a power of the order of some simple group of composite order.

154. Let now Γ be a minimum self-conjugate sub-group of a doubly transitive group G, and suppose that Γ is the direct product of the α simply isomorphic simple groups $H_1, H_2, \ldots\ldots,$ H_α. Since G is primitive, Γ is transitive. If H_1 is a cyclical group of prime order p, the order of Γ is p^α; therefore the degree of Γ, or what is the same thing, the degree of G, is p^α.

If H_1 is a simple group of composite order, and if $\alpha > 2$, then (§ 152) H_1 cannot be transitive. The transitive systems of H_1, since they form a set of imprimitive systems for Γ, must each contain the same number m of symbols. If m is less than the order of H_1, a sub-group of H_1 which leaves unchanged one symbol of one transitive system will leave unchanged one symbol of each transitive system. Now we have seen, in § 151, that the operations of an imprimitive self-conjugate sub-group of a doubly transitive group must displace all or all but one of the symbols. Hence m cannot be less than the order of H_1. We may similarly shew that, if m is equal to the order of H_1, and if the degree of G is less than m^α, some of the operations of Γ must keep more than one symbol fixed; and therefore the group assumed cannot exist. If the degree of G is equal to m^α, G must be a sub-group of the holomorph of Γ, and cannot obviously be doubly transitive. If $\alpha = 2$, H_1 may be transitive. In this case G would be a sub-group of the group (§ 64) whose order is twice that of the holomorph of H_1; and such a group cannot be doubly transitive. Hence finally no doubly transitive group can contain a minimum self-conjugate sub-group of the type assumed.

No general law can be stated regarding self-conjugate sub-groups of simply transitive primitive groups; but for groups which are at least doubly transitive the preceding results may be summed up as follows:—

THEOREM XIII. *A group G which is at least doubly transitive either must be simple or must contain a simple group H as a self-conjugate sub-group. In the latter case no operation of G, except identity, is permutable with every operation of H. The only exceptions to this statement are that a triply transitive group of degree* 2^m *may have a self-conjugate sub-group of order* 2^m*; and that a doubly transitive group of degree* p^m*, where p is a prime, may have a self-conjugate sub-group of order* p^m.

Corollary. If a primitive group is soluble, its degree must be the power of a prime*.

In fact, if a group is soluble, so also is its minimum self-conjugate sub-group. The latter must be therefore an Abelian group of order p^a: and since this group must be transitive, its order is equal to the degree of the primitive group.

155. As illustrating the occurrence of an imprimitive self-conjugate sub-group in a primitive group, we will construct a primitive group of degree 36 which has an imprimitive self-conjugate sub-group. For this purpose, let†

$$S = (1, 2, 3)(4, 5, 6)(7, 8, 9)(10, 11, 12)(13, 14, 15)(16, 17, 18)(19, 20, 21)(22, 23, 24)(25, 26, 27)(28, 29, 30)(31, 32, 33)(34, 35, 36),$$

and $$A = (3, 4)(5, 6)(9, 10)(11, 12)(15, 16)(17, 18)(21, 22)(23, 24)(27, 28)(29, 30)(33, 34)(35, 36);$$

so that $\{S, A\}$ is an intransitive group of degree 36, the symbols

* This result, stated in a somewhat different form, is given, among many others, in the letter written by Galois to his friend Chevalier on the evening of May 29th, 1832, the day before the duel in which he was killed. The letter was first printed in the *Revue Encyclopédique* (1832), p. 568; it was reprinted in the collection of Galois's mathematical writings in *Liouville's Journal*, t. XI (1846), pp. 381—444.

† The commas in the symbols for the permutations are here used to prevent confusion among the one-digit and two-digit numbers.

being interchanged in 6 transitive systems containing 6 symbols each. This group is simply isomorphic with

$$\{(123)(456),\ (34)(56)\};$$

and it may be easily verified that this group is simply isomorphic with the alternating group of 5 symbols, the order of which is 60.

Also let

$$J = (2, 7)(3, 13)(4, 19)(5, 25)(6, 31)(9, 14)(10, 20)(11, 26)$$
$$(12, 32)(16, 21)(17, 27)(18, 33)(23, 28)(24, 34)(30, 35).$$

Then

$$JSJ = (1, 7, 13)(19, 25, 31)(2, 8, 14)(20, 26, 32)$$
$$(3, 9, 15)(21, 27, 33)(4, 10, 16)(22, 28, 34)$$
$$(5, 11, 17)(23, 29, 35)(6, 12, 18)(24, 30, 36),$$

and $JAJ = (13, 19)(25, 31)(14, 20)(26, 32)(15, 21)(27, 33)$
$$(16, 22)(28, 34)(17, 23)(29, 35)(18, 24)(30, 36);$$

and $\{JSJ, JAJ\}$ is similar to and simply isomorphic with $\{S, A\}$.

Now it may be directly verified that S and A are, each of them, permutable with JSJ and JAJ; and therefore every operation of the group $\{S, A\}$ is permutable with every operation of the group $\{JSJ, JAJ\}$. Also these two groups can have no common operation, since the symbols into which $\{S, A\}$ changes any given symbol are all distinct from those into which $\{JSJ, JAJ\}$ change it. Hence $\{S, A, JSJ, JAJ\}$ is the direct product of $\{S, A\}$ and $\{JSJ, JAJ\}$; it is therefore a group of order 3600. It is also, from its mode of formation, a transitive group of degree 36; and it interchanges the symbols in two and only two distinct sets of imprimitive systems, of which

$$1, 2, 3, 4, 5, 6 \text{ and } 1, 7, 13, 19, 25, 31$$

may be taken as representatives.

Now J does not interchange the 36 symbols in either of these systems, and therefore it cannot occur in $\{S, A, JSJ, JAJ\}$. Further

$$J\{S, A, JSJ, JAJ\}J = \{S, A, JSJ, JAJ\};$$

and therefore $\{J, S, A\}$ is a transitive group of degree 36 and order 7200. Also, since J does not interchange the symbols in either of the two sets of imprimitive systems of $\{S, A, JSJ, JAJ\}$, it follows that $\{J, S, A\}$ is primitive.

156. Ex. 1. Shew that a group of order N, which has a set of n conjugate sub-groups, is composite if $n!/N$ is not an integer.

Ex. 2. An imprimitive group of order N permutes its symbols in r imprimitive systems of $n\,(>1)$ symbols each. Prove that, if r

is 2, the group has a self-conjugate sub-group of order $\frac{1}{2}N$; and that for the values 3 and 4 of r there is a self-conjugate sub-group whose order is either $\frac{1}{2}N$ or $\frac{1}{3}N$.

Ex. 3. Prove that, if n is the smallest number such that a transitive permutation-group of degree n is simply isomorphic with a group G, then n^a is the smallest number such that a transitive permutation-group of degree n^a is simply isomorphic with the direct product of a groups each of which is simply isomorphic with G.

Ex. 4. Shew that, if every sub-group of G contains a self-conjugate sub-group of G, no transitive permutation-group whose degree is less than the order of G can be simply isomorphic with G. In particular shew that no transitive group whose degree is less than 63 can be simply isomorphic with the group defined by

$$A^9 = E, \quad B^7 = E, \quad A^{-1}BA = B^2.$$

Ex. 5. Shew that a transitive permutation-group whose order is the power of a prime is necessarily imprimitive.

Ex. 6. Shew that an Abelian group of order 2^n and type (1, 1, ... to n units) can be expressed as an intransitive permutation-group of degree $2(2^n - 1)$, each of whose permutations except identity leaves $2(2^{n-1} - 1)$ symbols unchanged.

Ex. 7. Prove that the holomorph of an Abelian group of order 2^n and type (1, 1, ... to n units), when expressed as a permutation of degree 2^n, as on p. 87, is triply transitive; while the holomorph of an Abelian group of order p^n and type (1, 1, ... to n units), p being an odd prime, is only doubly transitive.

Ex. 8. If G is a simply transitive primitive group and H the sub-group of G which leaves one symbol unchanged and permutes the remaining symbols in two or more transitive sets, prove that a prime which divides the order of one transitive constituent of H must divide the orders of all of them. (Jordan.)

Ex. 9. If G is a transitive group of odd order and of degree $2n+1$, and H the sub-group of G which leaves one symbol unchanged and is necessarily intransitive in the remaining $2n$, prove that the degrees of the transitive constituents of H are equal in pairs.

Ex. 10. Prove that a doubly transitive group cannot contain an intransitive sub-group whose order is greater than that of a sub-group which leaves one symbol unchanged.

Ex. 11. Shew that the alternating group of 6 symbols can be expressed as a doubly transitive group of degree 10; and that in this form all the operations of order 3 are represented by similar permutations.

CHAPTER XI.

ON PERMUTATION-GROUPS: TRANSITIVITY AND PRIMITIVITY: (CONCLUDING PROPERTIES).

157. FROM the point of view of one of the problems of pure group-theory, namely, the determination of all distinct types of group of a given order, the analysis of the symmetric group of n symbols is not a succinct process, as it continually involves the redetermination of groups which have been already obtained. Thus a simple group of degree mn, in which the symbols are permuted in m imprimitive systems of n each, would in this analysis have been already obtained as a group of degree m. With reference then to the more restricted problem of determining all types of simple groups, it would certainly be sufficient to find all primitive sub-groups of the symmetric group.

158. We shall proceed to determine a superior limit to the order of a primitive group of degree n, other than the alternating or the symmetric group.

Let G be a primitive group of degree n, and suppose that G contains a sub-group H which leaves $n-m$ symbols unchanged and is transitive in the remaining m. Since G is primitive, H and the sub-groups conjugate to it must generate a transitive self-conjugate sub-group of G; and therefore there must be some sub-group H', conjugate to H, such that the m symbols operated on by H and the m operated on by H' are not all distinct. Suppose H' is chosen so that these two sets of m symbols have as great a number in common as possible, say s; and represent by

$$\alpha_1, \alpha_2, \ldots\ldots, \alpha_r, \gamma_1, \gamma_2, \ldots\ldots, \gamma_s,$$

and $$\beta_1, \beta_2, \ldots\ldots, \beta_r, \gamma_1, \gamma_2, \ldots\ldots, \gamma_s,$$

where $r + s = m$, the symbols operated on by H and H' respectively. Then $\{H, H'\}$ is a transitive group in the $2r + s$ symbols α, β, and γ, which leaves unaltered all the remaining symbols of G.

If S is an operation of H which changes α_2 into α_1, $S^{-1}H'S$ does not affect α_1. Hence, unless S interchanges the α's among themselves, the m symbols operated on by H' and the m operated on by $S^{-1}H'S$ will have more than s in common. Every operation of H which changes one α into another must therefore interchange all the α's among themselves; hence H must be imprimitive.

If then H is primitive, s must be equal to $m - 1$. In any case, if $s = m - 1$, $\{H, H'\}$ is a doubly transitive and therefore primitive group of degree $m + 1$, which leaves the remaining $n - m - 1$ symbols of G unchanged. We may reason about this sub-group as we have done about H. Among the sub-groups conjugate to $\{H, H'\}$, there must be one at least which operates on m of the symbols displaced by $\{H, H'\}$. This, with $\{H, H'\}$, generates a triply transitive group of degree $m + 2$, which leaves $n - m - 2$ symbols unchanged. Proceeding thus, we find finally that G itself must be $(n - m + 1)$-ply transitive.

159. If s is less than $m - 1$, we may again deal with the sub-group $\{H, H'\}$, or H_1, exactly as we have dealt with H. It is a transitive group of degree m_1 ($> m$), which leaves $n - m_1$ symbols unchanged. If, among the sub-groups conjugate to H_1, none operates on more than s_1 of the symbols affected by H_1, and if H_1' is a suitably chosen conjugate sub-group, then $\{H_1, H_1'\}$ is a transitive group of degree $2m_1 - s_1$, which leaves $n - 2m_1 + s_1$ symbols unchanged. Continuing this process, we must, before arriving at a group of degree n, reach a stage at which the number s_r is equal to $m_r - 1$.

For suppose, if possible, that among the groups conjugate to K, of degree $\rho + \sigma$, none displaces more than σ of the symbols acted on by K, while at the same time $2\rho + \sigma = n$. If

$$\alpha_1, \alpha_2, \ldots\ldots, \alpha_\rho, \gamma_1, \gamma_2, \ldots\ldots, \gamma_\sigma,$$

and

$$\beta_1, \beta_2, \ldots\ldots, \beta_\rho, \gamma_1, \gamma_2, \ldots\ldots, \gamma_\sigma$$

are the symbols affected by K and K' respectively, then since

G is primitive, it must contain an operation S which changes α_1 into α_2 without at the same time changing all the α's into α's. If then we transform K' by S, the two groups K' and $S^{-1}K'S$ must operate on more than σ common symbols, contrary to supposition.

Hence G must in this case certainly contain a transitive sub-group of degree $n-1$, and therefore is itself at least doubly transitive*.

160. Returning to the case in which H is primitive and G therefore $(n-m+1)$-ply transitive, we at once obtain an inferior limit for m. We have seen, in fact, in Theorem IV, § 138, that a group of degree n, other than the alternating or the symmetric group, cannot be more than $(\frac{1}{3}n+1)$-ply transitive. Hence

$$n - m + 1 \ngtr \tfrac{1}{3}n + 1,$$

or

$$m \nless \tfrac{2}{3}n.$$

We may sum up these results as follows:—

THEOREM I. *A primitive group G of degree n, which has a sub-group H that keeps $n-m$ symbols unchanged and is transitive in the remaining m symbols, is at least doubly transitive. If H is primitive and G does not contain the alternating group, m cannot be less than $\frac{2}{3}n$, and G is $(n-m+1)$-ply transitive.*

Corollary. The order of a primitive group of degree n cannot exceed $n!/2 . 3 ...... p$, where $2, 3, ... p$ are the distinct primes which are less than $\frac{2}{3}n$.

If q^{α} is the highest power of a prime q that divides $n!$, the sub-groups of order q^{α} of the symmetric group form a single conjugate set, and each of them must contain circular substitutions of order q. Hence if $q < \frac{2}{3}n$, it follows by the theorem that no primitive group of degree n, other than the alternating

* The results contained in §§ 158, 159 are due to Jordan (*Liouville's Journal*, Vol. XVI, 1871) and Netto (*Crelle's Journal*, Vol. CIII, 1889). They have been extended by Marggraff: "Ueber primitiven Gruppen mit transitiven Untergruppen geringeren Grades" (*Inaugural Dissertation*, Giessen, 1892). With the notation used in the text, Marggraff shews that, unless the symbols affected by H can be divided into imprimitive systems of r symbols each, in at least $r+1$ distinct ways, G will be $(n-m+1)$-ply transitive. In particular, if H is a cyclical group of degree m, G is $(n-m+1)$-ply transitive. He also shews that in any case $m \geqslant \frac{1}{2}n$.

or the symmetric group, can contain a sub-group of order q^a; and therefore q^{a-1} is the highest power of q that can divide the order of the group.

161. The ratio of $2 \,.\, 3 \ldots\ldots p$ to n increases rapidly as n increases, and it is at once obvious that, when $n > 7$, this ratio is greater than unity; hence for values of n greater than 7, the symmetric group can have no primitive sub-group of order $(n-1)!$.

The order of the greatest imprimitive sub-group of the symmetric group is $a!\,(n/a!)^a$, where a is the smallest factor of n. When $n > 4$, this is less than $(n-1)!$.

The order of the greatest intransitive sub-group of the symmetric group, other than the sub-groups that keep one symbol fixed, is $2!\,(n-2)!$. This is always less than $(n-1)!$.

Hence when $n > 7$, the only sub-groups of order $(n-1)!$ of the symmetric group are the sub-groups which each keep one symbol fixed; and these form a conjugate set of n sub-groups.

When $n = 7$, a sub-group of order $(n-1)!$ must be intransitive, and therefore the same result holds in this case; this also is true when n is 3, 4, or 5.

Lastly, when $n = 6$, there may, by the foregoing theorem, be primitive sub-groups of order $5!$. That such sub-groups actually exist may be verified at once by considering the symmetric group of 5 symbols. This group contains 6 cyclical sub-groups of order 5, and each of them is self-conjugate in a sub-group of order 20. When these 6 conjugate sub-groups of order 20 are transformed by the operations of the symmetric group, they are transitively permuted among themselves. Moreover no operation of the symmetric group transforms each of these sub-groups into itself. Hence there is a transitive group of degree 6 which is simply isomorphic with the symmetric group of 5 symbols; and, since the alternating group of degree 6 is simple, this transitive group of degree 6 must be one of 6 conjugate sub-groups in the symmetric group of degree 6. The symmetric group of degree 6 therefore contains a set of 6 conjugate doubly transitive sub-groups of order $5!$, which are simply isomorphic with the intransitive sub-groups that each keep one symbol fixed. Finally, if the 12 sub-groups of order 5!, which are thus accounted for, do not exhaust all the sub-groups of this order, any other would have in common with each of the 12 a sub-group of order 20; and therefore the operations of order 3 contained in it would be distinct from those in the previous 12. But these clearly contain all the operations of order 3 of the symmetric group, and therefore there can be no other sub-groups of order 5!. Hence:—

THEOREM II. *The symmetric group of degree n* ($n \neq 6$) *contains n and only n sub-groups of order* $(n-1)!$, *which form a single conjugate set. The symmetric group of degree* 6 *contains* 12 *sub-groups of order* 5!, *which are simply isomorphic with one another and form two conjugate sets of* 6 *each.*

162. It is an immediate result of the preceding theorem that, except when $n=6$, the symmetric group of degree n is a complete group. In fact with this exception the symmetric group of degree n contains just n sub-groups of order $n-1\,!$ forming a conjugate set, and no operation of the group is permutable with each sub-group of the set. Hence (Theorem III, Chapter VI) to every isomorphism of the group there corresponds a permutation of n symbols. There are therefore no outer isomorphisms, and since the group has no self-conjugate operations it is complete*.

When $n=6$, every isomorphism of the group must either change each of the two conjugate sets of sub-groups of order 5 ! into itself, or must permute the two sets. By the previous reasoning an isomorphism, which transforms each of the two conjugate sets into itself, can be represented as a permutation of 6 symbols and is therefore an inner isomorphism. There can therefore be, at most, a single class of outer isomorphisms which must permute the two conjugate sets.

That such a class of outer isomorphisms actually exists may be verified as follows. Let the symmetric group of degree 6 be set up on the symbols

$$a_1,\ a_2,\ a_3,\ a_4,\ a_5,\ a_6,$$

so that the sub-group which leaves a_1 unchanged is one of the first set of conjugate sub-groups of order 5 !; and again on the symbols

$$b_1,\ b_2,\ b_3,\ b_4,\ b_5,\ b_6,$$

so that the sub-group which leaves b_1 unchanged is one of the second set of sub-groups of order 5 !. The 36 products a_ib_j then obviously undergo a transitive permutation-group under the operations of the symmetric group.

* Hölder, *Math. Ann.* Vol. XLVI (1895), p. 345.

To the sub-group of the a's which leaves a_1 unchanged there corresponds a sub-group on the products which permutes

$$a_1b_1,\ a_1b_2,\ a_1b_3,\ a_1b_4,\ a_1b_5,\ a_1b_6$$

transitively and the remaining 30 products also transitively. To the sub-group of the b's which leaves b_1 unchanged there corresponds a sub-group on the products which permutes

$$a_1b_1,\ a_2b_1,\ a_3b_1,\ a_4b_1,\ a_5b_1,\ a_6b_1$$

transitively and the remaining 30 products transitively. Now it will be found that the permutation

$$\begin{pmatrix} a_ib_j \\ a_jb_i \end{pmatrix}$$

is permutable with the transitive group on the 36 products. Moreover it permutes

$$a_1b_1,\ a_1b_2,\ a_1b_3,\ a_1b_4,\ a_1b_5,\ a_1b_6$$

with $$a_1b_1,\ a_2b_1,\ a_3b_1,\ a_4b_1,\ a_5b_1,\ a_6b_1.$$

Hence it must permute a sub-group of order 5 ! of the first set with one of the second. The group of isomorphisms of the symmetric group of degree 6 is therefore a group of order 1440*.

163. We shall now discuss certain further limitations on the order of a primitive group of given degree. Though it will be seen that these do not lead to general results, similar to that given by Theorem I, § 160, yet in many special cases they are of considerable assistance in determining the possible existence of groups of given orders and degrees.

We consider first a group G of order N and of prime degree p. If G is not cyclical, it must contain permutations which keep only one symbol unchanged. For let P be a permutation of G of order p. The only permutations permutable with P are its own powers (§ 136); and the only permutations permutable with $\{P\}$ are permutations which keep one symbol unchanged and are regular in the remaining $p-1$ symbols (§ 140)†. Now if the only permutations permutable with $\{P\}$ are its own, then $\{P\}$ is one of N/p conjugate sub-groups; and these contain $N(p-1)/p$

* Hölder, *loc. cit.* p. 343. Compare also § 183 below.

† It is shewn in § 140 that $\{P\}$ is permutable with a circular permutation of $p-1$ symbols, which leaves one symbol a_1 unchanged. If there are other permutations which leave a_1 unchanged and are permutable with $\{P\}$, some such permutation will leave two symbols unchanged. This is clearly impossible. Hence the group of order $p(p-1)$ is the greatest group of the p symbols in which $\{P\}$ is self-conjugate.

permutations of order p. In this case, G would contain exactly N/p permutations whose orders are not divisible by p. But this is clearly impossible, since N/p is the order of a sub-group which keeps one symbol unchanged, and there are p such sub-groups. Hence there must be permutations in G, other than those of $\{P\}$, which are permutable with $\{P\}$; and each of these permutations keeps one symbol unchanged.

It follows from § 154 that G, if soluble, must contain a self-conjugate sub-group of order p: therefore no group of prime degree p, which contains more than one sub-group of order p, can be soluble.

If $1+kp$ is the number of sub-groups of order p contained in G, then

$$N = p\frac{p-1}{d}(1+kp),$$

where d is a factor of $p-1$; and a sub-group of order p is transformed into itself by every permutation of a cyclical sub-group of order $(p-1)/d$. When d is odd, a permutation which generates this cyclical sub-group is an odd permutation; and G then contains a self-conjugate sub-group of order $\frac{1}{2}N$.

If both p and $\frac{1}{2}(p-1)$ are primes, the order of a group of degree p, which contains more than one sub-group of order p, must be divisible by $\frac{1}{2}(p-1)$. For if the order is not divisible by $\frac{1}{2}(p-1)$, the order of the sub-group, within which a sub-group of order p is self-conjugate, must be $2p$. Now the permutations of order 2 in this sub-group consist of $\frac{1}{2}(p-1)$ transpositions, so that they are odd permutations. The group must therefore contain a self-conjugate sub-group in which these operations of order 2 do not occur. In such a sub-group, the only operations permutable with those of a sub-group of order p are its own; and we have seen that no such group can exist. The order of the group must therefore, as stated above, be divisible by $\frac{1}{2}(p-1)$.

164. Let G be a primitive group of degree n and order N; and let p be a prime, which is a factor of N but not of either n or $n-1$. Moreover, suppose that n is congruent to ν, mod. p; ν being less than p. If $n < p^2$, and if p^α is the highest power of

p which divides N, the sub-groups of order p^α must be Abelian groups of type (1, 1, ... to α units). In fact, such a sub-group must be intransitive, and, since $n < p^2$, the number of symbols in each transitive system of the sub-group must be p. In any case the number of symbols left unchanged by a sub-group of order p^α is of the form $kp + \nu$.

Suppose now that, in a sub-group of order N/n which leaves one symbol unchanged, a sub-group H of order p^α is one of $N/p^\alpha mn$ conjugate sub-groups. Then each of the n sub-groups that keep one symbol unchanged contains $N/p^\alpha mn$ sub-groups of order p^α; and each sub-group of order p^α belongs to $kp + \nu$ sub-groups that keep one symbol unchanged. Hence G contains $N/p^\alpha m(kp + \nu)$ sub-groups of order p^α; and any one of them, say H, is contained self-conjugately in a sub-group I of order $p^\alpha m(kp + \nu)$. This sub-group I must interchange transitively among themselves the $kp + \nu$ symbols left unchanged by H. For let a and b be any two of these symbols; and let S be an operation which changes a into b and transforms H into H'. There must be an operation T which keeps b unchanged and transforms H' into H, since in the sub-group that keeps b unchanged there is only one conjugate set of sub-groups of order p^α. Then ST changes a into b and transforms H into itself; and therefore I contains permutations which change a into b. Now it may happen that the existence of a sub-group such as I, transitive in the $kp + \nu$ symbols unchanged by H, requires that G is either the alternating or the symmetric group.

165. As a simple example, we will shew that the order of a group of degree 19 cannot be divisible by 7, unless it contains the alternating group. It follows from Theorem I, Corollary, § 160, that the order of a group of degree 19, which does not contain the alternating group, cannot be divisible by a power of 7 higher than the first, and that if the group contains a permutation of order 7, the permutation must consist of two cycles of 7 symbols each. The sub-group of order 7 must therefore leave 5 symbols unchanged; hence, by § 164, it must be contained self-conjugately in a sub-group whose order is divisible by 5. Now (§ 36) a group of order 35 is necessarily Abelian; so that the group of degree 19 must contain a permutation of order 5 which is permutable with a permutation of order 7. Such a permutation of order 5 must clearly consist of a single cycle, and its presence in a group of degree 19 requires that the latter should contain the alternating group. It follows that, if a group of degree 19 does not contain the alternating group, its order is not divisible by 7.

As a second example, we will determine the possible forms for the order of a group of degree 13, with more than one sub-group of order 13, which does not contain the alternating group. By Theorem I, Corollary, § 160, the order of such a group must be of the form $2^{\alpha} . 3^{\beta} . 5^{\gamma} . 11^{\delta} . 13$; where α, β, γ, δ do not exceed 9, 4, 1, 1 respectively.

Suppose, first, that γ is unity, if possible. A permutation of order 5 must consist of two cycles of 5 symbols each; and a sub-group of order 5 must therefore be self-conjugate in a sub-group of order 15. There is then a permutation of order 3 which is permutable with a permutation of order 5. Such a permutation must, as in the last example, consist of a single cycle; and its existence would imply that the group contains the alternating group. It follows that, for the group as specified, γ must be zero.

Suppose, next, that δ is unity, if possible. The group is then (Theorem I, § 160) triply transitive; and the order of the sub-group, that keeps two symbols fixed and is transitive in the remaining 11, is $2^{\alpha-2} . 3^{\beta-1} . 11$; and this sub-group must contain more than one sub-group of order 11. We have seen in § 163 that no such group can exist. Therefore δ must be zero.

The two smallest numbers of the form $2^m 3^n$ which are congruent to unity, mod. 13, are 3^3 and $2^4 3^2$; and every number of this form, which is congruent to unity, mod. 13, can be written $(2^4 3^2)^x 3^{3y}$. Hence the order of every group of degree 13, which contains no odd permutation, must be of the form $(2^4 3^2)^x . 3^{3y} . z . 13$, where z is 2, 3 or 6. Since 3^4 is the highest power of 3 that can divide the order of the group, the only admissible values of x and y are (i) $x = 0$, $y = 1$: (ii) $x = 2$, $y = 0$: (iii) $x = 1$, $y = 0$.

Suppose, first, that $x = 0$, $y = 1$. The order of the group is $2 . 3^3 . 13$, $3^4 . 13$, or $2 . 3^4 . 13$. There must be 13 sub-groups of order 3^4 (or 3^3), and since 13 is not congruent to unity, mod. 9, there must be sub-groups of order 3^3 (or 3^2) common to some two sub-groups of order 3^4 (or 3^3). Such a sub-group must be self-conjugate (Theorem III, § 123). This case therefore cannot occur.

Next, suppose that $x = 2$, $y = 0$. Then z must be 2, and the order of the group is $2^9 . 3^4 . 13$. Now it is easy to verify that a sub-group of order $2^9 . 3^4$ and degree 12 can be neither intransitive or imprimitive. The order of a sub-group of the group of degree 12 which keeps one symbol fixed is $2^7 . 3^3$. This sub-group can have no permutation consisting of a single cycle of 3 symbols, since no such permutation can occur in the original group. Hence it must permute the 11 symbols in two transitive sets of 9 and 2 symbols respectively. It must therefore contain a self-conjugate sub-group of order $2^6 . 3^3$ which keeps 3 of the 12 symbols unchanged; and this sub-group must occur self-conjugately in 3 of the 12 sub-groups which keep one symbol unchanged. This however makes the group of degree 12 imprimitive, contrary to supposition. Hence this case cannot occur.

Finally, then, the only possible values of x and y are $x=1$, $y=0$. The order of a group of degree 13, which has more than one sub-group of order 13 and no odd permutations, is $2^5 . 3^2 . 13$, $2^4 . 3^3 . 13$, or $2^5 . 3^3 . 13$. The order of a group of order 13 with odd permutations will be twice one of the preceding three numbers.

A further and much more detailed examination would be necessary to determine whether groups of degree 13 correspond to any or all of these orders. We shall see in Chapter XX that there is a group of degree 13 and order $2^4 . 3^3 . 13$.

Ex. If $n\,(> 3)$ and $2n+1$ are primes, shew that there is no triply transitive group of degree $2n+3$ which does not contain the alternating group.

166. As a further illustration, and for the actual value of the results themselves, we proceed to determine all types of primitive groups for degrees not exceeding 8.

(i) $n=3$.

The symmetric group of 3 symbols has a single sub-group, viz. the alternating group. Both these groups are necessarily primitive.

(ii) $n=4$.

Groups of degree 4 and order 2, 4 or 8 are obviously either intransitive or imprimitive. Hence the only primitive groups of degree 4 are the symmetric and the alternating groups.

(iii) $n=5$.

Since 5 is a prime, every transitive group of degree 5 is a primitive group. The symmetric group of degree 5 contains 6 cyclical sub-groups of order 5; and, by Sylow's theorem, every group of degree 5 must contain either 1 or 6 sub-groups of order 5. Since the alternating group is simple, every sub-group that contains 6 sub-groups of order 5 must contain the alternating group. Hence, besides the alternating and the symmetric groups, we have only sub-groups which contain a sub-group of order 5 self-conjugately. In such a group, an operation of order 5 can be permutable with its own powers only. Hence (§ 140) the only sub-groups of the type in question, other than cyclical sub-groups, are groups of orders 20 and 10. These are defined by

$$\{(12345),\ (2354)\},$$

and

$$\{(12345),\ (25)(34)\}.$$

(iv) $n = 6$.

If the order of a primitive group of degree 6 is not divisible by 5, the order must (§ 160) be equal to or be a factor of $2^3 \cdot 3$. The order of a sub-group that keeps one symbol fixed is equal to or is a factor of 2^2. Hence the sub-group must keep two symbols fixed, and therefore (§ 147) the group cannot be primitive. Hence the order of every primitive group of degree 6 is divisible by 5, and every such group is at least doubly transitive. The symmetric group contains 36 sub-groups of order 5; and hence, since no transitive group of degree 6 can contain a self-conjugate sub-group of order 5, every primitive group of degree 6, which does not contain the alternating group, must have 6 sub-groups of order 5.

If G is such a group, the sub-group of G that keeps one symbol fixed is a transitive group of degree 5 which has a self-conjugate sub-group of order 5. If this transitive group of degree 5 were cyclical, every operation of the doubly transitive group G of order 30 would displace all or all but one of the symbols. Since 6 is not the power of a prime, this is impossible (§ 134). Hence the sub-group of G which keeps one symbol fixed must be of one of the two types given above; and the order of G must be 120 or 60. Now we have seen, in § 161, that the symmetric group of degree 6 has a single conjugate set of primitive sub-groups of order 120 and a single set of order 60. Hence there is a single type of primitive group of degree 6, corresponding to each of the orders 120 and 60. These are defined by

$$\{(126)(354),\ (12345),\ (2354)\},$$

and

$$\{(126)(354),\ (12345),\ (25)(34)\}:$$

where the last two permutations in each case generate a sub-group that keeps one symbol unchanged.

(v) $n = 7$.

Every transitive group of degree 7 is primitive; and if it does not contain the alternating group, its order must (§ 160) be equal to or be a factor of $7 . 6 . 5 . 4$. A cyclical sub-group of order 7 must (footnote, p. 210), in a group of degree 7 that contains more than one such sub-group, be self-conjugate in a group of order 21 or 42. Now neither 20 nor 40 is congruent to unity, mod. 7; and therefore 5 cannot be a factor of the order of such a group. Hence the order of a transitive group of degree 7, that does not contain the alternating group, is equal to or is a factor of $7 . 6 . 4$. But 8 is the only factor of $7 . 6 . 4$ which is congruent to unity, mod. 7; and therefore, if the group contains more than one sub-group of order 7, its order must be equal to $7 . 6 . 4$ and it must contain 8 sub-groups of order 7.

Such a group must be doubly transitive; for if a sub-group of order 24, that leaves one symbol unchanged, interchanges the symbols in two intransitive systems, it is easily shewn that the group would contain permutations displacing three symbols only, and therefore that it would contain the alternating group. A sub-group of degree 24, transitive in 6 symbols, can contain no circular permutation of order 6, for it would be an odd permutation; it must therefore contain four sub-groups of order 3. Hence the sub-groups of order 24 must be simply isomorphic with the symmetric group of 4 symbols.

The actual construction of the group is now reduced to a limited number of trials. A group of degree 6, simply isomorphic with the symmetric group of 4 symbols, and containing no odd permutations, may always be represented in the form

$$\{(234)(567),\ (2763)(45)\};$$

and we have to find a circular permutation of the seven symbols 1, 2, 3, 4, 5, 6, 7 such that the group generated by it shall be permutable with this group. Moreover since, in the required group, every operation of order 3 transforms some operation of order 7 into its square, we may assume without loss of generality that the circular permutation of order 7 contains the sequence ..12.. and is transformed into its own square by (234) (567).

There are only three circular permutations satisfying these conditions, viz.

(1235476),

(1236457),

and (1237465).

It appears on trial that the group generated by the first of these is not permutable with the sub-group of order 24, while the groups generated by the other two are. There are therefore just two groups of order 7 . 6 . 4 which contain the given group of order 24. Now in the symmetric group of 7 symbols, a sub-group of order 7 . 6 . 4 must, from the foregoing discussion, be one of a set of 30 conjugate sub-groups. These all enter in the alternating group; and therefore, in that group, they must form two sets of 15 conjugate sub-groups each. Each of these contains 7 sub-groups of the type

$$\{(234)(567),\ (2763)(45)\};$$

and the alternating group contains a conjugate set of 105 such sub-groups. Hence each sub-group of this set will enter in two, and only in two, sub-groups of the alternating group of order 7 . 6 . 4; and in the symmetric group these two sub-groups are conjugate. Finally then, the sub-groups of order 7 . 6 . 4 form a single conjugate set in the symmetric group. They are defined by

$$\{(1236457),\ (234)(567),\ (2763)(45)\},$$

the two latter permutations giving a sub-group that keeps one symbol fixed.

These groups are simple; for since they are expressed as transitive groups of degree 7, there can be no self-conjugate sub-group whose order divides 24, while it is evident that a self-conjugate sub-group that contains an operation of order 7 must coincide with the group itself. Also since there are 8 sub-groups of order 7, these groups can be expressed as doubly transitive groups of eight symbols.

A group of degree 7, which has only one sub-group of order 7, must either be cyclical or be contained in the group of order 7 . 6 given by § 140. Such groups are defined by

$$\{(1234567),\ (243756)\},$$

or $$\{(1234567),\ (235)(476)\},$$

or $$\{(1234567),\ (27)(45)(36)\}.$$

The simple group of order 168, which here occurs as a transitive group of degree 7, is the only simple group of that order. For, if possible, let there be a simple group G of order 168 and of a distinct type from the above. It certainly cannot be expressed as a group of degree 7; and therefore it must have 21 sub-groups of order 8. If two of these sub-groups have a common sub-group of order 4, it must be contained self-conjugately (§ 123) in a sub-group of order 24 or 56; and this is inconsistent with the suppositions made. If on the other hand, 2 is the order of the greatest sub-group common to two sub-groups of order 8, such a common sub-group of order 2 must, on the suppositions made, be self-conjugate in a sub-group of order 12. But a group of order 12, which has a self-conjugate operation of order 2, must have a self-conjugate sub-group of order 3; and therefore G would only contain 7 sub-groups of order 3, and could be expressed as a group of degree 7; contrary to supposition. No other supposition is possible with regard to the sub-groups of order 8, since 21 is not congruent to unity, mod. 8. Hence, finally, there is no simple group of order 168 distinct from the group of degree 7.

(vi) $n = 8$.

The order of a primitive group of degree 8, which does not contain the alternating group, cannot (§ 160) be divisible by 5. Suppose, if possible, that the order of such a group is $2^{\alpha+3} . 3$ $(\alpha = 0, 1, 2, 3)$. A permutation of order 3 must consist of two cycles; and therefore the sub-group of order $2^{\alpha} . 3$, which keeps one symbol fixed, must interchange the others in two intransitive systems of 3 and 4 respectively. In this sub-group, a sub-group of order 3 must be one of four conjugate sub-groups, and therefore α is either 2 or 3. Now a group of order $2^5 . 3$ or $2^6 . 3$ is soluble, as is seen at once by considering the sub-groups of order 2^5 or 2^6. Hence a primitive group of order $2^5 . 3$ or $2^6 . 3$ must contain a transitive self-conjugate sub-group of order 8, whose operations are all of order 2.

If 7 is a factor of the order of the group, the group must be doubly transitive; and from the case of $n = 7$, it follows that the possible orders are 8 . 7, 8 . 7 . 2, 8 . 7 . 3, 8 . 7 . 6, and 8 . 7 . 6 . 4. Moreover, for the orders 8 . 7 . 2 and 8 . 7 . 6, the group contains odd permutations and therefore it contains self-conjugate sub-groups of order 8 . 7 and 8 . 7 . 3 respectively.

A simple group of order 8 . 7 . 3 is necessarily identical in type with the group of this order determined above; and a group of order 8 . 7 . 3, which is not simple, is certainly soluble. Hence a composite group of order 8 . 7 . 3, and a group of order 8 . 7 . 6 which does not contain a simple sub-group of order 8 . 7 . 3, must both, if expressible as primitive groups of degree 8, contain transitive self-conjugate sub-groups of order 8 whose operations are all of order 2. With the possible exception then of groups of order 8 . 7 . 6 . 4, the only primitive groups of degree 8, which do not contain a self-conjugate sub-group of order 8, are the simple group of order 8 . 7 . 3 and any group of 8 . 7 . 6 which contains this self-conjugately. We have seen that the simple group of order 8 . 7 . 3 contains a single set of 8 conjugate sub-groups of order 21, and therefore it can be expressed in one form only as a group of degree 8. A group of degree 8 and order 8 . 7 . 6, which contains this self-conjugately, can occur only in one form, if at all; for, if it exists, it must be triply transitive, and it must be given by combining the simple group with an operation of order 2 which transforms one of its operations of order 7 into its own inverse. That such a group does exist has been shewn in § 141. These two groups are actually given by

$$\{(15642378),\ (1234567),\ (243756)\},$$

and $$\{(1627)(5438),\ (1234567),\ (235)(476)\};$$

where in each case the last two permutations give a sub-group that keeps one symbol fixed.

A primitive group of degree 8 which contains a transitive self-conjugate sub-group of order 8 whose operations are all of order 2 must be the holomorph (§ 64) of the Abelian group of order 8, or a sub-group of the holomorph. The sub-group that leaves one symbol unchanged must be a group of isomorphisms of the Abelian group. The group of isomorphisms of a group of order 8, whose operations are all of order 2, will be shewn in Chapter XX to be identical with the simple group of order 168. This group has a single set of conjugate sub-groups of each of the orders 7 and 21, but no sub-group of order 14 or 42. When expressed as a group of degree 7, it has a single set of conjugate sub-groups of order 12 (or 24) which leave no symbols unchanged. There are therefore primitive groups of degree 8 containing transitive self-conjugate sub-groups of order 8 corresponding to each of the orders $8 . 7$, $8 . 7 . 3$, $2^5 . 3$, $2^6 . 3$, and $8 . 7 . 6 . 4$; and in each case there is a single type of such group.

It remains to determine whether there can be any type of group, of degree 8 and order $8 . 7 . 6 . 4$, other than that just obtained. Such a group must be one of 15 conjugate sub-groups in the alternating group of degree 8, and is therefore simply isomorphic with a group of degree 14. Since it certainly is not simply isomorphic with a group of degree 7, the group of degree 14 must be transitive. The order of the sub-group, in this form, that keeps one symbol fixed is $2^5 . 3$. If this keeps only one symbol unchanged, it must interchange the remaining symbols in four intransitive systems of 3, 3, 3 and 4 respectively, since a permutation of order 3 must clearly consist of 4 cycles. A group of order $2^5 . 3$ cannot however be so expressed; and therefore the sub-group that keeps one symbol fixed must keep two fixed. The group of degree 14 is therefore imprimitive, and the group must contain a sub-group of order $2^6 . 3$. Moreover, since the group is not simply isomorphic with a transitive group of degree 7, this sub-group of order $2^6 . 3$ must contain a sub-group which is self-conjugate in the group itself. The order of this sub-group must be a power of 2; since the group is primitive, it cannot be less than 2^3. On the other hand, the order cannot be greater than 2^3 since the group contains a simple sub-group of order $7 . 6 . 4$. Hence finally, there is no type of primitive group of degree 8 and order $8 . 7 . 6 . 4$ other than that already obtained.

There is no difficulty now in actually constructing the primitive groups of degree 8 which have a self-conjugate sub-group of order 8. They are all contained in the group of order $8 . 7 . 6 . 4$; and it will be found that this group is given by

$$\{(81)(26)(37)(45),\ (1236457),\ (234)(567),\ (2763)(45)\};$$

while the groups of orders $8 . 7 . 3$ and $8 . 7$ are given by omitting respectively the last and the two last of the four generating operations.

The construction of the two remaining groups, of order $2^5 . 3$ and $2^6 . 3$, is left as an exercise for the reader.

It may be noticed that it has been shewn incidentally, in discussing above the possibility of a second type of group of degree 8 and order 8 . 7 . 6 . 4, that the alternating group of degree 8 can be expressed as a doubly transitive group of degree 15.

It may similarly be shewn that the alternating group of degree 7 can be expressed as a doubly transitive group of degree 15, and the alternating group of degree 6 as a simply transitive and primitive group of degree 15.

167. We have seen in § 134 that a doubly transitive group, of degree n and order $n(n-1)$, can exist only when n is the power of a prime. For such a group, the identical operation is the only one which keeps more than one symbol unchanged. We shall now go on to consider the sub-groups of a doubly transitive group, of degree n and order $n(n-1)m$, which keep two symbols fixed. The order of any such sub-group is m; since the group contains operations changing any two symbols into any other two, the sub-groups which keep two symbols fixed must form a single conjugate set.

Suppose first that the sub-group, which keeps two symbols unchanged, displaces all the other symbols. The sub-group that keeps a and b unchanged cannot then be identical with that which keeps c and d unchanged, unless the symbols c and d are the same pair as a and b. Since there are $\frac{1}{2}n(n-1)$ pairs of n symbols, the conjugate set contains $\frac{1}{2}n(n-1)$ sub-groups; and each sub-group of order m keeping two symbols fixed must be self-conjugate in a sub-group of order $2m$, which consists of the operations of the sub-group of order m and of those operations interchanging the two symbols that the sub-group of order m keeps fixed.

Suppose next that all the operations of a sub-group H, which keeps two symbols fixed, keep x symbols fixed, while none of the remaining $n-x$ symbols are unchanged by all the operations of H. From x symbols $\frac{1}{2}x(x-1)$ pairs can be formed, and therefore the sub-group that keeps one pair unchanged must keep $\frac{1}{2}x(x-1)$ pairs unchanged. In this case, the conjugate set contains $n(n-1)/x(x-1)$ distinct sub-groups of order m, and H is therefore self-conjugate in a group K of order $x(x-1)m$. The operations of this sub-group which do not belong to H interchange among themselves the x symbols that are left unchanged by H. Now since the group itself is doubly transitive, there must be operations which change any two of these x symbols into any other two; and any such operation being permutable with H must belong to K. Hence if we consider the effect of K on the x symbols only which are left unchanged by H, K reduces to a doubly transitive group of degree x and order $x(x-1)$. It follows that x must be a prime or the power of a prime.

168. The preceding paragraph suggests the combinatorial problem of forming from n distinct symbols $n(n-1)/x(x-1)$ sets of x symbols, such that every pair of symbols occurs in one set of x and no pair occurs in more than one.

There is one class of cases in which a solution of this problem is given immediately by the theory of Abelian groups. Let G be an Abelian group of order p^m, where p is a prime, and type (1, 1, ... to m units). We have seen, in § 84, that G has $(p^m-1)/(p-1)$ sub-groups of order p, and $(p^m-1)(p^{m-1}-1)/(p-1)(p^2-1)$ sub-groups of order p^2. Now any pair of sub-groups of order p generates a sub-group of order p^2, and therefore every pair of sub-groups of order p occurs in one and only one sub-group of order p^2. Moreover, every sub-group of order p^2 contains $p+1$ sub-groups of order p. When p is a prime and m any integer, it is therefore always possible to form from $(p^m-1)/(p-1)$ symbols $(p^m-1)(p^{m-1}-1)/(p-1)(p^2-1)$ sets of $p+1$ symbols each, such that every pair of the symbols occurs in one set of $p+1$ and no pair occurs in more than one set.

Supposing that, for given values of n and x, such a distribution is possible, it is still of course an open question as to whether there is a doubly transitive permutation-group of the n symbols, such that every permutation which keeps any two symbols unchanged keeps also unchanged the whole set of x in which they occur. When x is greater than 3, the question as to the existence of such groups is one which still remains to be investigated. There is however an important class of groups, to be considered later (Chapter XX), that possess a closely analogous property. These groups are doubly transitive; and from the n symbols upon which they operate, we can form $n(n-1)/x(x-1)$ sets of x, that are interchanged transitively by the permutations of the group: the sets being such that every pair occurs in one set and no pair in more than one set.

If $n(n-1)m$ is the order of such a group, and if H is a sub-group of order m which keeps a given pair fixed, then H must interchange among themselves the remaining $x-2$ symbols of that set of x which contains the pair kept unchanged by H. H contains, as a self-conjugate sub-group, the group h which leaves every symbol of the set of x unchanged; and if m'' is the order of this sub-group, while $m=m'm''$, then m' is the order of the group to which H reduces when we consider its effect only on the $x-2$ symbols. Now h is self-conjugate in the group K that interchanges all the symbols of the set of x among themselves. But since the original group is doubly transitive, it must contain permutations which change any two of the set of x into any other two, and every such permutation must belong to K. Hence K must be doubly transitive in the x symbols, and therefore finally the order of the group, to which K reduces when we consider its effect on the x symbols only, is $x(x-1)m'$. Since the order of h, which keeps unchanged each of the x symbols, is m'', the order of K is $x(x-1)m$.

169. When $x=3$, n must be of the form $6k+1$ or $6k+3$, since otherwise $n(n-1)/x(x-1)$ would not be an integer. The permutations of a doubly transitive group of degree n, which possesses a complete set of $\frac{1}{6}n(n-1)$ triplets, must be such that every permutation which leaves two given symbols unchanged also leaves a third definite symbol unchanged.

The smallest possible value of n is 7; and the group of order 168, in § 166, satisfies all the conditions.

The complete set of triplets in this case is

$$126,\ 137,\ 145,\ 234,\ 257,\ 356,\ 467.$$

The next smallest value of n is 9, and in this case again, a group with the required properties exists.

Ex. Shew that the group

$$\{(26973854),\ (456)(798)\}$$

is an imprimitive group of order 48, each imprimitive system containing two symbols; and that the sub-group, which keeps the symbols of one imprimitive system unchanged, is isomorphic with the symmetric group of three symbols. Prove that this group is permutable with

$$\{(123)(456)(789),\ (147)(258)(369)\},$$

and thence that

$$\{(123)(456)(789),\ (26973854),\ (456)(798)\}$$

is a doubly transitive group of degree 9, which possesses a complete set of 12 triplets*, viz.

123, 147, 159, 168, 249, 258, 267, 348, 357, 369, 456, 789.

The reader is not to infer from the examples given that, when n is of the form $6k+1$ or $6k+3$, there is always a doubly transitive group of degree n which possesses a complete set of triplets. It is a good exercise to verify that there is no such group when n is 13.

The case $n=13$, $x=4$ is the simplest case that can occur of the division of n symbols into sets of x in the manner of § 168 when x is greater than 3. We shall see in Chapter XX that there is a doubly transitive group of degree 13 such that from the 13 symbols permuted by the group a complete set of 13 quartets can be formed, which are themselves permuted by the operations of the group. Of the operations forming a sub-group that keeps two given symbols fixed, half will keep fixed the two other symbols, which form a quartet with the two given symbols, and half will permute them.

On the question of the independent formation of a complete set of triplets of n symbols, and in certain cases of the group of degree n which interchanges the triplets among themselves, reference may be made to the memoirs mentioned in the subjoined footnote†.

170. We shall conclude the present Chapter with some applications of permutation-groups, which enable us to complete and extend certain earlier results.

We have seen in § 136 that the permutations of n symbols, which are permutable with each of the permutations of a regular permutation-group G of order n of the same n symbols, form another regular permutation-group of order n; and that, if G is Abelian, the latter group coincides with G. Hence the only permutations of n symbols, which are permutable with a circular permutation of the n symbols, are the powers of the circular permutation.

Let now S be a regular permutation of order m, in mn symbols. It must permute the symbols in n cycles of m symbols each; and so we may take

$$S=(a_{11}a_{12}\dots\dots a_{1m})(a_{21}a_{22}\dots\dots a_{2m})\dots\dots(a_{n1}a_{n2}\dots\dots a_{nm}).$$

* It may be pointed out that the tactical relation between the 9 symbols and the 12 triplets is the same as that of the inflections of a cubic and the 12 lines on which they lie 3 by 3.

† Netto: "Substitutionentheorie," pp. 220—235; "Zur Theorie der Tripelsysteme," *Math. Ann.* Vol. XLII (1892), pp. 143—152. Moore: "Concerning triple systems," *Math. Ann.* Vol. XLIII (1893), pp. 271—285. Heffter: "Ueber Tripelsysteme," *Math. Ann.* Vol. XLIX (1897), pp. 101—112.

If T is permutable with S, and if it changes a_{rp} into a_{rq}, it clearly must permute the m symbols

$$a_{r1}, a_{r2}, \ldots\ldots, a_{rm}$$

among themselves; and therefore, so far as regards its effect on these m symbols, T must be a power of

$$(a_{r1} a_{r2} \ldots\ldots a_{rm}).$$

Again, if T changes a_{rp} into a_{sq}, it must change the set

$$a_{r1}, a_{r2}, \ldots\ldots, a_{rm},$$

into the set

$$a_{s1}, a_{s2}, \ldots\ldots, a_{sm};$$

as otherwise it would not be permutable with S.

Now the totality of the permutations of the mn symbols, which are permutable with S, form a group G_S. This group must, from the properties of T just stated, be imprimitive, interchanging the symbols in n imprimitive systems of m symbols each; and the symbols in any cycle of S will form an imprimitive system. Moreover, the self-conjugate sub-group H_S of this group, which permutes the symbols of each system among themselves, is the group of order m^n generated by

$$(a_{11} a_{12} \ldots\ldots a_{1m}),\ (a_{21} a_{22} \ldots\ldots a_{2m}),\ \ldots\ldots,\ (a_{n1} a_{n2} \ldots\ldots a_{nm}).$$

In fact, every permutation of this group is clearly permutable with S; and conversely, every permutation of the mn symbols, which does not permute the systems, must belong to this group.

Now G_S/H_S is simply isomorphic with a group of degree n, for none of its operations changes every one of the n systems into itself. Hence $n!$ is the greatest possible order of G_S/H_S. On the other hand, every operation of the group, generated by

$$(a_{11} a_{21} \ldots\ldots a_{n1})(a_{12} a_{22} \ldots\ldots a_{n2}) \ldots\ldots (a_{1m} a_{2m} \ldots\ldots a_{nm})$$

and

$$(a_{11} a_{21})(a_{12} a_{22}) \ldots\ldots (a_{1m} a_{2m}),$$

is clearly permutable with S; and this group, being simply isomorphic with the group

$$\{(a_1 a_2 \ldots\ldots a_n),\ (a_1 a_2)\},$$

i.e. with the symmetric group of n symbols, is of order $n!$.

Hence, finally, the order of G_S is $m^n . n!$; and G_S is generated by

$$(a_{11}a_{21}\ldots\ldots a_{n1})(a_{12}a_{22}\ldots\ldots a_{n2})\ldots\ldots(a_{1m}a_{2m}\ldots\ldots a_{nm}),$$

$$(a_{11}a_{21})(a_{12}a_{22})\ldots\ldots(a_{1m}a_{2m}),$$

and

$$(a_{11}a_{12}\ldots\ldots a_{1m}).$$

171. Let h_r be a regular permutation-group of order m in the m symbols

$$a_{r1}, a_{r2}, \ldots\ldots, a_{rm},$$

and let S_{rt} be one of its permutations. Then if for r we write in turn 1, 2, ..., n, and if for each value of t from 1 to m we form the permutation

$$S_{1t}S_{2t}\ldots\ldots S_{nt},$$

the set of m permutations so formed constitute an intransitive group H in the mn symbols, simply isomorphic with h_r.

The method of § 170 can be applied directly to determine the group G_H of degree mn, each of whose permutations are permutable with every permutation of H. The order of this group is $m^n . n!$; and it can be generated by

$$(a_{11}a_{21}\ldots\ldots a_{n1})(a_{12}a_{22}\ldots\ldots a_{n2})\ldots\ldots(a_{1m}a_{2m}\ldots\ldots a_{nm}),$$

$$(a_{11}a_{21})(a_{12}a_{22})\ldots\ldots(a_{1m}a_{2m}),$$

and

$$h_1';$$

where h_1' is the regular group in the symbols

$$a_{11}, a_{12}, \ldots\ldots, a_{1m},$$

each of whose permutations is permutable with every permutation of h_1.

This group will contain H if, and only if, H is an Abelian group. Moreover, the only self-conjugate permutations of G_H are the permutations of H contained in it. For if G_H contained other self-conjugate permutations S_1, S_3, ..., every operation of G_H would be permutable with every operation of the group $\{H, S_1, S_2, \ldots\}$. Now G_H is transitive, so that S_1, S_2, ... must displace all the symbols; and therefore $\{H, S_1, S_2, \ldots\}$ has all its permutations regular in the mn symbols. If its order is mn_1, where $n = n_1n_2$, the order of the group formed of all the permutations of mn symbols, which are permutable with each of its operations, is $(mn_1)^{n_2} . n_2!$; and this number is less than $m^n . n!$. Thus the supposition, that G_H has self-conjugate operations other than the operations of H which it contains, leads to an impossibility.

By means of this and the preceding section, the reader will have no difficulty in forming the permutation-group of n symbols, which is permutable with every operation of any given permutation-group in the n symbols.

172. If a group, whose order is a power of a prime p, be expressed as a transitive permutation-group, the degree of the latter must also be a power of p. Moreover such a group, since it has self-conjugate operations, must necessarily be imprimitive.

The greatest value of m, for which a group of order p^m is simply isomorphic with a transitive group of degree p^n, where n is regarded as given, is determined at once by considering the symmetric group of degree p^n. The highest power of p that divides $p^n!$ is p^ν, where

$$\nu = p^{n-1} + p^{n-2} + \ldots\ldots + p + 1.$$

Hence the symmetric group of degree p^n contains a set of conjugate sub-groups of order p^ν and it contains no groups whose order is a higher power of p. Also, these groups are transitive in the p^n symbols; for any one of them must contain a circular permutation of order p^n. There are therefore groups of order p^ν which are simply isomorphic with transitive groups of degree p^n; but no groups of order $p^{\nu'}$ $(\nu' > \nu)$.

This group may be constructed synthetically as follows. The group necessarily has a self-conjugate sub-group of order p. This must consist of the powers of a regular permutation of order p, permuting the p^n symbols in p^{n-1} sets of p each; and these sets are imprimitive systems for the group. The group then is multiply isomorphic with a transitive group of degree p^{n-1}. This latter group has a self-conjugate sub-group of order p, which permutes the p^{n-1} symbols in p^{n-2} sets of p symbols each; and the corresponding self-conjugate sub-group of the original group permutes the p^n symbols in p^{n-2} sets of p^2 each. These again are imprimitive systems for the group, each being constituted by combining the p^{n-1} systems of p symbols each in sets of p. If $n > 2$ the process may be repeated to shew that the

p^{n-2} systems of p^2 symbols each may be combined in sets of p to form p^{n-3} systems of p^3 symbols each, and so on. If then with each of the p^{n-1} sets of p we form a circular permutation, the p^{n-1} permutable and independent circular permutations will generate an intransitive group of order $p^{p^{n-1}}$. It will be the self-conjugate sub-group of the group of order p^ν, which permutes the symbols of each system of p among themselves.

Next, with each set of p^2 symbols we can form a circular permutation, whose pth power is the product of the p circular permutations of order p, which have been previously formed from the p^2 symbols. The symbols of any set of p^2 will then be interchanged by a transitive group of order p^{p+1}; and since there are p^{n-2} such sets, we obtain in this way an intransitive group of $p^{p^{n-1}+p^{n-2}}$. The group thus formed is that self-conjugate sub-group of the original group, which interchanges among themselves the symbols of each system of p^2. This process may be continued, taking greater and greater systems, till at the last step we combine the p systems of p^{n-1} symbols each into a single system by means of a circular permutation of order p^n. The order of the resulting group is clearly p^ν, as it should be.

The self-conjugate operations of this group form a sub-group of order p.

For suppose, if possible, they form a sub-group of order p^r. Every operation of this sub-group displaces all the symbols; and therefore, when expressed as a permutation group in the p^n symbols, it must interchange them transitively in p^{n-r} sets of p^r each.

Now (§ 171) those permutations of the p^n symbols, which are permutable with every operation of this sub-group, form a group of order $p^{rp^{n-r}} . p^{n-r}!$; this number is only divisible by p^ν, as it must be, when $r=1$.

Ex. 1. Prove that the above group is generated by the n circular permutations

$$(1,\ 2,\ 3,\ \ldots\ldots\ldots\ldots,\ p^n-1,\ p^n)$$
$$(1,\ 1+p,\ 1+2p,\ \ldots\ldots\ldots\ldots,\ 1+(p^{n-1}-1)\,p)$$
$$(1,\ 1+p^2,\ 1+2p^2,\ \ldots\ldots\ldots\ldots,\ 1+(p^{n-2}-1)\,p^2)$$
$$\ldots\ldots\ldots\ldots\ldots\ldots\ldots\ldots\ldots\ldots\ldots\ldots$$
$$(1,\ 1+p^{n-1},\ 1+2p^{n-1},\ \ldots\ldots\ldots\ldots,\ 1+(p-1)\,p^{n-1})$$

and discuss the possibility of reducing the number of generating operations.

Ex. 2. Shew that, for the group of degree p^2 and order p^{p+1}, the factor-groups H_r/H_{r+1} (of § 93) are all of type (1) except the first, which is of type (1, 1).

The fact that ν is a function of p when n is given, explains why, in classifying all groups of order p^n, some of the lower primes may behave in an exceptional manner. Thus we saw, in § 117, that for certain groups of order p^4 it was necessary to consider separately the case $p = 3$. The present article makes it clear that, while there may be more than one type of group of order p^4 ($p > 3$), which is simply isomorphic with a transitive group of degree p^2, there is only a single type of group of order 3^4 which is simply isomorphic with a transitive group of degree 9.

173. In the memoirs referred to in the footnote on p. 182, M. Mathieu has demonstrated the existence of a remarkable group, of degree 12 and order 12 . 11 . 10 . 9 . 8, which is quintuply transitive. The verification of some of the more important properties of this group, as stated in the succeeding example, forms a good exercise on the results of this and the preceding Chapter.

Ex. 1. Shew that the permutations

$$(1254)(3867),\quad (1758)(2643),$$
$$(12)(48)(57)(69),\quad (a2)(58)(46)(79),$$
$$(ab)(57)(68)(49),\quad (bc)(47)(58)(69),$$

generate a quintuply transitive group of degree 12 and order

$$12 \,.\, 11 \,.\, 10 \,.\, 9 \,.\, 8.$$

Prove that this group is simple; that a sub-group of degree 11 and order 11 . 10 . 9 . 8, which leaves one symbol unchanged, is a simple group; and that a sub-group of degree 10 and order 10 . 9 . 8, which leaves two symbols unchanged, contains a self-conjugate sub-group simply isomorphic with the alternating group of degree 6.

Shew also that the group of degree 12 contains (i) 1728 sub-groups of order 11 each of which is self-conjugate in a group of order 55: (ii) 2376 sub-groups of order 5, each of which is self-conjugate in a group of order 40: (iii) 880 sub-groups of order 27, each of which is self-conjugate in a group of order 108: (iv) 1485 sub-groups of order 64.

Prove further that the group is a maximum sub-group of the alternating group of degree 12.

Ex. 2. Shew that the alternating group of degree 8 contains 30 regular Abelian sub-groups of order 8 and type (1, 1, 1), forming two conjugate sets of 15 sub-groups each.

If H_1, H_2 are any two sub-groups belonging to the same conjugate set of 15, prove that $\{H_1, H_2\}$ is a sub-group of order $2^6 . 3^2$, permuting the symbols in 2 imprimitive systems of 4 each; and that $\{H_1, H_2\}$ contains just one other sub-group H_3 belonging to the same set. Hence shew that from the 15 conjugate sub-groups a complete set of 35 triplets may be formed, which is invariant when the sub-groups are transformed by any operation of the alternating group. Prove also that when the sub-groups of the second set of 15 are transformed by the operations of H_1, 7 are transformed into themselves and the other 8 are permuted regularly.

Ex. 3. Prove that the permutations of

$$a,\ b,\ c,\ d,\ a',\ b',\ c',\ d',$$

for which the expression

$$abcd + a'b'c'd' + abc'd' + a'b'cd + acb'd' + a'c'bd + adb'c' + a'd'bc$$

remains invariant, form a transitive group of order $2^6 . 3$, which contains a self-conjugate operation of order 2.

Ex. 4. From the bilinear form

$$\xi_1 = a_1 b_1 + a_2 b_2 + a_3 b_3 + a_4 b_4 + a_5 b_5 + a_6 b_6 + a_7 b_7 + a_8 b_8$$

seven others ξ_i $(i = 2, 3, \ldots, 8)$ are constructed by carrying out on the b's the permutations of the Abelian group generated by

$$A \text{ or } (b_1 b_2)(b_3 b_4)(b_5 b_6)(b_7 b_8),$$
$$B \text{ or } (b_1 b_3)(b_2 b_4)(b_5 b_7)(b_6 b_8),$$
$$C \text{ or } (b_1 b_5)(b_2 b_6)(b_3 b_7)(b_4 b_8);$$

and simultaneously on the a's the corresponding substitutions of the Abelian group generated by

$$A \text{ or } \begin{matrix} a_1' = a_1, & a_2' = -a_2, & a_3' = \alpha a_3, & a_4' = -\alpha a_4, \\ a_5' = \beta a_5, & a_6' = -\beta a_6, & a_7' = -\alpha\beta a_7, & a_8' = \alpha\beta a_8; \end{matrix}$$

$$B \text{ or } \begin{matrix} a_1' = a_1, & a_2' = -\alpha a_2, & a_3' = -a_3, & a_4' = \alpha a_4, \\ a_5' = \gamma a_5, & a_6' = \alpha\gamma a_6, & a_7' = -\gamma a_7, & a_8' = -\alpha\gamma a_8; \end{matrix}$$

$$C \text{ or } \begin{matrix} a_1' = a_1, & a_2' = -\beta a_2, & a_3' = -\gamma a_3, & a_4' = -\beta\gamma a_4, \\ a_5' = -a_5, & a_6' = \beta a_6, & a_7' = \gamma a_7, & a_8' = \beta\gamma a_8; \end{matrix}$$

where $\alpha^2 = \beta^2 = \gamma^2 = 1$.

Prove that

$$\sum_1^8 \xi_i^2 = \sum_1^8 a_i^2 \sum_1^8 b_i^2,$$

and discuss this identity from the point of view of the permutations of the symbols involved in it.

CHAPTER XII.

ON THE REPRESENTATION OF A GROUP OF FINITE ORDER AS A PERMUTATION-GROUP*.

174. Definitions. If $S_1, S_2, \ldots\ldots, S_N$ are the operations of a group G of finite order N, and $s_1, s_2, \ldots$ the permutations of a permutation-group g of degree n, and if to each operation S_i of G there corresponds a single permutation s_i of g, so that when

$$S_i S_j = S_k,$$

then

$$s_i s_j = s_k,$$

the permutation-group g is said to give a *representation* of G.

It follows from this definition that G may be either simply or multiply isomorphic with g. In the latter case there is a self-conjugate sub-group of G to each of the operations of which there corresponds the identical permutation in g.

Let g and h be two permutation-groups of degree n which represent G, and let

$$\begin{pmatrix} x_1, & x_2, & \ldots\ldots, & x_n \\ x_1', & x_2', & \ldots\ldots, & x_n' \end{pmatrix} \text{ or } s_i$$

and

$$\begin{pmatrix} y_1, & y_2, & \ldots\ldots, & y_n \\ y_1', & y_2', & \ldots\ldots, & y_n' \end{pmatrix} \text{ or } \sigma_i$$

be the permutations of g and h which correspond to the operation S_i of G; then if a permutation of the symbols

$$\begin{pmatrix} x_1'', & x_2'', & \ldots\ldots, & x_n'' \\ y_1, & y_2, & \ldots\ldots, & y_n \end{pmatrix} \text{ or } t$$

exists, such that, for each i,

$$t\sigma_i t^{-1} = s_i,$$

* On the subject of this chapter the reader may consult Dyck, "Gruppentheoretische Studien, II," *Math. Ann.* Vol. XXII (1883), pp. 86—95.

the representations g and h are said to be *equivalent.* If no such permutation as t exists, or if the degrees of g and h are not equal, then the representations g and h are called *distinct.*

175. It has already been seen in § 20 that every group of order N admits a representation as a regular permutation-group in N symbols, and that such a representation can be set up in two ways. The permutations that correspond to the operation S_i in the two forms are

$$\begin{pmatrix} S \\ SS_i \end{pmatrix} \text{ and } \begin{pmatrix} S \\ S_i^{-1}S \end{pmatrix}.$$

Now the symbol

$$\begin{pmatrix} S^{-1} \\ S \end{pmatrix}$$

is a permutation of order two of the N symbols; and for each i

$$\begin{pmatrix} S^{-1} \\ S \end{pmatrix}\begin{pmatrix} S \\ SS_i \end{pmatrix}\begin{pmatrix} S \\ S^{-1} \end{pmatrix} = \begin{pmatrix} S^{-1} \\ SS_i \end{pmatrix}\begin{pmatrix} SS_i \\ S_i^{-1}S^{-1} \end{pmatrix} = \begin{pmatrix} S^{-1} \\ S_i^{-1}S^{-1} \end{pmatrix} = \begin{pmatrix} S \\ S_i^{-1}S \end{pmatrix}.$$

Hence, in the sense of the above definition, the two representations of G as a regular permutation-group of N symbols that arise by pre- and post-multiplication are equivalent.

176. We shall now consider the various sets of imprimitive systems that present themselves in the representation of G as a regular permutation-group. Let

$$S_1, S_2, \ldots\ldots, S_n$$

be that one of a set of imprimitive systems which contains S_1, the symbol of the identical operation. By the permutation

$$\begin{pmatrix} S \\ SS_i \end{pmatrix} \quad (i = 1, 2, \ldots\ldots, n)$$

S_1 is changed into S_i $(i = 1, 2, \ldots\ldots, n)$; and these are the only permutations of the group which change S_1 into another of the set. Hence this set of permutations combine among themselves by multiplication, and therefore

$$S_1, S_2, \ldots\ldots, S_n$$

constitute a sub-group H of G. In respect of this sub-group, let the operations of G fall into the sets

$$H, HT_2, HT_3, \ldots\ldots, HT_m,$$

where $mn = N$. On post-multiplication by any operation $S_i T_j$ of the group, the operations of the set HT_k are changed into the operations of the set $HT_k S_i T_j$. Now $T_k S_i T_j$ must belong to one of the m sets into which the operations fall in respect of H. If it belongs to the set HT_l, there is an operation S' of H such that

$$T_k S_i T_j = S' T_l,$$

and the set $HT_k S_i T_j$ is then the same as the set

$$HS'T_l \text{ or } HT_l.$$

Hence by any permutation

$$\begin{pmatrix} S \\ SS_i T_j \end{pmatrix}$$

the symbols of any one of the sets

$$H, HT_2, HT_3, \ldots\ldots, HT_m$$

are either permuted among themselves or are changed into the symbols of another one of the sets. The m sets therefore constitute a set of imprimitive systems for the regular permutation-group in the N symbols; and there is such a set of imprimitive systems corresponding to each sub-group of G. Moreover, no two of these modes of division into imprimitive systems can be identical with each other; since of the m sets of operations

$$H, HT_2, HT_3, \ldots\ldots, HT_m,$$

the first, and the first only, constitute a sub-group.

177. If each of the m sets

$$H, HT_2, HT_3, \ldots\ldots, HT_m$$

is regarded as a single symbol, these m symbols are, as seen in the preceding paragraph, permuted among themselves on post-multiplication by any operation of G. A permutation-group of degree m thus arises which, in accordance with the definition, is a representation of G. Since the symbol H may thus be changed into any one of the other symbols, the permutation-group is transitive. This representation will be denoted by G_H.

Now if
$$HS = H,$$
S must belong to H; and if
$$HT_iS = HT_i,$$
$T_iST_i^{-1}$ must belong to H. Hence the permutation of the m symbols that arises on post-multiplication by S will be the identical permutation, if, and only if, S and all its conjugates belong to H. Conversely, if I is the greatest self-conjugate sub-group of G contained in H, and if S is any operation of I, post-multiplication of the m symbols by S gives the identical permutation. Hence the representation of G under consideration is simply isomorphic with G/I. In this representation the permutations which leave the symbol H unchanged are those that correspond to the operations of H, and those which leave HT_i unchanged are the permutations that correspond to the operations of $T_i^{-1}HT_i$.

If the permutation-group on the symbols
$$H, HT_2, HT_3, \ldots, HT_m$$
is imprimitive, there must be (§ 147) a set of m_1 $(m = m_1m_2)$ of them,
$$H, HT_2, HT_3, \ldots, HT_{m_1},$$
such that every permutation, which changes H into another symbol of this set, permutes the m_1 symbols among themselves. But if this is the case, the totality of the operations in the m_1 sets constitute a sub-group of G; for the product of any two of them belongs again to one of the m_1 sets. The converse is obviously true. Hence the representation of G as a permutation-group that arises in respect of H is primitive if, and only if, H is a maximum sub-group of G.

If the conjugate sub-group $T_i^{-1}HT_i$ were used for forming the representation, in the place of H, the set of m symbols would be
$$T_i^{-1}HT_i,\ T_i^{-1}HT_2T_i,\ \ldots\ldots,\ T_i^{-1}HT_mT_i,$$
and the permutation corresponding to S would be
$$\begin{pmatrix} T_i^{-1}HT_i\ , & T_i^{-1}HT_2T_i\ , & \ldots\ldots, & T_i^{-1}HT_mT_i \\ T_i^{-1}HT_iS, & T_i^{-1}HT_2T_iS, & \ldots\ldots, & T_i^{-1}HT_mT_iS \end{pmatrix}$$

Now

$$\begin{pmatrix} HT_i, & HT_2T_i, & \ldots\ldots, & HT_mT_i \\ T_i^{-1}HT_i, & T_i^{-1}HT_2T_i, & \ldots\ldots, & T_i^{-1}HT_mT_i \end{pmatrix}$$

$$\begin{pmatrix} T_i^{-1}HT_i\ , & T_i^{-1}HT_2T_i\ , & \ldots\ldots, & T_i^{-1}HT_mT_i \\ T_i^{-1}HT_iS, & T_i^{-1}HT_2T_iS, & \ldots\ldots, & T_i^{-1}HT_mT_iS \end{pmatrix}$$

$$\begin{pmatrix} T_i^{-1}HT_i, & \ldots\ldots, & T_i^{-1}HT_mT_i \\ HT_i, & \ldots\ldots, & HT_mT_i \end{pmatrix}$$

$$= \begin{pmatrix} HT_i\ , & HT_2T_i\ , & \ldots\ldots, & HT_mT_i \\ HT_iS, & HT_2T_iS, & \ldots\ldots, & HT_mT_iS \end{pmatrix}$$

$$= \begin{pmatrix} H\ , & HT_2\ , & \ldots\ldots, & HT_m \\ HS, & HT_2S, & \ldots\ldots, & HT_mS \end{pmatrix}$$

Hence the representation of degree m that arises from the sub-group H is equivalent to that which arises from any conjugate sub-group $T_i^{-1}HT_i$.

178. When pre-multiplication is used the operations of G fall, in respect of H, into m sets which may be written

$$H,\ T_2^{-1}H,\ T_3^{-1}H,\ \ldots\ldots,\ T_m^{-1}H.$$

These are transitively permuted among themselves on pre-multiplication by the operations of G; and the permutation, which in this representation corresponds to the operation S of G, is

$$\begin{pmatrix} H, & T_2^{-1}H, & T_3^{-1}H, & \ldots\ldots, & T_m^{-1}H \\ S^{-1}H, & S^{-1}T_2^{-1}H, & S^{-1}T_3^{-1}H, & \ldots\ldots, & S^{-1}T_m^{-1}H \end{pmatrix}.$$

It may be formally proved, just as in the preceding paragraph, that the representation thus arising is equivalent to the representation arising from H by post-multiplication.

179. Suppose now that g is any representation of G as a transitive permutation-group on m symbols

$$a_1,\ a_2,\ \ldots\ldots,\ a_m.$$

Let H be that sub-group of G, whose operations correspond to the permutations which leave a_1 unchanged, and let

$$T_i\ (i = 2,\ \ldots\ldots,\ m)$$

be an operation of G that corresponds to a permutation changing a_1 into a_i ($i = 2, \ldots\ldots, m$). Then HT_i is the set of operations of G which correspond to the permutations that change a_1 into a_i; and therefore the set of symbols

$$H, HT_2, \ldots\ldots, HT_m$$

undergo, on post-multiplication by S, a permutation identical with the permutation of

$$a_1, a_2, \ldots\ldots, a_m,$$

that corresponds to S.

Hence the representation g of G, as a transitive permutation-group, may be set up by the method of § 177. It follows that the number of distinct representations of G as a transitive permutation-group cannot exceed the number of distinct sets of conjugate sub-groups in G.

180. Definition. Let g be any representation of G as a permutation-group (not necessarily transitive) of degree n; and in this representation let h be the permutation-group that corresponds to a given sub-group H of G. Denote by m the number of the n symbols which are left unchanged by every permutation of h. Then m is called the *mark* of H in the representation g.

The marks of any two conjugate sub-groups of G in g are clearly the same; for if H leaves $a_1, a_2, \ldots, a_m$ only unchanged, and if S changes these symbols in $b_1, b_2, \ldots, b_m$, then the latter are the only symbols unchanged by $S^{-1}HS$. Also from the definition of equivalent representations the mark of H in g is equal to the mark of H in any representation equivalent to g. No two representations of G can therefore be equivalent unless the mark of each sub-group in one is the same as its mark in the other.

Denote now by s the number of distinct sets of conjugate sub-groups in G, and choose

$$G_1, G_2, \ldots\ldots, G_s,$$

as representative sub-groups, one from each set. Let the orders of these sub-groups be

$$N_1, N_2, \ldots\ldots, N_s,$$

and suppose them chosen so that

$$N_1 \leqslant N_2 \leqslant \ldots\ldots \leqslant N_s.$$

This involves that G_1 is E, the identical operation; G_s is G itself; while N_1 is 1 and N_s is N, the order of G. Let

$$g_i \, (i = 1, 2, \ldots\ldots, s)$$

be the representation of G, as a transitive permutation-group, that arises by the method of § 177 when G_i is taken for H.

It has been seen that if G_i', a sub-group conjugate to G_i, is used instead of G_i an equivalent representation will arise. Hence $g_1, g_2, \ldots\ldots, g_s$ include all distinct representations of G as a transitive permutation-group. Of these g_1 is the representation as a regular permutation-group in N symbols, and g_s is the representation in which every operation of G corresponds to the identical permutation on a single symbol.

Denote by m_i^j the mark of G_i in g_j. Each such symbol is either zero or a positive integer. Since G_i is that sub-group of G which corresponds to the sub-group of g_i that leaves one symbol unchanged, m_i^i is necessarily equal to or greater than 1, and the only sub-groups of G whose marks in g_i are different from zero are those which are contained in G_i and its conjugates. Hence

$$m_i^j = 0, \text{ when } i > j,$$

and the table of marks is as follows:

	G_1	G_2	...	...	...	G_i	...	...	G_s
g_1	N	0	...	...	...	0	...	...	0
g_2	m_1^2	m_2^2	...	...	...	0	...	...	0
.	...	...	...	...	...	...	...	...	...
.	...	...	...	...	...	...	...	...	...
g_i	m_1^i	m_2^i	...	...	...	m_i^i	...	...	0
:	...	...	...	...	...	...	...	...	...
g_s	1	1	...	...	...	1	...	...	1

It is to be noticed that m_i^j is not necessarily different from zero if $i<j$. The symbol m_1^i is the degree of g_i, or with the previous notation, N/N_i.

An inspection of this table shews that in no two of the representations $g_i\,(i=1, 2, \ldots\ldots, s)$ can each sub-group of G have the same mark, and therefore these s representations are all distinct.

181. If g is a representation of G as an intransitive permutation-group, the symbols operated on by g will fall into a number of transitive sets, and each of these sets must undergo a transitive permutation-group equivalent to one of the groups $g_i\,(i=1, 2, \ldots\ldots, s)$. If a_i transitive permutation-groups equivalent to g_i thus occur, the representation g may be completely represented by the symbol

$$\sum_1^s a_i g_i,$$

denoting that the representation g is made up of a_1 representations equivalent to g_1, a_2 equivalent to g_2, and so on.

Moreover, if the marks of $G_1, G_2, \ldots, G_s$ in g are known, and if μ_j is the mark of G_j in g, then for each j

$$\mu_j = \sum_1^s a_i m_j^i.$$

Since the determinant of the marks

$$| \, m_j^i \, |$$

is necessarily different from zero, these equations determine the a's uniquely, and so give the complete reduction of g into its transitive constituents.

We may sum up the preceding results in the following form :

THEOREM I. *A group of finite order which contains s distinct sets of conjugate sub-groups admits s distinct representations as a transitive permutation-group. If these be denoted by $g_i\,(i=1, 2, \ldots\ldots, s)$, then every representation of the group as a permutation-group is given by the symbol $\sum_1^s a_i g_i$ in which the a's are zeroes or positive integers, and no two such representations, with different a's, are equivalent.*

182. It is to be noticed that two distinct representations of a group G may, when no attention is paid to the correspondence between the operations of G and the permutations of either permutation-group, be identical with each other; i.e. they may consist of exactly the same sets of permutations. Thus, to take a very simple instance, let G be the group of order 9, generated by two permutable operations P_1, P_2 of order 3. The cyclical permutation-group generated by $(a_1a_2a_3)$ gives four distinct representations of G. In one of the four the operations of $\{P_1\}$ correspond to the identical permutation; and in the other three the operations of $\{P_2\}$, $\{P_1P_2\}$ and $\{P_1P_2^2\}$ correspond to the identical permutation.

A less obvious case is offered by the representation of the symmetric-group of degree 6 as a transitive permutation-group in 6 symbols. It has been seen that the symmetric-group of 6 symbols, order 720, has two distinct conjugate sets of sub-groups of order 120, simply isomorphic with the symmetric-group of 5 symbols. It has therefore two distinct representations as a permutation-group of degree 6: and these regarded merely as permutation-groups are necessarily identical with each other, since each consists of all the permutations of the 6 symbols.

183. Let H and H' be sub-groups of G which are not conjugate, and g and g' the corresponding representations of G as a transitive permutation-group. If I and I' are the greatest self-conjugate sub-groups of G contained in H and H', then g, g' are simply isomorphic with G/I, G/I' respectively. Suppose now that, considered merely as permutation-groups, g and g' are identical with each other. Then G/I and G/I' are simply isomorphic, and in the isomorphism so established H/I and H'/I' are corresponding sub-groups, since they each correspond to the sub-groups of g and g' which leaves one symbol unchanged. If I and I' are each E, the identical operation, then the permutation-group g is simply isomorphic with G, and the isomorphism of G, in which H and H' are corresponding sub-groups, is necessarily an outer isomorphism. Hence:—

THEOREM II. *If a transitive permutation-group g, simply isomorphic with G, gives two distinct representations of G, then G must admit an outer isomorphism which changes the conjugate set of sub-groups of G that correspond to the sub-groups of g which leave one symbol unchanged in the first representation into the conjugate set which correspond to the sub-groups of g that leave one symbol unchanged in the second representation.*

184. Let g_i and g_j be constructed on the sets of symbols

$$x_1, x_2, \ldots\ldots, x_{m_1{}^i},$$

and

$$y_1, y_2, \ldots\ldots, y_{m_1{}^j},$$

and let

$$\binom{x_t}{x_{t'}}\ (t=1, 2, \ldots\ldots, m_1{}^i),$$

$$\binom{y_u}{y_{u'}}\ (u=1, 2, \ldots\ldots, m_1{}^j),$$

be the permutations which correspond to an operation S of G.

Then the $m_1{}^i m_1{}^j$ products $x_t y_u$ undergo, corresponding to the operations of G, permutations such that

$$\binom{x_t y_u}{x_{t'} y_{u'}}$$

is the permutation corresponding to S. This permutation-group of degree $m_1{}^i m_1{}^j$ is necessarily a representation of G; and by Theorem I it may be denoted by a symbol

$$\sum_1^s a_{ijk}\, g_k.$$

It is spoken of as the result of *compounding* the representations g_i and g_j, and from this point of view may be represented by the symbol $g_i g_j$ (or $g_j g_i$). In $g_i g_j$ the mark of G_t is obviously $m_t{}^i m_t{}^j$; and the coefficients a_{ijk} are therefore determined by the system of equations

$$m_t{}^i m_t{}^j = \sum_1^s a_{ijk} m_t{}^k\ (t=1, 2, \ldots\ldots, s).$$

The only operations of G for which one of the x's remain unchanged are those of a sub-group conjugate to G_i. Hence the only operations of G for which $x_t y_u$ remains unchanged are those of the sub-group common to $T^{-1}G_iT$ and $U^{-1}G_jU$, T and U being suitably chosen operations of G. The coefficients a_{ijk} are therefore necessarily zero unless k is not greater than the lesser of i and j. For the particular cases in which g_1 or g_s is compounded with another representation, the result is easily seen to be

$$g_1 g_i = m_1{}^i g_1,\quad g_s g_i = g_i.$$

185. The number of distinct ways in which a given group can be represented as a permutation-group of given degree is determined at once by the table of marks. Any such representation is equivalent to $\sum_1^s a_i g_i$, and the degree of this representation is $\sum_1^s a_i m_1^i$. Hence the sole relation between the a's in order that the degree of the group may be n is

$$\sum_1^s a_i m_1^i = n.$$

To each distinct solution of this equation in positive integers there corresponds a distinct representation of degree n.

The alternating group of degree 4, whose order is 12, has five different conjugate sets of sub-groups, viz. those of order 1, 2, 3, 4, 12. The student will find it a simple exercise to verify in this case the following results:

Ex. Shew that for the alternating group of degree 4 the table of marks is

	G_1	G_2	G_3	G_4	G_5
g_1	12	0	0	0	0
g_2	6	2	0	0	0
g_3	4	0	1	0	0
g_4	3	3	0	3	0
g_5	1	1	1	1	1

Prove that the composition of the representations is given by the relations

$$g_2^2 = 2g_1 + 2g_2, \quad g_3^2 = g_1 + g_3, \quad g_4^2 = 3g_4,$$
$$g_2 g_3 = 2g_1, \quad g_2 g_4 = 3g_2, \quad g_3 g_4 = g_1,$$

and that the group admits 6 distinct representations of degree 7.

186. The permutation-groups we are here discussing are quite special cases of the more general groups of linear substitutions to be considered in the following chapters. When a set of permutations are transformed by a linear substitution they become, in general, a set of linear substitutions; but it is always possible to choose the linear substitution so that the set of permutations is transformed into another set of permutations. When such more general transformations are admitted, the question of equivalence, as between permutation-groups, may and does take a new form. In fact two permutation-groups which are distinct in regard to transformation by permutations are not necessarily distinct in regard to transformation by linear substitutions. Though it is natural in dealing with permutation-groups, as such, to use the more narrow definition of equivalence here given, we shall later on (§ 217) resume the question and determine the equivalences that always exist, except in the case of a cyclical group, among the s representations of a group as a transitive permutation-group, when transformations by linear substitutions are admitted.

187. A second process apparently, but not really, different from that made use of in § 177 for presenting a group of finite order as a permutation-group, may be shortly referred to here, because of its convenience in many particular cases.

Let $$P_1, P_2, \ldots\ldots, P_m$$

be a set of conjugate operations or sub-groups of a group G. If S is any operation of G,

$$\begin{pmatrix} P_1 \;, & P_2 \;, \ldots\ldots, & P_m \\ S^{-1}P_1S, & S^{-1}P_2S, \ldots\ldots, & S^{-1}P_mS \end{pmatrix}$$

is a permutation of the m P's. To each operation of G will correspond a definite permutation of the m symbols, and the set of permutations so arising obviously constitute a transitive permutation-group with which G is isomorphic. In fact a representation of G thus arises. The sub-group of this permutation-group which leaves P_1 unchanged corresponds to those operations of G which are permutable with P_1. If then G_{P_1} is the greatest sub-group of G which contains the operation or sub-group P_1 self-conjugately, the representation thus arising is equivalent to that formed by the method of § 177 in respect of the sub-group G_{P_1}.

It may be noticed that however the P's are chosen, the permutation in this form that corresponds to any self-conjugate operation of G is the identical permutation, so that if G has self-conjugate operations no representation of the form considered can be simply isomorphic with G. Moreover the regular representation will never occur in this form; and in general there are other representations which do not occur. The process therefore, though often convenient, is not exhaustive as that of § 177 is.

CHAPTER XIII.

ON GROUPS OF LINEAR SUBSTITUTIONS; REDUCIBLE AND IRREDUCIBLE GROUPS*.

188. A SYSTEM of n linear equations

$$\begin{aligned} y_1 &= a_{11}x_1 + a_{12}x_2 + \dots + a_{1n}x_n, \\ y_2 &= a_{21}x_1 + a_{22}x_2 + \dots + a_{2n}x_n, \\ &\dots\dots\dots\dots\dots\dots\dots\dots \\ y_n &= a_{n1}x_1 + a_{n2}x_2 + \dots + a_{nn}x_n, \end{aligned}$$

in which the coefficients a_{ij} are regarded as given quantities, determine uniquely the n y's in terms of the n x's. Such a system of equations is called a *linear substitution* performed on the x's. It may be expressed in the abbreviated form

$$y_i = \sum_{j=1}^{j=n} a_{ij}x_j, \quad (i = 1, 2, \dots\dots, n)\dots\dots\dots\dots(\text{i}).$$

The determinant

$$\begin{vmatrix} a_{11} & a_{12} & \dots & a_{1n} \\ a_{21} & a_{22} & \dots & a_{2n} \\ \dots & \dots & \dots & \dots \\ \dots & \dots & \dots & \dots \\ a_{n1} & a_{n2} & \dots & a_{nn} \end{vmatrix}$$

* On the question of the reducibility of groups of linear substitutions the reader may consult the following memoirs: H. Maschke, "Beweis des Satzes dass diejenigen endlichen linearen Substitutionsgruppen, in welchen einige durchgehends verschwindende Coefficienten auftreten, intransitiv sind," *Math. Ann.* Vol. LII (1899), pp. 363—368; A. Loewy, "Zur Theorie der Gruppen linearer Substitutionen," *Ibid.* Vol. LIII. (1900), pp. 225—242; "Ueber die Reducibilität der Gruppen linearer homogener Substitutionen," *Trans. Amer. Math. Soc.* Vol. III (1902), pp. 44—64; "Ueber die Reducibilität der reellen Gruppen linearer homogener Substitutionen," *Ibid.* Vol. IV (1903), pp. 171—177; W. Burnside, "On the reduction of a group of homogeneous linear substitutions of finite order," *Acta Mathematica*, Vol. XXVIII (1904), pp. 369—387;

for which the abbreviation

$$|a_{ij}|$$

is used, is called the *determinant* of the substitution. If this determinant is different from zero, the linear substitution (i) also gives the x's uniquely in terms of the y's: but not otherwise. We shall be concerned here mainly with linear substitutions whose determinants are different from zero, and in what follows it is to be understood that this is the case.

The determinant $|a_{ij}|$ being different from zero, the system of equations (i) may be solved with respect to the x's in the form

$$x_j = \sum_{i=1}^{i=n} A_{ji} y_i, \quad (j = 1, 2, \ldots\ldots, n) \quad \ldots\ldots\ldots\text{(i)}',$$

where

$$|A_{ij}| \,.\, |a_{ij}| = 1.$$

Further, if

$$z_l = \sum_{k=1}^{k=n} b_{lk} y_k, \quad (l = 1, 2, \ldots\ldots, n) \quad \ldots\ldots\ldots\ldots\text{(ii)}$$

be another linear substitution on n symbols, the y's may be eliminated between (i) and (ii), giving the system of equations

$$z_t = \sum_{s=1}^{s=n} c_{ts} x_s, \quad (t = 1, 2, \ldots\ldots, n) \ldots\ldots\ldots\ldots\text{(iii)},$$

where

$$c_{ts} = \sum_{k=1}^{k=n} b_{tk} a_{ks}.$$

Moreover, from the rule for the multiplication of determinants

$$|c_{ts}| = |b_{ts}| \,.\, |a_{ts}|,$$

so that the determinant of (iii) is different from zero.

189. A linear substitution, as defined above, is an operation performed on a set of n symbols and leading to a new set of n symbols. It is completely specified by its coefficients, whatever letters may be used to represent the old and the new sets of n symbols. It is customary to use unaccented and accented letters to denote the old and the new sets of symbols. The operations A, A', B and C, given by the systems (i), (i)′, (ii)

"On the condition of reducibility of any group of linear substitutions," *Proc. L. M. S.* Series 2, Vol. III (1905), pp. 430—434. The question is also dealt with, less explicitly, in the memoirs by G. Frobenius referred to in the following chapter.

and (iii), thus expressed are

$$\begin{aligned} x_i' &= \sum_1^n a_{ij} x_j, \\ x_i' &= \sum_1^n A_{ij} x_j, \\ x_i' &= \sum_1^n b_{ij} x_j, \\ x_i' &= \sum_1^n c_{ij} x_j, \end{aligned} \qquad (i = 1, 2, \ldots\ldots, n),$$

and the relations between them are

$$A'A = AA' = E, \quad AB = C,$$

where, as usual, E denotes the identical substitution

$$x_i' = x_i, \quad (i = 1, 2, \ldots\ldots, n).$$

Linear substitutions on a given number of symbols are therefore such that any number of them carried out in succession lead to another linear substitution on the same symbols, while to each substitution A there corresponds a unique inverse A'. The existence of groups of linear substitutions follows immediately from these properties.

The permutations of n symbols that have been already considered are a very special case of linear substitutions. The number of these however is necessarily finite, so that the permutation-groups of n symbols are necessarily groups of finite order. This is obviously not in general the case with groups of linear substitutions.

190. Each of the two linear substitutions

$$x_i' = \sum_1^n a_{ij} x_j,$$

and

$$x_i' = \sum_1^n a_{ji} x_j, \qquad (i = 1, 2, \ldots\ldots, n),$$

is spoken of as the *transposed* of the other. If

$$A, A_t; \ B, B_t; \ C, C_t$$

are pairs of transposed substitutions, and if

$$AB = C,$$

then

$$c_{ij} = \sum_{s=1}^{s=n} b_{is} a_{sj}.$$

But if $B_t A_t = D$, then

$$d_{ij} = \sum_{s=1}^{s=n} b_{js} a_{si} = c_{ji},$$

and therefore

$$D = C_t.$$

Hence, if

$$AB = C,$$

then

$$A_t^{-1} B_t^{-1} = C_t^{-1}.$$

It follows that if the linear substitutions

$$E,\ A,\ B,\ C,\ \ldots\ldots$$

form a group G, then

$$E,\ A_t,\ B_t,\ C_t,\ \ldots\ldots$$

form a simply isomorphic group G_t, the substitutions A_t^{-1}, B_t^{-1}, C_t^{-1}, ... of G_t corresponding to the substitutions A, B, C, ... of G.

Each of the groups G and G_t is called the *transposed* of the other.

Denoting by $\bar{a}_{ij}$ the conjugate imaginary of a_{ij}, and by $\bar{A}$ the linear substitution

$$x_i' = \sum_1^n \bar{a}_{ij} x_j, \quad (i = 1, 2, \ldots\ldots, n),$$

the relation

$$c_{ij} = \sum_1^n b_{is} a_{sj}$$

involves

$$\bar{c}_{ij} = \sum_1^n \bar{b}_{is} \bar{a}_{sj},$$

and therefore if the linear substitutions

$$E,\ A,\ B,\ C,\ \ldots\ldots$$

form a group G, then

$$E,\ \bar{A},\ \bar{B},\ \bar{C},\ \ldots\ldots$$

form a simply isomorphic group $\bar{G}$ in which $\bar{A}$, $\bar{B}$, ... correspond to A, B, ...

Each of the groups G and $\bar{G}$ is called the *conjugate* of the other.

If G and G' are two simply isomorphic groups of linear substitutions, there are always a variety of one-to-one correspondences that can be established between the individual substitutions of the two groups. Thus, S and S_t^{-1} being corresponding substitutions of a group and its transposed group, so also, for another isomorphism, are $\Sigma^{-1}S\Sigma$ and S_t^{-1}, Σ being any substitution of the original group. In regard to this latter isomorphism the groups are not to be regarded as transposed groups, though the totality of the substitutions of the second is constituted by the totality of the transposed substitutions of the first. The phrases "transposed groups" and "conjugate groups" imply the isomorphisms in which S, S_t^{-1} and S, $\bar{S}$ are respectively pairs of corresponding substitutions.

Rather more generally if the coefficients a_{ij} are rational numbers in an algebraic field determined by an algebraic number ξ, and if when ξ is replaced by one of its conjugate values ξ', a_{ij} becomes a'_{ij} and A becomes A', then

$$E,\ A,\ B,\ C,\ \ldots\ldots$$

and

$$E,\ A',\ B',\ C',\ \ldots\ldots$$

are simply isomorphic groups of linear substitutions, in which A and A' are corresponding substitutions. In fact the relation

$$c_{ij} = \sum_1^n b_{is} a_{sj}$$

involves necessarily

$$c'_{ij} = \sum_1^n b'_{is} a'_{sj}.$$

191. Let G be a group of linear substitutions on n symbols of which A, or

$$x_i' = \sum_1^n a_{ij} x_j, \quad (i = 1, 2, \ldots\ldots, n),$$

is any one; and G' a simply isomorphic group on m symbols, in which A', or

$$y_u' = \sum_1^m a'_{uv} y_v, \quad (u = 1, 2, \ldots\ldots, m),$$

is the substitution corresponding to A. By multiplying together these systems of equations we have

$$x_i' y_u' = \sum_{j=1}^{j=n} \sum_{v=1}^{v=m} a_{ij} a'_{uv} x_j y_v, \quad \begin{pmatrix} i = 1, 2, \ldots\ldots, n \\ u = 1, 2, \ldots\ldots, m \end{pmatrix},$$

a linear substitution on the mn products of the x's and y's. Denote this linear substitution by α: and the similar ones that arise from B and B' and from C and C' by β and γ. Then $\alpha\beta$ is

$$x_i' y_u' = \sum_{s=1}^{s=n} \sum_{t=1}^{t=m} b_{is} b'_{ut} \sum_{j=1}^{j=n} \sum_{v=1}^{v=m} a_{sj} a'_{tv} x_j y_v.$$

Now if $AB = C$, then

$$\sum_{s=1}^{s=n} b_{is} a_{sj} = c_{ij};$$

while in consequence of the isomorphism of G and G',

$$A'B' = C',$$

and

$$\sum_{t=1}^{t=m} b'_{ut} a'_{tv} = c'_{uv}.$$

Hence $\alpha\beta$ is

$$x_i' y_u' = \sum_{j=1}^{j=n} \sum_{v=1}^{v=m} c_{ij} c'_{uv} x_j y_v,$$

i.e.

$$\alpha\beta = \gamma.$$

The set of linear substitutions on the mn products of the x's and y's thus formed, by multiplying together the equations defining corresponding substitutions of G and G', therefore constitute a group Γ simply isomorphic with G or G'.

If between G and G' there exists an isomorphism of the most general kind (§ 32), such that to every substitution of G there correspond p substitutions of G' and to every substitution of G' there correspond q substitutions of G, a similar construction may be effected. Let Σ_i ($i = 1, 2, \ldots\ldots$) be the operations of an abstract group simply isomorphic with G, and Σ_j' ($j = 1, 2, \ldots\ldots$) those of an abstract group simply isomorphic with G'; and suppose that every operation of one of these groups is permutable with every operation of the other. Further, let

$$\Sigma'_{i1}, \Sigma'_{i2}, \ldots\ldots, \Sigma'_{ip}$$

be the p operations of the second group which, in respect of the isomorphism between G and G', correspond to the operation Σ_i of the first. Then the set of operations

$$\Sigma_i\Sigma'_{i1}, \Sigma_i\Sigma'_{i2}, \ldots\ldots, \Sigma_i\Sigma'_{ip}, \quad (i = 1, 2, \ldots\ldots),$$

constitute an abstract group g of order N which is multiply isomorphic with both G and G'. To every operation of g there corresponds a single substitution of G (or G'), and to every substitution of G (or G') there correspond p (or q) operations of g.

Let S_k ($k = 1, 2, \ldots\ldots, N$) be the operations of g; and let

$$x_i' = \sum_1^n a_{ijk} x_j, \quad (i = 1, 2, \ldots\ldots, n),$$

and

$$y_u' = \sum_1^m a'_{uvk} y_v, \quad (u = 1, 2, \ldots\ldots, m),$$

be the substitutions of G and G' which correspond to S_k. With this notation, of the N substitutions whose coefficients are a_{ijk} ($k = 1, 2, \ldots\ldots, N$) only N/p are distinct, each one occurring p times; and a similar statement may be made with respect to the substitutions whose coefficients are a'_{ijk}. It may however be verified, exactly as above, that the set of N substitutions on the mn products of the x's and y's,

$$x_i' y_u' = \sum_{j=1}^{j=n} \sum_{v=1}^{v=m} a_{ijk} a'_{uvk} x_j y_v \quad \begin{pmatrix} i = 1, 2, \ldots\ldots, n \\ u = 1, 2, \ldots\ldots, m \end{pmatrix},$$

$$(k = 1, 2, \ldots\ldots, N),$$

constitute a group simply isomorphic with g, the substitution written being that which corresponds to the operation S_k.

This process of forming from two isomorphic groups of linear substitutions a third group which is simply or multiply isomorphic with each of them, on a number of symbols equal to the product of the numbers affected by the two given groups, is spoken of as a *composition* of the two groups. It should be noticed that, although for brevity we speak of compounding two groups, the process involves not only a given pair of groups of linear substitutions but also a given isomorphism between them.

192. Suppose that $\sum_i k_i x_i$ is a linear function of the x's which is changed into a multiple of itself by A, so that

$$\sum_{ij} k_i a_{ij} x_j \equiv \lambda \sum_i k_i x_i.$$

Then

$$\sum_i k_i a_{ij} = \lambda k_j, \quad (j = 1, 2, \ldots\ldots, n),$$

and
$$\begin{vmatrix} a_{11}-\lambda, & a_{12} \;, & \ldots & a_{1n} \\ a_{21} \;, & a_{22}-\lambda, & \ldots & a_{2n} \\ \cdots & \cdots & \cdots & \cdots \\ a_{n1} \;, & a_{n2} \;, & \ldots & a_{nn}-\lambda \end{vmatrix} = 0.$$

This equation is called the *characteristic equation* of A. Corresponding to any root λ of this equation there is clearly at least one linear function of the x's which is changed into λ times itself by A.

If $S^{-1}AS=B$, and the notation of § 189 is used for the substitutions A, B, S and S^{-1} (or S'), then
$$b_{ij}=\sum_{u,v} s_{iu}\, a_{uv}\, S_{vj}.$$

Now
$$\sum_k s_{ik}S_{kj}=0, \qquad i\neq j,$$
$$=1, \qquad i=j.$$

Therefore if
$$\lambda_{ij}=0, \qquad i\neq j,$$
$$=\lambda, \qquad i=j,$$

then
$$b_{ij}-\lambda_{ij}=\sum_{uv} s_{iu}\,(a_{uv}-\lambda_{uv})\,S_{vj}.$$

Hence the determinants of the substitutions, whose coefficients are $a_{ij}-\lambda_{ij}$ and $b_{ij}-\lambda_{ij}$, are equal; in other words the substitutions A and B have the same characteristic equation. The characteristic equation of a linear substitution is therefore the same as that of any one of the substitutions into which it may be transformed. In particular, in a group of linear substitutions the characteristic equations of any two conjugate substitutions are the same.

The sum of the roots of the characteristic equation of a substitution, in other words the sum of the coefficients in the leading diagonal of the substitution, i.e.
$$a_{11}+a_{22}+\ldots+a_{nn},$$
is called the *characteristic* of the substitution. In a group of linear substitutions each one of a set of conjugate substitutions has the same characteristic.

193. The foregoing results in regard to linear substitutions and groups of linear substitutions involve no limitations with respect to the order either of the substitutions or of the groups. The general theory of groups of linear substitutions whose order is not finite lies, however, outside the range of this treatise, and in what follows we shall consider almost exclusively groups of linear substitutions of finite order. In such groups each substitution is also necessarily of finite order. For such a substitution the roots of the characteristic equation must obviously be roots of unity, for a substitution which replaces a linear function of the variables by λ times itself is clearly not of finite order unless some power of λ is unity. The condition that the roots of the characteristic equation should be roots of unity is however clearly not sufficient to ensure that the substitution should be of finite order. Thus this condition is satisfied for the substitution

$$x' = x, \quad y' = x + y,$$

which is not of finite order, since its nth power is

$$x' = x, \quad y' = nx + y.$$

It is essential then to determine the general form of a linear substitution of finite order. To this we now proceed.

Suppose that A is a linear substitution of order N performed on $x_1, x_2, \ldots\ldots, x_n$. Let y_1 be any linear function of the x's, and suppose that A changes y_1 into y_2, y_2 into y_3, and so on. Since A is of order N, y_{N+1} is the same as y_1; and if y_{n_1+1} is the first y which is the same as y_1, then n_1 must be a factor of N. Let ω be a primitive n_1th root of unity, and put

$$\begin{aligned}
&y_1 + y_2 + y_3 + \ldots + y_{n_1} = \eta_0, \\
&y_1 + \omega^{-1}y_2 + \omega^{-2}y_3 + \ldots + \omega^{-n_1+1}y_{n_1} = \eta_1, \\
&y_1 + \omega^{-2}y_2 + \omega^{-4}y_3 + \ldots + \omega^{-2n_1+2}y_{n_1} = \eta_2, \\
&\ldots\ldots\ldots\ldots\ldots\ldots\ldots\ldots\ldots\ldots\ldots\ldots \\
&y_1 + \omega y_2 + \omega^2 y_3 + \ldots + \omega^{n_1-1}y_{n_1} = \eta_{n_1-1}.
\end{aligned}$$

If all the η's were zero, y_1 would be zero contrary to supposition. Hence a certain number, say m_1, of the η's are different from zero; and A replaces each one of them by a distinct multiple of itself. In fact, if η_k is not zero, it is the only one of the η's which A replaces by ω^k times itself. The m_1 non-vanishing η's are therefore linearly independent.

If m_1 is less than n, there must be a linear function z_1 of the x's, which is not a linear function of the η's. Treat this in the same way as y_1. If z_{n_2+1} is the first of the series of z's which is identical with z_1, n_2 is a factor of N. Let ω' be a primitive n_2th root of unity and form as before the n_2 functions

$$\zeta_0,\ \zeta_1,\ \ldots\ldots,\ \zeta_{n_2-1}.$$

These cannot be all identically zero, or z_1 would be zero. They also cannot all be either zero or linear functions of the η's or z_1 would be such, contrary to supposition. Hence if m_1 is less than n, at least one more linear function of the x's can be formed which A replaces by a multiple of itself. This process can therefore be continued until n independent linear functions of the x's have been formed, each of which is replaced by a multiple of itself under the operation of A. Moreover each of the multipliers is necessarily an Nth root of unity. Hence:

THEOREM I. *If*

$$x_i' = \sum_1^n a_{ij} x_j, \quad (i = 1, 2, \ldots\ldots, n)$$

is a linear substitution A of finite order N, it is always possible to find a substitution S, such that $S^{-1}AS$ is of the form

$$x_1' = \omega_1 x_1,\ x_2' = \omega_2 x_2,\ \ldots\ldots,\ x_n' = \omega_n x_n,$$

where $\omega_1, \omega_2, \ldots\ldots, \omega_n$ are Nth roots of unity.

The n roots of unity $\omega_1, \omega_2, \ldots\ldots, \omega_n$ are called the *multipliers* of A. Their sum is the characteristic (§ 192) of A; and their product is the determinant of A.

Ex. Prove that every linear substitution of order two on three symbols is of one of the forms

(i) $$x' = -x, \quad y' = -y, \quad z' = -z,$$

(ii) $$x' = x + \alpha (ax + by + cz),$$
$$y' = y + \beta (ax + by + cz),$$
$$z' = z + \gamma (ax + by + cz),$$

(iii) $$x' = -x - \alpha (ax + by + cz),$$
$$y' = -y - \beta (ax + by + cz),$$
$$z' = -z - \gamma (ax + by + cz),$$

where $$a\alpha + b\beta + c\gamma = -2.$$

194. In the preceding paragraph we have determined a canonical form to which any linear substitution of finite order may be brought. It is obviously not unique unless the multipliers of the substitution are all distinct. It is not therefore to be expected that a unique canonical form should exist for a group of linear substitutions of finite order. There is, however, a certain standard form to which any group of linear substitutions of finite order may be brought, the coefficients of each substitution of the group satisfying certain relations, the same for all. This form is directly connected with the existence of a bilinear invariant for any group and its conjugate, which we proceed to consider.

A bilinear form in n variables and their conjugates $x_1, x_2, \ldots\ldots, x_n, \bar{x}_1, \bar{x}_2, \ldots\ldots, \bar{x}_n$, viz.

$$\sum_{i,j} c_{ij} x_i \bar{x}_j,$$

the coefficients of which satisfy the relations

$$c_{ij} = \bar{c}_{ji}, \quad (i, j = 1, 2, \ldots\ldots, n),$$

is called an *Hermitian form.*

The coefficients being regarded as given numerical (complex) quantities, such a form takes a real numerical value whatever (complex) numerical values be assigned to the variables. If the form is such that it cannot take a negative value, whatever values are assigned to the variables, it is said to be *definite.* For instance

$$x_1\bar{x}_1 + x_2\bar{x}_2 + \ldots\ldots + x_n\bar{x}_n$$

is a definite form.

If, in a definite form, c_{11} is not zero, it must obviously be positive, for otherwise the values $x_2 = x_3 = \ldots = x_n = 0$ would make the form negative.

If, in a definite form, c_{11} is zero, then c_{1i} $(i = 2, 3, \ldots\ldots, n)$ must also be zero. In fact for the values $x_3 = x_4 = \ldots = x_n = 0$ the form becomes

$$c_{22}x_2\bar{x}_2 + c_{12}x_1\bar{x}_2 + c_{21}\bar{x}_1x_2.$$

If c_{22} is not zero, this may be written

$$[(c_{22}x_2 + c_{12}x_1)(c_{22}\bar{x}_2 + c_{21}\bar{x}_1) - c_{12}c_{21}x_1\bar{x}_1]/c_{22},$$

and is negative, when $c_{22}x_2 + c_{12}x_1 = 0$, unless $c_{12} = 0$.

If c_{22} is zero, the form may be written

$$(x_2 + c_{12}x_1)(\bar{x}_2 + c_{21}\bar{x}_1) - x_2\bar{x}_2 - c_{12}c_{21}x_1\bar{x}_1,$$

and again is negative, when $x_2 + c_{12}x_1 = 0$, unless $c_{12} = 0$.

A definite Hermitian form may be brought in an infinite number of ways to a standard expression. Put

$$\sqrt{c_{11}}\,\xi_1 = c_{11}x_1 + c_{21}x_2 + \ldots + c_{n1}x_n,$$
$$\sqrt{c_{11}}\,\bar{\xi}_1 = c_{11}\bar{x}_1 + c_{12}\bar{x}_2 + \ldots + c_{1n}\bar{x}_n.$$

The form then becomes

$$\xi_1\bar{\xi}_1 + \sum_2^n d_{ij}x_i\bar{x}_j,$$

where $$d_{ij} = c_{ij} - \frac{c_{i1}c_{1j}}{c_{11}}, \text{ so that } d_{ij} = \bar{d}_{ji}.$$

If $d_{22} = 0$, then $d_{2i} = 0$ ($i = 3, 4, \ldots\ldots, n$). If d_{22} is not zero, it is positive and we may take

$$\sqrt{d_{22}}\,\xi_2 = d_{22}x_2 + d_{32}x_3 + \ldots + d_{n2}x_n,$$
$$\sqrt{d_{22}}\,\bar{\xi}_2 = d_{22}\bar{x}_2 + d_{23}\bar{x}_3 + \ldots + d_{2n}\bar{x}_n.$$

For a definite form this process may be continued, and it leads to the expression

$$\xi_1\bar{\xi}_1 + \xi_2\bar{\xi}_2 + \ldots + \xi_s\bar{\xi}_s$$

for the form, where the number of terms, s, is equal to or less than n, while $\xi_1, \xi_2, \ldots, \xi_s$ are independent linear functions of the original variables.

The form will take the value zero if, and only if,

$$\xi_1 = \xi_2 = \ldots = \xi_s = 0.$$

When $s = n$, this involves

$$x_1 = x_2 = \ldots = x_n = 0,$$

so that the form is zero only for simultaneous zero values of the variables. In this case we shall call the form a *non-zero* definite form*.

* This is not a recognised phraseology.

When $s < n$, the form will vanish for other values of the original variables besides simultaneous zero values, and when it is necessary to emphasize this point the form may be called a *zero* definite form. It may be shewn that the determinant $|c_{ij}|$ of the form is zero in the second case and not zero in the first.

195. Let G and $\bar{G}$ be two conjugate groups of linear substitutions (§ 190), for which corresponding pairs of substitutions are

$$\left.\begin{aligned} x_i' &= \sum_1^n a_{ij}x_j, \\ y_i' &= \sum_1^n \bar{a}_{ij}y_j, \end{aligned}\right\} \quad (i = 1, 2, \ldots\ldots, n).$$

If the y's are the conjugate imaginaries of the x's, then for each corresponding pair of substitutions the y''s are the conjugate imaginaries of the x''s: and the equations defining corresponding pairs of operations may be written

$$\left.\begin{aligned} x_i' &= \sum_1^n a_{ij}x_j, \\ \bar{x}_i' &= \sum_1^n \bar{a}_{ij}\bar{x}_j, \end{aligned}\right\} \quad (i = 1, 2, \ldots\ldots, n).$$

When the x's and $\bar{x}$'s undergo any pair of corresponding substitutions of G and $\bar{G}$,

$$\sum_i x_i\bar{x}_i$$

becomes

$$\sum_{i,s,t} a_{is}\bar{a}_{it}x_s\bar{x}_t.$$

Hence, if G is of finite order and if $\sum_a$ denotes a summation with respect to corresponding pairs of substitutions of G and $\bar{G}$,

$$I = \sum_{a,i,s,t} a_{is}\bar{a}_{it}x_s\bar{x}_t$$

is a bilinear invariant for G and $\bar{G}$.

Now the coefficient of $x_s\bar{x}_s$ in I is $\sum_{a,i} a_{is}\bar{a}_{is}$, which is a real positive non-zero quantity. Also the coefficients of $x_s\bar{x}_t$ and $\bar{x}_sx_t$ are $\sum_{a,i} a_{is}\bar{a}_{it}$ and $\sum_{a,i} a_{it}\bar{a}_{is}$, and these are conjugate imaginaries.

If the abbreviation $x_i^{(a)}$ be used for $\sum_1^n a_{ij}x_j$,

$$I = \sum_a (x_1^{(a)}\bar{x}_1^{(\bar{a})} + x_2^{(a)}\bar{x}_2^{(\bar{a})} + \ldots + x_n^{(a)}\bar{x}_n^{(\bar{a})}).$$

Each term in this sum is a real positive quantity unless

$$x_1 = x_2 = \ldots = x_n = 0.$$

It follows that I is a non-zero definite Hermitian form. Hence*:—

THEOREM II. *For any two conjugate groups of linear substitutions of finite order G and $\bar{G}$ there exists a non-zero definite Hermitian form which is invariant when the two sets of variables in the form undergo corresponding substitutions of G and $\bar{G}$.*

It should be noticed that the form $\sum_i x_i\bar{x}_i$ on which the substitutions have been effected may be replaced by any non-zero definite Hermitian form in the x's and their conjugates. There may therefore very well be more than one such invariant form. The essence of the theorem is that when G is of finite order there is always at least one such invariant form. If G is not of finite order this is not, in general, the case.

196. Suppose now that I is an invariant non-zero definite Hermitian form for G and $\bar{G}$, and that by the process of § 194 or otherwise it has been brought to the expression

$$I = \xi_1\bar{\xi}_1 + \xi_2\bar{\xi}_2 + \ldots + \xi_n\bar{\xi}_n,$$

where

$$\xi_i = \sum_1^n t_{ij}x_j, \qquad \bar{\xi}_i = \sum_1^n \bar{t}_{ij}\bar{x}_j, \qquad (i = 1, 2, \ldots\ldots, n).$$

Denoting these two substitutions by T and $\bar{T}$, the groups G and $\bar{G}$ become when the ξ's and $\bar{\xi}$'s are used as variables $T^{-1}GT$ and $\bar{T}^{-1}\bar{G}\bar{T}$. These are clearly still conjugate groups and for them

$$\sum_i \xi_i\bar{\xi}_i$$

is invariant.

* A. Loewy, *Comptes Rendus*, Vol. CXXIII (1896), pp. 168—171; E. H. Moore, *Math. Ann.* Vol. L (1898), pp. 213—219.

If

$$\xi_i' = \sum_1^n \alpha_{ij}\xi_j, \qquad (i = 1, 2, \ldots\ldots, n)$$
$$\bar{\xi}_i' = \sum_1^n \bar{\alpha}_{ij}\bar{\xi}_j,$$

be typical corresponding substitutions of $T^{-1}GT$ and $\bar{T}^{-1}\bar{G}\bar{T}$, then

$$\sum_i \xi_i\bar{\xi}_i = \sum_{i,\, s,\, t} \alpha_{is}\bar{\alpha}_{it}\xi_s\bar{\xi}_t.$$

Hence

$$\sum_i \alpha_{is}\bar{\alpha}_{is} = 1,$$
$$\sum_i \alpha_{is}\bar{\alpha}_{it} = 0, \quad (t \neq s).$$

If A_{ij} is the minor of α_{ij} in the determinant $|\alpha_{ij}|$, and if D is the value of the determinant, these relations are equivalent to

$$\bar{\alpha}_{is} = \frac{A_{is}}{D}.$$

The substitution $\bar{A}$ therefore is

$$\bar{x}_i' = \sum_1^n \frac{A_{is}}{D}\bar{x}_s, \quad (i = 1, 2, \ldots\ldots, n).$$

Now the inverse of this is

$$\bar{x}_i' = \sum_1^n \alpha_{si}\bar{x}_s, \quad (i = 1, 2, \ldots\ldots, n)$$

which is the transposed substitution of A, so that

$$\bar{A} = A_t^{-1}.$$

These results may be summed up as follows:

THEOREM III. *Any group of linear substitutions of finite order may be transformed so that the coefficients of its substitutions satisfy the relations*

$$\sum_i \alpha_{is}\bar{\alpha}_{is} = 1, \quad \sum_i \alpha_{is}\bar{\alpha}_{it} = 0, \quad (t \neq s).$$

In this form the bilinear expression $\sum_i \xi_i\bar{\xi}_i$ *is invariant for the group and its conjugate, while the conjugate group and the transposed group are identical with each other; i.e.* $\bar{A} = A_t^{-1}$, *if* A *is any substitution of the group.*

197. Definition. A group of linear substitutions in n symbols

$$x_1, x_2, \ldots\ldots, x_n,$$

is called *reducible*, when it is possible to find $s\,(< n)$ linear functions

$$\xi_1, \xi_2, \ldots\ldots, \xi_s$$

of the n symbols which are transformed among themselves by every substitution of the group. When this is not possible the group is called *irreducible*.

A permutation-group is always reducible. In fact the sum of the symbols operated on by the group is unchanged by every permutation. Again the group that results from the composition of any group of linear substitutions of finite order with its conjugate is always reducible; for the Hermitian bilinear form which is invariant for the group and its conjugate is a linear function of the symbols $x_i\bar{x}_j$ operated on by the compounded group.

Definition. When it is possible to form $t\,(> 1)$ sets of independent linear functions of the x's,

$$\begin{array}{l} \xi_{11}, \xi_{12}, \ldots\ldots, \xi_{1s_1}, \\ \xi_{21}, \xi_{22}, \ldots\ldots, \xi_{2s_2}, \\ \ldots\ldots\ldots\ldots\ldots\ldots\ldots \\ \xi_{t1}, \xi_{t2}, \ldots\ldots, \xi_{ts_t}, \end{array}$$

where

$$s_1 + s_2 + \ldots + s_t = n,$$

such that the functions of each set are transformed among themselves by every substitution of the group, while the group of linear substitutions in each set is by itself irreducible, the group is called *completely reducible*.

A group of linear substitutions of finite order is either irreducible or completely reducible. This theorem which is fundamental in connection with groups of finite order we now go on to prove.

198. The step-by-step process by which any non-zero definite Hermitian form, in n variables and their conjugates, is brought to the form

$$\xi_1\bar{\xi}_1 + \xi_2\bar{\xi}_2 + \ldots + \xi_n\bar{\xi}_n,$$

must break off at some step before the last, when applied to a zero form.

Suppose that for a group G and its conjugate $\bar{G}$, the zero definite Hermitian form

$$\Sigma\, a_{ij} x_i \bar{x}_j$$

is invariant. By the above process this form may be expressed as

$$\xi_1\bar{\xi}_1 + \xi_2\bar{\xi}_2 + \ldots + \xi_s\bar{\xi}_s,$$

where s is less than n.

Take $$\xi_1, \xi_2, \ldots\ldots, \xi_s, \xi_{s+1}, \ldots\ldots, \xi_n,$$

a set of n linearly independent functions of the x's, and their conjugates, as the new variables for G and $\bar{G}$. The transformed groups will still be conjugate, and for them

$$\sum_1^s \xi_i\bar{\xi}_i$$

is invariant.

If $$\begin{aligned} \xi_i' &= \sum_1^n a_{ij}\xi_j, \\ \bar{\xi}_i' &= \sum_1^n \bar{a}_{ij}\bar{\xi}_j, \end{aligned} \qquad (i = 1, 2, \ldots\ldots, n)$$

are typical corresponding substitutions for the transformed groups,

$$\sum_1^s \xi_i\bar{\xi}_i \equiv \sum_{i=1}^{i=s} \sum_{u=1}^{u=n} \sum_{v=1}^{v=n} a_{iu}\bar{a}_{iv}\xi_u\bar{\xi}_v.$$

Hence if $$u > s,$$

$$0 = \sum_{i=1}^{i=s} a_{iu}\bar{a}_{iu}$$

or $$a_{iu} = 0.$$

The s variables $\xi_1, \xi_2, \ldots\ldots, \xi_s$ are therefore transformed among themselves by G. Hence:

THEOREM IV. *If a zero definite Hermitian form is invariant for a group of linear substitutions G and its conjugate $\bar{G}$, then G is reducible.*

199. Suppose now that the bilinear form

$$\Sigma\, a_{ij} x_i y_j$$

is invariant when the m x's and the n y's undergo corresponding substitutions of two isomorphic groups. By a suitable choice of new variables, the bilinear form can be written

$$\sum_1^s \xi_i \eta_i,$$

where $\xi_1, \xi_2, \ldots\ldots, \xi_s$ and $\eta_1, \eta_2, \ldots\ldots, \eta_s$ are linearly independent functions of the x's and y's respectively. Replace the x's by

$$\xi_1, \xi_2, \ldots\ldots, \xi_s, \xi_{s+1}, \ldots\ldots, \xi_m,$$

m linearly independent functions of themselves, and the y's by

$$\eta_1, \eta_2, \ldots\ldots, \eta_s, \eta_{s+1}, \ldots\ldots, \eta_n.$$

With these as variables let

$$\xi_i' = \sum_1^m \alpha_{ij} \xi_j \quad (i = 1, 2, \ldots\ldots, m)$$

and

$$\eta_i' = \sum_1^n \beta_{ij} \eta_j \quad (i = 1, 2, \ldots\ldots, n)$$

be corresponding substitutions of the two groups. Then

$$\sum_1^s \xi_i \eta_i \equiv \sum_{i=1}^{i=s} \sum_{u=1}^{u=m} \sum_{v=1}^{v=n} \alpha_{iu} \beta_{iv} \xi_u \eta_v.$$

Hence

$$\sum_1^s \alpha_{iu} \beta_{iv} = 0, \quad v \neq u,$$

$$\sum_1^s \alpha_{iu} \beta_{iu} = 1, \quad u \leqslant s,$$

$$\sum_1^s \alpha_{iu} \beta_{iu} = 0, \quad u > s.$$

Every determinant of s rows and columns formed from the scheme

$$\begin{array}{l} \alpha_{11}, \alpha_{12}, \alpha_{13}, \ldots\ldots, \alpha_{1s}, \ldots\ldots, \alpha_{1m}, \\ \alpha_{21}, \alpha_{22}, \alpha_{23}, \ldots\ldots, \alpha_{2s}, \ldots\ldots, \alpha_{2m}, \\ \ldots\ldots\ldots\ldots\ldots\ldots\ldots\ldots\ldots\ldots\ldots\ldots \\ \alpha_{s1}, \alpha_{s2}, \alpha_{s3}, \ldots\ldots, \alpha_{ss}, \ldots\ldots, \alpha_{sm}, \end{array}$$

cannot be zero, for then the determinant of the linear substitution

$$\xi_i' = \sum_1^m \alpha_{ij} \xi_j \quad (i = 1, 2, \ldots\ldots, m)$$

would be zero. Suppose

$$\begin{vmatrix} \alpha_{1a_1} & \alpha_{1a_2} & \cdots & \alpha_{1a_s} \\ \alpha_{2a_1} & \alpha_{2a_2} & \cdots & \alpha_{2a_s} \\ \cdots & \cdots & \cdots & \cdots \\ \alpha_{sa_1} & \alpha_{sa_2} & \cdots & \alpha_{sa_s} \end{vmatrix}$$

is different from zero. Then from the relations

$$\sum_1^s \alpha_{iu}\beta_{iv} = 0, \quad v \neq u$$
$$(u = a_1, a_2, \ldots\ldots, a_s)$$

it follows that $\beta_{iv}\,(i = 1, 2, \ldots\ldots, s)$ is zero, except when v has one of the values $a_1, a_2, \ldots\ldots, a_s$.

Now the relations

$$\sum_1^s \alpha_{iu}\beta_{iu} = 1, \quad u \leqslant s$$

shew that if u is not greater than s, each one of

$$\beta_{iu}\,(i = 1, 2, \ldots\ldots, s)$$

cannot be zero. Hence $a_1, a_2, \ldots\ldots, a_s$ must be $1, 2, \ldots\ldots, s$; and β_{iu} is zero if u is greater than s. Similarly α_{iu} is zero if $u > s$. Hence if

$$\sum_1^s \xi_i \eta_i$$

is an invariant bilinear form, both the first s ξ's and the first s η's must be transformed among themselves by every substitution of their respective groups.

Moreover, when corresponding substitutions on the first s ξ's and the first s η's are taken to be

$$\xi_i' = \sum_1^s \alpha_{ij}\xi_j,$$
$$(i = 1, 2, \ldots\ldots, s),$$
$$\eta_i' = \sum_1^s \beta_{ij}\eta_j,$$

the coefficients must satisfy the relations

$$\sum_{i=1}^{i=s} \alpha_{ij}\beta_{ik} = 0, \quad j \neq k,$$
$$\sum_{i=1}^{i=s} \alpha_{ij}\beta_{ij} = 1.$$

If A_{ij} is the minor of α_{ij} in the determinant D of the substitution on the s ξ's, then

$$D\beta_{ij}=A_{ij}.$$

Hence the corresponding substitution on the s η's is

$$D\eta_i' = \sum_1^s A_{ij}\eta_j,$$

and its inverse is

$$\eta_i' = \sum_1^s \alpha_{ji}\eta_j.$$

When $\sum_1^s \xi_i\eta_i$ is invariant, it therefore follows that the s ξ's and the s η's must undergo corresponding substitutions of a group and its transposed group.

The most important application of this result is to the case in which the group G of linear substitutions on the m x's is irreducible. When this is the case, s is necessarily equal to m, and the ξ's may be taken to be any m linearly independent linear functions of the x's. Suppose them so chosen that, when taken as variables, G has the standard form of Theorem III. The η's are then m linearly independent functions of the y's; and when the ξ's undergo any substitution of G, the η's undergo the corresponding substitution of the transposed group, or what is the same thing (since G is in standard form) of the conjugate group. Hence:—

THEOREM V. *If G is an irreducible group of linear substitutions on the variables $x_1, x_2, \ldots\ldots, x_m$ in the standard form of Theorem III, then the only bilinear form in the x's and another set of variables which is invariant when the x's and the other set of variables undergo corresponding substitutions of G and of an isomorphic group H is $\sum_1^m x_iy_i$ where the y's undergo the substitutions of $\bar{G}$.*

200. Let G be a reducible group of linear substitutions of finite order in the $s+t$ symbols

$$x_1, x_2, \ldots\ldots, x_s, x_{s+1}, \ldots\ldots, x_{s+t},$$

which transforms the symbols

$$x_1, x_2, \ldots\ldots, x_s$$

among themselves. Suppose that

$$I = \Sigma\, a_{ij} x_i \bar{x}_j$$

is a non-zero definite Hermitian form, invariant for G and $\bar{G}$. Use the step-by-step process of § 194 to bring I to standard form, taking the symbols in the order

$$x_{s+1},\ x_{s+2},\ \ldots\ldots,\ x_{s+t},\ x_1,\ x_2,\ \ldots\ldots,\ x_s,$$

so that I becomes

$$\xi_{s+1}\bar{\xi}_{s+1} + \xi_{s+2}\bar{\xi}_{s+2} + \ldots + \xi_{s+t}\bar{\xi}_{s+t} + \xi_1\bar{\xi}_1 + \ldots + \xi_s\bar{\xi}_s,$$

where

$$\xi_1,\ \xi_2,\ \ldots\ldots,\ \xi_s$$

are functions of

$$x_1,\ x_2,\ \ldots\ldots,\ x_s$$

only. When the ξ's and their conjugates are taken as variables, G and $\bar{G}$ are reducible conjugate groups for which

$$\sum_1^{s+t} \xi_i \bar{\xi}_i$$

is invariant, while the first s ξ's and the first s $\bar{\xi}$'s are transformed among themselves by G and $\bar{G}$ respectively.

Since $\sum_1^{s+t} \xi_i\bar{\xi}_i$ is invariant for G and $\bar{G}$, it follows that $\bar{G}$ is identical with G_t. Now if G does not transform the symbols $\xi_{s+1},\ \xi_{s+2},\ \ldots\ldots,\ \xi_{s+t}$ among themselves, G_t (or $\bar{G}$) would not transform the symbols $\xi_1,\ \xi_2,\ \ldots\ldots,\ \xi_s$ among themselves as it actually does. Hence G must transform each of the sets

$$\xi_1,\ \xi_2,\ \ldots\ldots,\ \xi_s$$

and

$$\xi_{s+1},\ \xi_{s+2},\ \ldots\ldots,\ \xi_{s+t}$$

among themselves. If the group in either of these sets is reducible, the same reasoning may be applied again. Hence:—

THEOREM VI. *A group of linear substitutions of finite order is either irreducible or is completely reducible.*

The condition that the group should be of finite order has only been used in establishing the existence of an invariant non-zero definite Hermitian form for the group and its conjugate. It follows that any group of linear substitutions which, with its conjugate possesses such an invariant form, is either irreducible or is completely reducible.

Ex. 1. Prove that the group of order 16 in four variables, generated by

$$x' = ix, \quad y' = -iy, \quad u' = -iu, \quad v' = iv;$$
$$x' = y, \quad y' = -x, \quad u' = v, \quad v' = -u;$$
$$x' = u, \quad y' = v, \quad u' = -x, \quad v' = -y;$$

where

$$i^2 = -1,$$

is reducible, transforming the variables in two sets of two each.

Ex. 2. Prove that the group of order 32 in four variables, generated by

$$x' = \alpha x, \quad y' = \alpha^{-1}y, \quad u' = \alpha^3 u, \quad v' = \alpha^{-3}v;$$
$$x' = y, \quad y' = -x, \quad u' = v, \quad v' = -u;$$
$$x' = u, \quad y' = v, \quad u' = -x, \quad v' = -y;$$

where

$$\alpha^4 = -1,$$

is irreducible.

201. The coefficients in a non-zero definite Hermitian form, formed as in § 195,

$$I = \Sigma\, a_{ij} x_i \bar{x}_j,$$

which is invariant for a group of linear substitutions and its conjugate, are rational functions of the coefficients in the two groups. The reduction of the form to the expression

$$\xi_1 \bar{\xi}_1 + \xi_2 \bar{\xi}_2 + \dots + \xi_n \bar{\xi}_n,$$

as explained in § 194, involves the introduction of the quantities $\sqrt{a_{11}}$, etc.; and the coefficients in the transformed groups are not therefore, in general, rational functions of the coefficients in the original groups. The process may, however, be modified so that no new irrational quantities are introduced. To effect this, put

$$\eta_1 = x_1 + \frac{a_{21}}{a_{11}} x_2 + \dots + \frac{a_{n1}}{a_{11}} x_n,$$

$$\bar{\eta}_1 = \bar{x}_1 + \frac{a_{12}}{a_{11}} \bar{x}_2 + \dots + \frac{a_{1n}}{a_{11}} \bar{x}_n.$$

Then

$$I = a_{11} \eta_1 \bar{\eta}_1 + \Sigma\, \beta_{ij} x_i \bar{x}_j, \quad (i, j = 2, 3, \dots\dots, n).$$

Hence I can be expressed in the form

$$\alpha_1 \eta_1 \bar{\eta}_1 + \alpha_2 \eta_2 \bar{\eta}_2 + \dots + \alpha_n \eta_n \bar{\eta}_n,$$

where the η's are linear functions of the x's with coefficients which are rational in the coefficients of the substitutions of the groups, as also are the α's. When the η's and $\bar{\eta}$'s are taken as new variables, the transformed groups are still conjugate, and the coefficients in their substitutions are rational functions of the original coefficients. With this modification the coefficients of the transformed groups are subject to the relations

$$\sum_i a_i \alpha_{is} \bar{\alpha}_{it} = 0, \quad t \neq s,$$

$$\sum_i a_i \alpha_{is} \bar{\alpha}_{is} = a_s.$$

If the first m of the η's are transformed among themselves, then

$$\alpha_{is} = 0, \text{ when } i \leqslant m, \ s > m.$$

Hence, if $t > m$, the equation

$$\sum_i a_i \alpha_{is} \bar{\alpha}_{it} = 0, \quad s \neq t$$

becomes

$$0 = a_{m+1}\alpha_{m+1,s}\bar{\alpha}_{m+1,t} + \dots + a_n \alpha_{n,s} \bar{\alpha}_{n,t}.$$

If $s \leqslant m$, this equation holds for $t = m+1, m+2, \dots\dots, n$. Now the determinant

$$\begin{vmatrix} \bar{\alpha}_{m+1,m+1} & \bar{\alpha}_{m+1,m+2} & \cdots & \bar{\alpha}_{m+1,n} \\ \bar{\alpha}_{m+2,m+1} & \bar{\alpha}_{m+2,m+2} & \cdots & \bar{\alpha}_{m+2,n} \\ \dots & \dots & \dots & \dots \\ \bar{\alpha}_{n,m+1} & \bar{\alpha}_{n,m+2} & \cdots & \bar{\alpha}_{n,n} \end{vmatrix}$$

cannot be zero, since it is a factor of the determinant of one of the substitutions of the group. Hence

$$\alpha_{m+1,s} = \alpha_{m+2,s} = \dots = \alpha_{n,s} = 0,$$

for all values of s from 1 to m. The variables $\eta_{m+1}, \eta_{m+2}, \dots\dots, \eta_n$ are therefore transformed among themselves; while the coefficients in the groups of substitutions on the two sets of η's are rational functions of the coefficients in the original form of the groups.

This is equivalent to the statement that, even when the coefficients in the groups dealt with are limited to a given field of rationality, a group of linear substitutions is either irreducible or completely reducible, relatively to the field*. This generalized idea of reducibility relatively to a given field may be defined as follows. A group of linear substitutions on n symbols is irreducible, relatively to a given field (which necessarily contains the coefficients of its substitutions), when it is impossible to choose m $(< n)$ linear functions of the variables with coefficients in the given field which are transformed among themselves by every substitution of the group.

202. Let T be a linear substitution on n symbols which is permutable with every substitution of a group G of linear

* Loewy, *Trans. Amer. Math. Soc.* Vol. III (1902), pp. 62—64.

substitutions on the same variables. Then $S^{-1}TS$ is permutable with every substitution of $S^{-1}GS$. If λ_1 is a root of the characteristic equation of T, S may be chosen so that $S^{-1}TS$ replaces a certain number of the variables by λ_1 times themselves. Every substitution which is permutable with $S^{-1}TS$ must obviously transform these variables among themselves; and therefore this must be true of every substitution of $S^{-1}GS$. Hence, unless $S^{-1}TS$, and therefore also T, replaces each variable by λ_1 times itself, $S^{-1}GS$, and therefore also G, must be reducible.

THEOREM VII. *The only substitutions which are permutable with every substitution of an irreducible group of linear substitutions are those which replace each variable by the same multiple of itself.*

It may be pointed out that the above reasoning holds even when the determinant of T is zero. In this case, $S^{-1}TS$ replaces a certain number of the variables by zero, when S is suitably chosen, and these must be transformed among themselves by every substitution of $S^{-1}GS$. Hence:—

Corollary. The only substitution of zero determinant, which is permutable with every substitution of an irreducible group of linear substitutions, is the substitution which replaces each variable by zero.

203. The result of the last article may also be expressed as follows. If $x_1, x_2, \ldots\ldots, x_n$ are the variables operated on by an irreducible group of linear substitutions, then the only linear functions of the x's which undergo for every operation of the group the same linear substitution as the x's are

$$kx_1, kx_2, \ldots\ldots, kx_n,$$

where k is any constant.

Suppose now that the mn variables

$$x_{i1}, x_{i2}, \ldots\ldots, x_{in},$$

$$(i = 1, 2, \ldots\ldots, m),$$

are transformed among themselves by a reducible group of linear substitutions G, such that each set of n variables with the same first suffix undergo among themselves the substitutions of an irreducible group, while the substitution that any set undergo corresponding to a given operation of G is independent of the first suffix, or in other words is the same for each of the m sets. Then it follows at once from the previous statement that the most general set of n linear functions of the mn variables, which undergo for every operation of G the same linear substitution as

$$x_{11}, x_{12}, \ldots\ldots, x_{1n},$$

is

$$\sum_{t=1}^{t=m} \alpha_t x_{tj}, \quad (j = 1, 2, \ldots\ldots, n),$$

where the α's are arbitrary constants.

Suppose now that the linear substitution T, or

$$x'_{ij} = y_{ij}, \quad (i = 1, 2, \ldots\ldots, m;\ j = 1, 2, \ldots\ldots, n),$$

where for each double suffix y_{ij} is a linear function of the x's, is permutable with every operation of G. The necessary and sufficient condition for this is that for each i,

$$y_{i1}, y_{i2}, \ldots\ldots, y_{in},$$

and

$$x_{i1}, x_{i2}, \ldots\ldots, x_{in},$$

shall undergo, corresponding to each operation of G, the same linear substitution. The most general form of T is therefore

$$x'_{ij} = \sum_{t=1}^{t=m} \alpha_{it} x_{tj}, \quad (i = 1, 2, \ldots\ldots, m;\ j = 1, 2, \ldots\ldots, n),$$

where the m^2 symbols α_{it} denote arbitrary constants. The totality of linear substitutions of this form, subject to the condition that the determinant $|\alpha_{it}|$ is different from zero, constitutes the most general group of linear substitutions on the mn variables, each of whose operations is permutable with every operation of G.

With this result the reader will be able to form the most general group of linear substitutions each of whose operations is permutable with every operation of any group G of linear substitutions of finite order on a given set of variables.

Ex. 1. The sub-group of a transitive permutation-group of degree n, which leaves x_1 unchanged, permutes the remaining $n-1$ symbols in $m-1$ transitive sets; and ξ_s represents the sum of the symbols in the sth set. A permutation of the group which changes x_1 into x_i changes the set of symbols whose sum is ξ_s into a set whose sum is $\xi_s^{(i)}$. Prove that every permutation of the group which changes x_1 into x_i also changes ξ_s into $\xi_s^{(i)}$; and that the most general linear substitution which is permutable with every permutation of G is

$$x_i' = \alpha_1 x_i + \sum_2^m \alpha_s \xi_s^{(i)},$$

$$(i = 1, 2, \ldots\ldots, n),$$

where the α's are arbitrary constants.

Ex. 2. If the coefficients of all the substitutions of a group of linear substitutions of finite order are real, prove that there is a quadratic function of the variables which (i) is invariant for all the substitutions of the group, and (ii) vanishes only, when the variables are real, for simultaneous zero values of the variables.

Shew also that when new variables are chosen such that the invariant quadratic function is the sum of their squares, the coefficients of every substitution of the transformed group satisfy the relations

$$\sum_i a_{is} a_{it} = 0, \quad (s \neq t), \quad \sum_i a_{is}^2 = 1.$$

Note to §§ 188, 189.

If D_A, D_B, D_C are the determinants of three linear substitutions A, B, C, and if $AB = C$, we have seen that $D_A D_B = D_C$; while also

$$D_{B^{-1}AB} = D_{B^{-1}} D_A D_B = D_A.$$

Hence if the determinants of some of the substitutions of a group differ from unity, those substitutions whose determinants are unity constitute a self-conjugate sub-group. Moreover the corresponding factor-group is cyclical, if the group is one of finite order.

CHAPTER XIV.

ON THE REPRESENTATION OF A GROUP OF FINITE ORDER AS A GROUP OF LINEAR SUBSTITUTIONS*.

204. Definitions. Let S_i $(i = 1, 2, \ldots\ldots, N)$ be the operations of an abstract group G of finite order N; and let

$$s_k \quad (k = 1, 2, \ldots\ldots)$$

or

$$x_i' = \sum_{j=1}^{j=n} a_{ijk} x_j \quad (i = 1, 2, \ldots\ldots, n)$$

be the substitutions of a group of linear substitutions Γ.

If to each operation S_i of G there corresponds a single operation s_i of Γ, such that when

$$S_i S_j = S_k,$$

then

$$s_i s_j = s_k,$$

Γ is said to give a *representation* of G as a group of linear substitutions.

* The theory of the representation of a group of finite order as a group of linear substitutions was largely, and the allied theory of group-characteristics was entirely, originated by Prof. Frobenius. His original memoirs on the subject all appeared in the *Berliner Sitzungsberichte*, and the most important of them are: "Ueber Gruppencharaktere" (1896), pp. 985—1021; "Ueber die Primfactoren der Gruppendeterminante" (1896), pp. 1343—1382; "Ueber Relationen zwischen den Charakteren einer Gruppe und denen ihrer Untergruppen" (1898), pp. 501—515, "Ueber die Darstellung der endlichen Gruppen durch linearer Substitutionen" (1897), pp. 994—1015; "Do. do. II" (1899), pp. 482—500; "Ueber die Composition der Charaktere einer Gruppe" (1899), pp. 330—339. In this series of memoirs Prof. Frobenius's methods are, to a considerable extent, indirect; and the same is true of two memoirs "On the continuous group that is defined by any given group of finite order," I and II, *Proc. L. M. S.* Vol. XXIX (1898) in which the author obtained independently the chief results of Prof. Frobenius's earlier memoirs. More recently in the memoir "On the reduction of a group of homogeneous linear substitutions of finite order," *Acta Mathematica*, Vol. XXVIII (1904), pp. 369—387, and "On the representation of a group of finite order as

It is to be noticed that this definition of the representation of an abstract group as a group of linear substitutions, does not involve or assume that G and Γ are simply isomorphic. If G is not a simple group it may be multiply isomorphic with Γ. If

$$\sigma_k \quad (k = 1, 2, \ldots\ldots)$$

or

$$x_i' = \sum_{j=1}^{j=n} \alpha_{ijk} x_j \quad (i = 1, 2, \ldots\ldots, n)$$

be another representation Γ' of G in the same number of symbols as a group of linear substitutions, and if a linear substitution T on the n symbols exists, such that

$$T^{-1} s_k T = \sigma_k,$$

for each k, the representations Γ and Γ' are said to be *equivalent.* If no such linear substitution as T exists, the representations are called *distinct.*

The two groups of linear substitutions Γ and Γ' may consist of the same set of substitutions and yet may give distinct representations of G.

For instance in the case of the non-cyclical group, defined by

$$S_1^p = S_2^p = E, \quad S_1 S_2 = S_2 S_1,$$

we may take s_1 and s_2 to be

$$x' = \omega_1 x \text{ and } x' = \omega_2 x,$$

ω_1 and ω_2 being any two pth roots of unity. Unless both ω_1 and ω_2 are unity, the set of linear substitutions that thus arises, giving a representation of the group, is

$$x' = \omega^i x, \quad (i = 0, 1, 2, \ldots\ldots, p-1),$$

where ω is a primitive pth root of unity.

Hence in this case the same set of linear substitutions gives $p^2 - 1$ distinct representations of the group.

A less simple case, and one in which G and Γ are simply isomorphic, is given by the abstract group G defined by

$$S_1^7 = E, \quad S_2^3 = E, \quad S_2^{-1} S_1 S_2 = S_1^2.$$

an irreducible group of linear substitutions and the direct establishment of the relations between the group-characteristics," *Proc. L. M. S.* Series 2, Vol. I (1903), pp. 117—123, the author has established the chief results of the theory by direct and comparatively simple methods. The exposition in the text mainly follows the lines of the two last mentioned memoirs.

Some account of the theory of group-characteristics is also given in Prof. Weber's *Lehrbuch der Algebra*, 2nd Edition, Vol. II, pp. 193—218.

Here we may take s_1 and s_2 to be

$$x' = \omega x, \quad y' = \omega^2 y, \quad z' = \omega^4 z, \qquad \omega^7 = 1$$

and

$$x' = z, \quad y' = x, \quad z' = y;$$

and the group of linear substitutions on x, y, z is a representation of G. If we take s_1 and s_2 to be

$$x' = \omega^3 x, \quad y' = \omega^6 y, \quad z' = \omega^5 z,$$

and

$$x' = z, \quad y' = x, \quad z' = y,$$

we obtain another representation of G by means of the same group of linear substitutions. It is however certainly distinct, for the two substitutions

$$x' = \omega x, \quad y' = \omega^2 y, \quad z' = \omega^4 z,$$

and

$$x' = \omega^3 x, \quad y' = \omega^6 y, \quad z' = \omega^5 z,$$

having different characteristics, cannot be transformed the one into the other.

205. Since any group of linear substitutions of finite order is either irreducible or completely reducible, the most important representations of an abstract group are clearly the irreducible representations. From these any representation whatever can be built up. Among the irreducible representations there necessarily occurs what is known as the *identical representation*, viz. that in which every operation of the group corresponds to the identical substitution

$$x' = x$$

in a single symbol. This identical representation will always be denoted by Γ_1 and the other irreducible representations by

$$\Gamma_2, \Gamma_3, \ldots\ldots$$

Any representation whatever of the abstract group as a group of linear substitutions may then be denoted by the symbol

$$\Sigma c_i \Gamma_i,$$

where each c is either zero or a positive integer. In fact, when the group of linear substitutions is completely reduced, each separate irreducible group of linear substitutions that arises must be equivalent to one of the Γ's, and the symbol $\Sigma c_i \Gamma_i$ denotes that of these separate irreducible groups just c_i arise which are equivalent to Γ_i.

The separate irreducible groups that thus arise on the complete reduction of a group of linear substitutions are called its *irreducible components.*

The sets of variables which are transformed among themselves by the irreducible components are called the *reduced variables.*

206. Suppose that when a group of linear substitutions has been completely reduced the two sets of variables $x_1, x_2, \ldots\ldots, x_s$ and $y_1, y_2, \ldots\ldots, y_t$ are transformed, each among themselves, irreducibly.

We have seen in § 199 that, unless the x's and the y's undergo equivalent representations of the group, there can be no invariant bilinear form in the x's and $\bar{y}$'s. Hence for the group and its conjugate, when expressed in terms of the reduced variables, there can be no invariant Hermitian form containing a product $x\bar{y}$, unless the same condition is satisfied.

Suppose that, in the completely reduced form of the group considered, there are just t sets of variables

$$x_{i1}, x_{i2}, \ldots\ldots, x_{is}$$
$$(i = 1, 2, \ldots\ldots, t),$$

the irreducible components corresponding to which are equivalent to a given irreducible representation of the group.

The variables of each set may be chosen so that (i) corresponding to any operation of the group, those of each set undergo the same substitution, and (ii) the invariant Hermitian forms for each separate set are

$$x_{i1}\bar{x}_{i1} + x_{i2}\bar{x}_{i2} + \ldots\ldots + x_{is}\bar{x}_{is}.$$

Let
$$f = \Sigma a_{ip,jq}\, x_{ip}\bar{x}_{jq}$$

be an invariant Hermitian form; and

$$x'_{ip} = \sum_{q=1}^{q=s} \alpha_{pqk} x_{iq} \quad (p = 1, 2, \ldots\ldots, s)$$

a typical substitution for any one of the sets. Then

$$\Sigma a_{ip,jq} x_{ip}\bar{x}_{jq} \equiv \Sigma a_{ip,jq} \alpha_{puk}\bar{\alpha}_{qvk} x_{iu}\bar{x}_{jv},$$

and therefore

$$a_{iu,jv} = \sum_{p,q} a_{ip,jq}\alpha_{puk}\bar{\alpha}_{qvk}.$$

These relations express that

$$\Sigma a_{iu,jv} x_u \bar{x}_v$$

is invariant for the group of linear substitutions

$$x_p' = \sum_1^s \alpha_{pqk} x_q$$

and its conjugate.

But the only invariant form for this group is

$$\sum_1^s x_i \bar{x}_i.$$

Hence $$a_{ip,jq} = 0, \quad p \neq q,$$

$$a_{ip,jp} = a_{iq,jq}.$$

If then $$a_{ip,jp} = b_{ij},$$

the most general invariant Hermitian form in the st variables and their conjugates is

$$\sum_{i,j,p} b_{ij} x_{ip} \bar{x}_{jp}.$$

This form contains just t^2 arbitrary constants

$$b_{ij} \quad (i, j = 1, 2, \ldots\ldots, t).$$

Hence combining this result and the immediately previous one, we may state the following:

THEOREM I. *The representation of an abstract group, as a group of linear substitutions, denoted by* $\Sigma c_i \Gamma_i$ *and its conjugate has exactly* Σc_i^2 *linearly independent invariant Hermitian forms.*

207. Let G_H be the representation of a group of finite order G as a transitive permutation-group in respect of a sub-group H of order N_1 (§ 177); and suppose that in this representation H permutes the symbols in m transitive sets,

$$x_1; \quad x_2, x_3, \ldots\ldots, x_i; \quad x_{i+1}, x_{i+2}, \ldots\ldots, x_j; \quad \ldots\ldots$$

The Hermitian invariant for G_H and $\bar{G}_H$ that arises from

$$x_1\bar{x}_2 + \bar{x}_1 x_2$$

is the same as that which arises from $x_1\bar{x}_3 + \bar{x}_1 x_3$, and is distinct from that which arises from $x_1\bar{x}_{i+1} + \bar{x}_1 x_{i+1}$. Hence for G_H and $\bar{G}_H$ there are just m linearly independent Hermitian invariants. On the other hand, if

$$G_H = \Sigma c_s \Gamma_s$$

gives the complete reduction of G_H, the number of these independent Hermitian invariants is Σc_s^2. Therefore

$$m = \Sigma c_s^2.$$

Suppose that there are just m_s independent linear functions of the symbols operated on by Γ_s which are invariant for H. From any one of them N/N_1 linear functions arise, under the operations of Γ_s, which formally undergo the permutations of G_H; and when this permutation-group is completely reduced it must obviously contain Γ_s as an irreducible component. Hence, if $m_s \geqslant 1$, Γ_s must occur among the irreducible components of G_H. Now in $\Sigma c_s \Gamma_s$ the number of independent linear invariants for H is $\Sigma c_s m_s$. On the other hand the number of independent linear invariants for H in G_H is obviously m. Hence

$$m = \Sigma c_s m_s,$$

and therefore

$$\Sigma c_s^2 = \Sigma c_s m_s.$$

Omitting the suffix s in c_s and Γ_s, let

$$\xi_{i1}, \xi_{i2}, \ldots\ldots, \xi_{in}$$
$$(i = 1, 2, \ldots\ldots, c)$$

be the c sets of symbols (linear functions of the x's) which undergo the linear substitutions of the irreducible representation Γ when G_H is completely reduced; and suppose the symbols chosen so that those of each set undergo the same linear substitution for each operation of G. The original variables

$$x_1, x_2, \ldots\ldots, x_{N/N_1}$$

of G_H are linear functions of the reduced variables; and in the expression for x_1 a linear function of each separate reduced set of variables must occur; since x_1 assumes N/N_1 linearly independent values under the substitutions of the group.

Suppose that

$$x_1 = \ldots\ldots + \Xi_{11} + \Xi_{22} + \ldots\ldots + \Xi_{cc} + \ldots\ldots,$$

where $\Xi_{ii} = \sum_j \alpha_j^{(i)} \xi_{ij}$ is a linear function of the symbols of the ith set.

If the c functions $\sum_j \alpha_j^{(i)} y_j$, $(i = 1, 2, \ldots\ldots, c)$ are not linearly independent, put

$$\sum_j \alpha_j^{(c)} y_j = A_1 \sum_j \alpha_j^{(1)} y_j + A_2 \sum_j \alpha_j^{(2)} y_j + \ldots\ldots + A_{c-1} \sum_j \alpha_j^{(c-1)} y_j.$$

Then

$$\Xi_{11} + \Xi_{22} + \dots\dots + \Xi_{cc} = \Xi'_{11} + \Xi'_{22} + \dots\dots + \Xi'_{c-1,c-1},$$

where

$$\Xi'_{ii} = \sum_j \alpha_j^{(i)} [\xi_{ij} + A_i \xi_{cj}].$$

Now each of the $c-1$ sets

$$\xi_{i1} + A_i\xi_{c1},\quad \xi_{i2} + A_i\xi_{c2},\ \dots\dots,\ \xi_{in} + A_i\xi_{cn},\quad (i=1, 2, \dots, c-1)$$

undergo the substitutions of Γ; and therefore, on the supposition made, when the substitutions of the group are carried out on x_1, fewer than N/N_1 independent linear functions would arise. It follows that the c linear functions $\sum_j \alpha_j^{(i)} y_j$ are linearly independent. Now for the operations of H, x_1 is invariant and therefore also $\Xi_{11}, \Xi_{22}, \dots\dots, \Xi_{cc}$. Hence, if Ξ_{1t} is the same linear function of the symbols of the first set that Ξ_{tt} is of those of the tth set, $\Xi_{11}, \Xi_{12}, \dots\dots, \Xi_{1c}$ are invariant for the substitutions of Γ which correspond to the operations of H; and they have just been shewn to be linearly independent.

There are therefore at least c linear functions of the symbols operated on by Γ, which are invariant for H. Hence with the notation of the earlier part of the paragraph

$$m_s \geqslant c_s.$$

Combining this with

$$\Sigma c_s^2 = \Sigma m_s c_s,$$

it follows that

$$c_s = m_s.$$

THEOREM II. *If G_H is the representation of a group G of finite order as a transitive permutation-group in respect of a sub-group H, the complete reduction of G_H is given by the formula*

$$G_H = \Sigma m_s \Gamma_s,$$

where Γ_s is any irreducible representation of G and m_s is the number of independent linear invariants for H in Γ_s. Moreover, if m is the number of transitive sets in which the sub-group of G_H, which leaves one symbol unchanged, permutes the symbols, then

$$m = \sum_s m_s^2.$$

208. When a group G, of finite order N, is represented as a regular permutation-group in N symbols, the sub-group that leaves one symbol unchanged consists of the identical operation E. Now in any group of linear substitutions the number of independent linear invariants for E is equal to the number of variables.

Hence, when the theorem of the previous paragraph is applied to the reduction of G_E, it takes the form

$$G_E = \sum_{s=1}^{s=\mu} n_s \Gamma_s,$$

where n_s is the number of symbols operated on by the irreducible representation Γ_s, μ being the number of distinct representations.

Suppose the reduction of G_E carried out, and let

$$x_{i1}, x_{i2}, \ldots\ldots, x_{in}$$
$$(i = 1, 2, \ldots\ldots, n)$$

be the n sets of symbols, each of which are transformed among themselves by the substitutions of the irreducible representation Γ. Suppose, moreover, the symbols chosen so that for each operation of G those of each set undergo the same substitution.

Any linear substitution on the original variables which is permutable with every substitution of G_E, must, when expressed in terms of the reduced variables, transform among themselves the n^2 symbols x_{ij} $(i, j = 1, 2, \ldots\ldots, n)$. This is an obvious consequence of the fact that the different irreducible representations are distinct, so that one cannot be transformed into another.

Hence (§ 203) a substitution which is permutable with every operation of G_E must so far as it affects the n^2 variables be of the form

$$x'_{ij} = \sum_{k=1}^{k=n} a_{ik} x_{kj},$$
$$(i, j = 1, 2, \ldots\ldots, n).$$

Such a linear substitution therefore effects the same transformation of the symbols in each column of the scheme

$$\begin{array}{l} x_{11}, x_{12}, \ldots\ldots, x_{1n}, \\ x_{21}, x_{22}, \ldots\ldots, x_{2n}, \\ \ldots\ldots\ldots\ldots\ldots\ldots\ldots\ldots \\ x_{n1}, x_{n2}, \ldots\ldots, x_{nn}, \end{array}$$

while each substitution of Γ effects the same transformation of the symbols in each row.

Now (§ 136) there is a group G', of order N, of regular permutations on the N original symbols, which is simply isomorphic with G, while every operation of G' is permutable with every operation of G.

Hence, when G is completely reduced as above, G' is simultaneously completely reduced; and, as regards the above scheme of n^2 symbols,

(i) Every operation of G gives the same substitution of the set of symbols in each line;

(ii) Every operation of G' gives the same substitution of the set of symbols in each column;

(iii) The group of substitutions of the symbols in each line, corresponding to the operations of G, and the group of substitutions of the symbols in each column, corresponding to the operations of G', are each irreducible.

Hence, for the group $\{G, G'\}$, the set of n^2 symbols in the scheme undergo an irreducible group of linear substitutions. In fact a linear substitution on the n^2 symbols, which is permutable with every operation of G, must be of the form

$$x'_{ij} = \sum_{k=1}^{k=n} \alpha_{ik} x_{kj} \quad (i, j = 1, 2, \ldots\ldots, n),$$

while if it is also permutable with every operation of G' it must be of the form

$$x'_{ij} = \sum_{k=1}^{k=n} \beta_{kj} x_{ik} \quad (i, j = 1, 2, \ldots\ldots, n).$$

It is therefore

$$x'_{ij} = \alpha x_{ij} \quad (i, j = 1, 2, \ldots\ldots, n).$$

The group of permutations $\{G, G'\}$ therefore, when completely reduced, transforms the N variables in μ reduced sets of $n_1^2, n_2^2, \ldots\ldots, n_\mu^2$ variables respectively. Moreover, since Γ_s and Γ_t are distinct representations of G, the μ representations of $\{G, G'\}$ that thus arise are also distinct. It follows, by § 206, that there are just μ independent Hermitian invariants for the permutation-group $\{G, G'\}$ and its conjugate. On the other hand it has been seen in § 207 that the number of independent

Hermitian invariants for any transitive permutation-group and its conjugate is equal to the number of transitive sets into which the symbols fall for the sub-group that leaves one symbol unchanged. Now for the permutation-group $\{G, G'\}$ it has been seen (§ 136) that this number is equal to r, the number of conjugate sets of operations in G. Thus

$$\mu = r.$$

THEOREM III. *A group of finite order, with r sets of conjugate operations, has just r distinct irreducible representations. When the representation of the group as a regular permutation-group is completely reduced, every irreducible representation occurs; and the number of times that any one occurs is equal to the number of symbols on which it operates.*

209. Let H, of order M, be a self-conjugate sub-group of G, of order N; and consider the representation G_H of G, as a transitive permutation-group, in respect of H. We have seen in § 177 that G is multiply isomorphic with G_H, every operation of H corresponding to the identical permutation in G_H.

Considered merely as a group of permutations, G_H is a regular permutation-group of degree N/M, simply isomorphic with the abstract group G/H of order N/M. If r' is the number of conjugate sets in this abstract group, just r' distinct irreducible representations of G/H arise when G_H is completely reduced. Each of these is an irreducible representation of G; and being distinct representations of G/H, they are necessarily distinct representations of G. Hence:—

THEOREM IV. *If H is a self-conjugate sub-group of G, and if G/H has r' sets of conjugate operations, there are at least r' distinct irreducible representations of G, in each of which the identical substitution corresponds to every operation of H.*

The converse of this theorem will be considered in the following chapter (§ 228), and it will be seen that r' is the actual number of representations of G which have the property in question.

210. If G is an Abelian group, every operation of it is self-conjugate and $r = N$. Hence for an Abelian group the number of irreducible representations is equal to the order of the group, and each of them is in a single symbol.

Now a group of linear substitutions in a single symbol is necessarily cyclical. Hence if a group G admits such a representation other than the identical one, G must contain a self-conjugate sub-group H such that G/H is a cyclical group; i.e. G must be distinct from its derived group G_1. On the other hand, when G is distinct from G_1 every distinct irreducible representation of G/G_1 gives a distinct representation of G, and G/G_1 is Abelian. Hence:—

THEOREM V. *If a group G of finite order N has a derived group G_1 of order N_1, there are just N/N_1 distinct representations of G in a single symbol.*

CHAPTER XV.

ON GROUP-CHARACTERISTICS.

211. In the present chapter we shall investigate a number of remarkable and important relations between the various representations of a group of finite order as an irreducible group of linear substitutions. A uniform notation is essential for this purpose, and, at the risk of a certain amount of repetition, this notation will first be explained in some detail.

The abstract group considered is called G. Its order is N, and the number of distinct sets of conjugate operations which it contains is r. The first set is that consisting of the identical operation E alone, and the numbers of operations in the r sets are

$$h_1 (= 1),\ h_2,\ \ldots\ldots,\ h_r;$$

so that

$$N = h_1 + h_2 + \ldots\ldots + h_r.$$

The r distinct irreducible representations of G will be called $\Gamma_1, \Gamma_2, \ldots\ldots, \Gamma_r$; the first of these is the identical representation (§ 205) in which every operation of the group corresponds to $x' = x$.

The number of symbols operated on by Γ_i is represented by $\chi_1^{(i)}$; but usually for convenience of printing the brackets round the i will be omitted. From Theorem III of the preceding chapter it follows that

$$N = (\chi_1^1)^2 + (\chi_1^2)^2 + \ldots\ldots + (\chi_1^r)^2.$$

An irreducible representation of the group in a single symbol is susceptible of one form only; but those in more than one symbol may be transformed (i.e. the variables may be chosen) in an infinite number of ways. In particular Γ_i may always be thrown into such a form that for Γ_i and its conjugate $\overline{\Gamma}_i$ the Hermitian invariant is of canonical form. $\overline{\Gamma}_i$ is obviously an irreducible representation if Γ_i is. The two may or may not be distinct. The suffixes are understood to be chosen so that $\overline{\Gamma}_i$ is equivalent to $\Gamma_{i'}$; and i' and i are the same or different according as Γ_i and $\overline{\Gamma}_i$ are equivalent or distinct.

If Γ_i and Γ_j are two irreducible representations of G, to each operation of G there corresponds a single substitution of Γ_i and a single substitution of Γ_j. A definite isomorphism is thus established between Γ_i and Γ_j. Hence when they are compounded as in § 191, there results another representation of G as a group of linear substitutions which may or may not be irreducible. This representation will be denoted by

$$\sum_{s=1}^{s=r} g_{ijs}\Gamma_s,$$

where each g_{ijs} is either zero or a positive integer; and the formula expresses that when the compounded group is completely reduced the irreducible representation Γ_s occurs just g_{ijs} times. The compounded group, i.e. the group of linear substitutions on the products of the symbols operated on by Γ_i and Γ_j, may be denoted by the symbol $\Gamma_i\Gamma_j$ or $\Gamma_j\Gamma_i$, and the formula

$$\Gamma_i\Gamma_j = \Gamma_j\Gamma_i = \sum_1^r g_{ijs}\Gamma_s$$

gives the complete reduction of the compounded group.

The occurrence of Γ_1 on the right-hand side of this formula, i.e. the case when g_{ij1} is not zero, indicates the existence of one or more bilinear invariants for Γ_i and Γ_j. It therefore follows, from § 199, that g_{ij1} is different from zero only when Γ_j is equivalent to $\overline{\Gamma}_i$ (or, which is the same thing, when Γ_i is equivalent to $\overline{\Gamma}_j$), i.e. when j is i' or i is j'; and that then

$$g_{ii'1} = 1.$$

212. The characteristics (§ 192) of any two conjugate operations in a group of linear substitutions are the same; and it is therefore legitimate to speak of the characteristic of a conjugate set of operations, meaning thereby the characteristic of any one of the operations of the conjugate set.

The characteristics of the r conjugate sets in the representation Γ_i will be denoted by

$$\chi_1^{(i)},\ \chi_2^{(i)},\ \ldots\ldots,\ \chi_r^{(i)},$$

where again the brackets round the i's will generally be omitted. If S is an operation of the jth set, and if the order of S is m, then χ_j^i, being the sum of the multipliers of S (§ 193), is the sum of as many mth roots of unity as there are symbols operated on by Γ_i. In particular χ_1^i, the characteristic of E, is, as already defined, the number of symbols operated on by Γ_i.

The set of quantities (each of them a cyclotomic integer)

$$\chi_1^i,\ \chi_2^i, \ldots\ldots,\ \chi_r^i$$

is called a set of *group-characteristics.*

There are r such sets corresponding to the r irreducible representations of G.

For the identical representation Γ_1, each one of the set of group-characteristics is 1. Hence in this representation

$$\sum_S \chi_S^1 = \sum_i h_i \chi_i^1 = N,$$

where the first summation is extended to all the operations and the second to all the conjugate sets of G.

From the definition of $\overline{\Gamma}_i$, it follows that the set of group-characteristics for it are

$$\chi_1^i,\ \overline{\chi}_2^i,\ \overline{\chi}_3^i,\ \ldots\ldots,\ \overline{\chi}_r^i.$$

Hence Γ_i and $\Gamma_{i'}$ are certainly distinct unless each group-characteristic for Γ_i is real; and when Γ_i and $\Gamma_{i'}$ are distinct, their sets of group-characteristics are sets of conjugate imaginary quantities. It will be seen presently that when each group-characteristic for Γ_i is real, Γ_i and $\overline{\Gamma}_i$ (or $\Gamma_{i'}$) are equivalent.

213. We have had occasion in Chapters III and IV, when considering the properties of groups apart from any special mode of representation, to deal with expressions such as

$$A + B + \ldots + D,$$

where $A, B, \ldots, D$ are operations belonging to a given group. We now consider what will correspond to such a sum of operations when we have to do with groups of linear substitutions. The essential property of such sums is that they obey (subject to the multiplication table of the group) the associative law of multiplication. In fact if

$$AC = S, \quad AD = T, \quad BC = U, \quad BD = V,$$

then
$$(A+B)(C+D) = S + T + U + V.$$

With the notation used at the beginning of Chapter XIII, let the linear substitutions that correspond to $A, B, \ldots, V$ be

$$\begin{aligned} x_i' &= \sum_1^n a_{ij}x_j, \\ x_i' &= \sum_1^n b_{ij}x_j, \qquad (i = 1, 2, \ldots, n) \\ &\ldots\ldots\ldots\ldots, \\ x_i' &= \sum_1^n v_{ij}x_j. \end{aligned}$$

Consider now the linear substitutions

$$\begin{aligned} x_i' &= \sum_1^n (a_{ij} + b_{ij})\, x_j, \\ x_i' &= \sum_1^n (c_{ij} + d_{ij})\, x_j. \end{aligned} \qquad (i = 1, 2, \ldots, n)$$

Their determinants are not necessarily different from zero; but they may be carried out successively, and the resulting linear substitution is

$$x_i' = \sum_{k=1}^{k=n} \sum_{j=1}^{j=n} (c_{ik} + d_{ik})(a_{kj} + b_{kj})\, x_j, \qquad (i = 1, 2, \ldots, n).$$

Now, since $AC = S$,

$$\sum_{k=1}^{k=n} c_{ik}a_{kj} = s_{ij},$$

and so for the other products. Hence the resulting substitution is

$$x_i' = \sum_{j=1}^{j=n} (s_{ij} + t_{ij} + u_{ij} + v_{ij})\, x_j, \qquad (i = 1, 2, \ldots, n).$$

It follows that, when the operations of the abstract group are represented by the linear substitutions as indicated, we may take as corresponding to the sum $A+B+\ldots+D$ the linear substitution

$$x_i' = \sum_{j=1}^{j=n} (a_{ij}+b_{ij}+\ldots+d_{ij})\,x_j, \quad (i=1, 2, \ldots\ldots, n);$$

and that then any relation which holds among such sums of operations of the abstract group will also hold among the corresponding linear substitutions.

With this notation if

$$T^{-1}AT = B, \text{ and } T^{-1}BT = A,$$

then $A+B$ is clearly permutable with T; and if $A_1, A_2, \ldots\ldots, A_s$ are a number of linear substitutions which are permuted among themselves on transformation by T, then $A_1 + A_2 + \ldots\ldots + A_s$ is permutable with T.

Moreover it follows, from the definition of the characteristic of a substitution, that the characteristic of $A_1 + A_2 + \ldots\ldots + A_s$ is the sum of the characteristics of $A_1, A_2, \ldots\ldots, A_s$.

Suppose now that

$$S_1, S_2, \ldots\ldots, S_{h_i}$$

are the operations of the ith conjugate set of a group G; and, as in § 41, put

$$C_i = S_1 + S_2 + \ldots\ldots + S_{h_i}.$$

In any irreducible representation of G, the substitution corresponding to C_i, whether of non-zero determinant or not, is permutable with every substitution of G. Hence (§ 202) C_i must replace every symbol operated on by the same multiple, α, of itself. The number of symbols being χ_1, the characteristic of C_i is $\alpha\chi_1$. On the other hand the characteristic of

$$S_1 + S_2 + \ldots\ldots + S_{h_i} \text{ is } h_i\chi_i.$$

Hence

$$\alpha\chi_1 = h_i\chi_i,$$

and the substitution C_i is

$$x_1' = \frac{h_i\chi_i}{\chi_1}x_1, \quad x_2' = \frac{h_i\chi_i}{\chi_1}x_2, \quad \ldots\ldots$$

Now the relations (§ 42) between the conjugate sets of G, viz.

$$C_iC_j = \sum_{s=1}^{s=r} c_{ijs}C_s,$$

being identities, in virtue of the multiplication table of G, must hold for this concrete representation. The linear substitutions denoted by the two sides of the equations are therefore the same, and hence

$$\frac{h_i\chi_i}{\chi_1}\frac{h_j\chi_j}{\chi_1}=\sum_{s=1}^{s=r} c_{ijs}\frac{h_s\chi_s}{\chi_1}.$$

These equations hold for each irreducible representation. They may be rather more conveniently expressed in the form

$$h_ih_j\chi_i^k\chi_j^k=\chi_1^k\sum_1^r c_{ijs}h_s\chi_s^k,$$

$$(i, j, k=1, 2, \ldots\ldots, r).$$

214. In the representation of G as a regular permutation-group of N symbols,

$$x_1,\ x_2,\ \ldots\ldots,\ x_N,$$

the substitution denoted with the previous notation by

$$C_1+C_2+\ldots\ldots+C_r,$$

i.e. the sum of all the substitutions of the group, is

$$x_1'=\sigma,\ x_2'=\sigma,\ \ldots\ldots,\ x_N'=\sigma,$$

where σ denotes the sum of the N symbols. With

$$\sigma,\ x_2-x_1,\ x_3-x_1,\ \ldots\ldots,\ x_N-x_1$$

as new symbols, this substitution is

$$\sigma'=N\sigma,\ (x_2-x_1)'=0,\ (x_3-x_1)'=0,\ \ldots\ldots,\ (x_N-x_1)'=0.$$

Now in the completely reduced form of G_E the identical representation occurs just once (Theorem III, Chapter XIV), and the corresponding reduced variable is σ. Hence the reduced variables for any other irreducible component must be linear functions of the differences x_2-x_1, x_3-x_1, ..., x_N-x_1.

Hence in each irreducible component of G, except the identical one, $C_1+C_2+\ldots\ldots+C_r$ replaces each symbol by zero. By the preceding paragraph, $C_1+C_2+\ldots\ldots+C_r$, in any irreducible representation, replaces each symbol in $\sum_i \frac{h_i\chi_i}{\chi_1}$ times itself. Hence

$$\sum_S \chi_S^k=\sum_i h_i\chi_i^k=0, \qquad k\neq 1,$$

where the first summation is extended to the operations and the second to the conjugate sets of G.

215. In the group on the $\chi_1^i\chi_1^j$ products of the variables that arises by compounding the representations Γ_i and Γ_j, the characteristic of any substitution is the product of the corresponding characteristics in Γ_i and Γ_j. In fact if

$$x_p' = \Sigma\, a_{pq} x_q,$$

and

$$y_u' = \Sigma\, b_{uv} y_v,$$

are corresponding substitutions of Γ_i and Γ_j, the resulting substitution of the compounded group is

$$(x_p y_u)' = \Sigma\, a_{pq} b_{uv} x_q y_v,$$

and the sum of the coefficients in the leading diagonal of this is $\Sigma\, a_{pp} b_{qq}$ or $\Sigma\, a_{pp} \,.\, \Sigma\, b_{qq}$. Now in two equivalent groups the characteristics of any substitution are the same. It follows that the relation

$$\Gamma_i \Gamma_j = \sum_1^r g_{ijs} \Gamma_s,$$

expressing the complete reduction of the group compounded from Γ_i and Γ_j, involves, for each p, the equation

$$\chi_p^i \chi_p^j = \sum_1^r g_{ijs} \chi_p^s;$$

the two sides of this equation being different forms of the characteristic of the pth conjugate set in the compounded group.

If the last equation be multiplied by h_p, and a summation be carried out with respect to p, i.e. with respect to the conjugate sets, there results

$$\sum_{p=1}^{p=r} h_p \chi_p^i \chi_p^j = \sum_{s=1}^{s=r} g_{ijs} \sum_{p=1}^{p=r} h_p \chi_p^s.$$

Now we have seen, in §§ 212, 214, that

$$\sum_{p=1}^{p=r} h_p \chi_p^1 = N,$$

$$\sum_{p=1}^{p=r} h_p \chi_p^s = 0, \qquad s \neq 1.$$

Hence

$$\sum_{p=1}^{p=r} h_p \chi_p^i \chi_p^j = g_{ij1} N.$$

Also it has been seen, in § 211, that g_{ij1} is unity or zero, according as j is or is not i'; so that

$$\sum_{p=1}^{p=r} h_p \chi_p^{\,i} \chi_p^{\,i'} = N$$

and

$$\sum_{p=1}^{p=r} h_p \chi_p^{\,i} \chi_p^{\,j} = 0, \qquad j \neq i'.$$

216. From these equations it immediately follows that no two distinct irreducible representations have the same set of group-characteristics.

For if $\chi_p^{\,i} = \chi_p^{\,j}$, for each p,

then $\chi_p^{\,i'} = \chi_p^{\,j'}$, for each p,

and

$$\sum_1^r h_p \chi_p^{\,i} \chi_p^{\,j'} = \sum_1^r h_p \chi_p^{\,i} \chi_p^{\,i'} = N,$$

in contradiction of the equation

$$\sum_1^r h_p \chi_p^{\,i} \chi_p^{\,j'} = 0, \qquad j' \neq i'.$$

In particular, if the characteristics of Γ_i are all real, Γ_i is equivalent to $\overline{\Gamma}_i$, or $i' = i$. Moreover the sets of group-characteristics are linearly independent, in the sense that their determinant $|\chi_p^{\,i}|$ is not zero. For suppose that a relation

$$\sum_{k=1}^{k=r} A_k \chi_p^{\,k} = 0$$

holds for each p. Then

$$\sum_{p=1}^{p=r} h_p \chi_p^{\,k'} \sum_{k=1}^{k=r} A_k \chi_p^{\,k} = 0,$$

and in virtue of the above relations

$$A_k N = 0,$$

so that each A_k is zero.

Suppose now that in any representation of G as a group of linear substitutions the characteristics of the r conjugate sets are ψ_s $(s = 1, 2, \ldots\ldots, r)$. When completely reduced let the representation be equivalent to $\Sigma c_i \Gamma_i$. Then for each s

$$\psi_s = \Sigma c_i \chi_s^{\,i}.$$

Since the determinant $|\chi_s^{\,i}|$ is not zero, these equations determine the c's uniquely. Hence:—

THEOREM I. *The necessary and sufficient condition that two representations of a group of finite order, as a group of linear substitutions, should be equivalent is that the characteristic of each conjugate set shall be the same in the two.*

Further, the actual solution of the last equations is

$$c_i = \frac{\sum\limits_s h_s \psi_s \chi_s^{i'}}{N}.$$

217. With the aid of this theorem, we can now complete the discussion of the equivalence of two representations of a group as a permutation-group when transformations by linear substitutions are admitted, i.e. when two representations are regarded as equivalent if a linear substitution can be found which will transform one into the other.

If g is any representation of G as a permutation-group, the characteristic of any operation S of G in g is the mark (§ 180) of the cyclical sub-group $\{S\}$ in g. In fact if $(a_1 a_2 \ldots\ldots a_n)$ is any cycle of the permutation of g which corresponds to S, the characteristic, so far as these n symbols are concerned, is zero.

Unless G is a cyclical group, the s distinct sets of conjugate sub-groups in G are not all cyclical. Denote the number of distinct conjugate sets of cyclical sub-groups by ρ; and (departing slightly from the notation of § 180) let

$$G_1,\ G_2,\ \ldots\ldots,\ G_\rho$$

be representative sub-groups, one from each set. Then the necessary and sufficient conditions, when transformation by linear substitutions is admitted, that the two representations

$$\sum_1^s a_i g_i \text{ and } \sum_1^s b_i g_i$$

should be equivalent is that

$$\Sigma a_i m_t^i = \Sigma b_i m_t^i \qquad (t = 1, 2, \ldots\ldots, \rho).$$

For if these equations are satisfied every operation of G will have the same characteristic in the two representations.

Writing
$$a_i - b_i = c_i,$$

the system of equations

$$\sum_{i=1}^{i=s} c_i m_t^i = 0 \qquad (t = 1, 2, \ldots\ldots, \rho)$$

must have $s - \rho$ linearly independent systems of solutions in integers, since the determinant $|m_t^i|$ $(i, t = 1, 2, \ldots\ldots, \rho)$ is certainly different from zero. Moreover for such a system of equations there is a set of $s-\rho$ solutions*,

$$c_1^{(n)},\ c_2^{(n)},\ \ldots\ldots,\ c_s^{(n)}\qquad (n=1,\ 2,\ \ldots\ldots,\ s-\rho),$$

in terms of which the general solution can be expressed in the form

$$c_i=\sum_n k_n c_i^{(n)},$$

where the k's are arbitrary positive or negative integers.

Every possible equivalence will therefore arise from the $s-\rho$ fundamental equivalences

$$\sum_1^s c_i^{(n)} g_i=0\qquad (n=1,\ 2,\ \ldots\ldots,\ s-\rho).$$

Of the c's some are positive and some are negative; and the equation expresses the fact that the representation given by the terms with positive coefficients is equivalent to (i.e. can be transformed into) the representation given by the terms with negative coefficients.

It is clear that though such an equivalence as

$$g_i=g_j$$

may occur, there will not necessarily be equivalences of this form.

Ex. 1. For the alternating group of four symbols (§ 185), prove that the fundamental equivalences are

$$g_3+g_4=g_2+g_5,\quad g_1+2g_4=3g_2,$$

and verify them directly by transformation.

Ex. 2. The simple group of order 168 contains two distinct conjugate sets of sub-groups of order 24, in respect of each of which it may be represented as a transitive permutation-group of degree 7. Shew that in the representation (§ 166) in which the group is generated by

$$(x_1x_2x_3x_6x_4x_5x_7),\ (x_2x_3x_4)(x_5x_6x_7),\ (x_2x_7x_6x_3)(x_4x_5),$$

the two permutations

$$(x_2x_3x_4)(x_5x_6x_7),\ (x_1x_7x_5x_6)(x_2x_3)$$

generate a sub-group of order 24 which does not leave one symbol unchanged; and that the given representation is transformed into the representation in respect of this sub-group by the linear substitution

$$x_1'=x_2+x_3+x_4,\quad x_2'=x_3+x_5+x_6,\quad x_3'=x_4+x_6+x_7,$$
$$x_4'=x_2+x_5+x_7,\quad x_5'=x_1+x_3+x_7,\quad x_6'=x_1+x_4+x_5,$$
$$x_7'=x_1+x_2+x_6.$$

* Elliott, *Algebra of Quantics*, p. 192.

218. In the representation of G as a regular permutation-group, the characteristic of every operation except E is zero. The completely reduced form of this group is (Theorem III, Chap. XIV)

$$\sum_{i=1}^{i=r} \chi_1^i \Gamma_i.$$

Hence for each p except 1,

$$\sum_{i=1}^{i=r} \chi_1^i \chi_p^i = 0,$$

while, as has already been seen,

$$\sum_{i=1}^{i=r} (\chi_1^i)^2 = N.$$

If now the equation of § 213,

$$h_p h_q \chi_p^k \chi_q^k = \chi_1^k \sum_{s=1}^{s=r} c_{pqs} h_s \chi_s^k,$$

be summed with respect to k, i.e. with respect to the distinct representations,

$$h_p h_q \sum_{k=1}^{k=r} \chi_p^k \chi_q^k = \sum_{s=1}^{s=r} c_{pqs} h_s \sum_{k=1}^{k=r} \chi_1^k \chi_s^k$$
$$= c_{pq1} N$$

from the above equations.

Now c_{pq1} is h_p or zero according as q is or is not p'.

Hence
$$\sum_{k=1}^{k=r} \chi_p^k \chi_q^k = 0, \qquad q \neq p',$$
$$\sum_{k=1}^{k=r} \chi_p^k \chi_{p'}^k = N/h_p.$$

The latter equation may obviously also be written

$$\sum_{k=1}^{k=r} \chi_p^k \chi_p^{k'} = N/h_p.$$

For convenience of reference the various relations among the group-characteristics obtained in the preceding paragraphs are collected here. They are clearly not all independent of each other, but they form a complete system of relations all of which will be required in the sequel,

$$h_p h_q \chi_p^k \chi_q^k = \chi_1^k \sum_{s=1}^{s=r} c_{pqs} h_s \chi_s^k, \quad (p, q, k = 1, 2, \ldots, r),$$

$$\chi_p^i \chi_p^j = \sum_{s=1}^{s=r} g_{ijs} \chi_p^s, \qquad (p, i, j = 1, 2, \ldots, r),$$

$$\sum_{p=1}^{p=r} h_p \chi_p^k \chi_p^{k'} = N,$$

$$\sum_{p=1}^{p=r} h_p \chi_p^k \chi_p^l = 0, \qquad l \neq k',$$

$$\sum_{k=1}^{k=r} \chi_p^k \chi_{p'}^k = N/h_p,$$

$$\sum_{k=1}^{k=r} \chi_p^k \chi_q^k = 0, \qquad q \neq p'.$$

219. The coefficients g_{ijk} that occur in the expressions for the composition of the irreducible representations, satisfy certain relations analogous to those connecting the coefficients c_{ijk}.

From their definition it follows that

$$g_{ijk} = g_{jik}.$$

As has already been seen, by equating the characteristics of $\Gamma_i \Gamma_j$ to those of $\Sigma g_{ijk} \Gamma_k$, we have

$$\chi_p^i \chi_p^j = \Sigma g_{ijk} \chi_p^k, \qquad (p = 1, 2, \ldots, r).$$

Since the determinant $|\chi_p^k|$ is not zero, these equations determine the g's in terms of the characteristics, giving

$$N g_{ijk} = \sum_p h_p \chi_p^i \chi_p^j \chi_p^{k'}.$$

Similarly $$N g_{i'kj} = \sum_p h_p \chi_p^{i'} \chi_p^k \chi_p^{j'},$$

and $$N g_{i'j'k'} = \sum_p h_p \chi_p^{i'} \chi_p^{j'} \chi_p^k.$$

Now the sums on the right-hand sides of the two latter equations are the conjugate imaginaries of the sum on the right-hand side of the first; and the sums, all being real, are therefore all equal. Hence

$$g_{ijk} = g_{i'kj} = g_{j'ki} = g_{i'j'k'} = g_{ik'j'} = g_{jk'i'}.$$

Further, since the multiplication involved in the composition of Γ_i and Γ_j is associative,

$$\Gamma_i\Gamma_j \,.\, \Gamma_s = \sum_k g_{ijk}\Gamma_k\Gamma_s = \sum_{k,\,t} g_{ijk}g_{kst}\Gamma_t,$$

and

$$\Gamma_i \,.\, \Gamma_j\Gamma_s = \sum_k g_{jsk}\Gamma_i\Gamma_k = \sum_{k,\,t} g_{jsk}g_{kit}\Gamma_t.$$

Hence $\sum_k g_{ijk}g_{kst}$ is unaltered by any permutation of the symbols i, j, s.

That the numbers g_{ijk} are comparatively small follows from their definition. Moreover a simple expression holds for the sum of their squares. Thus

$$N g_{ijk} = \sum_p h_p \chi_p{}^i \chi_p{}^j \chi_p{}^{k'}$$

$$= \sum_q h_q \chi_q{}^{i'} \chi_q{}^{j'} \chi_q{}^{k},$$

so that

$$N^2 g^2{}_{ijk} = \sum_{p,\,q} h_p h_q \chi_p{}^i \chi_q{}^{i'} \chi_p{}^j \chi_q{}^{j'} \chi_p{}^{k'} \chi_q{}^{k}.$$

Now

$$\sum_i \chi_p{}^i \chi_q{}^{i'} = 0, \qquad p \neq q,$$

$$= N/h_p, \qquad p = q.$$

Hence

$$N^2 \sum_{i,\,j,\,k} g^2{}_{ijk} = \sum_p \frac{N^3}{h_p},$$

or

$$\sum_{i,\,j,\,k} g^2{}_{ijk} = N \sum_p \frac{1}{h_p}.$$

220. The representations of a group in a single symbol clearly combine among themselves by composition. Denote them by $\Gamma_i\,(i = 1, 2, \ldots\ldots, t)$ where t is the ratio of the order of the group G to the order of its derived group H. Then the system of relations

$$\Gamma_i\Gamma_j = \Gamma_k$$

between these t representations is easily seen to be in effect the multiplication table of an Abelian group simply isomorphic with G/H.

If Γ is any other representation of G then $\Gamma_i\Gamma\,(i = 1, 2, \ldots\ldots, t)$ are clearly irreducible representations of G. Moreover if K is the self-conjugate sub-group of G, whose operations correspond to the identical substitution in Γ_i, $\Gamma_i\Gamma$ and Γ are distinct representations unless the characteristic in Γ of each operation of G not contained in K is zero. In fact it is obviously only when this condition is satisfied that every operation of G has the same characteristic in Γ and $\Gamma_i\Gamma$.

When this condition is satisfied, then

$$\Gamma_i \Gamma = \Gamma,$$

and therefore, since

$$g_{ijk} = g_{j'ki},$$

Γ_i occurs just once in the reduced form of $\Gamma\Gamma'$, where Γ' is the inverse representation of Γ. Now if

$$\Gamma_i \Gamma = \Gamma,$$

then

$$\Gamma_i^s \Gamma = \Gamma.$$

Hence each of the representations in a single symbol

$$\Gamma_i^s \ (s = 1, 2, \ldots\ldots)$$

occurs once in the reduced form of $\Gamma\Gamma'$. If the order of G/K is m, the number of these representations which are distinct is m.

On the other hand if Γ_k and Γ_l are two representations of G in more than one symbol, and if $l \neq k'$, then in the reduced form of $\Gamma_k \Gamma_l$ there is no representation in a single symbol. For if $\Gamma_i \ (i \leqslant t)$ occurred, then Γ_l and $\Gamma_i \Gamma_{k'}$ would be equivalent representations, and as has been seen above this can only be the case if $l = k'$.

221. If S is an operation of order m, the characteristic of S in any irreducible representation is the sum of a number of powers of ω, a primitive mth root of unity, say

$$\chi_S = \omega^{a_1} + \omega^{a_2} + \ldots\ldots + \omega^{a_t}.$$

The characteristic of S^μ in the same representation is

$$\chi_{S^\mu} = \omega^{\mu a_1} + \omega^{\mu a_2} + \ldots\ldots + \omega^{\mu a_t}.$$

If S and S^μ are conjugate operations, these characteristics must be the same, so that in each irreducible representation χ_S is unchanged on writing ω^μ for ω.

Conversely, if this last condition is satisfied, S and S^μ must be conjugate operations. For suppose if possible that S and S^μ belong to the ith and jth conjugate sets respectively, where $j \neq i$ and therefore $j' \neq i'$. For two such sets

$$\sum_k \chi_i^k \chi_{j'}^k = 0.$$

But on the supposition made χ_i^k and $\chi_{j'}^k$ are conjugate imaginaries, and therefore the supposition that $j \neq i$ leads to a contradiction. In particular if S is not conjugate to any of its powers there must be representations in which χ_S is changed when any other primitive mth root of unity is written for ω.

222. The case of a group of odd order presents peculiarities that should be noticed. In such a group no operation can be conjugate to its inverse. For if $R^{-1}SR=S^{-1}$, then $R^{-2}SR^2=S$. But, R being an operation of odd order, R must be permutable with S if R^2 is; so that the assumption made is not true. Hence some of the characteristics of every conjugate set must be imaginary. For the same reason r, the number of conjugate sets, is necessarily odd, for E is the only set which is not distinct from its inverse. Moreover, of such a group there can be no irreducible representation in which the characteristics are all real. In fact, if the characteristic χ_S of S is real, then $\sum_\mu \chi_{S^\mu}$ extended to the μ powers of S which are of the same order as S, which is a real integer (positive or negative) in any case, is an even integer because

$$\chi_S = \chi_{S^{-1}}.$$

Hence if the characteristic of every operation were real, the equation

$$\sum_S \chi_S = 0$$

would be χ_E + an even number $=0$, which is impossible, since χ_E is necessarily odd (§ 225 below). Hence:—

THEOREM II. *No irreducible representation of a group of odd order, other than the identical representation, is equivalent to its conjugate.*

Corollary. No group of linear substitutions of odd order with real coefficients is irreducible.

This theorem involves a remarkable relation between the (odd) order N of a group and the number r of its conjugate sets. It has been seen (§ 218) that

$$N = \sum_{s=1}^{s=r} (\chi_1^s)^2.$$

For a group of odd order r is odd, say $2\rho+1$, and each irreducible representation, except the identical one, is distinct from its conjugate, while the number of symbols in any irreducible representation is odd. Hence the above equation takes the form

$$N = 1 + \sum_{s=1}^{s=\rho} 2(2a_s + 1)^2$$

$$= r + \sum_{s=1}^{s=\rho} 8a_s(a_s + 1),$$

and therefore

$$N \equiv r \pmod{16}.$$

223. The actual determination of the group-characteristics involves only algebraical processes when the numbers c_{ijk} are known. Moreover these numbers can always be calculated from the multiplication table of the group.

Multiplying each side of the equation (§ 213)

$$\frac{h_i\chi_i^k}{\chi_1^k}\frac{h_j\chi_j^k}{\chi_1^k} = \sum_{s=1}^{s=r} c_{ijs}\frac{h_s\chi_s^k}{\chi_1^k}$$

by an arbitrary coefficient A_i, and summing with respect to i, we have

$$\xi\frac{h_j\chi_j^k}{\chi_1^k} = \sum_{i,s=1}^{i,s=r} A_i c_{ijs}\frac{h_s\chi_s^k}{\chi_1^k},$$

where

$$\xi = \sum_{i=1}^{i=r}\frac{A_i h_i\chi_i^k}{\chi_1^k}.$$

Eliminating the r quantities $\dfrac{h_s\chi_s^k}{\chi_1^k}$ from the r equations that arise by putting $j = 1, 2, \ldots\ldots, r$, there results

$$0 = \begin{vmatrix} \sum_i A_i c_{i11} - \xi, & \sum_i A_i c_{i12}, & \ldots\ldots, & \sum_i A_i c_{i1r} \\ \sum_i A_i c_{i21}, & \sum_i A_i c_{i22} - \xi, & \ldots\ldots, & \sum_i A_i c_{i2r} \\ \ldots & \ldots & \ldots & \ldots \\ \sum_i A_i c_{ir1}, & \sum_i A_i c_{ir2}, & \ldots\ldots, & \sum_i A_i c_{irr} - \xi \end{vmatrix}$$

or

$$f(\xi, A_1, A_2, \ldots\ldots, A_r) = 0,$$

where the left-hand side is an integral homogeneous function of the rth degree of $\xi, A_1, A_2, \ldots\ldots, A_r$ with rational integral coefficients, the coefficient of ξ^r being unity. The r roots of this equation are the r values of

$$\sum_1^r A_i \frac{h_i \chi_i^k}{\chi_1^k},$$

for $k = 1, 2, \ldots\ldots, r$; and the homogeneous function f must therefore fall into r homogeneous linear factors. The coefficients in these linear factors are rational functions of roots of unity, since χ_i is the sum of χ_1 m_ith roots of unity, where m_i is the order of an operation of the ith set. Hence if m is the least common multiple of the orders of the operations of the group, the linear factors of f are rationally determinable in terms of the mth roots of unity.

If now
$$\xi - \Sigma \alpha_i A_i$$
is one of the linear factors, then the equations

$$\frac{h_i \chi_i}{\chi_1} = \alpha_i \qquad (i = 2, \ldots\ldots, r)$$

determine the ratios of the corresponding set of group-characteristics. Using these values in the equation

$$\sum_i h_i \chi_i \bar{\chi}_i = N,$$

we have
$$\chi_1^2 \sum_i \frac{\alpha_i \bar{\alpha}_i}{h_i} = N,$$

determining χ_1, which is necessarily a positive integer, and thereby completing the determination of the set of characteristics.

224. In illustration of this process a simple example will be given, viz. the non-cyclical group of order 10. This is defined by

$$S^5 = E, \quad T^2 = E, \quad TST = S^{-1}.$$

The conjugate sets are

$$E; \quad S, S^{-1}; \quad S^2, S^{-2}; \quad T, TS, TS^2, TS^3, TS^4.$$

Representing these in the order written by

$$C_1, \quad C_2, \quad C_3, \quad C_4,$$

the multiplication table of the conjugate sets is at once found to be

$$\begin{aligned}
C_2^2 &= 2C_1 + C_3, \\
C_2C_3 &= C_2 + C_3, \\
C_2C_4 &= 2C_4, \\
C_3^2 &= 2C_1 + C_2, \\
C_3C_4 &= 2C_4, \\
C_4^2 &= 5C_1 + 5C_2 + 5C_3.
\end{aligned}$$

The equation for ξ is therefore

$$\begin{vmatrix} A_1-\xi & A_2 & A_3 & A_4 \\ 2A_2 & A_1+A_3-\xi & A_2+A_3 & 2A_4 \\ 2A_3 & A_2+A_3 & A_1+A_2-\xi & 2A_4 \\ 5A_4 & 5A_4 & 5A_4 & A_1+2A_2+2A_3-\xi \end{vmatrix} = 0.$$

By adding the first three rows and then adding or subtracting the last, two of the factors are obviously

$$\xi - A_1 - 2A_2 - 2A_3 \pm 5A_4.$$

By combining the first three rows the other two factors are found to be

$$\xi - A_1 + \frac{1}{2}(A_2 + A_3) \pm \frac{\sqrt{5}}{2}(A_2 - A_3).$$

The first two factors give

$$\frac{2\chi_2}{\chi_1} = 2, \quad \frac{2\chi_3}{\chi_1} = 2, \quad \frac{5\chi_4}{\chi_1} = \pm 5$$

leading to $\chi_1 = 1, \quad \chi_2 = 1, \quad \chi_3 = 1, \quad \chi_4 = 1;$

and $\chi_1 = 1, \quad \chi_2 = 1, \quad \chi_3 = 1, \quad \chi_4 = -1.$

The other two factors give

$$\frac{2\chi_2}{\chi_1} = \frac{-1 \pm \sqrt{5}}{2}, \quad \frac{2\chi_3}{\chi_1} = \frac{-1 \mp \sqrt{5}}{2}, \quad \frac{5\chi_4}{\chi_1} = 0$$

leading to

$$\chi_1 = 2, \quad \chi_2 = \frac{-1+\sqrt{5}}{2}, \quad \chi_3 = \frac{-1-\sqrt{5}}{2}, \quad \chi_4 = 0;$$

and $\chi_1 = 2, \quad \chi_2 = \dfrac{-1-\sqrt{5}}{2}, \quad \chi_3 = \dfrac{-1+\sqrt{5}}{2}, \quad \chi_4 = 0.$

225. If in the equation for ξ (§ 223) arbitrary rational integral values are given to the A's, ξ will satisfy an equation with rational integral coefficients in which the coefficient of the leading term is unity. In other words ξ is an algebraic integer. In particular this is the case if all the A's except one are zero and that one unity. Hence, for each i and k, $h_i\chi_i^k/\chi_1^k$ is an algebraic integer.

The relation (§ 218)

$$h_p h_q \chi_p^k \chi_q^k = \chi_1^k \sum_1^r c_{pqs} h_s \chi_s^k$$

gives, when p' is written for q, and the relation (§ 43)

$$c_{pqs} h_s = c_{ps'q'} h_q$$

is taken account of,

$$h_p \chi_p^k \chi_{p'}^k = \chi_1^k \sum_1^r c_{ps'p} \chi_s^k.$$

Summing this equation with respect to p,

$$\sum_p h_p \chi_p^k \chi_{p'}^k = \chi_1^k \sum_{p,\,s=1}^{p,\,s=r} c_{ps'p} \chi_s^k,$$

or

$$N = \chi_1^k \sum_{p,\,s=1}^{p,\,s=r} c_{ps'p} \chi_s^k,$$

and therefore N is divisible by χ_1^k. Hence:—

THEOREM III. *The number of variables in terms of which a group of finite order can be represented as an irreducible group of linear substitutions is a factor of the order of the group.*

226. Let $\Sigma a_i \Gamma_i$ or Γ be any representation of G in which the characteristics are $\psi_p\,(p = 1, 2, \ldots\ldots, r)$. If the result of compounding Γ with itself n times and completely reducing the compounded group be denoted by the formula

$$\Gamma^n = \sum_i \gamma_{ni} \Gamma_i,$$

then

$$(\psi_p)^n = \sum_i \gamma_{ni} \chi_p^i, \qquad (p = 1, 2, \ldots\ldots, r),$$

from which we obtain

$$N\gamma_{ni} = \sum_p h_p \chi_p^{i'} (\psi_p)^n,$$

and

$$N \sum_n x^n \gamma_{ni} = \sum_{n,p} h_p \chi_p^{i'} (x\psi_p)^n,$$

where x is arbitrary. If $|x|$ is small enough, the r series on the right are certainly convergent when extended to infinity, and their sum is

$$\sum_p \frac{h_p \chi_p^{i'}}{1 - x\psi_p};$$

so that, if $\gamma_{ni} = 0$, for each n, then

$$\sum_p \frac{h_p \chi_p^{i'}}{1 - x\psi_p} \equiv 0.$$

Suppose now that G is simply isomorphic with Γ. Then the characteristic ψ_1 of E is different from the characteristic of every other operation of G, and therefore the preceding identity cannot hold. In this case, for each i, it is possible to find n so that $\gamma_{ni} \neq 0$. Hence:—

THEOREM IV. *If Γ is a representation of G as a group of linear substitutions, and if G is simply isomorphic with Γ, then, when the process of compounding Γ with itself is carried far enough, every irreducible representation of G will arise.*

Corollary. If $s\,(< r)$ of the irreducible representations of G, viz. $\Gamma_1, \Gamma_2, \ldots\ldots, \Gamma_s$, combine among themselves by composition, then G has a self-conjugate sub-group H, each of whose operations is represented by the identical substitution in these s representations of G and in no others.

If the representation $\sum_1^s a_i\Gamma_i$ were such that G was simply isomorphic with it, every irreducible representation would arise by compounding this representation with itself and therefore by compounding $\Gamma_1, \Gamma_2, \ldots\ldots, \Gamma_s$ among themselves. Hence there are operations of G other than E which correspond to the identical substitution in $\sum_1^s a_i\Gamma_i$, whatever positive integers a_i may be. Let H be the self-conjugate sub-group of G constituted of these operations. Then to the operations of H there correspond the identical substitution in each of the representations $\Gamma_1, \Gamma_2, \ldots\ldots, \Gamma_s$. Suppose now, if possible, that $\Gamma_t\,(t > s)$ is another representation of G to the identical substitution of which the operations of H correspond. Since Γ_t does not occur when $\sum_1^s a_i\Gamma_i$ is compounded continually with itself,

$$\sum_p \frac{h_p \chi_p^{t'}}{1 - x\psi_p} \equiv 0,$$

where ψ_p is the characteristic of the pth conjugate set in

$$\sum_1^s a_i\Gamma_i.$$

Now for each conjugate set in H, and for these only,

$$\psi_p = \psi_1;$$

and for each conjugate set in H,

$$\chi_p^{t'} = \chi_1^{t'}.$$

Hence the left-hand side of the last identity contains the term

$$\frac{n_H \chi_1^{t'}}{1 - x\psi_1},$$

where n_H is the order of H, while all the other terms have denominators different from this one. The identity therefore cannot hold; in other words the supposed existence of the representation Γ_t leads to a contradiction. The proof of the corollary is thus completed. Its converse is obviously true.

The expression

$$\frac{1}{N}\sum_p \frac{h_p \chi_p^{i'}}{1 - x\psi_p}$$

is a generating function for determining the number of times that the irreducible representation Γ_i occurs when the representation in which $\psi_p\,(p = 1, 2, \ldots\ldots, r)$ are the characteristics is compounded continually with itself.

227. If a set of variables

$$x_1, x_2, \ldots\ldots, x_m$$

undergo a group of linear substitutions which is a representation of G, their homogeneous products of n dimensions also undergo a group of linear substitutions which is a representation of G, and the question arises as to what the reduced form of this group is. Herr Molien* has obtained a series of generating functions for determining this reduction. If

$$\omega_1^{(p)}, \omega_2^{(p)}, \ldots\ldots, \omega_m^{(p)}$$

are the multipliers of an operation of the pth conjugate set in the given group of linear substitutions, then the sum of the homogeneous products of the ω's of n dimensions, i.e. the coefficient of x^n in the expansion of

$$\frac{1}{(1 - x\omega_1^{(p)})(1 - x\omega_2^{(p)})\ldots\ldots(1 - x\omega_m^{(p)})},$$

is the characteristic of the pth conjugate set in the group of linear substitutions on the homogeneous products of the x's of n dimensions.

Consider now the expression

$$\frac{1}{N}\sum \frac{h_p \chi_p^{i'}}{(1 - x\omega_1^{(p)})\ldots\ldots(1 - x\omega_m^{(p)})}.$$

* "Ueber die Invarianten der linearen Substitutionsgruppen," *Berliner Sitzungsberichte* (1898), pp. 1152—1156.

The coefficient of x^n in this is

$$\frac{1}{N}\sum_p h_p \chi_p^{i'} \psi_p,$$

where ψ_p is the characteristic of the pth conjugate set in the group on the homogeneous products of the x's of n dimensions. Hence, § 216, this coefficient is the number of times Γ_i occurs in the reduced form of the group on the homogeneous products of the x's of n dimensions. The expression given is therefore the required generating function. In particular, the coefficient of x^n in

$$\frac{1}{N}\sum_p \frac{h_p}{(1-x\omega_1^{(p)})\ldots\ldots(1-x\omega_m^{(p)})}$$

is the number of linearly independent functions of the x's of the nth degree which are invariant for all the substitutions of the group.

As a simple illustration of the last result we take the group of order 10 generated by S and T, viz.

$$x' = \omega x, \quad y' = \omega^{-1}y; \quad \omega^5 = 1$$
$$x' = y, \quad y' = x;$$

already considered in § 224. Here

$$\frac{1}{N}\sum_p \frac{h_p}{(1-x\omega_1^{(p)})\ldots\ldots(1-x\omega_m^{(p)})}$$
$$= \frac{1}{10}\left(\frac{1}{(1-x)^2} + \frac{2}{(1-x\omega)(1-x\omega^{-1})} + \frac{2}{(1-x\omega^2)(1-x\omega^{-2})} + \frac{5}{1-x^2}\right)$$
$$= 1 + x^2 + x^4 + x^5 + x^6 + x^7 + x^8 + x^9 + 2x^{10} + \ldots\ldots.$$

The reader will have no difficulty in verifying directly the results indicated by this series. (Compare § 266.)

228. If $\Gamma_1, \Gamma_2, \ldots\ldots, \Gamma_{r'}$ $(r' < r)$ are r' irreducible representations of G, which combine among themselves by composition, and if H is the self-conjugate sub-group of G, each of whose operations correspond to the identical substitution in each of the r' representations, then $\Gamma_1, \Gamma_2, \ldots\ldots, \Gamma_{r'}$ are obviously irreducible representations of G/H.

Let $H, S_2H, \ldots\ldots, S_mH$ be the sets into which the operations of G fall in respect of H, and

$$e, s_2, \ldots\ldots, s_m,$$

the corresponding operations of G/H.

In $\Gamma_i\,(i \leqslant r')$ there corresponds the same substitution to each of the operations of the set S_pH of G, and this substitution corresponds to the operation s_p of G/H. Now, because Γ_i and Γ_j are distinct representations of G,

$$\sum_S \chi^i{}_S \chi^{j'}{}_S = 0,$$

the summation extending to all the operations of G.

But if T is any operation of H,

$$\begin{aligned} \chi^i{}_S &= \chi^i{}_{ST}, \text{ and } & \chi^{j'}{}_S &= \chi^{j'}{}_{ST} \\ &= \chi^i{}_s & &= \chi^{j'}{}_s. \end{aligned}$$

Hence, summing first for the operations of the set S_pH, and then for the sets,

$$n_H \sum_s \chi_s{}^i \chi_s{}^{j'} = 0,$$

where n_H is the order of H. The representations Γ_i and Γ_j, considered as representations of G/H, are therefore distinct. Now every irreducible representation of G/H must obviously occur among the irreducible representations of G; and

$$\Gamma_1,\ \Gamma_2,\ \ldots\ldots,\ \Gamma_{r'}$$

are the only representations of G in which each operation of H corresponds to the identical substitution. Hence

$$\Gamma_1,\ \Gamma_2,\ \ldots\ldots,\ \Gamma_{r'}$$

are the distinct irreducible representations of G/H; and the number of conjugate sets in this group is r'.

229. We shall now proceed to consider further the actual reduction of the representation of G as a regular permutation-group. It has been seen how the r sets of group-characteristics

$$\chi_1{}^p,\ \chi_2{}^p,\ \ldots\ldots,\ \chi_r{}^p,$$
$$(p = 1, 2, \ldots\ldots, r)$$

may be determined; and for the present purpose they will be regarded as known.

Denoting as before the sum of the operations in the ith conjugate set by C_i, form the r expressions

$$K_p = \sum_{i=1}^{i=r} \chi_{i'}{}^{p} C_i = \sum_S \chi^p{}_{S^{-1}} S,\ \ (p = 1, 2, \ldots\ldots, r)$$

where the first sum is extended to the r conjugate sets, and the second to the N operations of G. Then

$$K_p C_j = \sum_{i=1}^{i=r} \chi_i^{p'} C_i C_j = \sum_{i,s=1}^{i,s=r} c_{ijs} \chi_i^{p'} C_s.$$

Now
$$\sum_i c_{ijs} \chi_i^{p'} = \sum_i c_{js'i'} \frac{h_{i'}}{h_{s'}} \chi_i^{p'} \qquad (\S\ 43)$$
$$= \frac{1}{h_{s'}} \sum_{i'} c_{js'i'} h_{i'} \chi_{i'}^{p}$$
$$= \frac{1}{h_{s'}} h_j h_{s'} \frac{\chi_j^{p} \chi_{s'}^{p}}{\chi_1^{p}} \qquad (\S\ 218)$$
$$= \frac{h_j \chi_j^p}{\chi_1^p} \chi_s^{p'}.$$

Hence
$$K_p C_j = \sum_s \frac{h_j \chi_j^p}{\chi_1^p} \chi_s^{p'} C_s = \frac{h_j \chi_j^p}{\chi_1^p} K_p.$$

In particular
$$K_p K_q = K_p \sum_j \chi_j^{q'} C_j$$
$$= \frac{1}{\chi_1^p} K_p \Sigma h_j \chi_j^p \chi_j^{q'}$$
$$= 0, \text{ unless } q = p.$$

It follows that the N expressions

$$K_p S_1,\ K_p S_2,\ \ldots\ldots,\ K_p S_N$$

are certainly not linearly independent.

Suppose that just m of these expressions are linearly independent, and let them be

$$K_p S_x, \qquad (x = 1, 2, \ldots\ldots, m).$$

If S_u is any operation of G, each of the m expressions

$$K_p S_x S_u \qquad (x = 1, 2, \ldots\ldots, m)$$

can be represented as linear functions of

$$K_p S_x, \qquad (x = 1, 2, \ldots\ldots, m).$$

If
$$K_p S_i S_u = \sum_{j=1}^{j=m} \alpha_{iju} K_p S_j$$
and
$$K_p S_i S_v = \sum_{j=1}^{j=m} \alpha_{ijv} K_p S_j$$
$$(i = 1, 2, \ldots\ldots, m),$$

then
$$K_p S_i S_u S_v = \sum_{j=1}^{j=m} \alpha_{iju} K_p S_j S_v$$
$$= \sum_{j=1}^{j=m} \sum_{k=1}^{k=m} \alpha_{iju} \alpha_{jkv} K_p S_k.$$

Hence, on post-multiplication of the m expressions

$$K_p S_x \qquad (x = 1, 2, \ldots\ldots, m)$$

by the operations of G, a group of linear substitutions on m symbols arises which gives a representation of G. The same is obviously true if pre-multiplication is used instead of post-multiplication. Moreover, since in simplifying the expression $S_v K_p S_i S_u$, the same expression necessarily results whether we first form $K_p S_i S_u$ and then $S_v . K_p S_i S_u$, or first $S_v K_p S_i$ and then $S_v K_p S_i . S_u$, every linear substitution that arises from a post-multiplication is permutable with every linear substitution that arises from a pre-multiplication.

Further, since

$$K_p S_i S_u = \sum_{j=1}^{j=m} \alpha_{iju} K_p S_j$$

is, when the multiplication-table of the group is taken account of, an identical relation, the coefficients in the linear substitutions are rational functions of the group-characteristics of the particular set dealt with.

230. We next consider how this representation of G as a group of linear substitutions on m symbols may be expressed in terms of the irreducible representations. For this purpose it is necessary to know its set of characteristics.

In any representation the characteristic of C_i is h_i times the characteristic of any operation of the ith set.

Now it has been seen that

$$K_p C_i = \frac{h_i \chi_i^p}{\chi_1^p} K_p,$$

and therefore for each x

$$K_p S_x C_i = \frac{h_i \chi_i^p}{\chi_1^p} K_p S_x.$$

Hence the characteristic of any operation of the ith set is $m\chi_i^p/\chi_1^p$. From this it follows (§ 216) that the group of linear substitutions in question is equivalent to $(m/\chi_1^p)\,\Gamma_p$, and therefore that m is necessarily a multiple of χ_1^p. So also the group of linear substitutions that arises by pre-multiplication on the same set of the symbols, is equivalent to $(m/\chi_1^p)\,\Gamma'_p$. Since every substitution of the one group is permutable with every substitution of the other, m/χ_1^p cannot be less than χ_1^p. In fact if we suppose the first group completely reduced, and the symbols of each irreducible component

$$\begin{array}{llll} x_{11}, & x_{21}, & \ldots\ldots, & x_{t1}, \\ & & & \quad (t=\chi_1), \\ x_{12}, & x_{22}, & \ldots\ldots, & x_{t2}, \\ \multicolumn{4}{l}{\ldots\ldots\ldots\ldots\ldots\ldots\ldots\ldots \quad (s=m/\chi_1),} \\ x_{1s}, & x_{2s}, & \ldots\ldots, & x_{ts}, \end{array}$$

chosen so that each set undergoes the same linear substitution corresponding to each operation of the group, then the second group must transform among themselves the symbols in each column of the table. Hence the number of symbols in each column is equal to or a multiple of χ_1^p. The number m is therefore equal to or a multiple of $(\chi_1^p)^2$. From each of the r expressions K_p $(p=1, 2, \ldots, r)$ a corresponding set of symbols arises. Those arising from the different K's are necessarily independent, since the representations they give correspond to distinct irreducible components.

Now
$$\sum_p (\chi_1^p)^2 = N,$$

and the number of linearly independent symbols in all the sets cannot exceed N, the original number of symbols. Hence finally $m=(\chi_1^p)^2$.

THEOREM V. *If $\chi_1, \chi_2, \ldots, \chi_r$ are the group characteristics for the irreducible representation Γ of a group G, then*

$$\sum_i \chi_i C_{i'} \left(= \sum_S \chi_{S^{-1}} S\right)$$

takes just $(\chi_1)^2$ linearly independent values on post-multiplication by the operations of G. The $(\chi_1)^2$ linearly independent functions of the S's that so arise are transformed among themselves by post-multiplication, and give the component denoted by $\chi_1\Gamma$ in the reduction of the regular permutation-group which is simply isomorphic with G. The coefficients in the group of linear sub-

stitutions thus formed are rational functions of the characteristics of the set chosen. Every substitution of this group of linear substitutions is permutable with every substitution of the conjugate group on the same $(\chi_1)^2$ *functions that arises by using pre-multiplication in the place of post-multiplication.*

231. Let $x_1, x_2, \ldots, x_m$ $(m = \chi_1^2)$ be the χ_1^2 symbols which are transformed among themselves by the two groups, arising by pre- and post-multiplication, of the preceding theorem; and denote these groups by G_1 and G_2. Each of them is equivalent to the representation $\chi_1\Gamma$ of G. Suppose that

$$\xi_1 = \sum_{i=1}^{i=m} A_i x_i,$$

where the A's are arbitrary coefficients, is changed into

$$\xi_2, \xi_3, \ldots, \xi_n$$

by the linear substitutions of G_2 that correspond to a sub-group H of order n contained in G. Then $\sum_{j=1}^{j=n} \xi_j$ is the most general linear invariant for H in the representation G_2 of G. If in Γ there are just a linear invariants for H, $\Sigma\xi_j$ must contain just $a\chi_1$ independent linear functions of the x's. In other words $\Sigma\xi_j$ contains just $a\chi_1$ arbitrary coefficients; and the $a\chi_1$ linear functions of the x's which multiply these arbitrary coefficients are the $a\chi_1$ independent linear invariants of H in G_2. Moreover the coefficients of the x's in these linear functions are rational functions of the characteristics. Since every substitution of G_1 is permutable with every substitution of G_2, these $a\chi_1$ linear functions are transformed among themselves by every substitution of G_1, and the coefficients in the linear substitutions that so arise are rational in the characteristics. Hence $a\Gamma$ can be expressed in a form in which the coefficients are rational in the characteristics.

The group $\chi_1\Gamma$ is therefore in general further reducible without introducing any irrational quantity beyond the characteristics themselves. The only exception* is when the

* The author has shewn that this exceptional case can only occur when the Sylow sub-groups of G of odd order are cyclical, while the Sylow sub-group of even order is either cyclical or of the type given on p. 132. Cf. *Messenger of Mathematics*, Vol. xxxv. (1905), pp. 51—55.

number denoted by a is zero for every sub-group of G except E. In particular, whenever G contains a sub-group H which has only one linear invariant in Γ, this process completes the reduction of $\chi_1\Gamma$; and Γ itself can be expressed in a form in which the coefficients are rational in the characteristics.

232. When for a given group G, i.e. a group whose multiplication table is known, the characteristics have been calculated, the process that has just been described for constructing the representation $\chi_1\Gamma$ and partly or wholly reducing it is undoubtedly a lengthy one. An alternative process is to start from some other representation G_H of the group as a transitive permutation-group in the place of G_E.

If in the irreducible representation Γ, the sub-group H has just a linear invariants, then (Theorem II, Chapter XIV) Γ occurs just a times in the completely reduced form of G_H. In particular, if a is unity, there must be χ_1 linear functions of the symbols operated on by G_H, which are transformed among themselves by the permutations of G_H, the numerical coefficients which occur being rational functions of the characteristics of Γ.

In illustration of this process we will now actually set up one of the irreducible representations of the alternating group of degree 5; assuming for that purpose a knowledge of the characteristics of the group. These, as we have seen, may be calculated from the multiplication table. They are given in Ex. 3, p. 319.

The alternating group G of degree 5 admits an irreducible representation in three symbols for which the characteristics of identity, operations of orders 2, 3 and two sets of operations of order 5 are respectively 3, -1, 0 and $\frac{1}{2}(1 \pm \sqrt{5})$. If ω is a primitive fifth root of unity, the multipliers of an operation of order 5 are therefore 1, ω, ω^{-1}; and a cyclical sub-group of order 5 has a single linear invariant. Hence when the representation of G as a transitive permutation-group of degree 12 is completely reduced, the representation in question will occur just once. If $S_i\,(i=1, 2, \ldots\ldots, 12)$ are a set of 12 conjugate operations of order 5 and U any operation of the group, the permutations of the transitive group of degree 12 are given by

$$\begin{pmatrix} S_i \\ U^{-1}S_iU \end{pmatrix}.$$

Hence there must be three linear functions

$$\xi_i = \sum_{j=1}^{j=12} a_{ij} S_j \quad (i=1, 2, 3)$$

of the S's such that

$$U^{-1}\xi_1 U, \quad U^{-1}\xi_2 U, \quad U^{-1}\xi_3 U$$

are expressible linearly in terms of ξ_1, ξ_2, ξ_3 for every operation U

of the group. Moreover it must be possible to choose these functions so that when U is an assigned operation of order 5,

$$U^{-1}\xi_1 U = \xi_1, \quad U^{-1}\xi_2 U = \omega\xi_2, \quad U^{-1}\xi_3 U = \omega^{-1}\xi_3.$$

The operations of the group are most readily specified by the permutations of five symbols. Write

$$S = (abcde), \quad T = (ab)(cd),$$
$$T^{-1}ST = S_1, \quad S^{-1}S_1S = S_2, \quad S^{-1}S_2S = S_3,$$
$$S^{-1}S_3S = S_4, \quad S^{-1}S_4S = S_5.$$

Then since an operation of order 5 and its inverse are conjugate operations, S, S_1, S_2, S_3, S_4, S_5 and their inverses form the set of conjugate operations. Now S permutes S_1, S_2, S_3, S_4, S_5 cyclically. Hence the only linear function of the S's which is changed into itself on transformation by S is

$$\xi_1 = S + aS^{-1} + \beta(S_1 + S_2 + S_3 + S_4 + S_5)$$
$$+ \beta'(S_1^{-1} + S_2^{-1} + S_3^{-1} + S_4^{-1} + S_5^{-1}).$$

Similarly the only linear functions which are changed respectively in ω and ω^{-1} times themselves on transformation by S are

$$\xi_2 = S_1 + \omega^{-1}S_2 + \omega^{-2}S_3 + \omega^{-3}S_4 + \omega^{-4}S_5$$
$$+ \gamma(S_1^{-1} + \omega^{-1}S_2^{-1} + \omega^{-2}S_3^{-1} + \omega^{-3}S_4^{-1} + \omega^{-4}S_5^{-1}),$$

and $\xi_3 = S_1 + \omega S_2 + \omega^2 S_3 + \omega^3 S_4 + \omega^4 S_5$

$$+ \delta(S_1^{-1} + \omega S_2^{-1} + \omega^2 S_3^{-1} + \omega^3 S_4^{-1} + \omega^4 S_5^{-1}).$$

Now by using the permutations it is immediately verified that

$$TST = S_1, \quad TS_1T = S, \quad TS_2T = S_5,$$
$$TS_3T = S_3^{-1}, \quad TS_4T = S_4^{-1}, \quad TS_5T = S_2;$$

and it is certainly possible to determine a, β, β', γ, δ so that

$$T\xi_1T = \lambda\xi_1 + \mu\xi_2 + \nu\xi_3,$$
$$T\xi_2T = \lambda'\xi_1 + \mu'\xi_2 + \nu'\xi_3,$$
$$T\xi_3T = \lambda''\xi_1 + \mu''\xi_2 + \nu''\xi_3;$$

where the coefficients are numerical constants. Moreover, since S and T generate the group, when a, β, β', γ, δ are so determined, $U^{-1}\xi_1U$, $U^{-1}\xi_2U$, $U^{-1}\xi_3U$ will be linearly expressible in terms of ξ_1, ξ_2, ξ_3 for every operation U of the group. The actual calculation presents no difficulty. Thus the comparison of the coefficients of S, S_1, S_2, S_5 on either side of

$$T\xi_2T = \lambda'\xi_1 + \mu'\xi_2 + \nu'\xi_3$$

gives
$$\lambda' = 1,$$
$$0 = \beta + \mu' + \nu',$$
$$\omega^{-1} = \beta + \mu'\omega + \nu'\omega^{-1},$$
$$\omega = \beta + \mu'\omega^{-1} + \nu'\omega.$$

These, on solution, give
$$\beta = \frac{1}{\omega + \omega^{-1} - \omega^2 - \omega^{-2}} = \frac{1}{\sqrt{5}},$$
$$\mu'\sqrt{5} = \omega^2 + \omega^{-2},$$
$$\nu'\sqrt{5} = \omega + \omega^{-1}.$$

The complete solution, by using all three relations, gives in addition to the above
$$\alpha = \gamma = \delta = -1, \quad \beta' = -\frac{1}{\sqrt{5}},$$
$$\lambda = \frac{1}{\sqrt{5}}, \quad \mu = \nu = \frac{2}{5},$$
$$\lambda'' = 1, \quad \mu''\sqrt{5} = \omega + \omega^{-1}, \quad \nu''\sqrt{5} = \omega^2 + \omega^{-2}.$$

The substitution corresponding to T may be slightly simplified by writing ξ_2 and ξ_3 in the place of $\frac{2}{\sqrt{5}}\xi_2$ and $\frac{2}{\sqrt{5}}\xi_3$, a change which leaves the substitution corresponding to S unaltered. When this is done the alternating group of degree 5 is represented as an irreducible group of linear substitution in three variables, which is generated by
$$\xi_1' = \xi_1, \quad \xi_2' = \omega\xi_2, \quad \xi_3' = \omega^{-1}\xi_3;$$
and
$$\sqrt{5}\xi_1' = \xi_1 + \xi_2 + \xi_3,$$
$$\sqrt{5}\xi_2' = 2\xi_1 + (\omega^2 + \omega^{-2})\,\xi_2 + (\omega + \omega^{-1})\,\xi_3,$$
$$\sqrt{5}\xi_3' = 2\xi_1 + (\omega + \omega^{-1})\,\xi_2 + (\omega^2 + \omega^{-2})\,\xi_3;$$
these being the substitutions that correspond to $(abcde)$ and $(ab)(cd)$ respectively.

In the form of the group thus obtained the coefficients are not rational functions of the characteristics; but it is certainly possible to transform the group so that this condition shall be satisfied. If
$$\xi_1 + \xi_2 + \xi_3 = \eta_1, \quad \xi_1 + \omega\xi_2 + \omega^{-1}\xi_3 = \eta_2, \quad \xi_1 + \omega^2\xi_2 + \omega^{-2}\xi_3 = \eta_3,$$
it will be found that, in the transformed group with the η's as variables, the coefficients of the substitutions are rational functions of $\sqrt{5}$.

As a further illustration of methods that may be used for setting up an irreducible representation (whose characteristics are known) of a given group, we will consider the simple group of order 168 defined as a permutation-group of degree 7 in § 166. This group has an irreducible representation in which the characteristics of identity, operations of orders 2, 3, 4 and two sets of operations of order 7 are respectively 3, -1, 0, 1 and $\frac{1}{2}(-1 \pm \sqrt{-7})$. If α is a seventh root of unity the multipliers of an operation of order 7 are α, α^2, α^4; and the substitution corresponding to the operation may be taken to be

$$\xi_1' = \alpha\xi_1, \quad \xi_2' = \alpha^2\xi_2, \quad \xi_3' = \alpha^4\xi_3.$$

The multipliers of an operation of order 2 are 1, -1, -1. Now (Example, p. 252) any such substitution may be written in the form

$$\begin{aligned} \xi_1' &= -\xi_1 + a(l\xi_1 + m\xi_2 + n\xi_3), \\ \xi_2' &= -\xi_2 + b(l\xi_1 + m\xi_2 + n\xi_3), \\ \xi_3' &= -\xi_3 + c(l\xi_1 + m\xi_2 + n\xi_3), \\ al &+ bm + cn = 2. \end{aligned}$$

Moreover, by taking $l\xi_1$, $m\xi_2$, $n\xi_3$ as new variables, the former substitution is unaltered and the latter takes the simpler form

$$\begin{aligned} \xi_1' &= -\xi_1 + a(\xi_1 + \xi_2 + \xi_3), \\ \xi_2' &= -\xi_2 + b(\xi_1 + \xi_2 + \xi_3), \quad a + b + c = 2. \\ \xi_3' &= -\xi_3 + c(\xi_1 + \xi_2 + \xi_3). \end{aligned}$$

Hence it must be possible to choose a, b, c so that these two substitutions correspond to any operation of order 7 and any operation of order 2 of the group.

Now with the group defined as in § 166, (1673524) and (26) (37) are a pair of permutations which generate the group, and they are such that

$$(1673524)(26)(37) = (124)(356).$$

Hence if the two substitutions correspond to (1673524) and (26) (37) respectively, they generate the group, and their product is a substitution of order 3 with zero characteristic. In order that the latter condition may be satisfied, it is at once found that

$$a\alpha + b\alpha^2 + c\alpha^4 = \alpha + \alpha^2 + \alpha^4,$$

and $$a(\alpha^5 + \alpha^3) + b(\alpha^3 + \alpha^6) + c(\alpha^6 + \alpha^5) = \alpha^6 + \alpha^5 + \alpha^3,$$

while $$a + b + c = 2.$$

These equations determine a, b, c uniquely, giving

$$a - 1 = \frac{\alpha^5 - \alpha^2}{\sqrt{-7}}, \quad b - 1 = \frac{\alpha^3 - \alpha^4}{\sqrt{-7}}, \quad c - 1 = \frac{\alpha^6 - \alpha}{\sqrt{-7}},$$

where $$\alpha + \alpha^2 + \alpha^4 - \alpha^6 - \alpha^5 - \alpha^3 = \sqrt{-7}.$$

If we put

$$x_1 = \xi_1 (\alpha^2 - \alpha^5), \quad x_2 = \xi_2 (\alpha^4 - \alpha^3), \quad x_3 = \xi_3 (\alpha - \alpha^6),$$

this substitution takes a more symmetric expression while the previous one is unaltered. Hence an irreducible representation of the simple group of order 168 in 3 variables is generated by

$$x_1' = \alpha x_1, \quad x_2' = \alpha^2 x_2, \quad x_3' = \alpha^4 x_3;$$

and
$$\sqrt{-7}\, x_1' = (\alpha^5 - \alpha^2)\, x_1 + (\alpha^6 - \alpha)\, x_2 + (\alpha^3 - \alpha^4)\, x_3,$$
$$\sqrt{-7}\, x_2' = (\alpha^6 - \alpha)\, x_1 + (\alpha^3 - \alpha^4)\, x_2 + (\alpha^5 - \alpha^2)\, x_3,$$
$$\sqrt{-7}\, x_3' = (\alpha^3 - \alpha^4)\, x_1 + (\alpha^5 - \alpha^2)\, x_2 + (\alpha^6 - \alpha)\, x_3;$$

these two substitutions corresponding to the permutations (1673524) and (26) (37). It will be found that if

$$x_1 + x_2 + x_3 = y_1, \quad \alpha x_1 + \alpha^2 x_2 + \alpha^4 x_3 = y_2, \quad \alpha^2 x_1 + \alpha^4 x_2 + \alpha x_3 = y_3,$$

the coefficients in the substitutions of the transformed group with y_1, y_2, y_3 as variables are rational functions of $\sqrt{-7}$.

233. The general question as to the nature of the irrational quantities in terms of which the coefficients of any group of linear substitutions may be expressed has not yet received a complete answer. In every case that has been actually examined the coefficients may be expressed rationally in terms of the mth roots of unity, where m is the least common multiple of the orders of the operations of the group. Herr Schur* has shewn, among other results, that this is certainly the case for soluble groups; and the author† has shewn that, unless there is a number a, greater than unity, such that each multiplier of each operation of the group occurs a or a multiple of a times, it is the case.

234. We have seen in § 223 that

$$\prod_{k=1}^{k=r} \left(\xi - \sum_{i=1}^{i=r} \frac{A_i h_i \chi_i^k}{\chi_1^k} \right)$$

is a rational homogeneous function of ξ, A_1, A_2, ..., A_r with rational integral coefficients. Let m be the least common

* I. Schur, "Arithmetische Untersuchungen über endliche Gruppen linear Substitutionen," *Berliner Sitzungsberichte*, 1906, p. 181.

† W. Burnside, "On the arithmetical nature of the coefficients in a group of linear substitutions of finite order," *Proc. L. M. S.*, Series 2, Vol. IV. (1905), p. 8.

multiple of the orders of the operations of the group, and let ω be an assigned primitive mth root of unity. Then χ_i^k is, for each value of k and i, the sum of χ_1^k powers of ω; and each factor in the above product is a linear homogeneous function of $\xi, A_1, A_2, \ldots, A_r$ with coefficients which are rational functions of ω. Now the primitive mth roots of unity satisfy an irreducible equation with rational coefficients. Hence if in each of the factors of the product ω is replaced by ω^μ, where μ is relatively prime to m, the factors will be permuted among themselves. From this it follows that if

$$\chi_s = \omega^{a_{1s}} + \omega^{a_{2s}} + \ldots + \omega^{a_{ms}}, \quad (s = 1, 2, \ldots, r)$$

are the characteristics of the r conjugate sets in an irreducible representation of a group, so also are

$$\chi_{s\,(\mu)} = \omega^{\mu a_{1s}} + \omega^{\mu a_{2s}} + \ldots + \omega^{\mu a_{ms}}, \quad (s = 1, 2, \ldots, r),$$

where μ is any number relatively prime to m.

Moreover if Γ and $\Gamma_{(\mu)}$ denote the irreducible representations to which these two sets of group-characteristics belong, the result of writing ω^μ for ω in each characteristic is to give a permutation of the r sets of characteristics (or of the r irreducible representations) which is denoted by the symbol

$$\begin{pmatrix} \Gamma_1, & \Gamma_2, & \ldots, & \Gamma_r \\ \Gamma_1, & \Gamma_{2\,(\mu)}, & \ldots, & \Gamma_{r\,(\mu)} \end{pmatrix}.$$

If
$$S_1, S_2, \ldots, S_h$$
are the distinct operations of any conjugate set C, and if μ still denote a number which is relatively prime to the least common multiple of the orders of the operations, then

$$S_1^\mu, S_2^\mu, \ldots, S_h^\mu$$

are distinct and constitute a conjugate set, which may be denoted by $C^{(\mu)}$. If then every operation of the group be replaced by its μth power, a permutation of the conjugate sets arises which is denoted by the symbol

$$\begin{pmatrix} C_1, & C_2, & \ldots, & C_r \\ C_1, & C_2^{(\mu)}, & \ldots, & C_r^{(\mu)} \end{pmatrix}.$$

Consider now the r symbols

$$K_p = \sum_i \chi_i^{p'} C_i = \sum_S \chi^p{}_{S^{-1}} S, \quad (p = 1, 2, \ldots, r)$$

that have already been used in § 229. For any permutation of the r sets of group-characteristics they are merely permuted among themselves. In particular a definite permutation of the K's will arise from the permutation of the sets of characteristics denoted by

$$\begin{pmatrix} \Gamma_1, & \Gamma_2, & \ldots, & \Gamma_r \\ \Gamma_1, & \Gamma_{2(\mu)}, & \ldots, & \Gamma_{r(\mu)} \end{pmatrix}$$

which is given on replacing ω by ω^μ in each characteristic. On the other hand K_p remains unchanged, for each p, when ω^μ is written for ω in each characteristic and at the same time S^μ is written in the place of S for each operation. In other words each K remains unaltered when the sets of characteristics undergo the permutation denoted by

$$\begin{pmatrix} \Gamma_1, & \Gamma_2, & \ldots, & \Gamma_r \\ \Gamma_1, & \Gamma_{2(\mu)}, & \ldots, & \Gamma_{r(\mu)} \end{pmatrix},$$

and the conjugate sets undergo simultaneously the permutation denoted by

$$\begin{pmatrix} C_1, & C_2, & \ldots, & C_r \\ C_1, & C_2^{(\mu)}, & \ldots, & C_r^{(\mu)} \end{pmatrix}.$$

The K's are therefore permuted among themselves when the sets of characteristics are unpermuted, while the conjugate sets undergo the permutation denoted by the last symbol; and this permutation is the inverse of that which arises when the conjugate sets are unpermuted, and the sets of characteristics undergo the permutation

$$\begin{pmatrix} \Gamma_1, & \Gamma_2, & \ldots, & \Gamma_r \\ \Gamma_1, & \Gamma_{2(\mu)}, & \ldots, & \Gamma_{r(\mu)} \end{pmatrix}$$

The group of permutations of the C's which arises when for μ is taken each of the $\phi(m)$ numbers less than and prime to m is an Abelian group, since

$$\begin{pmatrix} C \\ C^{(\mu_1\mu_2)} \end{pmatrix} = \begin{pmatrix} C \\ C^{(\mu_1)} \end{pmatrix}\begin{pmatrix} C \\ C^{(\mu_2)} \end{pmatrix} = \begin{pmatrix} C \\ C^{(\mu_2)} \end{pmatrix}\begin{pmatrix} C \\ C^{(\mu_1)} \end{pmatrix}.$$

It is also intransitive since C_1 is necessarily unpermuted. If C_i and C_j belong to the same transitive set in this permutation-group, the cyclical sub-group generated by any operation belonging to C_i must be conjugate to the cyclical sub-group generated by any operation belonging to C_j; and conversely, unless this condition is satisfied C_i and C_j do not belong to the same transitive set. Hence the number of transitive sets in which the C's are permuted is equal to ρ, the number of distinct conjugate sets of cyclical sub-groups in the group.

Now the K's are linearly independent functions of the C's, equal to them in number, which are permuted among themselves when the C's undergo the permutation-group considered. The group in the K's and the group in the C's must therefore have the same number of linear invariants; and the number of transitive sets of the group in the K's is therefore ρ.

But this group also arises from the permutations of the r sets of characteristics given on replacing ω by ω^μ in each characteristic, the conjugate sets being unpermuted.

Hence finally the permutation-group of the r sets of characteristics (or of the corresponding r irreducible representations) consisting of the permutations

$$\begin{pmatrix} \Gamma_1, \Gamma_2, & \ldots, \Gamma_r \\ \Gamma_1, \Gamma_{2(\mu)}, & \ldots, \Gamma_{r(\mu)} \end{pmatrix}$$

(μ and m relatively prime)

permutes the sets (or the irreducible representations) in ρ transitive sets.

The irreducible representations that belong to the same transitive set may be called a *family* of representations.

235. If χ_i $(i=1, 2, \ldots, r)$ are the characteristics for one member of a family, the expression

$$\sum_i \chi_i C_i^{(\mu)},$$

when for μ is taken in turn each number less than and prime to m, takes just m_1 distinct values if m_1 is the number of members in the family.

If $$\sum_i \chi_i C_i = \sum_i \chi_i C_i^{(\mu_1)},$$

then $$\sum_i \chi_i C_i^{(\mu)} = \sum_i \chi_i C_i^{(\mu\mu_1)}.$$

Also if $$\mu\mu' \equiv 1 \pmod{m},$$

$$\sum_i \chi_i C_i^{(\mu)} = \sum_i \chi_{i(\mu')} C_i.$$

Hence m_1 must be a factor of $\phi(m)$, and if

$$\phi(m) = m_1 m_2,$$

there are just m_2 values of μ' such that

$$\chi_{i(\mu')} = \chi_i, \quad (i = 1, 2, \ldots, r).$$

Now the χ's are rational functions of ω, a primitive mth root of unity. Since they are unaltered when ω is replaced by any one of a set of m_2 primitive mth roots of unity, they must be rational functions of an algebraic number ξ, which itself is a rational function of ω taking just m_1 values when ω is replaced by any other primitive mth root. The irreducible equation with rational coefficients which ξ satisfies is therefore of degree m_1, and the field of rationality which it determines is the same as that determined by the set of characteristics.

If the members of the family are

$$\Gamma_{i_1}, \Gamma_{i_2}, \ldots, \Gamma_{i_{m_1}},$$

every operation necessarily has a rational characteristic in the representation denoted by $\Gamma_{i_1} + \Gamma_{i_2} + \ldots + \Gamma_{i_{m_1}}$. Conversely it follows, from the formula of § 216 for the complete reduction of any representation, that a representation in which the characteristics are rational must, when completely reduced, contain each of the representations $\Gamma_{i_1}, \Gamma_{i_2}, \ldots, \Gamma_{i_{m_1}}$ the same number of times.

THEOREM VI. *If r is the number of sets of conjugate operations of a group, and ρ the number of sets of conjugate cyclical sub-groups, the r irreducible representations of the group fall into ρ distinct families. The characteristics of the distinct members of a family are derived from the characteristics of any one of them, expressed as rational functions of ω, on replacing ω by ω^μ. Here μ is any number relatively prime to m the least common multiple of the orders of the operations of the group, and ω is a primitive mth root of unity. Any representation of the group in which all the characteristics are rational, when completely reduced contains each member of a family the same number of times.*

236. The results of the last two paragraphs may be used to prove a remarkable property of the multiplication table of the conjugate sets (§ 44) from which they have been obtained.

It has been shewn in § 229 that, if

$$K_p = \sum_i \chi_i^{p'} C_i, \quad (p = 1, 2, \ldots, r)$$

then $$K_p K_q = 0;$$
and in a similar way it may be proved that

$$K_p^2 = \frac{N}{\chi_1^p} K_p.$$

Since the determinant of the characteristics is different from zero, the C's can be expressed in terms of the K's, and the expression is

$$C_i = \frac{h_i}{N} \sum_p \chi_i^p K_p.$$

It has also been seen in § 234 that if

$$K_{p(\mu)} = \sum_i \chi_{i'}^p C_i^{(\mu)},$$

then the r symbols $K_{p(\mu)}$ $(p = 1, 2, \ldots, r)$ are the symbols K_p $(p = 1, 2, \ldots, r)$ in some altered sequence. The last relations give, on solution with respect to $C_i^{(\mu)}$,

$$C_i^{(\mu)} = \frac{h_i}{N} \sum_p \chi_i^p K_{p(\mu)}.$$

Hence
$$C_i^{(\mu)} C_j^{(\mu)} = \frac{h_i h_j}{N^2} \sum_{p,q} \chi_i^p \chi_j^q K_{p(\mu)} K_{q(\mu)}$$

$$= \frac{h_i h_j}{N^2} \sum_p \chi_i^p \chi_j^p \frac{N}{\chi_1^p} K_{p(\mu)}$$

$$= \frac{h_i h_j}{N} \sum_{p,s} \frac{\chi_i^p \chi_j^p \chi_{s'}^p}{\chi_1^p} C_s^{(\mu)}.$$

Now the relations (§ 218)

$$h_i h_j \chi_i^p \chi_j^p = \chi_1^p \sum_s c_{ijs} h_s \chi_s^p \quad (p = 1, 2, \ldots, r)$$

give on solution with respect to c_{ijs}

$$\sum_p h_i h_j \chi_i^p \chi_j^p \chi_{s'}^p = \chi_1^p N c_{ijs}.$$

Hence $$C_i^{(\mu)} C_j^{(\mu)} = \sum_s c_{ijs} C_s^{(\mu)}.$$

THEOREM VII. *The multiplication table of the conjugate sets of a group is invariant for the Abelian group of permutations of the conjugate sets that arises on replacing every operation of the group by its μth power, where μ is any number relatively prime to the least common multiple of the orders of the operations.*

237. It may be shewn in a precisely similar manner that the multiplication table

$$\Gamma_i \Gamma_j = \Sigma g_{ijs} \Gamma_s,$$

which gives the composition of the irreducible representations, is invariant for the permutations of the representations denoted by

$$\begin{pmatrix} \Gamma_1, & \Gamma_2, & \dots, & \Gamma_r \\ \Gamma_1, & \Gamma_{2(\mu)}, & \dots, & \Gamma_{r(\mu)} \end{pmatrix},$$

where $\Gamma_{i(\mu)}$ is that representation whose characteristics are obtained from those of Γ_i on replacing ω by ω^μ.

In fact it will be found that the r symbols

$$H_i = \sum_k \chi_i^k \Gamma_k \quad (i = 1, 2, \dots, r)$$

are merely permuted among themselves when, in them, the Γ's undergo any one of the above permutations; while the H's are such that

$$H_i^2 = \frac{N}{h_i} H_i,$$

$$H_i H_j = 0, \quad (i \neq j).$$

Now $$\Gamma_k = \frac{1}{N} \sum_i h_i \chi_{i'}^k H_i.$$

Hence $$\Gamma_{k(\mu)} \Gamma_{l(\mu)} = \frac{1}{N^2} \sum_{i,j} h_i h_j \chi_{i'}^k \chi_{j'}^l H_i^{(\mu)} H_j^{(\mu)}$$

$$= \frac{1}{N} \sum_i h_i \chi_{i'}^k \chi_{i'}^l H_i^{(\mu)}$$

$$= \frac{1}{N} \sum_{i,s} h_i \chi_{i'}^k \chi_{i'}^l \chi_{i'}^{s'} \Gamma_{s(\mu)}.$$

Now (§ 219) $$N g_{kls} = \sum_i h_{i'} \chi_{i'}^{\,k} \chi_{i'}^{\,l} \chi_{i'}^{\,s'},$$

and therefore $$\Gamma_{k(\mu)} \Gamma_{l(\mu)} = \sum_s g_{kls} \Gamma_{s(\mu)}.$$

238. Ex. 1. Prove that the numbers $(\chi_1^{\,i})^2$, $(i = 1, 2, \ldots\ldots, r)$ are the roots of the equation

$$\begin{vmatrix} \sum\limits_{pq} c_{1pq} c_{1'qp} - \dfrac{h_1 N}{x} & \sum\limits_{pq} c_{1pq} c_{2'qp} & \cdots\cdots & \sum\limits_{pq} c_{1pq} c_{r'qp} \\ \sum\limits_{pq} c_{2pq} c_{1'qp} & \sum\limits_{pq} c_{2pq} c_{2'qp} - \dfrac{h_2 N}{x} & \cdots\cdots & \sum\limits_{pq} c_{2pq} c_{r'qp} \\ \cdots & \cdots & \cdots & \cdots \\ \cdots & \cdots & \cdots & \cdots \\ \sum\limits_{pq} c_{rpq} c_{1'qp} & \sum\limits_{pq} c_{rpq} c_{2'qp} & \cdots\cdots & \sum\limits_{pq} c_{rpq} c_{r'qp} - \dfrac{h_r N}{x} \end{vmatrix} = 0$$

(Frobenius).

Ex. 2. Shew that the representation of G as a permutation-group, that arises on transforming the N operations of G by each of themselves in turn, when completely reduced contains the irreducible representation Γ_k just $\sum\limits_i \chi_i^{\,k}$ times.

Ex. 3. If C_1, C_2, C_3, C_4, C_5 are the conjugate sets consisting of identity, the operations of order 2, those of order 3, and the two sets of order 5 respectively, in the alternating group of 5 symbols, prove that

$$\begin{aligned}
C_2^2 &= 15C_1 + 2C_2 + 3C_3 + 5C_4 + 5C_5, \\
C_2C_3 &= 4C_2 + 6C_3 + 5C_4 + 5C_5, \\
C_2C_4 &= 4C_2 + 3C_3 + 5C_5, \\
C_2C_5 &= 4C_2 + 3C_3 + 5C_4, \\
C_3^2 &= 20C_1 + 8C_2 + 7C_3 + 5C_4 + 5C_5, \\
C_3C_4 &= 4C_2 + 3C_3 + 5C_4 + 5C_5, \\
C_3C_5 &= 4C_2 + 3C_3 + 5C_4 + 5C_5, \\
C_4^2 &= 12C_1 + 3C_3 + 5C_4 + C_5, \\
C_4C_5 &= 4C_2 + 3C_3 + C_4 + C_5, \\
C_5^2 &= 12C_1 + 3C_3 + C_4 + 5C_5.
\end{aligned}$$

Thence or otherwise shew that the sets of group-characteristics are given by the table

C_1	1	3	3	4	5
C_2	1	-1	-1	0	1
C_3	1	0	0	1	-1
C_4	1	$\frac{1+\sqrt{5}}{2}$	$\frac{1-\sqrt{5}}{2}$	-1	0
C_5	1	$\frac{1-\sqrt{5}}{2}$	$\frac{1+\sqrt{5}}{2}$	-1	0

Ex. 4. Form the sets of group-characteristics for the two types of non-Abelian groups of order p^3, and shew that they are identical.

Ex. 5. Prove that in every representation of a group of finite order as an irreducible group of linear substitutions in $m\,(>1)$ variables there are operations with zero characteristics.

(*Proc. L. M. S.* New Series, Vol. I. p. 115.)

Ex. 6. Shew that if, in a representation of a group of order N as an irreducible group of linear substitutions, the characteristic of every operation is either zero or a multiple of a rational integer n, then not more than N/n^2 operations can have non-zero characteristics.

Ex. 7. Shew that

$$\sum_k \frac{\chi_i^k}{\chi_1^k} = 0$$

is the necessary and sufficient condition that an operation of the ith conjugate set should not be a commutator; and determine, in a similar form, the conditions that it should not be the product of two or more commutators.

Ex. 8. Prove that the group defined by

$$A^9 = E, \quad B^7 = E, \quad A^{-1}BA = B^2$$

has 15 conjugate sets; and admits 9 representations in a single symbol and 6 representations in 3 symbols. Shew that in the latter B and A may be represented by

$$x' = \omega x, \quad y' = \omega^2 y, \quad z' = \omega^4 z;$$
$$x' = y, \quad y' = z, \quad z' = ax;$$

where ω is any primitive seventh root of unity and a is any cube root of unity. Shew also that, when a is a primitive cube root of unity, it is not possible to represent the group in a form in which the coefficients are rational functions of the characteristics.

Ex. 9. Prove that the group of order 2^n defined by

$$A^{2^{n-1}} = E, \quad B^2 = A^{2^{n-2}}, \quad B^{-1}AB = A^{-1},$$

which has only one operation of order 2, admits $2^{n-2} + 3$ irreducible representations of which four are in a single symbol, while $2^{n-2} - 1$ are in two symbols. Shew also that, in any irreducible representation which is simply isomorphic with the group itself, A and B may be taken to be

$$x' = ax, \; y' = \alpha^{-1}y; \text{ and } x' = y, \; y' = -x;$$

where α is a primitive 2^{n-1}th root of unity.

Ex. 10. Shew that the numbers g_{ijk} satisfy the relations

$$\sum_i g_{pp'i} g_{qq'i} = \sum_i g^2_{pqi}$$

for all values of the suffixes p and q.

Ex. 11. Prove that if each prime that divides the order of a group is congruent to unity (mod. 4), then the order of the group and the number of conjugate sets are congruent (mod. 32).

CHAPTER XVI.

SOME APPLICATIONS OF THE THEORY OF GROUPS OF LINEAR SUBSTITUTIONS AND OF GROUP-CHARACTERISTICS.

239. WE shall now apply some of the methods and results of the preceding three chapters to obtain a series of special theorems some of which give properties of a group independent of its mode of representation, while others are directly concerned with permutation-groups.

The theorem, due to Prof. Frobenius, that a transitive permutation-group whose operations except E permute all or all but one of the symbols, contains a self-conjugate subgroup whose order is equal to its degree, and the theorem that every group whose order contains only two distinct primes is soluble, are good examples of the power of this method. Before the development of the theory of group-characteristics these theorems, though special cases of them had been established, presented difficulties which had not been overcome. It cannot be doubted that further important results await the investigator in this line.

240. It has been seen in § 225 that $h_i\chi_i/\chi_1$ is an algebraic integer. If m is the order of the operations of the ith set, χ_i is the sum of χ_1 mth roots of unity; and unless these are all the same, mod. χ_i/χ_1 is zero or a real positive quantity less than unity. This is immediately obvious when the roots of unity are represented graphically.

If S is any operation of the ith set, and if μ is a number less than and prime to m, then S^μ belongs to a conjugate set of h_i operations, whose characteristic is obtained from χ_i on replacing each root of unity in it by its μth power. Denote this as before by $\chi_{i(\mu)}$. Then $M, = (h_i/\chi_1)^{\phi(m)} \prod_{\mu} \chi_{i(\mu)}$, where in the product μ takes each of the $\phi(m)$ values which are less than and prime to m, is (i) an algebraic integer, and (ii) a rational number. The latter statement follows from the fact that the product is a symmetric function of the $\phi(m)$ primitive mth roots of unity. Hence M, being both an algebraic integer and a rational number, is a rational integer. Also

$$\prod_{\mu} \chi_{i(\mu)} = \prod_{\mu} \text{mod. } \chi_{i(\mu)},$$

and therefore $(h_i/\chi_1)^{\phi(m)} \prod_{\mu} \text{mod. } \chi_{i(\mu)}$ is a rational integer. Hence if h_i and χ_1 are relatively prime, $\prod_{\mu} \text{mod. } \chi_{i(\mu)}$ must be divisible by $\chi_1^{\phi(m)}$ or else must be zero. Now it has been seen that unless the mth roots whose sum is χ_i are all the same, mod. $\chi_{i(\mu)}/\chi_1$, if not zero, is a real number less than unity. Finally then we may state the following:—

THEOREM I. *If in a representation of a group of finite order as an irreducible group of linear substitutions the number of variables and the number of operations in some conjugate set are relatively prime, then either* (i) *the characteristic of the set is zero, or* (ii) *all the multipliers of any operation of the set are the same.*

Corollary I. An irreducible group of linear substitutions in p (prime) variables, whose order is divisible by p^2, must contain self-conjugate substitutions.

For if p^α is the highest power of p which divides the order of the group, and if a sub-group of order p^α is not Abelian, it is necessarily irreducible; and therefore contains self-conjugate operations, which must be self-conjugate operations of the group.

If the sub-group of order p^α is Abelian, the conditions of the theorem are satisfied for each of its operations, and it is immediately obvious that, when $\alpha > 1$, their characteristics cannot all be zero.

Corollary II. If the number of operations in some conjugate set of a group of finite order is a power of a prime, the group cannot be simple.

Let $h_i = p^n$, so that N, the order of the group, is divisible by p^n. Since

$$N = \sum_1^r (\chi_1^i)^2,$$

there must be representations, other than the identical one, in which χ_1 is not divisible by p. In such a representation, either χ_i is zero or $\chi_i = \chi_1 \omega$, where ω is a root of unity. In the latter case, if $\chi_1 > 1$, the group has a self-conjugate sub-group containing the ith conjugate set, and, if $\chi_1 = 1$, the group is distinct from its derived group. Now χ_i cannot be zero in each representation, except the identical one, in which χ_1 is not divisible by p. For

$$\sum_{k=1}^{k=r} \chi_1^k \chi_i^k = 0,$$

and, on the supposition made, this relation would involve the contradiction

$$1 \equiv 0 \ (\text{mod. } p).$$

The group is therefore in any case composite.

Corollary III. A group whose order contains only two distinct primes is soluble.

If $N = p^\alpha q^\beta$, an operation which is self-conjugate in a sub-group of order p^α is one of q^b ($b \leqslant \beta$) conjugate operations. The group G therefore, by the previous corollary, contains a self-conjugate sub-group H; and the same reasoning applies both to G/H and to H. Hence G is soluble.

241. The author has shewn* that, subject to exceptions when p is 2 and q of the form $1 + 2^{2^n}$ or when p is of the form $2^n - 1$ and q is 2, a group of order $p^\alpha q^\beta$ ($p^\alpha > q^\beta$) has a characteristic sub-group of order p^a, where a satisfies the inequality $p^a > p^\alpha q^{-\beta}$. This result may be used as a basis for the discussion of such groups. The following comparatively simple results are proposed as an exercise for the reader.

Ex. 1. Shew that if a group of order $p^\alpha q^\beta$ has more than one sub-group of order p^α, and if no two sub-groups of order p^α have a common operation except E, then these sub-groups must be cyclical.

Ex. 2. Shew that if p^a is the order of the smallest self-conjugate sub-group of a group of order $p^\alpha q^\beta$, and if the group contains no operation of order pq, then q^β is a factor of $(p^a - 1)$, and the sub-groups of order q^β are cyclical.

* "On groups of order $p^\alpha q^\beta$," *Proc. L. M. S.*, Series 2, Vol. II. (1904), pp. 432—437.

242. If H is a sub-group of G, and if

$$H, HT_2, HT_3, \ldots\ldots, HT_n$$

are the sets into which the operations of G fall in respect of H, it has been seen in § 177 that these sets are permuted among themselves on post-multiplication by any operation of G, and that a transitive permutation-group thus arises, which is a representation of G.

Let H' be a self-conjugate sub-group of H such that H/H' is a cyclical group of order m. Unless H is identical with its derived group, there must be such a sub-group for some value of m greater than unity. In respect of H' the operations of H fall into the sets

$$H', H'S, H'S^2, \ldots\ldots, H'S^{m-1},$$

where S is an operation of H, whose mth power is the first that occurs in H'.

If ω is an mth root of unity

$$H' + \omega^{-1}H'S + \omega^{-2}H'S^2 + \ldots\ldots + \omega^{-m+1}H'S^{m-1}$$

is unaltered on multiplication by any operation of H' and is changed into ω times itself on multiplication by S. Denote this expression by K, and consider the n expressions

$$K, KT_2, KT_3, \ldots\ldots, KT_n.$$

If, on post-multiplication by U, any operation of G, HT_i becomes HT_j, there must be an operation Σ of H, such that

$$T_iU = \Sigma T_j,$$

and then $$KT_iU = K\Sigma T_j = \omega^a KT_j,$$

if Σ belongs to the set $H'S^a$.

Hence, when the n above expressions are post-multiplied by any operation of G, each is changed into one of the set multiplied by some power of ω. Neglecting the factors so introduced, the permutation of

$$K, KT_2, \ldots\ldots, KT_n$$

is the same as that of

$$H, HT_2, \ldots\ldots, HT_n.$$

A representation of G is thus set up as a group of linear substitutions of a specially simple kind. They are not mere permutations, but permutations affected by factors, all of which are mth roots of unity.

Whatever the factors may be such substitutions are called *monomial* substitutions.

This representation of G as a group of monomial substitutions cannot be equivalent to the representation as a permutation-group in respect of H. In fact, when the latter representation is reduced, it necessarily contains the identical representation, while the former one clearly does not.

The product of the symbols operated on by the monomial group of substitutions is changed into a multiple of itself by every operation of the group; the factor in each case being a power of ω. It may happen that this factor is unity for every operation. If this is not so, a representation of G in a single symbol, other than the identical representation, arises; and therefore G must be isomorphic with a cyclical group whose order is equal to or is a factor of m.

243. We proceed to apply the representation of a group as a group of monomial substitutions to obtain results connected with the solubility of the group.

Let p^α be the highest power of p which divides the order of G, H be a sub-group of G of order p^α, and I the greatest sub-group of G which contains H self-conjugately. Suppose further that every operation of I is permutable with every operation of H, so that H is Abelian.

If S, of order p^β, is one of a set of independent generating operations of H, there is a sub-group H' of H of order $p^{\alpha-\beta}$ in respect of which the operations of H fall into the sets

$$H',\ H'S,\ H'S^2,\ \ldots\ldots,\ H'S^{p^\beta-1}.$$

Take H' and S for the group and operation denoted by the same symbols in the previous paragraph and form the representation of G as a group of monomial substitutions in respect of them, using a primitive p^βth root of unity for ω.

If KT_i is changed into a multiple of itself on multiplication by S

$$T_iS = S'T_i,$$

where S' is some operation of H; or

$$T_iST_i^{-1} = S'.$$

But the operations S and S' of H cannot be conjugate in G unless they are conjugate in I (§ 123). Hence if KT_i is changed into a multiple of itself on multiplication by S, T_i is permutable with S, and $KT_iS = \omega KT_i$. Moreover the number of sets KT_i, each of which is changed into ω times itself on multiplication by S, which is $1/p^a$ of the number of operations of G permutable with S, is not a multiple of p. The product of the factors for these symbols is therefore a primitive p^βth root of unity. Consider now a set of the symbols KT_j which are permuted cyclically by S. Denote them by $x_1, x_2, \ldots\ldots, x_{p^b}$ $(b \leqslant \beta)$. The corresponding part of the monomial substitution which represents S is

$$x_1' = \omega_1 x_2,$$

$$x_2' = \omega_2 x_3,$$

$$\ldots\ldots\ldots\ldots$$

$$x'_{p^b} = \omega_{p^b} x_1,$$

where $\omega_1, \omega_2, \ldots\ldots, \omega_{p^b}$ are p^βth roots of unity.

The p^βth power of this substitution is identity, and therefore

$$(\omega_1\omega_2\ldots\ldots\omega_{p^b})^{p^{\beta-b}} = 1.$$

Hence $\omega_1\omega_2\ldots\ldots\omega_{p^b}$ is *not* a primitive p^βth root of unity.

Combining the two results it follows that the product of all the symbols is changed by the substitution that corresponds to S into ω' times itself, where ω' is a primitive p^βth root of unity. Hence G must contain a self-conjugate sub-group in respect of which it is isomorphic with a cyclical group of order p^β, and neither S nor any power of S occurs in this sub-group.

This self-conjugate sub-group satisfies the same condition as G, as regards the prime p, and may be treated in the same way. Hence :—

THEOREM II. *If p^α is the highest power of p which divides the order N of G, while H is a sub-group of G of order p^α and I the greatest sub-group of G which contains H self-conjugately; and if every operation of I is permutable with every operation of H, then G has a self-conjugate sub-group of order N/p^α.*

244. A number of particular cases of this theorem are of sufficient importance to be stated explicitly.

Corollary I. If $p^\alpha m$, where m is not divisible by p, is the order of G, and if every operation of G whose order is a power of p is permutable with every operation whose order is prime to p, then G is the direct product of two groups of orders p^α and m.

Under the given conditions G contains a self-conjugate sub-group H of order p^α. If H is Abelian, the conditions of the theorem apply, and G contains a self-conjugate sub-group M of order m. Then since M and H can contain no common operation except E, G is the direct product of M and H.

If H is not Abelian, let H_1 of order p^{α_1} be the derived group of H. Since H_1 is a characteristic sub-group of H, it is a self-conjugate sub-group of G. The conditions of the theorem apply then to G/H_1, which therefore has a self-conjugate sub-group of order m, containing all its operations whose orders are relatively prime to p. Hence G has a self-conjugate sub-group of order $p^{\alpha_1}m$, with the same property. Similar reasoning may be applied to this sub-group. Hence, finally, G again contains a self-conjugate sub-group M of order m; and G is therefore the direct product of M and H.

Corollary II. If, in G, the Sylow sub-group H, of order p^α, is Abelian; and if k is the greatest number of a set of independent generators of H which have the same order; then when N, the order of G, and $(p^k-1)(p^{k-1}-1)\ldots\ldots(p-1)$, are relatively prime, G has a self-conjugate sub-group of order N/p^α. In fact, when these conditions are satisfied, it has been seen in § 86 that every operation of G which is permutable with H is permutable with every operation of H, and therefore the conditions of the theorem are satisfied.

Corollary III*. The order N of G is $p_1^{a_1} p_2^{a_2} \ldots\ldots p_n^{a_n} m$, where $p_1, p_2, \ldots\ldots, p_n$ are primes in ascending order and m is relatively prime to each of them. For each i from 1 to n, the sub-groups of order $p_i^{a_i}$ are Abelian, and k_i is the greatest number of a set of independent generating operations which have the same order. Then if, for each i, $N/p_1^{a_1} p_2^{a_2} \ldots\ldots p_{i-1}^{a_{i-1}}$ and $(p_i^{k_i} - 1)(p_i^{k_i-1} - 1) \ldots\ldots (p_i - 1)$ are relatively prime, G has a series of self-conjugate sub-groups of orders

$$N/p_1^{a_1} p_2^{a_2} \ldots\ldots p_i^{a_i} \quad (i = 1, 2, \ldots\ldots, n).$$

The existence of the self-conjugate sub-group of order $N/p_1^{a_1}$ follows from the preceding Corollary. Applying the same reasoning to this, it has a self-conjugate sub-group of order $N/p_1^{a_1} p_2^{a_2}$. This clearly consists of all operations of G whose orders are relatively prime to $p_1 p_2$, and is therefore a self-conjugate sub-group of G; and this reasoning may be repeated.

Corollary IV†. If the Sylow sub-groups of G, for all primes dividing the order of G except the highest, are Abelian groups with either one or two generating operations and if 12 is not a factor of the order, then G is soluble. In fact

$$(p^2 - 1)(p - 1)$$

can only be divisible by a prime greater than p if $p = 2$; and then 3 is the divisor. With this exception the conditions of the previous Corollary are certainly satisfied. In particular, a group whose order is not divisible by the cube of a prime or by 12 is certainly soluble‡.

245. If the order of a group is $2^a n$, where n is odd, there are other cases besides those covered by the preceding Theorem in which it may be shewn that there is a self-conjugate sub-group of order n.

Suppose first that the sub-groups of order 2^a are of one of the types

* Frobenius, "Ueber auflösbare Gruppen, II." *Berliner Sitzungsberichte* (1895), p. 1035.

† Frobenius, *loc. cit.* p. 1041.

‡ By a method similar to that used in Theorem II, the author has shewn that if p^3 is the highest power of p which divides N, and the sub-groups of order p^3 are non-Abelian, there is a self-conjugate sub-group of order N/p^3, if N and $(p^2 - 1)(p - 1)$ are relatively prime. (*Proc. L. M. S.*, Vol. XXXIII. p. 265 (1900).)

$$A^{2^{\alpha-1}}=E,\quad B^2=E,\quad BAB=A^{-1},$$
$$A^{2^{\alpha-1}}=E,\quad B^2=E,\quad BAB=A^{1+2^{\alpha-2}},$$
$$A^{2^{\alpha-1}}=E,\quad B^2=E,\quad BAB=A^{-1+2^{\alpha-2}}.$$

In each case $\{A^{2^{\alpha-2}}, B\}$ is a group of order 4 and type (1, 1), and there is no Abelian sub-group of order 8 and type (1, 1, 1). If $A^{2^{\alpha-2}}$ and B are conjugate operations in the group, there must (§ 124) be an operation S of odd order such that

$$A^{2^{\alpha-2}},\ S^{-1}A^{2^{\alpha-2}}S\ (=B),\ S^{-2}A^{2^{\alpha-2}}S^2, \ldots\ldots$$

are permutable operations. Since there is no Abelian sub-group of order 8 and type (1, 1, 1), this is only possible if S^3 is permutable with $A^{2^{\alpha-2}}$. Hence if n is not divisible by 3, $A^{2^{\alpha-2}}$ and B are not conjugate operations, and therefore B is not contained in any sub-group conjugate to $\{A\}$. Now A is one of 2μ conjugate operations, where μ is odd. No one of these can be permutable with B; for if $BA'=A'B$, then $\{A', B\}$ would be an Abelian group of order 2^α, and the sub-groups of order 2^α are not Abelian. Hence the permutation that arises when the 2μ operations conjugate to A are transformed by B is an odd permutation; and therefore the group has a self-conjugate sub-group of index 2 in which B does not occur. In this sub-group the sub-groups of order $2^{\alpha-1}$ are cyclical; and therefore the group has a self-conjugate sub-group of order n. If the sub-groups of order 2^α are of the type

$$A^{2^{\alpha-1}}=E,\ B^2=A^{2^{\alpha-2}},\ B^{-1}AB=A^{-1},$$

it may be shewn, as in the former case, that when n is not divisible by 3, B and $A^{2^{\alpha-3}}$ are not conjugate operations. Here $A^{2^{\alpha-3}}$ is one of 2μ conjugate operations, where μ is odd, and since the group contains no two permutable operations of order 4, which are not inverses of each other, just 2 of the 2μ operations remain unchanged on transforming by $A^{2^{\alpha-3}}$. For the same reason none of the 2μ operations remain unchanged on transforming by B. Hence, since $A^{2^{\alpha-2}}=B^2$, one of the two permutations corresponding to $A^{2^{\alpha-2}}$ or B must be an odd permutation, and the group has a self-conjugate sub-group of index 2. In this the sub-groups of order $2^{\alpha-1}$ are either cyclical or of the type under consideration; and in the latter case the same reasoning may be repeated. Hence again there is a self-conjugate sub-group of order n. The types considered cover all non-Abelian groups of order 2^a with operations of order 2^{a-1}. Hence:—

THEOREM III. *A group of order $2^a n$, where n is odd and not divisible by 3, which contains operations of order 2^{a-1} has a self-conjugate sub-group of order n.*

Corollary. The order, if even, of a simple group must be divisible by 12, 16 or 56. For groups whose orders are not divisible by 16, the two preceding theorems cover all cases except that where the order is divisible by 2^3 and the groups of order 2^3 are of type (1, 1, 1). In this case, if the order is relatively prime to $(2^3-1)(2^2-1)$ there is a self-conjugate sub-group of order n; i.e. unless 12 or 56 divides the order the group must be composite*.

246. Let G be a group of order N and G' a sub-group of G of order N'. For G we use the ordinary notation for the irreducible representations and the characteristics, viz. Γ_u is any irreducible representation of G, χ_S^u is the characteristic of S in Γ_u, and h_S is the number of operations in the conjugate set to which S belongs. For G' let γ_v denote any irreducible representation, ψ_P^v the characteristic in γ_v of any operation P of G', and h'_P he number of operations in the conjugate set of G' to which P belongs. As usual the representation of both G and G' with suffix 1 is the identical representation. In the representation Γ_u of G, the set of linear substitutions corresponding to the operations of G' will, in general, form a reducible group. For each u, the completely reduced form of this group will be denoted by

$$\sum_v k_{uv}\gamma_v.$$

Now the characteristic of P, an operation of G', in Γ_u is χ_P^u. Its characteristic in $\sum_v k_{uv}\gamma_v$ is $\sum_v k_{uv}\psi_P^v$. Hence

$$\chi_P^u = \sum_v k_{uv}\psi_P^v$$

* An examination of the orders of known non-cyclical simple groups brings out the remarkable fact that all of them are divisible by 12.

for each u. Multiply this equation by $\psi^w_{P^{-1}}$, and sum for the operations of G'. Then

$$\sum_P \chi^u_P \psi^w_{P^{-1}} = \sum_{v, P} k_{uv} \psi^v_P \psi^w_{P^{-1}}.$$

Now (§ 218)
$$\sum_P \psi^v_P \psi^w_{P^{-1}} = 0, \qquad w \neq v,$$
$$\sum_P \psi^w_P \psi^w_{P^{-1}} = N'.$$

Hence
$$N' k_{uw} = \sum_P \chi^u_P \psi^w_{P^{-1}} = \sum_P \chi^u_{P^{-1}} \psi^w_P,$$

and if S is any operation of G,

$$N' \sum_u k_{uv} \chi^u_S = \sum_{u, P} \chi^u_S \chi^u_{P^{-1}} \psi^v_P.$$

But (§ 218)
$$\sum_u \chi^u_S \chi^u_{P^{-1}} = \frac{N}{h_P} \text{ or } 0,$$

according as S is or is not conjugate to P.

Hence
$$\sum_u k_{uv} \chi^u_S = \frac{N}{N' h_P} \sum_P \psi^v_P,$$

where the summation with respect to P is extended to all the operations of G' which, in G, are conjugate to S.

The result thus obtained* connects, without exception, the characteristics of G with those of any sub-group of G.

247. We now make the particular supposition that G contains N/N' sub-groups conjugate to G', no two of which have a common operation other than E, so that G can be represented as a permutation-group of degree N/N', whose operations, except E, displace all or all but one of the symbols.

If P is an operation of G', all the operations permutable with P must belong to G', for if

$$Q^{-1}PQ = P,$$
$$Q^{-1}G'Q = G'',$$

then P would belong to both G' and G''. Hence the number of operations in G conjugate to P is Nh'_P/N', i.e.

$$Nh'_P = N'h_P.$$

* Frobenius, "Ueber Relationen zwischen den Charakteren einer Gruppe und denen ihrer Untergruppen," *Berliner Sitzungsberichte* (1898), p. 502.

If now, in this case, the equation

$$\sum_u k_{uv}\chi_S^u = \frac{N}{N'h_P}\sum_P \psi_P^v$$

be applied to P, there are h'_P terms in the sum on the right, and they are all equal. Hence

$$\sum_u k_{uv}\chi_P^u = \psi_P^v.$$

This holds for all operations of G' except E. When we write E for S, the relation is

$$\sum_u k_{uv}\chi_E^u = \psi_E^v N/N'.$$

Combining the last two results with

$$\chi_P^u = \sum_v k_{uv}\psi_P^v,$$

which holds for all operations of G' without exception, we have

$$\psi_P^w = \sum_{u,v} k_{uv}k_{uw}\psi_P^v, \qquad P \neq E,$$

$$\psi_E^w N/N' = \sum_{u,v} k_{uv}k_{uw}\psi_E^v.$$

Now

$$\sum_v \psi_E^v\psi_E^v = N',$$

$$\sum_v \psi_E^v\psi_P^v = 0, \qquad P \neq E.$$

Hence for all operations of G' without exception

$$\psi_P^w + \frac{N-N'}{N'^2}\psi_E^w\sum_v\psi_E^v\psi_P^v = \sum_{u,v} k_{uv}k_{uw}\psi_P^v.$$

From this it follows, since the sets of group-characteristics are linearly independent (§ 216), that

$$\sum_u k_{uv}k_{uw} = \frac{N-N'}{N'^2}\psi_E^v\psi_E^w, \qquad v \neq w,$$

$$\sum_u (k_{uv})^2 = \frac{N-N'}{N'^2}(\psi_E^v)^2 + 1.$$

If now from these equations we calculate the values of $\sum_u (k_{uv} - \psi_E^v k_{u1})^2$, we obtain

$$\sum_u (k_{uv} - \psi_E^v k_{u1})^2 = 1 + (\psi_E^v)^2.$$

Also $k_{11}=1$, and if $v>1$, $k_{1v}=0$, so that

$$(k_{1v}-\psi_E^v k_{11})^2=(\psi_E^v)^2.$$

Hence, if $v>1$,

$$\sum_{u=2}^{u=r}(k_{uv}-\psi_E^v k_{u1})^2=1.$$

Now each of the $r-1$ terms on the left is either zero or a positive integer. Hence $r-2$ of them must be zero, and the remaining one unity.

In just the same way it may be shewn that if $v>1$, $w>1$, $v\neq w$, then

$$\sum_{u=2}^{u=r}(k_{uv}-\psi_E^v k_{u1})(k_{uw}-\psi_E^w k_{u1})=0.$$

Hence the values of u for which $k_{uv}-\psi_E^v k_{u1}$ and $k_{uw}-\psi_E^w k_{u1}$ are ± 1 cannot be the same. The notation may therefore be chosen so that

$$k_{\alpha\alpha}-\psi_E^\alpha k_{\alpha 1}=\pm 1, \quad (\alpha=2, 3, \ldots\ldots, r'),$$

$$k_{\alpha\beta}-\psi_E^\beta k_{\alpha 1}=0, \qquad \beta\neq\alpha, \alpha>1.$$

Moreover, as pointed out above, the values

$$k_{11}=1, \quad k_{1\alpha}=0$$

follow from the meaning of the symbols.

Now $$\sum_u k_{uv}\chi_E^u=\psi_E^v N/N'$$

and $$\sum_u k_{u1}\chi_E^u=N/N',$$

give $$\sum_u (k_{uv}-\psi_E^v k_{u1})\chi_E^u=0.$$

The term on the left, arising from $u=1$ (when $v>1$), is $-\psi_E^v$. The coefficients of all the other terms, except $u=v$, are zero, and the coefficient of this is ± 1. Hence

$$-\psi_E^v\pm\chi_E^v=0.$$

The positive sign must therefore be taken in each of the $r'-1$ cases.

Further, if S is an operation of G which is not conjugate to any operation of G',

$$\sum_u k_{uv}\chi_S^u = 0,$$

$$\sum_u k_{u1}\chi_S^u = 0,$$

so that

$$\sum_u (k_{uv} - \psi_E^v k_{u1})\,\chi_S^u = 0.$$

The only terms on the left which are different from zero are those for which $u = 1$ and $u = v$: and the equation becomes

$$\psi_E^v - \chi_S^v = 0,$$

so that in this representation

$$\chi_S^v = \chi_E^v,$$

and every operation of G which does not belong to G' and its conjugates corresponds to the identical substitution. The N/N' operations of G which do not belong to G' and its conjugates therefore generate a self-conjugate sub-group, which necessarily consists of themselves with identity. Hence*:—

THEOREM IV. *If G is a transitive permutation-group of degree n, whose operations except E permute all or all but one of the symbols, then the $n-1$ operations which permute all the symbols constitute with E a self-conjugate sub-group.*

248. If in the preceding theorem the self-conjugate sub-group consisting of E and the permutations that change all the symbols be denoted by H, then to every operation of G' there corresponds an isomorphism of H in which E is the only operation that is not altered. If h is a Sylow sub-group of H, of order p^a, and is therefore one of the same number of conjugate sub-groups in G and in H, then h and every characteristic sub-group of h admits a group of isomorphisms simply isomorphic with G', no one of which leaves any operation unaltered except E. Now h necessarily has a characteristic Abelian sub-group h' whose operations, except E, are all of order p.

Suppose, if possible, that G' contains a non-cyclical sub-group of order q^2, where q is prime. The corresponding group of

* Frobenius, "Ueber auflösbare Gruppen, IV." *Berliner Sitzungsberichte* (1901), pp. 1223—1225. Prof. Frobenius's proof has been closely followed in the text.

isomorphisms must permute the operations of h' transitively in sets of q^2; and, as affecting one set, its generators Q_1 and Q_2 may be taken to be

$$(P_{11}P_{12}\dots P_{1q})\dots\dots(P_{i1}P_{i2}\dots P_{iq})\dots\dots(P_{q1}P_{q2}\dots P_{qq}),$$

and $$(P_{11}P_{21}\dots P_{q1})\dots\dots(P_{1j}P_{2j}\dots P_{qj})\dots\dots(P_{1q}P_{2q}\dots P_{qq}).$$

Then in $Q_1Q_2^i$ the cycle containing P_{11} is

$$(P_{11}P_{1+i,2}P_{1+2i,3}\dots P_{1-i,q}).$$

Since no one of these isomorphisms changes any operation of h' except E into itself, the product of the operations in any cycle must be E.

Hence
$$P_{11}P_{12}\dots P_{1q}=E,$$
$$P_{11}P_{21}\dots P_{q1}=E,$$
$$P_{11}P_{1+i,2}\dots P_{1-i,q}=E,\quad (i=1,2,\dots,q-1),$$

and therefore
$$P_{11}^q\prod_{i,j}P_{ij}=E,\qquad (i,j=1,2,\dots,q),$$

or
$$P_{11}^q=E.$$

This is not the case, and therefore G' contains no non-cyclical sub-group of order q^2. Hence (§§ 104, 105) the Sylow sub-groups of G' of odd order are cyclical and those of even order are either cyclical or of the non-cyclical type that contains a single sub-group of order 2.

Let Q, R of orders q^α, r^β $(q>r)$ be operations of G' generating Sylow sub-groups of order q^α, r^β. Then (§ 129) G' contains a sub-group of order $q^\alpha r^\beta$ defined by

$$Q^{q^\alpha}=E,\quad R^{r^\beta}=E,\quad R^{-1}QR=Q^\gamma,$$

where
$$\gamma^{r^{\beta'}}\equiv 1 \pmod{q^\alpha},\quad \beta'\leqslant\beta.$$

Such a sub-group permutes the operations of h' transitively in sets of $q^\alpha r^\beta$; and, as affecting one set, Q and R may be taken to be

$$\prod_i(P_{i,0}P_{i,1}\dots P_{i,q^\alpha-1}),\qquad (i=1,2,\dots,r^\beta),$$

$$\prod_t(P_{1,t}P_{2,t\gamma}\dots P_{r^\beta,t\gamma^{r^\beta-1}}),\quad (t=0,1,\dots,q^\alpha-1).$$

Then in $Q^{-j}RQ^j$ the cycle containing $P_{1,0}$ is

$$(P_{1,0}P_{2,(1-\gamma)j}P_{3,(1-\gamma^2)j}\dots P_{r^\beta,(1-\gamma^{-1})j}),$$

and
$$P_{1,0}P_{2,(1-\gamma)j}\dots P_{r^\beta,(1-\gamma^{-1})j}=E,\quad (j=0,1,\dots,q^\alpha-1).$$

If γ is not unity, this leads to

$$P_{1,0}{}^{q^\alpha}=E,$$

a contradiction. Hence γ must be unity, and the group of order $q^\alpha r^\beta$ is cyclical. If r is 2 and the corresponding Sylow sub-group non-cyclical, it may be shewn in a similar way that the sub-group of order $q^\alpha 2^\delta$ is the direct product of sub-groups of orders q^α and 2^δ. Hence finally if the order of G' is odd, G' is cyclical; and if even, it is either cyclical or the direct product of a cyclical group of odd order and a non-cyclical group containing a single operation of order 2.

THEOREM V. *If a group admits a group of isomorphisms I, each of which leaves unchanged no operation of the group except E, then I is either a cyclical group, or the direct product of a cyclical group of odd order and a non-cyclical group of order 2^α containing a single operation of order* 2.

249. Returning to the relations between the characteristics of a group and one of its sub-groups obtained in § 246, we now suppose with the notation there used that G' is a self-conjugate sub-group of G while N/N' is prime. We also assume that every two operations of G' which are conjugate in G are also conjugate in G', so that if P is an operation of G', then $h'_P=h_P$; while if the operations of G' fall into r' conjugate sets in G', they also fall into r' conjugate sets in G. If S is an operation of G, not contained in G', the operations of the set SG' are transformed among themselves by every operation of G. Any operation P of G' is permutable with N'/h'_P operations of G' and with N/h'_P operations of G. It is therefore permutable with N'/h'_P operations of the set SG'. Further if S is permutable with m operations of G', it is permutable with m operations of the set SG'.

Hence when the two sets G' and SG' are transformed by any operation of G, the number of operations left unchanged in each set is the same. It follows from Theorem VII, Chapter X, that the permutation-groups which arise on transforming the operations G' and the operations SG' by every operation of G have the same number of transitive sets. Hence the operations of the set SG' form r' conjugate sets in G, and therefore

$$r = \frac{N}{N'} r'.$$

Now the relation

$$\sum_u k_{uv} \chi_S^u = \frac{N}{N' h_P} \sum_P \psi_P^v$$

of § 246, applied to any operation of G', gives

$$\sum_u k_{uv} \chi_P^u = \frac{N}{N'} \psi_P^v.$$

Combining this with

$$\chi_P^u = \sum_w k_{uw} \psi_P^w$$

we have

$$\sum_{u, w} k_{uv} k_{uw} \psi_P^w = \frac{N}{N'} \psi_P^v,$$

which is true for every operation of G'. Hence

$$\sum_u k_{uv} k_{uw} = 0, \quad (v \neq w),$$

$$\sum_u k_{uv}^2 = \frac{N}{N'}.$$

The first equation shews that, for each u, of the r' numbers k_{uv} ($v = 1, 2, \ldots\ldots, r'$) one and only one can be different from zero. From the second equation it follows that

$$\sum_{u, v} k_{uv}^2 = \frac{N}{N'} r' = r.$$

Hence each k_{uv} which is not zero is unity. Every irreducible representation of G is therefore irreducible as regards G', and there are N/N' irreducible representations of G which contain any given irreducible representation of G'. Slightly altering the notation this result gives the following:—

THEOREM VI. *If a group G of order N with r conjugate sets is contained self-conjugately in the group H of order Np (p-prime)* *and if the isomorphism of G given by any operation of H leaves each conjugate set in G unchanged, then* (i) *the number of conjugate sets in H is pr*; (ii) *in each of the pr irreducible representations of H, G is irreducible*; *and* (iii) *each irreducible representation of G occurs in just p distinct irreducible representations of H.*

If $\Gamma_1, \Gamma_2, \ldots, \Gamma_p$ are the p representations of H in a single symbol, in which the operations of G correspond to the identical substitution, and if Γ is any representation of H, then $\Gamma_1\Gamma$, $\Gamma_2\Gamma, \ldots, \Gamma_p\Gamma$ are all distinct and each of them give the same irreducible representation of G.

Ex. A group G of order N with r conjugate sets is contained self-conjugately in a group H of order Np (p-prime). Prove that if the isomorphism of G corresponding to an operation of H not contained in G leaves r_1 conjugate sets of G unchanged and permutes the $r - r_1$ remaining ones in sets of p, then the number of conjugate sets in H is $\{r + (p^2 - 1) r_1\}/p$.

250. If m is the number of transitive sets in which the sub-group of a transitive permutation-group which leaves one symbol unchanged permutes the symbols, and if $\Sigma c_s\Gamma_s$ gives the complete reduction of the permutation-group, we have seen, in § 207, that

$$m = \Sigma c_s^2.$$

The identical representation necessarily occurs just once in the reduced form, so that c_1 is 1. If the group is doubly transitive, m is 2, and the reduced form is $\Gamma_1 + \Gamma$, just one representation besides the identical one occurring. If the group is simply transitive m is not less than 3. The relation

$$m = \Sigma c_3^2,$$

if m is of the form $1 + \mu^2$, might be satisfied by just two c's, viz.

$$c_1 = 1, \quad c_2 = \mu,$$

but $\Gamma_1 + \mu\Gamma_2$ is not a possible form for the reduced group. In fact if χ were the characteristic in Γ_2 of an operation which, as a permutation, displaces all the symbols, then

$$0 = 1 + \mu\chi.$$

The permutation-group necessarily contains such operations, but $-1/\mu$ is not an admissible value for χ, which is an algebraical integer.

Hence if a permutation-group is simply transitive, at least three distinct representations must occur in its completely reduced form.

It may be noticed in passing that when m is less than 6 for a group of even order, or less than 11 for a group of odd order, the irreducible components are necessarily all distinct and therefore equal in number to m.

If in the completely reduced form of a permutation-group an irreducible component Γ occurs c times, each irreducible representation which belongs to the same family as Γ will also occur c times.

251. Consider now a simply transitive permutation-group G of prime degree p. A permutation P of order p contained in the group may be taken to be

$$(x_0 x_1 \ldots\ldots x_{p-1}).$$

Since G is simply transitive, so that at least three distinct irreducible representations occur in its reduced form, the characteristic of P in each of the irreducible components, except Γ_1, must be irrational. Suppose that for one irreducible representation χ_1 is s. Then in this representation

$$\chi_P = \omega^{a_1} + \omega^{a_2} + \ldots\ldots + \omega^{a_s},$$

where ω is a primitive pth root of unity, and $a_1, a_2, \ldots\ldots, a_s$ are s distinct residues (mod. p). If ω^i be written for ω in χ_P, the resulting expression is the characteristic of P in the same or another irreducible component. If when each primitive pth root of unity is written in turn for ω, just t distinct χ's arise,

$$st = p - 1,$$

since each primitive root must occur in one and only one χ. Hence if g is a primitive root of

$$g^s \equiv 1 \text{ (mod. } p),$$

then
$$\chi_P = \omega + \omega^g + \omega^{g^2} + \ldots\ldots + \omega^{g^{s-1}}.$$

Now $x_0 + \omega^{-1}x_1 + \omega^{-2}x_2 + \ldots\ldots + \omega^{-p+1}x_{p-1}$

is the only linear function of the x's which is changed into ω times itself by P.

Hence if

$$\xi_t = x_0 + \omega^{-t}x_1 + \omega^{-2t}x_2 + \ldots\ldots + \omega^{(-p+1)t}x_{p-1},$$

the symbols $\xi_1, \xi_g, \xi_{g^2}, \ldots\ldots, \xi_{g^{s-1}}$ are transformed among themselves by the irreducible component in which χ_P is the characteristic of P.

This and the other irreducible components, except Γ_1, are therefore groups of linear substitutions in s symbols, in which the coefficients of the substitutions are rational functions of ω. If Q is any operation of G whose order is relatively prime to p, its characteristic in the representation considered is a rational function of ω and is therefore zero or a rational number. It follows that the characteristic of Q in each of the t representations, other than Γ_1, is the same. Suppose now if possible that G contains a permutation Q, of order prime to p, which displaces all the symbols. Its characteristic in G is zero. In Γ_1 it is unity, and in each of the t conjugate representations it is the same rational number χ_Q. Therefore

$$0 = 1 + t\chi_Q.$$

This is an inadmissible value for χ_Q, and therefore the only operations of G which displace all the symbols are the operations of order p. If a permutation Q, whose order is prime to p, leaves just n symbols unchanged, then $n = 1 + t\chi_Q$, and therefore χ_Q is either zero or a positive integer; while the number of symbols unchanged by any permutation whose order is prime to p is of the form $1 + xt$. Let ν_x be the number of permutations of G which leave $1 + xt$ symbols unchanged; and let ν be the number of operations of G whose characteristic in the chosen representation is χ_P. Then the equation

$$\Sigma h_i \chi_i^k = 0$$

for this representation is

$$\nu\Sigma\chi_P^k + \nu_1 + 2\nu_2 + \ldots\ldots + s\nu_s = 0;$$

and the equation

$$\Sigma h_i \chi_i^k \chi_i^l = 0 \quad (k \neq l')$$

is
$$\nu \Sigma \chi_P^k \chi_P^l + \nu_1 + 2^2\nu_2 + \ldots\ldots + s^2\nu_s = 0;$$

the summations extending to the t conjugate values of χ_P^k and $\chi_P^k \chi_P^l$.

Now
$$\Sigma \chi_P^k = -1,$$

$$\Sigma \chi_P^k \chi_P^l = -s \quad (k \neq l').$$

Hence

$$s(\nu_1 + 2\nu_2 + \ldots\ldots + s\nu_s) = \nu_1 + 2^2\nu_2 + \ldots\ldots + s^2\nu_s,$$

so that
$$\nu_1 = \nu_2 = \ldots\ldots = \nu_{s-1} = 0.$$

The permutation-group is therefore such that every permutation except the identical one displaces all or all but one of the symbols. The order of the group is therefore pq, where q is a factor of $p-1$, and it contains a self-conjugate sub-group of order p. Hence:—

THEOREM VII. *A simply transitive permutation-group of prime degree p is of order pq, where q is a factor of $p-1$, and it therefore contains a self-conjugate sub-group of order p.*

252. A similar result may be proved for any simply transitive permutation-group G of degree p^m, which contains a permutation of order p^m. Let

$$(x_0 x_1 \ldots\ldots x_{p^m-1})$$

be a permutation P of order p^m contained in G.

If
$$\xi_i = \sum_0^{p^m-1} \omega^{-ij} x_j,$$

then ξ_i is the only linear function of the x's which P replaces by ω^i times itself, ω being an assigned primitive p^mth root of unity.

The multipliers of P are all distinct, and therefore when G is completely reduced no irreducible component can occur more than once. Moreover, it follows from Theorem II, Chapter XIV, that in each irreducible component the sub-group of G which leaves x_0 unchanged has just one linear invariant.

Suppose now that Γ is an irreducible component of G, and that in Γ the multipliers of P are $\omega, \omega^{a_2}, \ldots\ldots, \omega^{a_s}$. Then Γ must transform among themselves $\xi_1, \xi_{a_2}, \ldots\ldots, \xi_{a_s}$. Unless pth roots of unity occur among $\omega, \omega^{a_2}, \ldots, \omega^{a_s}$, there must be irreducible components in which no multiplier of P is a primitive p^mth root of unity. In such an irreducible component $P^{p^{m-1}}$ would correspond to the identical substitution, so that G would contain a self-conjugate sub-group generated by $P^{p^{m-1}}$ and its conjugates; in other words G would be imprimitive.

Suppose now that in the sub-group of G which leaves x_0 unchanged,

$$x_{b_1}, x_{b_2}, x_{b_3}, \ldots\ldots, x_{b_t}$$

are permuted transitively. Then

$$x_{b_1} + x_{b_2} + \ldots\ldots + x_{b_t}$$

is an invariant for this sub-group.

Now $$x_0 = \sum_0^{p^m - 1} \xi_i / p^m,$$

so that in Γ

$$\xi_1 + \xi_{a_2} + \ldots\ldots + \xi_{a_s}$$

is an invariant, and therefore the only invariant for the sub-group of G which leaves x_0 unchanged.

Further $$p^m (x_{b_1} + x_{b_2} + \ldots\ldots + x_{b_t})$$

$$= \sum_b \sum_{i=0}^{i=p^m - 1} \omega^{ib_j} \xi_i.$$

Hence

$$(\omega^{b_1} + \omega^{b_2} + \ldots\ldots + \omega^{b_t}) \xi_1$$
$$+ (\omega^{a_2 b_1} + \omega^{a_2 b_2} + \ldots\ldots + \omega^{a_2 b_t}) \xi_{a_2}$$
$$+ \ldots\ldots\ldots\ldots\ldots\ldots\ldots\ldots$$
$$+ (\omega^{a_s b_1} + \omega^{a_s b_2} + \ldots\ldots + \omega^{a_s b_t}) \xi_{a_s}$$

is an invariant for the sub-group of G which leaves x_0 fixed; and therefore this quantity must be zero or a multiple of

$$\xi_1 + \xi_{a_2} + \ldots\ldots \xi_{a_s}.$$

It follows that

$$\omega^{b_1} + \omega^{b_2} + \ldots\ldots + \omega^{b_t}$$
$$= \omega^{a_2 b_1} + \omega^{a_2 b_2} + \ldots\ldots + \omega^{a_2 b_t}$$
$$= \ldots\ldots\ldots\ldots\ldots\ldots\ldots\ldots$$
$$= \omega^{a_s b_1} + \omega^{a_s b_2} + \ldots\ldots + \omega^{a_s b_t}.$$

If one of the multipliers of P in Γ is a pth root of unity, we may assume that a_2 is a multiple of p^{m-1}, so that ω^{a_2} is a pth root of unity. Then

$$\omega^{b_1} + \omega^{b_2} + \ldots\ldots + \omega^{b_t} = \omega^{a_2 b_1} + \omega^{a_2 b_2} + \ldots\ldots + \omega^{a_2 b_t};$$

and this equation can obviously be true only if $t = p^m - 1$; while, G being simply transitive, this is not the case. Hence among the multipliers of P in Γ no pth root of unity can occur.

It follows that $P^{p^{m-1}}$ and its conjugates generate a self-conjugate sub-group of G, so that G is imprimitive. Hence:—

THEOREM VIII. *A simply transitive permutation-group of degree p^m, which contains a permutation P of order p^m, is necessarily imprimitive and contains an intransitive self-conjugate sub-group generated by $P^{p^{m-1}}$ and its conjugates.*

That a corresponding result is true for any simply transitive permutation-group containing a transitive Abelian sub-group whose order is equal to the degree of the group is highly probable; but the proof on the above lines presents difficulties which do not occur in the cases considered.

253. We now add some further applications of the methods considered which, though they lead to less general results, are of importance as indicating the lines on which investigation may be pursued.

The coefficients in the relations

$$\Gamma_i \Gamma_j = \sum_s g_{ijs} \Gamma_s$$

are directly determined by actually carrying out the reduction of the group represented by $\Gamma_i \Gamma_j$. In general it is not possible to say, *a priori*, whether the group represented by $\Gamma_i \Gamma_j$ is reducible or not; but it will now be shewn that the group denoted by Γ_i^2 is always reducible, and a consideration of the process of compounding an irreducible representation of a group with itself is of some importance.

If
$$x_i' = \sum_j a_{ijk} x_j \quad (i = 1, 2, \ldots\ldots, n)$$

is a substitution of Γ, the corresponding substitution of Γ^2 is

$$x_i' y_u' = \sum_{j,v} a_{ijk} a_{uvk} x_j y_v.$$

This substitution may be written in the form

$$x_i' y_u' \pm x_u' y_i' = \sum_{j,v} (a_{ijk} a_{uvk} \pm a_{ujk} a_{ivk})(x_j y_v \pm x_v y_j),$$

and therefore the symmetric bilinear functions of the x's and y's are transformed among themselves as also are the alternating. There are $\frac{1}{2}n(n+1)$ independent symmetric and $\frac{1}{2}n(n-1)$ independent alternating bilinear functions of the x's and y's. The n^2 symbols operated on by Γ^2 may therefore be separated into two sets, each of which are transformed among themselves, so that Γ^2 is certainly reducible.

If $\omega_1, \omega_2, \ldots\ldots, \omega_n$ are the multipliers of an operation in Γ, and if ψ_s, ψ_a are the sums of the multipliers of the same operations in the group on the symmetric and the group on the alternating functions, then

$$\psi_s = \sum_{i,j} \omega_i \omega_j \quad (i, j = 1, 2, \ldots\ldots, n),$$

$$\psi_a = \sum_{i,j} \omega_i \omega_j \quad (i \neq j;\ i, j = 1, 2, \ldots\ldots, n).$$

In fact these relations are given at once by the preceding expression for a substitution of Γ^2. Now

$$\psi_s = \psi_a + \omega_1^2 + \omega_2^2 + \ldots\ldots + \omega_n^2.$$

For a group of even order the series of quantities

$$\omega_1^2 + \omega_2^2 + \ldots\ldots + \omega_n^2$$

for the r conjugate sets is *not* a set of group-characteristics in general*; but for a group of odd order the set in question is always a set of group-characteristics, and the irreducible repre-

* They will be so for the direct product of a group of odd order and a group of order two.

sentation in n variables to which they belong has been denoted (§ 234) by $\Gamma_{(2)}$. Hence in this case, when the group on the symmetric functions is completely reduced, it contains the same irreducible components as the group on the alternating functions and the component $\Gamma_{(2)}$ in addition. This is expressed by the relation

$$\Gamma^2 = \Gamma_{(2)} + 2\Sigma a_i \Gamma_i.$$

On the other hand, for a group of even order there is no necessary relation between the irreducible components of the two groups on the symmetric and the alternating functions. When each y is put equal to the corresponding x, the alternating functions all vanish identically, and the symmetric functions become quadratic functions of the x's. Hence for a group of odd order each irreducible component of Γ^2 can be represented as a group of linear substitutions on quadratic functions of the variables. For groups of even order this result is not in general true.

In particular $\Gamma_{(2)}$ can be represented as a group of linear substitutions on n linearly independent quadratic functions of the x's. Let these functions be $X_1, X_2, \ldots\ldots, X_n$. Being linearly independent it is easy to see that they must also be algebraically independent, and therefore that the Jacobian

$$\frac{\partial (X_1, X_2, \ldots\ldots, X_n)}{\partial (x_1, x_2, \ldots\ldots, x_n)}$$

does not vanish identically. Since the X's are linearly transformed among themselves when the x's undergo any substitution of Γ, the Jacobian must be changed into ω times itself by any substitution of the group, ω being a root of unity. This Jacobian is a function of the nth degree of the variables. Hence:—

THEOREM IX. *For any irreducible group of odd order on n variables there is always* (i) *a set of n linearly independent homogeneous quadratic functions of the variables which are transformed among themselves by every operation of the group, and* (ii) *a homogeneous function of the nth degree of the variables which is changed into a multiple of itself by every operation of the group.*

254. If m_i is the order of the operations of the ith conjugate set, χ_i is the sum of χ_1 m_ith roots of unity. For any representation in which χ_i is not rational there must be some smallest number $\mu_i (> 2)$ such that χ_i can be expressed as a rational function of a primitive μ_ith root of unity, and cannot be expressed as a rational function of a μ_i'th root of unity $(\mu_i' < \mu_i)$.

Suppose now that in an irreducible representation Γ of G, p_1^a and p_2^b, where p_1 and p_2 are distinct primes, are the numbers referred to for the ith and jth sets. Also let $m, = p_1^{a_1} p_2^{a_2} p_3^{a_3} \ldots$, be the least common multiple of the orders of the operations of G. Of the $\phi(m)$ numbers, μ, less than and prime to m, there are just $\phi(m)/p_1^{a-1} p_2^{b-1} (p_1 - 1)(p_2 - 1)$, say m_1, which satisfy the congruences

$$\mu \equiv 1 \ (\text{mod.}\ p_1^a),$$
$$\mu \equiv 1 \ (\text{mod.}\ p_2^b).$$

We have seen that if μ is any number less than and prime to m, the relation

$$h_i h_j \chi_i \chi_j = \chi_1 \sum_s c_{ijs} h_s \chi_s$$

involves the relation

$$h_i h_j \chi_{i(\mu)} \chi_{j(\mu)} = \chi_1 \sum_s c_{ijs} h_s \chi_{s(\mu)}.$$

Sum these equations for the m_1 values of μ which satisfy

$$\mu \equiv 1 \ (\text{mod.}\ p_1^a), \quad \mu \equiv 1 \ (\text{mod.}\ p_2^b).$$

Since
$$\chi_{i(\mu)} = \chi_i, \quad \chi_{j(\mu)} = \chi_j,$$
the left-hand side is $m_1 h_i h_j \chi_i \chi_j$. Let ω be one of the χ_1 roots of unity whose sum is χ_s and write $\omega = \omega_1 \omega_2 \omega_3 \ldots$, where ω_1, ω_2, ω_3, ... are roots of unity whose indices are powers of p_1, p_2, p_3, ... If the index of ω_1 is greater than p_1^a, *or* if that of ω_2 is greater than p_2^b, *or* if that of ω_3 is greater than p_3, ..., then

$$\sum_\mu \omega^\mu = 0.$$

If the indices of ω_1 and ω_2 are equal to or less than p_1^a and p_2^b respectively, while the indices of $\omega_3, \omega_4, \ldots\ldots, \omega_t$ are $p_3, p_4, \ldots\ldots, p_t$ respectively and the remaining indices are zero, then

$$\sum_\mu \omega^\mu = (-1)^{t-2} \frac{m_1}{(p_3 - 1)(p_4 - 1) \ldots\ldots (p_t - 1)} \omega_1 \omega_2.$$

Hence, after the summation, the right-hand side of the equation is a rational function of p_1^ath and p_2^bth roots of unity. Moreover unless, for some value of s, the order of the operations of the sth set is equal to or a multiple of $p_1^a p_2^b$, no one of the $p_1^a p_2^b$th roots of unity which occur on the right-hand side of the equation will be a primitive root. Suppose now that, on each side of the equation expressed rationally in terms of ξ a primitive p_1^ath and of η a primitive p_2^bth root of unity, the equations

$$\xi^{p_1^{a-1}(p_1-1)} + \xi^{p_1^{a-1}(p_1-2)} + \ldots\ldots + \xi^{p_1^{a-1}} + 1 = 0$$

and $$\eta^{p_2^{b-1}(p_2-1)} + \eta^{p_2^{b-1}(p_2-2)} + \ldots\ldots + \eta^{p_2^{b-1}} + 1 = 0$$

are used to replace all powers of ξ and η higher than $\xi^{p_1^{a-1}(p_1-1)-1}$ and $\eta^{p_2^{b-1}(p_2-1)-1}$ by lower powers. In this form the relation must be an identity. But on the assumption made it cannot be so, since the left-hand side contains terms $\xi^x\eta^y$ in which neither x is divisible by p_1 nor y by p_2; while the right-hand side contains no such terms. The group therefore must contain operations whose orders are divisible by $p_1^a p_2^b$.

If χ_k is a rational function of a p_3^cth root of unity and is not a rational function of a p_3^{c-1}th root of unity, the equation

$$h_i h_j h_k \chi_i \chi_j \chi_k = \chi_1 \sum_s c_{ijs} h_s h_k \chi_s \chi_k$$
$$= \chi_1^2 \sum_{s,t} c_{ijs} c_{skt} h_t \chi_t$$

may be used in a similar way to shew that the group must contain operations of order $p_1^a p_2^b p_3^c$; and so on. Hence:—

THEOREM X. *If, $p_1, p_2, p_3, \ldots$ being primes, a group has operations whose characteristics in some irreducible representations are rational functions of $p_1^{a_1}$th, $p_2^{a_2}$th, $p_3^{a_3}$th, ... roots of unity respectively, and are not rational functions of $p_1^{a_1-1}$th, $p_2^{a_2-1}$th, $p_3^{a_3-1}$th, ... roots of unity, then the group has operations of order $p_1^{a_1} p_2^{a_2} p_3^{a_3} \ldots$.*

255. Let G, of order $p^\alpha q^\beta \ldots\ldots r^\gamma m$, (where m is not divisible by the primes $p, q, \ldots\ldots, r$) be an irreducible group of linear substitutions in n variables. Suppose further that $p, q, \ldots\ldots, r$ are greater than $n+1$ and that the prime factors of m are equal to or less than $n+1$. If G has a self-conjugate operation P whose order is a power of p, its determinant is necessarily different from unity. The same is true if G has self-conjugate operations whose orders are powers of q, ... r. Hence (note, p. 268) G must have a self-conjugate sub-group G_1, of order

$$p^a q^b \ldots\ldots r^c m \quad (a \leqslant \alpha,\ b \leqslant \beta,\ \ldots\ldots),$$

and G_1 contains no self-conjugate operation whose order is a power of $p, q, \ldots\ldots, r$.

A sub-group of G_1, of order p^a, is necessarily Abelian, since when completely reduced it must consist of n components each in a single variable. Moreover, since $n+1$ is less than either $p, q, \ldots\ldots$, or r, every operation of G_1 whose order is a power of $p, q, \ldots\ldots$, or r necessarily has an irrational characteristic. Hence, by Theorem X, G_1 must contain operations whose orders are divisible by pq.

Let P_1 and Q_1 be permutable operations of G_1 of orders p and q; and let H_1 be an Abelian sub-group of G_1, of order p^a, which contains P_1. Then P_1 is contained self-conjugately in the sub-group $\{H_1, Q_1\}$; and since P_1 is not a self-conjugate operation of G_1, this sub-group must be reducible.

Each irreducible component of this sub-group may be dealt with as G has been treated. In it P_1 is a self-conjugate operation whose determinant is different from unity; and its self-conjugate sub-group which does not contain P_1 may be treated like G_1. It is thus shewn that G_1 has an Abelian sub-group $\{H_1, Q\}$, where Q is an operation whose order is a power of q. Let K_1 be a sub-group of G_1, of order q^b, containing Q. Then Q is self-conjugate in $\{H_1, K_1\}$, which is therefore reducible; in other words G_1 has a reducible sub-group whose order is divisible by $p^a q^b$. This sub-group may be dealt with in the same way, and therefore G_1 has an Abelian sub-group whose order is divisible by $p^a q^b$. Repeating this reasoning with each of the primes $p, q, \ldots\ldots, r$, it is shewn similarly that G_1 has an Abelian sub-group of order $p^a q^b \ldots\ldots r^c$, and that G therefore has an Abelian sub-group of order $p^\alpha q^\beta \ldots\ldots r^\gamma$. Hence*:—

* H. F. Blickfeldt, "On the order of linear homogeneous groups" (Second Paper), *Trans. Amer. Math. Soc.* (1904), p. 319.

THEOREM XI. *An irreducible group of linear substitutions in n variables, of order $m_1 m_2$, where the prime factors of m_1 are greater than and those of m_2 are equal to or less than $n+1$, has an Abelian sub-group of order m_1.*

256. If $S_1, S_2, \ldots, S_N$ are the operations of a group G, and χ_S the characteristic of S in some irreducible representation, it is obvious that the only operation S, such that

$$\chi_{S_i} = \chi_{S_i S} \quad (i = 1, 2, \ldots, N),$$

is the identical operation.

Let R be a field of rationality which contains that determined by the coefficients of the substitutions in the representation considered, so that each characteristic is an integer in R. Then it is possible that, in certain cases, the system of congruences

$$\chi_{S_i} \equiv \chi_{S_i S} \pmod{\alpha}, \quad (i = 1, 2, \ldots, N),$$

where α is a suitably chosen integer or ideal in the field R, may hold for operations other than E. When this is the case the operations S for which this system of congruences holds constitute a self-conjugate sub-group of G. In fact, if

$$\chi_{S_i} \equiv \chi_{S_i S} \pmod{\alpha},$$

then $$\chi_{S_i} = \chi_{S_j^{-1} S_i S_j} \equiv \chi_{S_j^{-1} S_i S_j S} = \chi_{S_i S_j S S_j^{-1}}, \pmod{\alpha}.$$

A simple illustration is given by the group

$$S^7 = E, \quad T^3 = E, \quad T^{-1} S T = S^2,$$

as represented in the form

$$\begin{array}{llll} S & x' = \omega x, & y' = \omega^2 y, & z' = \omega^4 z; \quad \omega^7 = 1, \\ T & x' = y, & y' = z, & z' = x. \end{array}$$

If Σ is any operation of the group it is found that

$$\chi_\Sigma \equiv \chi_{\Sigma S} \pmod{1-\omega} \text{ for each } \Sigma,$$

while $$\chi_\Sigma \not\equiv \chi_{\Sigma T} \pmod{1-\omega} \text{ for each } \Sigma;$$

and this agrees with the fact that $\{S\}$ is a self-conjugate sub-group.

It may of course happen in particular cases that

$$\chi_{S_i} \equiv \chi_{S_i S} \pmod{\alpha}$$

for every operation S. This for instance is the case, with $\alpha \equiv p$, for an irreducible group in p symbols of order p^3. Since however, for every irreducible group in more than one symbol, there are necessarily operations with zero characteristic, the congruence

$$\chi_S \equiv \chi_T \pmod{\alpha}$$

for all pairs of operations can only hold if each non-zero characteristic is a multiple of α. Thus if χ_E is not divisible by α, the existence of operations S for which

$$\chi_{S_i} \equiv \chi_{S_iS} \pmod{\alpha} \quad (i=1, 2, \ldots, N)$$

ensures the existence of an actual self-conjugate sub-group, distinct from the group itself.

257. In illustration of the preceding paragraph, consider a group of linear substitutions

$$x_i' = \sum_j s_{ij} x_j, \quad (i = 1, 2, \ldots, n),$$

in which all the coefficients are algebraic integers, and suppose that the group contains a substitution P of canonical form

$$x_1' = \omega_1 x, \quad x_2' = \omega_2 x, \ldots, x_n' = \omega_n x,$$

where the multipliers are powers of ω, a primitive mth root of unity, m being the power of a prime. Then

$$\chi_S = s_{11} \quad + s_{22} \quad + \ldots + s_{nn},$$

and

$$\chi_{SP} = \omega_1 s_{11} + \omega_2 s_{22} + \ldots + \omega_n s_{nn}.$$

Hence, each of the s's being an algebraic integer,

$$\chi_S \equiv \chi_{SP} \pmod{1-\omega},$$

for every substitution of the group. If then $1-\omega$ is not a factor of n, the number of variables, the group has an actual self-conjugate sub-group containing P. This condition is certainly satisfied for a group, whose coefficients are algebraic integers, which contains a substitution, of prime order greater than the number of variables, in canonical form.

As a second example we take the case of an irreducible group on n variables which contains an operation P of prime-power order p^a $(p^a > n)$, whose multipliers are all distinct. Transform the group so that P occurs in canonical form

$$x_1' = \omega_1 x_1, \; x_2' = \omega_2 x_2, \; \ldots\ldots, \; x_n' = \omega_n x_n,$$

where $\omega_1, \omega_2, \ldots\ldots, \omega_n$ are n distinct p^ath roots of unity. If in this form any operation S of the group is

$$x_i' = \sum_j a_{ij} x_j \quad (i, j = 1, 2, \ldots\ldots, n),$$

then

$$\sum_1^n a_{ii} \omega_i^x = \chi_{SP^x}, \quad (x = 0, 1, \ldots\ldots, p^a - 1).$$

The number of these equations is greater than n. The determinant of the first n of them, viz.

$$\begin{vmatrix} 1 & 1 & \ldots\ldots & 1 \\ \omega_1 & \omega_2 & \ldots\ldots & \omega_n \\ \ldots & \ldots & \ldots & \ldots \\ \omega_1^{n-1} & \omega_2^{n-2} & \ldots\ldots & \omega_n^{n-1} \end{vmatrix}$$

is equal to $\prod_{i,j} (\omega_i - \omega_j)$, and its norm is known to be a power of p, say p^a. Hence when the first n are solved for a_{ii} $(i = 1, 2, \ldots\ldots, n)$, the result is

$$a_{ii} = \frac{\beta_i}{p^a},$$

where β_i is an algebraic integer.

Suppose now that the group has an operation Q of prime order $q\,(\neq p)$, and permutable with P. The corresponding substitution must be

$$x_1' = \alpha_1 x_1, \quad x_2' = \alpha_2 x_2, \quad \ldots\ldots, \quad x_n' = \alpha_n x_n,$$

where $\alpha_1, \alpha_2, \ldots\ldots, \alpha_n$ are qth roots of unity. Then

$$\chi_S - \chi_{SQ} = \frac{\sum \beta_i (1 - \alpha_i)}{p^a}.$$

If α is a primitive qth root of unity, the numerator is divisible by $1 - \alpha$, while the denominator certainly is not. Hence for each operation of the group

$$\chi_S \equiv \chi_{SQ} \ (\text{mod. } 1 - \alpha).$$

Unless then every characteristic is divisible by $1 - \alpha$, the group will have an actual self-conjugate sub-group containing Q. For instance, if q does not divide n, there will be such a sub-group.

258. We shall conclude this chapter by considering the representation of groups of prime-power order as irreducible groups of linear substitutions.

Let G be such a group, of order p^a, and suppose that Γ_i is one of its irreducible representations. The number of variables for Γ_i is necessarily a power of p, say p^a. Consider now the reduction of $\Gamma_i\Gamma_{i'}$. It is given by the formula

$$\Gamma_i\Gamma_{i'} = \sum_s g_{ii's}\Gamma_s.$$

Since $g_{ii'1}$ is unity, while χ_1^s is either unity or a power of p, there must be at least $p-1$ other representations, besides Γ_1, in a single symbol in the complete reduction of $\Gamma_i\Gamma_{i'}$.

There must therefore be a bilinear function of the variables operated on by Γ_i and $\Gamma_{i'}$ which is changed into ϵ times itself by any operation of G, ϵ being a pth root of unity. This function is unchanged by the operations of a sub-group G_1, whose order is $1/p$th of the order of G. Hence in $\Gamma_i\,\Gamma_{i'}$ the self-conjugate sub-group G_1 has more than one bilinear invariant.

Now if G_1 were irreducible in the representation Γ_i, it would only have a single bilinear invariant in $\Gamma_i\Gamma_{i'}$. Hence G_1 must be reducible, and it therefore transforms the variables in p sets of p^{a-1} each.

Suppose now that every irreducible group of linear substitutions in p^{a-1} variables, whose order is a power of p, can be so transformed that the product of the variables is changed into a multiple of itself by every substitution of the group. Then it follows that the same is true for every group in p^a variables, whose order is a power of p. But for a group in p variables the above process shews that the supposition is true. Hence*:—

THEOREM XII. *Every representation of a group of prime-power order as an irreducible group of linear substitutions can be so transformed that the product of the variables is changed into a multiple of itself by every substitution of the group; in other words, it can be represented as a group of monomial substitutions.*

259. It may be noticed that this mode of representing a prime-power group is not necessarily unique. The first two of the following examples illustrate the possibility of representing such a group as a group of monomial substitutions in more than one way.

* A proof of this theorem, which is not quite complete, is given by H. F. Blickfeldt, *l.c.*, p. 314.

Ex. 1. An irreducible group of order p^3 in p symbols is generated by the two substitutions

$$x_i' = x_{i+1}, \quad (i = 0, 1, \ldots, p-1),$$
$$x_i' = a^i x_i,$$

where a is a primitive pth root of unity. Prove that if

$$\xi_{m,n} = \sum_{i=0}^{i=p-1} a^{mi^2+ni} x_i,$$

the p symbols $\xi_{m,0}, \xi_{m,1}, \ldots, \xi_{m,p-1}$ are permuted among themselves with factors by every substitution of the group; so that there are $p+1$ distinct sets of variables in which the group can be represented as a set of monomial substitutions*.

Ex. 2. Prove that if p is prime, the four substitutions

$$x'_{i,j} = x_{i+1,j}; \quad x'_{i,j} = x_{i,j+1};$$
$$x'_{i,j} = a^i x_{i,j}; \quad x'_{i,j} = a^j x_{i,j};$$
$$(i, j = 0, 1, \ldots, p-1)$$

where a is a primitive pth root of unity, generate an irreducible group of order p^5 in the p^2 symbols; and that the variables can be chosen in $p^3 + p^2 + p + 1$ distinct ways so that the group is a group of monomial substitutions.

Ex. 3. A group of order p^n has p^{n_1} $(n_1 < n)$ self-conjugate operations and all the rest belong to conjugate sets containing p operations in each. Prove that (i) $n - n_1$ is even, (ii) the derived group is of order p, and (iii) the irreducible representations consist of p^{n-1} each in a single symbol and $p^{n_1-1}(p-1)$ each in $p^{\frac{1}{2}(n-n_1)}$ symbols. (Compare Ex. 1, p. 126.)

Ex. 4. Prove that the most general monomial group of substitutions on p^{n-1} symbols, whose order is a power of p and in which the multipliers are pth roots of unity, is irreducible; and that it is simply isomorphic with the sub-group of order p^ν of the symmetric group of degree p^n, where

$$\nu = p^{n-1} + p^{n-2} + \ldots + p + 1.$$

Ex. 5. Prove that the alternating group of degree 5 can be represented as an irreducible group of monomial substitutions on 5 symbols, the multipliers being cube roots of unity.

* Burnside, "On soluble irreducible groups in a prime number of variables," *Acta Mathematica*, Vol. XXVIII. p. 222 (1903).

Ex. 6. Prove that the simple group of order 168 can be represented as an irreducible group of monomial substitutions on 7 symbols the multipliers being ± 1; and also as an irreducible group of monomial substitutions on 8 symbols the multipliers being cube roots of unity.

Ex. 7. Prove that an irreducible group of odd order which contains the substitution

$$x_0' = \omega x_0, \quad x_1' = \omega^2 x_1, \quad x_2' = \omega^{2^2} x_2, \; \ldots, \; x_{2n}' = \omega^{2^{2n}} x_{2n},$$

where ω is a primitive $(2^{2n+1} - 1)$th root of unity, must be a group of monomial substitutions, and is soluble.

Ex. 8. Prove that a group of linear substitutions of odd order in 3 variables can be expressed as a group of monomial substitutions and is soluble.

Ex. 9. Prove that a group of linear substitutions of odd order in 5 variables is soluble, and that, if its order is not divisible by 3, it can be expressed as a group of monomial substitutions. Construct, on the lines of Ex. 1, an irreducible group of linear substitutions on 5 variables, of order 375, which contains a non-Abelian self-conjugate sub-group of order 125 and which cannot be expressed as a group of monomial substitutions on 5 variables.

Ex. 10. An irreducible group of linear substitutions in n variables has an Abelian sub-group H of order $M (> n^2)$. Shew that if E is the only operation common to H and any conjugate sub-group, then H is contained self-conjugately in a sub-group whose order is not less than nM.

Ex. 11. Shew that every irreducible representation of a metabelian group can be transformed into a group of monomial substitutions.

Ex. 12. Prove that the number of operations of order two contained in a group increased by unity is not greater than the sum of the numbers of variables operated on by the self-inverse irreducible representations.

CHAPTER XVII.

ON THE INVARIANTS OF GROUPS OF LINEAR SUBSTITUTIONS.

260. We have already considered, in certain particular cases, functions of the variables which are invariant for all the substitutions of a group of linear substitutions of finite order. In the present Chapter we shall deal with the general theory of such functions.

Definitions. If

$$x_1, x_2, \ldots, x_n$$

are the variables operated on by a group G of linear substitutions of finite order N, and if

$$x_1^{(S)}, x_2^{(S)}, \ldots, x_n^{(S)}$$

are the linear functions into which the variables are changed by a substitution S of the group, then a rational function

$$F(x_1, x_2, \ldots, x_n)$$

of the variables is called an *invariant* of the group, if

$$F(x_1^{(S)}, x_2^{(S)}, \ldots, x_n^{(S)}) \equiv F(x_1, x_2, \ldots, x_n)$$

for each substitution S of the group. It is obvious that such invariants always exist. In fact if from any rational function

$$f(x_1, x_2, \ldots, x_n),$$

which is not identically zero, the N functions

$$f(x_1^{(S)}, x_2^{(S)}, \ldots, x_n^{(S)})$$

be formed, where for S each of the N substitutions of G is taken in turn, then any symmetric function of the N functions is an invariant of G.

A rational function of the variables such that

$$F(x_1^{(S)}, x_2^{(S)}, \ldots, x_n^{(S)}) = k_S F(x_1, x_2, \ldots, x_n),$$

where k_S is a constant which for some substitutions is different from unity, is called a *relative invariant* of the group. Since every substitution of the group is of finite order, the multipliers k_S must be roots of unity. If among the multipliers mth roots of unity occur, but no roots of a higher index, the substitutions of the group for which F is an invariant clearly constitute a self-conjugate sub-group of index m, and in respect of this sub-group the group is isomorphic with a cyclical group of order m. If therefore a group of linear substitutions is identical with its derived group, it can have no relative invariants.

On the other hand a group which is not identical with its derived group will necessarily have relative invariants. To prove this, let H be a self-conjugate sub-group of G such that G/H is a cyclical group of prime order p. Construct, as we shall see can always be done, an invariant F of H which is not an invariant of G. Then if S is a substitution of G which does not belong to H, and if α is a primitive pth root of unity,

$$F + \alpha F^{(S)} + \alpha^2 F^{(S^2)} + \ldots + \alpha^{p-1} F^{(S^{p-1})}$$

is clearly a relative invariant of G.

261. Any rational invariant of G can be put in the form of a rational fraction N/D, where N and D are integral functions of the variables without a common factor. The relation

$$\frac{N}{D} = \frac{N^{(S)}}{D^{(S)}}$$

implies a relation among the variables unless $N^{(S)}$ and $D^{(S)}$ are the same constant multiples of N and D. Hence N and D must be invariants or relative invariants; and from N/D an integral invariant may be formed by multiplying by a suitable power of D.

Any rational function of a set of invariants of G is necessarily another invariant. Moreover it is an immediate consequence of the definition of a covariant that every covariant of an invariant of G, or of a number of invariants of G, is either an invariant or a relative invariant of G.

That a covariant of a set of invariants of a group may in certain cases be a relative invariant is shewn by the following simple example. The Jacobian of n functions of n variables, viz.

$$\frac{\partial (f_1, f_2, \dots, f_n)}{\partial (x_1, x_2, \dots, x_n)},$$

is a covariant of the functions.

Now for the group generated by E and (x_1x_2), the functions $x_1 + x_2$ and x_1x_2 are independent invariants. But

$$\frac{\partial (x_1 + x_2, x_1x_2)}{\partial (x_1, x_2)} = x_2 - x_1,$$

which is a relative invariant for the group.

262. Since an invariant of G is a function of n independent variables, any $n+1$ invariants are connected by an algebraic equation; while a smaller number than n may be connected by such an equation. We shall first shew that a set of n algebraically independent invariants must always exist.

If $x_1, x_2, \dots, x_n$ are the n independent variables operated on by a group of linear substitutions, and if

$$x_1^{(S)}, \quad (S = S_1, S_2, \dots, S_N),$$

are the N values that x_1 takes under the substitutions of the group, we have seen in § 260 that the symmetric functions of the N quantities $x_1^{(S)}$ are invariants. Hence x_1 satisfies an algebraic equation whose coefficients are invariants of the group. In other words x_1 is an algebraic function of invariants. Similarly each of the other variables is an algebraic function of invariants. If then the number of algebraically independent invariants were $n' (< n)$, the n independent variables would be algebraic functions of the n' invariants. This involves a contradiction. Hence:—

THEOREM I. *For a group of linear substitutions in n variables there always exist systems of n algebraically independent invariants.*

263. Suppose that $I_r (r = 1, 2, \dots, n)$ is such a set of n algebraically independent invariants, and consider the simultaneous equations

$$I_r = a_r, \qquad (r = 1, 2, \dots, n)$$

where the a's are constants.

If $$x_1 = \alpha_1,\ x_2 = \alpha_2,\ \ldots,\ x_n = \alpha_n$$
is a solution of these equations, so also is
$$x_1 = \alpha_1^{(S)},\ x_2 = \alpha_2^{(S)},\ \ldots,\ x_n = \alpha_n^{(S)},$$
where S is any substitution of the group.

Two such solutions will be called "equivalent"; and the solutions that arise, when for S is taken each substitution of the group in turn, will be called a system of equivalent solutions, or more shortly a "system."

In general $\alpha_1, \alpha_2, \ldots, \alpha_n$ are algebraic functions of the a's. A system of solutions for which this is the case will be called a variable system. The n equations may however also admit systems of solutions which are independent of the a's. Such systems will be called fixed systems. The number of distinct variable systems of equivalent solutions that the n equations admit is necessarily finite; and, when different values are assigned to $a_1, a_2, \ldots, a_n$, this number must have a greatest value M.

Suppose now that J is any other invariant. It is connected with $I_1, I_2, \ldots, I_n$ by an irreducible equation
$$f(I_1, I_2, \ldots, I_n, J) = 0.$$
When the values $a_1, a_2, \ldots, a_n$ are assigned to $I_1, I_2, \ldots, I_n$, the invariant J as determined directly from this equation is an algebraic function of $a_1, a_2, \ldots, a_n$. It is possible however to determine J by first determining the variables from
$$I_1 = a_1, I_2 = a_2, \ldots, I_n = a_n,$$
and then substituting their values in the expression for J. When this is done the variable systems give for J an algebraic function of $a_1, a_2, \ldots, a_n$; but the fixed systems give values for J which are independent of $a_1, a_2, \ldots, a_n$. Since the same value of J arises from all the equivalent solutions contained in any variable system, it follows that the degree in J of the equation
$$f(I_1, I_2, \ldots, I_n, J)$$
cannot exceed M*.

* In connection with the point here discussed the reader should compare the investigation of a similar but more general question in article 79 of Dr H. F. Baker's *Multiply periodic functions* (1907).

Suppose now the a's are such that the equations

$$I_1 = a_1,\ I_2 = a_2,\ \ldots,\ I_n = a_n$$

have M distinct variable systems of solutions; and denote by

$$x_1 = \alpha_{t1},\ x_2 = \alpha_{t2},\ \ldots,\ x_n = \alpha_{tn}, \qquad (t = 1, 2, \ldots, M)$$

a solution belonging to the tth system.

Take MN distinct arbitrary constants

$$k_t^S\ (t = 1, 2, \ldots, M;\ S = S_1, S_2, \ldots, S_N)$$

and a rational function $F(x_1, x_2, \ldots, x_n)$ such that

$$F(\alpha_{t1}^{(S)}, \alpha_{t2}^{(S)}, \ldots, \alpha_{tn}^{(S)}) = k_t^S.$$

These conditions can certainly be satisfied by taking for F a polynomial of sufficiently high degree. Further denote the invariant

$$\prod_S F(x_1^{(S)}, x_2^{(S)}, \ldots, x_n^{(S)})$$

by I_{n+1}. Then if the constants k_t^S are chosen so that no two of the M numbers $\prod_S k_t^S$ are the same, the invariant I_{n+1} takes M different values for the M distinct variable systems of solutions of

$$I_1 = a_1,\ I_2 = a_2,\ \ldots,\ I_n = a_n.$$

Hence the irreducible equation

$$\phi(I_1, I_2, \ldots, I_n, I_{n+1}) = 0$$

connecting I_{n+1} with the previous n invariants is of degree M in I_{n+1}. To a set of values of the $n+1$ invariants, consistent with the equation

$$\phi = 0,$$

there therefore corresponds just one variable system of values for the variables, and therefore just one value of any other invariant. Every invariant can therefore be expressed rationally in terms of $I_1, I_2, \ldots, I_n, I_{n+1}$. Hence:—

THEOREM II. *Given a set of n algebraically independent invariants of a group of linear substitutions on n variables, it is always possible to determine an $(n+1)$th invariant such that every invariant is rationally expressible in terms of the set of $n+1$ invariants so formed.*

264. Let

$$I_r = f_r(x_1, x_2, \ldots, x_n) \qquad (r = 1, 2, \ldots, n+1)$$

be a set of invariants in terms of which every invariant of a group of linear substitutions on the n variables is rationally expressible, and let

$$\phi(I_1, I_2, \ldots, I_{n+1}) = 0$$

be the irreducible algebraic equation connecting them. If there is a set of n (not $n+1$) invariants in terms of which every invariant of the group is rationally expressible, there must be n rational functions of $I_1, I_2, \ldots, I_{n+1}$, viz.

$$J_i = F_i(I_1, I_2, \ldots, I_{n+1}), \qquad (i = 1, 2, \ldots, n)$$

such that, in virtue of the equation

$$\phi = 0,$$

each I can be rationally expressed in terms of the J's.

For the case $n = 2$ this is always possible. In fact Prof. Castelnuovo * has proved the much more general theorem that if

$$x_1 = f_1(u, v), \quad x_2 = f_2(u, v), \quad x_3 = f_3(u, v),$$

where f_1, f_2, f_3 are rational functions, then there are always two rational functions of x_1, x_2, x_3 in terms of which x_1, x_2, x_3 can themselves be expressed rationally. From this it follows that for a group of linear substitutions on 2 variables there are always two invariants in terms of which all others can be expressed rationally.

For a group of linear substitutions on 3 variables, which contains no self-conjugate substitutions, the possibility of always obtaining a set of three invariants in terms of which all others are rationally expressible may be deduced from Castelnuovo's theorem. Examples of such sets are given below. For groups on more than 3 variables it is not at present known whether such reduction is always possible or not.

265. Just as a group of linear substitutions on n variables determines a class of rational functions which are invariant for the group, so a given set of rational functions of n variables defines a certain group of linear substitutions on the n variables

* "Sulla razionalitá delle involuzioni piane," *Math. Ann.* Vol. XLIV.

that consists of all those substitutions for which each of the functions is invariant. This group may consist of the identical substitution only; and on the other hand may be a group whose order is not finite.

For a group G of finite order the question arises as to whether the class of functions which are invariant for G may not be invariant for some greater group containing G. The preceding investigation shews immediately that this question must be answered in the negative. Let

$$I_1, I_2, \ldots, I_{n+1}$$

be the set of invariants of G, considered in § 263, in terms of which all the others are expressible rationally; and suppose that the first n of them are invariant for a greater group H containing G as a group of index μ. The equations

$$I_r = a_r, \qquad (r = 1, 2, \ldots, n)$$

which give M systems of values of the variables for G, will give M/μ systems for H. Hence if I_{n+1} is also invariant for H, it will take at most M/μ values when the other invariants are given. The supposition that all the $n+1$ invariants for G are also invariant for H leads therefore to a contradiction. Hence:—

THEOREM III. *The class of rational functions which are defined as the invariants of a group of linear substitutions G, themselves define G as the greatest group of linear substitutions for which they are invariant.*

Corollary. If the greatest common factor of the degree of the homogeneous invariants of a group of linear substitutions is greater than unity, the group must contain self-conjugate substitutions which multiply every variable by the same root of unity. In fact if the degree of every homogeneous invariant is a multiple of p, the substitution

$$x_i' = \omega x_i, \qquad \omega^p = 1, \qquad (i = 1, 2, \ldots, n),$$

leaves every invariant unchanged and therefore by the theorem belongs to the group.

266. In illustration of the preceding results we will now take some particular cases. Consider first the irreducible group of order $2n$ on 2 variables, generated by the substitutions

$$x' = \omega x, \quad y' = \omega^{-1} y;$$

and
$$x' = y, \quad y' = x;$$

where
$$\omega^n = 1.$$

The simplest invariants are obviously xy and $x^n + y^n$. Now the equations

$$xy = a_1, \quad x^n + y^n = a_2$$

have, for general values of a_1 and a_2, just $2n$ solutions which form a single system. Hence every invariant of the group can be expressed rationally in terms of these two.

As a second example we take the irreducible representation of the alternating group of degree 5 as a group of linear substitutions on 3 variables (§ 232). It is generated by

$$x_0' = x_0, \quad x_1' = \omega x_1, \quad x_2' = \omega^{-1} x_2;$$

and
$$\sqrt{5}x_0' = x_0 + x_1 + x_2, \qquad \omega^5 = 1,$$
$$\sqrt{5}x_1' = 2x_0 + (\omega^2 + \omega^{-2})\, x_1 + (\omega + \omega^{-1})\, x_2,$$
$$\sqrt{5}x_2' = 2x_0 + (\omega + \omega^{-1})\, x_1 + (\omega^2 + \omega^{-2})\, x_2.$$

The substitution of order 2 which transforms

$$x_0' = x_0, \quad x_1' = \omega x_1, \quad x_2' = \omega^{-1} x_2$$

into its inverse must change x_0 into $-x_0$; and therefore x_0^2 is invariant for a sub-group of order 10, and takes just six values under the substitutions of the group. These are

$$x_0^2, \quad \tfrac{1}{5}(x_0 + \omega^n x_1 + \omega^{-n} x_2)^2. \qquad (n = 0, 1, 2, 3, 4)$$

The symmetric functions of these six quantities are therefore invariants of the group.

It is easily verified that the sum of their squares and the sum of their fourth powers are not algebraically independent of the sum of the first powers and the sum of the cubes; while the sum of the fifth powers is algebraically independent of the simpler symmetric functions. Hence

$$f_2 = 5x_0^2 + \sum_0^4 (x_0 + \omega^n x_1 + \omega^{-n} x_2)^2,$$

$$f_6 = 5^3 x_0^6 + \sum_0^4 (x_0 + \omega^n x_1 + \omega^{-n} x_2)^6,$$

$$f_{10} = 5^5 x_0^{10} + \sum_0^4 (x_0 + \omega^n x_1 + \omega^{-n} x_2)^{10}$$

is a set of algebraically independent invariants. The set of equations

$$f_2 = a_2, \quad f_6 = a_6, \quad f_{10} = a_{10}$$

admits 120 solutions forming two systems, and therefore every other invariant must be connected with f_2, f_6, f_{10} by an equation of the first or second degree.

Since the group is simple, so that there can be no relative invariant, the Jacobian of f_2, f_6, f_{10} is an absolute invariant. Its degree is 15, and therefore it cannot be rationally expressed in terms of f_2, f_6, f_{10}. Hence if the Jacobian be denoted by f_{15}, every invariant can be expressed rationally in terms of

$$f_2, \ f_6, \ f_{10}, \ f_{15};$$

and these are connected by an algebraic equation which is quadratic in f_{15}.

Consider now the three invariants

$$I_1 = \frac{f_6}{f_2^3}, \quad I_2 = \frac{f_{10}}{f_6 f_2^2}, \quad I_3 = \frac{f_{10} f_6}{f_{15}}.$$

The equations $\qquad I_1 = a_1, \quad I_2 = a_2,$

being homogeneous equations of degrees 6 and 10 in the variables, determine 60 values of the ratios $x_0 : x_1 : x_2$. For given values of the ratios, the further equation

$$I_3 = a_3$$

determines x_0, x_1, x_2 uniquely. Hence to given values of I_1, I_2, I_3 there corresponds a single system of values of the variables. It follows that every invariant of the group can be expressed rationally in terms of I_1, I_2, I_3.

267. For the simple group of order 168, expressed as a group of linear substitutions on 3 variables as in § 232, the generating function for determining the numbers of invariants of various degrees (§ 227) is

$$\frac{1}{168}\left[\frac{1}{(1-x)^3} + \frac{21}{(1-x)(1-x^2)} + \frac{56}{1-x^3} + \frac{42}{(1-x)(1+x^2)} \right.$$
$$\left. + \frac{24}{(1-\alpha x)(1-\alpha^2 x)(1-\alpha^4 x)} + \frac{24}{(1-\alpha^6 x)(1-\alpha^5 x)(1-\alpha^3 x)}\right]$$
$$= 1 + x^4 + x^6 + x^8 + x^{10} + 2x^{12} + 2x^{14} + \dots.$$

This indicates the existence of invariants of degrees 4, 6, 14 which are rationally independent. Now for the substitution

$$x_1' = \alpha x_1, \quad x_2' = \alpha^2 x_2, \quad x_3' = \alpha^4 x_3, \quad \alpha^7 = 1$$

the only invariants of degree 4 are $x_1x_2^3$, $x_2x_3^3$ and $x_3x_1^3$. The only linear function of $x_1x_2^3$, $x_2x_3^3$ and $x_3x_1^3$, which is invariant for the other generating substitution of the group, is found to be

$$x_1x_2^3 + x_2x_3^3 + x_3x_1^3.$$

Denoting this by f_4, its Hessian (which since the group is simple is necessarily an absolute invariant) is of degree 6 and may be denoted by f_6. From the above considerations it is the only invariant of degree 6. Every covariant of f_4 and f_6 is an absolute invariant of the group. Denote by f_{14} the covariant

$$\begin{vmatrix} \dfrac{\partial^2 f_4}{\partial x_1^2} & \dfrac{\partial^2 f_4}{\partial x_1 \partial x_2} & \dfrac{\partial^2 f_4}{\partial x_1 \partial x_3} & \dfrac{\partial f_6}{\partial x_1} \\ \dfrac{\partial^2 f_4}{\partial x_1 \partial x_2} & \dfrac{\partial^2 f_4}{d x_2^2} & \dfrac{\partial^2 f_4}{\partial x_2 \partial x_3} & \dfrac{\partial f_6}{\partial x_2} \\ \dfrac{\partial^2 f_4}{\partial x_1 \partial x_3} & \dfrac{\partial^2 f_4}{\partial x_2 \partial x_3} & \dfrac{\partial^2 f_4}{\partial x_3^2} & \dfrac{\partial f_6}{\partial x_3} \\ \dfrac{\partial f_6}{\partial x_1} & \dfrac{\partial f_6}{\partial x_2} & \dfrac{\partial f_6}{\partial x_3} & 0 \end{vmatrix}$$

It will be found on calculating its leading terms that it does not vanish identically. Moreover as will be seen immediately it is algebraically independent of f_4 and f_6. Hence f_4, f_6 and f_{14} are the only rationally independent invariants whose degrees do not exceed 14. Now when the Jacobian of f_4, f_6, f_{14} is calculated it is found not to be identically zero. Denote it by f_{21}. Being of odd degree it cannot be expressed rationally in terms of f_4, f_6, f_{14}. The equations

$$f_4 = a, \quad f_6 = b, \quad f_{14} = c$$

determine 2.168 sets of values of the variables forming two systems. Hence the equation connecting f_4, f_6, f_{14}, f_{21} is of degree 2 in f_{21}, and every invariant can be expressed rationally in terms of these four. Finally if

$$I_1 = \frac{f_6^2}{f_4^3}, \quad I_2 = \frac{f_{14}}{f_6 f_4^2}, \quad I_3 = \frac{f_{21}}{f_{14} f_6},$$

the equations

$$I_1 = a_1, \quad I_2 = a_2$$

determine just 168 values of the ratios $x_1 : x_2 : x_3$, and when the ratios are known

$$I_3 = a_3$$

determines x_1, x_2, x_3 uniquely. Hence

$$I_1 = a_1, \quad I_2 = a_2, \quad I_3 = a_3$$

determine just one system for the variables, and therefore every other invariant of the group is expressible rationally in terms of these three.

268. In the last two examples, the groups of substitutions (birational) on the ratios of the variables are simply isomorphic with the groups of linear substitutions themselves, and the groups have invariants of degree 1 in the variables. If the group of linear substitutions has self-conjugate substitutions and is irreducible, these conditions are not satisfied. As a further example we will consider a simple case of such a group. The two substitutions

$$x_0' = x_1, \quad x_1' = x_2, \quad x_2' = x_0;$$

and

$$x_0' = x_0, \quad x_1' = \omega x_1, \quad x_2' = \omega^2 x_2; \qquad \omega^3 = 1;$$

generate a group of order 27. Its invariants are obviously xyz and all symmetric and alternating functions of x^3, y^3 and z^3. The three invariants

$$a = x^3 + y^3 + z^3,$$
$$b = y^3 z^3 + z^3 x^3 + x^3 y^3,$$
$$c = xyz,$$

are algebraically independent, and to given values of them there correspond two systems for the variables. If

$$d = (x^3 + \omega y^3 + \omega^2 z^3)^3,$$

d is invariant, and it will be found that

$$d^2 - d(2a^3 - 9ab + 27c^3) + (a^2 - 3b)^3 = 0.$$

Hence every invariant of the group is rationally expressible in terms of a, b, c and d. If, in this case again, there are three invariants in terms of which all invariants of the group are rationally expressible, there must be three rational functions of a, b, c, d in terms of which, in virtue of the preceding equation, a, b, c and d can be expressed rationally.

Now if

$$\frac{d}{(a^2-3b)(a-3\omega c)}=u, \quad \frac{(a^2-3b)^2}{d(a-3\omega^2 c)}=v,$$

the equation may be written

$$u(a-3\omega c)+v(a-3\omega^2 c)-\frac{1}{uv}(a-3c)-3a=0,$$

or

$$c=\frac{a\left(u+v-\frac{1}{uv}-3\right)}{3\left(\omega u+\omega^2 v-\frac{1}{uv}\right)}.$$

Hence b, c and d can be expressed rationally in terms of a, u and v. It follows that

$$x^3+y^3+z^3,$$

$$\frac{(x^3+\omega y^3+\omega^2 z^3)^2}{(x^3+\omega^2 y^3+\omega z^3)(x^3+y^3+z^3-3\omega xyz)},$$

$$\frac{(x^3+\omega^2 y^3+\omega z^3)^2}{(x^3+\omega y^3+\omega^2 z^3)(x^3+y^3+z^3-3\omega^2 xyz)}$$

is a set of three invariants in terms of which all the invariants of the group can be expressed rationally.

269. From the equations

$$x_i'=\sum_j a_{ij}x_j, \qquad (i, j=1, 2, \ldots, n)$$

defining a linear substitution, there follow the equations

$$\frac{\partial}{\partial x_i}=\sum_j a_{ji}\frac{\partial}{\partial x_j'}, \qquad (i, j=1, 2, \ldots, n)$$

giving the relations between differential coefficients with respect to the old and new variables. This is equivalent to the statement that if the variables x_i undergo any substitution of a group G, then the operators $\frac{\partial}{\partial x_i}$ undergo the corresponding substitution of the transposed group G_t. Suppose that

$F(x_1, x_2, \ldots, x_n)$ is an invariant for G. Then it follows that when the x's undergo any substitution of G, the n functions

$$\frac{\partial F}{\partial x_1}, \frac{\partial F}{\partial x_2}, \ldots, \frac{\partial F}{\partial x_n},$$

undergo the corresponding substitution of G_t. If when new variables $\xi_i\,(i = 1, 2, \ldots, n)$, linearly independent linear functions of the x's, are taken G becomes G' and $F(x_1, x_2, \ldots, x_n)$ becomes $F'(\xi_1, \xi_2, \ldots, \xi_n)$, then when the ξ's undergo any substitution of G', the n functions

$$\frac{\partial F'}{\partial \xi_1}, \frac{\partial F'}{\partial \xi_2}, \ldots, \frac{\partial F'}{\partial \xi_n}$$

undergo the corresponding substitution of G_t'. Suppose now that in the function F' only the first s ξ's actually occur. Then since

$$\frac{\partial F'}{\partial \xi_1}, \frac{\partial F'}{\partial \xi_2}, \ldots, \frac{\partial F'}{\partial \xi_s}, 0, 0, \ldots, 0$$

undergo formally the substitutions of G_t', this group and therefore also G' must be reducible, transforming the first s ξ's among themselves. Hence:—

THEOREM IV. *If G is an irreducible group of linear substitutions on n variables and if F is an invariant for G, it is not possible, by any linear substitution performed on the variables, to express F as a function of less than n variables.*

270. A group of linear substitutions in which all the coefficients are real has obviously at least one quadratic invariant (see Ex. 2, p. 268). The conditions under which an irreducible group of linear substitutions may have a quadratic invariant (by the preceding result there cannot be more than one) can be expressed in a form which depends only on the characteristics.

Suppose that for an irreducible group of linear substitutions G, the quadratic function $F(x_1, x_2, \ldots, x_n)$ is invariant. Then when the x's undergo the substitutions of G, the n linear functions of the x's

$$\frac{\partial F}{\partial x_1}, \frac{\partial F}{\partial x_2}, \ldots, \frac{\partial F}{\partial x_n}$$

undergo the corresponding substitutions of the transposed group G_t. Hence G and G_t are equivalent. Now it has been seen that in any case G_t and $\bar{G}$, the conjugate group, are equivalent; and therefore G and $\bar{G}$ are equivalent. The characteristics in G must therefore be real.

Now in § 227 we have obtained an expression for the number of invariants of any given degree m in the variables, which may be written

$$\frac{1}{N}\sum_S \psi_m(S),$$

$\psi_m(S)$ being the sum of the homogeneous products of m dimensions of the multipliers of S. If $\omega_1, \omega_2, \ldots, \omega_n$ are the multipliers of S,

$$\begin{aligned} 2\psi_2(S) &= (\omega_1 + \omega_2 + \ldots + \omega_n)^2 + \omega_1^2 + \omega_2^2 + \ldots + \omega_n^2 \\ &= (\chi_S)^2 + \chi_{S^2}. \end{aligned}$$

Hence the number of quadratic invariants is

$$\frac{1}{2N}\sum_S ((\chi_S)^2 + \chi_{S^2}).$$

Now (§ 218) for a group which is equivalent to its conjugate

$$\sum_S (\chi_S)^2 = N.$$

The number of invariants is therefore

$$\frac{1}{2} + \frac{1}{2N}\sum_S \chi_{S^2}.$$

This number is either zero or unity. Hence for a group which is equivalent to its conjugate $\sum\limits_S \chi_{S^2}$ is either $\pm N$; and the condition that the group should have a quadratic invariant is

$$\sum_S \chi_{S^2} = N.$$

The simplest instance of an irreducible group whose characteristics are real, for which there is no quadratic invariant, is given by the quaternion group in two variables. This is generated by

$$x_1' = ix_1, \qquad x_2' = -ix_2;$$

and

$$x_1' = x_2, \qquad x_2' = -x_1.$$

The characteristics of the five conjugate sets are 2, − 2, 0, 0, 0; and

$$\sum_S \chi_{S^2} = -8.$$

271. A quadratic invariant of an irreducible group of linear substitutions stands in a different relation to the group from that of the other invariants. In fact a quadratic function of n variables has no covariant which is algebraically independent of itself; and it is invariant for a group of linear substitutions whose order is not finite. Thus

$$x_1^2 + x_2^2 + \dots + x_n^2$$

is invariant for the linear substitution

$$x_i' = \sum_j a_{ij} x_j, \qquad (i, j = 1, 2, \dots, n)$$

if
$$\sum_i a_{is}^2 = 1 \quad \text{and} \quad \sum_i a_{is} a_{it} = 0, \qquad (s \neq t)$$

and these equations are known to have an infinite number of solutions.

On the other hand, a homogeneous function f of degree $m\,(> 2)$, which is not the product of homogeneous functions of lower degree, has in general* an algebraically independent system of covariants; so that covariants $f_1, f_2, \dots, f_{n-1}$ can in general be found such that the system of equations

$$f = a_0, \quad f_1^{m_1} = a_1, \quad \dots, \quad f_{n-1}^{m_{n-1}} = a_{n-1},$$

where the a's are assigned constants, have only a finite number of solutions. Now if f is an invariant of a group of linear substitutions of the variables, the covariants of f are absolute or relative invariants for the same group, and suitably chosen powers of them are absolute invariants. If the group were not of finite order, there would arise from any set of values of the variables satisfying the above equations an infinite number of sets of values, in contradiction of the fact that the equations have only a finite number of solutions.

Hence, in general, any homogeneous invariant, of degree greater than two, of a group of linear substitutions, which is not

* That there are exceptions to this statement is well known. For instance, any invariant of a general quantic, when in it the coefficients are regarded as independent variables, gives an exception.

expressible as a product of factors of lower degree, will, in the sense of § 265, determine either the group itself or a group of finite order containing it.

272. Ex. 1. Prove that if

$$x_1 + x_2 + x_3 + x_4 = s, \qquad x_1 + x_2 - x_3 - x_4 = z_1,$$

$$x_1 + x_3 - x_2 - x_4 = z_2, \qquad x_1 + x_4 - x_2 - x_3 = z_3,$$

$$z_1^2 + z_2^2 + z_3^2 = a, \qquad z_1^4 + z_2^4 + z_3^4 = b,$$

$$(z_1^2 + \omega z_2^2 + \omega^2 z_3^2)^3 = c, \qquad z_1 z_2 z_3 = d,$$

$$\omega^3 = 1,$$

then all the invariants of the alternating group in x_1, x_2, x_3, x_4 can be expressed rationally in terms of s, a/d, b/d, c/d.

Ex. 2. Shew that for the group of order 20 generated by the two substitutions

$$x_1' = \omega x_1, \quad x_2' = \omega^2 x_2, \quad x_3' = \omega^4 x_3, \quad x_4' = \omega^3 x_4; \qquad \omega^5 = 1$$

and $$x_1' = x_2, \quad x_2' = x_3, \quad x_3' = x_4, \quad x_4' = x_1;$$

four invariants in terms of which all others can be rationally expressed are

$$\frac{x_1x_2}{x_4} + \frac{x_2x_3}{x_1} + \frac{x_3x_4}{x_2} + \frac{x_4x_1}{x_3},$$

$$\left(\frac{x_1x_2}{x_4} + i\frac{x_2x_3}{x_1} - \frac{x_3x_4}{x_2} - i\frac{x_4x_1}{x_3}\right)^4,$$

$$\left(\frac{x_1x_2}{x_4} + i\frac{x_2x_3}{x_1} - \frac{x_3x_4}{x_2} - i\frac{x_4x_1}{x_3}\right)^2 \left(\frac{x_1x_2}{x_4} - \frac{x_2x_3}{x_1} + \frac{x_3x_4}{x_2} - \frac{x_4x_1}{x_3}\right),$$

and $$\left(\frac{x_1x_2}{x_4} + i\frac{x_2x_3}{x_1} - \frac{x_3x_4}{x_2} - i\frac{x_4x_1}{x_3}\right) \left(\frac{x_1x_2}{x_4} - i\frac{x_2x_3}{x_1} - \frac{x_3x_4}{x_2} + i\frac{x_4x_1}{x_3}\right),$$

where $i^2 = -1$.

Ex. 3. Shew that for the sub-group of order 10 of the group in the previous example, x_1x_3, $x_1^5 + x_3^5$, $x_1^3x_2 + x_3^3x_4$, $x_1^2x_4 + x_3^2x_2$ is a set of invariants in terms of which all can be rationally expressed.

Ex. 4. The sub-group of a transitive permutation-group, which leaves one symbol unchanged, permutes the symbols in m transitive sets. Prove that if the order of the group is odd, it has $\frac{1}{2}(m+1)$ independent quadratic invariants; and that if the order is even the number of quadratic invariants is greater than $\frac{1}{2}(m+1)$.

Ex. 5. Determine the group of linear substitutions for which $x^5y + y^5z + z^5x$ is invariant.

Ex. 6. Prove that

$$x' = \frac{1}{2i}(x + y - iz + it), \qquad y' = \frac{1}{2i}(x - y - iz - it),$$

$$z' = \frac{1}{2i}(-x - y - iz + it), \qquad t' = \frac{1}{2i}(-x + y - iz - it),$$

is a substitution of order 5 for which the homogeneous quartic function

$$x^4 + y^4 + z^4 + t^4 + 12xyzt$$

is invariant. Hence prove that this expression is invariant for a group of linear substitutions of order $2^6 . 120$, which contains a self-conjugate substitution of order 4.

(From this it follows that the quartic surface

$$x^4 + y^4 + z^4 + t^4 + 12xyzt = 0$$

is invariant for a group of $2^4 . 120$ collineations. It may be shewn that no quartic surface which is not projectively equivalent to the above admits so large a group of collineations of finite order for which it is unaltered.)

Ex. 7. Prove that the necessary and sufficient condition that an irreducible group Γ of odd order shall have a cubic invariant is that $\Gamma_{(2)}$ and $\overline{\Gamma}$ are equivalent.

Ex. 8. Shew that the group of linear substitutions on $x_1^2, x_2^2, x_3^2, x_2x_3, x_3x_1, x_1x_2$, when x_1, x_2, x_3 undergo the substitutions of the second group of § 232, is irreducible. Prove that this group of linear substitutions on 6 symbols has an invariant of degree 3 which does *not* possess a system of algebraically independent covariants.

CHAPTER XVIII.

ON THE GRAPHICAL REPRESENTATION OF A GROUP*.

273. OUR discussions hitherto have been confined mainly to groups of finite order. When however, as we now propose to do, we consider a group in relation to the operations that generate it, it becomes almost necessary to deal, incidentally at least, with groups whose order is not finite; for it is not possible to say a priori what must be the number and the nature of the relations between the given generating operations, which will ensure that the order of the resulting group is finite.

Many of the definitions given in respect of finite groups may obviously be extended at once to groups containing an infinite number of operations. Among these may be specially mentioned the definitions of a sub-group, of conjugate operations and sub-groups, of self-conjugate sub-groups, of the relation of isomorphism between two groups and of the factor-group given by this relation. In regard to the last of them, the isomorphism between two groups, one at least of which is not of finite order, may be such that to one operation of the one group there correspond an infinitely great number of operations of the other. On the other hand, all the results obtained for finite groups, which depend directly or indirectly on the order of the group, necessarily become meaningless when the group is not a group of finite order.

* The investigations of this Chapter are due to Dyck, "Gruppentheoretische Studien," *Math. Ann.*, Vol. xx (1882), pp. 1—44. We have followed Dyck's memoir closely except in two respects. Firstly, we have used a rather more definite geometrical operation than that of the memoir; and secondly, we have not specially considered a regular and symmetric division of a closed surface, apart from a merely regular division.

274. Suppose that

$$S_1, S_2, \ldots, S_n$$

represent any n distinct operations which can be performed, directly or inversely, on a common object, and that between these operations no relations exist. Then the totality of the operations represented by

$$\ldots S_p^{\alpha} S_q^{\beta} S_r^{\gamma} \ldots,$$

where the number of factors is any whatever and the indices are any positive or negative integers, form a group G of infinite order, which is generated by the n operations. If, moreover, whenever such a succession of factors as $S_p^{\alpha} S_p^{\beta}$ occurs in the above expression, it is replaced by $S_p^{\alpha+\beta}$, each operation of the group can be expressed in one way and in one way only by an expression of the above form, which is then called *reduced*.

It will sometimes be convenient to avoid the use of negative indices in the expression of any operation of the group. To this end we may write

$$S_1 S_2 \ldots S_n S_{n+1} = E,$$

so that S_{n+1} is a definite operation of the group; then

$$S_r^{-1} = S_{r+1} S_{r+2} \ldots S_n S_{n+1} S_1 \ldots S_{r-1}, \quad (r = 1, 2, \ldots, n).$$

By using these relations to replace all negative powers of operations wherever they occur, we may represent every operation of the group in a single definite way by means of the $n+1$ operations

$$S_1, S_2, \ldots, S_n, S_{n+1},$$

with positive indices only.

The group, thus defined and represented, is the most general group conceivable that is generated by n distinct operations. Any two such groups, for which n is the same, are simply isomorphic with each other.

Suppose now that

$$\bar{S}_1, \bar{S}_2, \ldots, \bar{S}_n$$

represent n distinct operations, but that, instead of being entirely independent, they are connected by a relation of the form

$$\bar{S}_p^{a} \bar{S}_q^{b} \ldots \bar{S}_r^{c} = E,$$

which will be represented by

$$f(\bar{S}_i) = E.$$

If $\bar{G}$ is the group generated by these operations, an isomorphism may be established between G and $\bar{G}$ by taking $\bar{S}_i$ $(i=1, 2, \ldots n)$ as the operation of $\bar{G}$ that corresponds to the operation S_i of G.

Then to every operation of G

$$\ldots S_p^{\alpha} S_q^{\beta} S_r^{\gamma} \ldots$$

will correspond a single definite operation

$$\ldots \bar{S}_p^{\alpha} \bar{S}_q^{\beta} \bar{S}_r^{\gamma} \ldots$$

of $\bar{G}$; for the supposition that two distinct operations of $\bar{G}$ correspond to the same operation of G leads to the result that between the generating operations of G there is a relation, which is not the case. On the other hand, to the identical operation of $\bar{G}$ there will correspond an infinite number of distinct operations of G, namely those which are formed by combining together in every possible way all operations of G of the form

$$R^{-1} f(S_i) R,$$

where R is any operation of G. These operations of G form a self-conjugate sub-group H, and the corresponding factor-group G/H is simply isomorphic with $\bar{G}$.

If between the generating operations of $\bar{G}$ there are several independent relations

$$f_1(\bar{S}_i) = E, \quad f_2(\bar{S}_i) = E, \ldots, f_m(\bar{S}_i) = E,$$

it may be shewn exactly as before that the groups G and $\bar{G}$ are isomorphic in such a way that to the identical operation of $\bar{G}$ there corresponds that self-conjugate sub-group of G, which is formed by combining in every possible way all the operations of G of the form

$$R^{-1} f_j(S_i) R, \quad (j = 1, 2, \ldots, m).$$

275. We may at once extend the result of the preceding paragraph in the following way:—

THEOREM I. *If G is the group generated by the n operations*

$$S_1, S_2, \ldots, S_n,$$

between which the m relations

$$f_1(S_i) = E, \quad f_2(S_i) = E, \ldots, f_m(S_i) = E,$$

exist; and if $\bar{G}$ is the group generated by the n operations

$$\bar{S}_1, \bar{S}_2, \ldots, \bar{S}_n,$$

which are connected by the same m relations

$$f_1(\bar{S}_i) = E, \quad f_2(\bar{S}_i) = E, \ldots, \quad f_m(\bar{S}_i) = E,$$

as hold between the generating operations of G, and by the further m′ relations

$$g_1(\bar{S}_i) = E, \quad g_2(\bar{S}_i) = E, \ldots, g_{m'}(\bar{S}_i) = E;$$

then $\bar{G}$ is simply isomorphic with the factor-group G/H; where H is that self-conjugate sub-group of G, which results from combining in every possible way all operations of the form

$$R^{-1} g_j(S_i) R, \quad (j = 1, 2, \ldots, m'),$$

R being any operation of G.

In proving this theorem, it is sufficient to notice that, if we take $\bar{S}_i (i = 1, 2, \ldots, n)$ as the operation of $\bar{G}$ which corresponds to the operation S_i of G, then to each operation of G a single definite operation of $\bar{G}$ will correspond, while to the identical operation of $\bar{G}$ there corresponds the self-conjugate sub-group H of G.

The theorem just stated is of such a general nature that it is perhaps desirable to illustrate it by considering shortly some simple examples.

Let us take first the case of a group G, generated by two independent operations S_1 and S_2, subject to no relations; and let us suppose that the single relation

$$\bar{S}_1 \bar{S}_2 = \bar{S}_2 \bar{S}_1$$

holds between the generating operations of $\bar{G}$. The self-conjugate sub-group H of G then consists of all the operations

$$\ldots S_1^{\alpha_n} S_2^{\beta_n} \ldots$$

of G which reduce to identity if we regard S_1 and S_2 as permutable; or, in other words, of those operations of G for which the relations

$$\Sigma\alpha_n = 0, \quad \Sigma\beta_n = 0$$

simultaneously hold.

In respect of this sub-group, the operations of G can be divided into an infinite number of classes of the form

$$S_1^p S_2^q H.$$

For the operations of the class $S_1^pS_2^qH$, multiplied by those of the class $S_1^{p'}S_2^{q'}H$, give always operations of the class

$$S_1^pS_2^qS_1^{p'}S_2^{q'}H,$$

since H is a self-conjugate sub-group; and, because

$$S_1^p S_2^q S_1^{p'} S_2^{q'} = S_1^{p+p'} . S_1^{-p'} S_2^q S_1^{p'} S_2^{-q} . S_2^{q+q'},$$

while $S_1^{-p'}S_2^qS_1^{p'}S_2^{-q}$ belongs to H, the class $S_1^pS_2^qS_1^{p'}S_2^{q'}H$ is the same as $S_1^{p+p'}S_2^{q+q'}H$. Hence the operations of any two given classes, multiplied in either order, give the same third class; and therefore the group G/H is an Abelian group generated by two permutable, but otherwise unrestricted, operations.

As a second illustration, we will choose a case in which $\overline{G}$ is of finite order. Let G be generated by the operations S and T, which satisfy the relations

$$S^3 = E, \quad T^3 = E, \quad (ST)^3 = E;$$

and for $\overline{G}$, suppose that the generating operations satisfy the additional relation

$$(ST^2)^3 = E.$$

Then H is formed by combining in all possible ways the operations

$$R^{-1}(ST^2)^3 R.$$

Now it may be easily verified that, in G, the operation ST^2 belongs to a set of three conjugate operations

$$ST^2, \quad TST, \quad T^2S;$$

and that these three operations are permutable among themselves, while their product is identity. Hence H consists of the Abelian group whose operations are

$$(ST^2)^{3\alpha}(TST)^{3\beta}, \quad (\alpha, \beta = 0, 1, 2, \ldots);$$

and in respect of H, G may be divided into 27 classes of the form

$$S^x(ST^2)^y(TST)^z H, \quad (x, y, z = 0, 1, 2).$$

The group $\overline{G}$ will be defined by the laws according to which these 27 classes combine among themselves; and the reader will have no difficulty in verifying that it is simply isomorphic with the non-Abelian group of order 27, whose operations are all of order 3 (§ 117).

276. For the further discussion of a group, as defined by its generating operations and the relations between them, a suitable graphical mode of representation becomes of the greatest assistance. To this we shall now proceed.

In the simple case in which the group is generated by a single unrestricted operation, such a representation may be constructed as follows. Let C_1 and C_{-1} be two circles which touch each other; C_2 and C_{-2} the inverses of C_{-1} in C_1 and C_1 in C_{-1}; C_3 and C_{-3} the inverses of C_{-2} in C_1 and C_2 in C_{-1}, and so on. These circles (fig. 1) divide the plane in which they are drawn into an infinite number of crescent-shaped spaces. Suppose now that the space between C_1 and C_{-1} is left white, and the spaces between C_1 and C_2 and between C_{-1} and C_{-2} (on either side of this white space) are coloured black; the next pair on either side left white, the next coloured black, and so on. Then any white space may be transformed into any other (and any black into any other) by an even number of inversions at

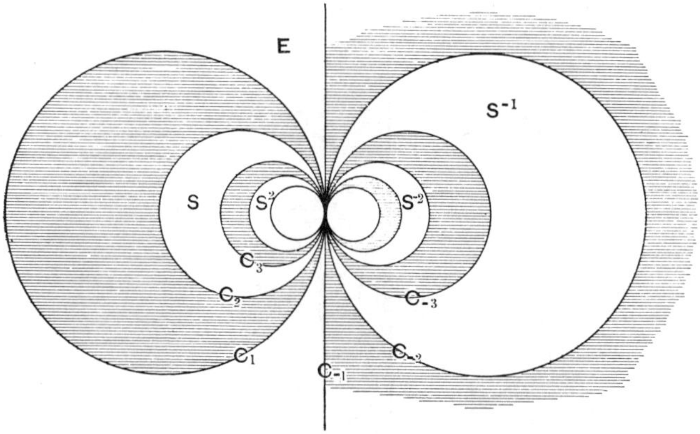

Fig. 1.

the circles C_{-1} and C_1; and if S denote the operation consisting of an inversion at C_{-1} followed by an inversion at C_1, the space between C_{-1} and C_1 will be transformed into another perfectly definite white space by the operation S^n, while conversely the operation necessary to transform the space between C_{-1} and C_1 into any other given white space will be a definite power of S. Hence if one of the white spaces, say that between C_{-1} and C_1, is taken to correspond to the identical operation, there is then a unique correspondence between the white spaces and the operations of the group generated by the unrestricted operation S; and the figure that has been constructed gives a graphical representation of the group. It should be noticed that the actual geometrical process of inversion, which has been here used to construct the spaces corresponding to the operations of the group, is in no way essential to the graphical representation. It is however convenient as giving definiteness to the construction; and later, when we deal with the case of a general group, such definiteness becomes almost a necessity.

In a precisely similar manner, the group generated by a single operation S, satisfying the relation

$$S^n = E,$$

may be treated. In this case, we take two circles C_{-1} and C_1 intersecting at an angle π/n, and from these form, as before,

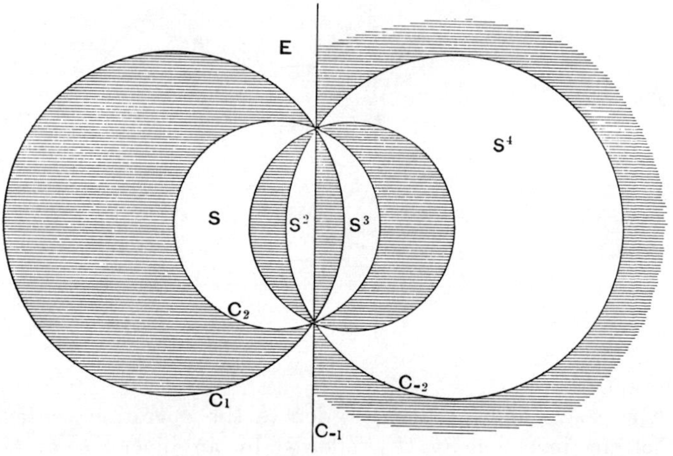

Fig. 2.

the circles obtained by successive inversions. This gives a finite series of n circles, each of which intersects the two next to it on either side at angles π/n, while the n circles divide the plane into $2n$ spaces. If these are left white and coloured black in alternate succession, and if one of the white is taken to correspond to the identical operation, there is a unique correspondence between the white spaces and the operations of the group generated by S, where S represents the result of successive inversions first at C_{-1} and then at C_1.

This operation obviously satisfies the relation

$$S^n = E$$

and no simpler relation; so that the figure gives a graphical representation of a cyclical group of order n.

The systems of circles in figures 1 and 2 have a common geometrical property which may be noticed here as it will be of use in the sequel. Successive inversions at any one of the pairs C_{-1} and C_1, C_1 and C_2, C_2 and C_3 are equivalent to the operation S; and therefore successive inversions at C_{-1} and C_r are equivalent to the operation S^r. Hence the result of an even number of inversions at any of the circles in either figure is equivalent to some operation of the group that the figure represents.

277. We may now proceed to construct a graphical representation of the group which is generated by n operations subject to no relations. To this end, suppose $n+1$ circles drawn, each of which is external to all the others while each touches two and only two of the rest. Such a system can be drawn in an infinite variety of ways: we will suppose, to give definiteness and simplicity to the resulting figure, that the $n+1$ points of contact lie on a circle, which cuts the $n+1$ circles orthogonally. If these $n+1$ points taken in order are A_1, A_2, ..., A_{n+1}, the successive circles are $A_{n+1}A_1$, A_1A_2, ..., A_nA_{n+1}. We will suppose that only so much of these circles is drawn as lies within the common orthogonal circle $A_1A_2 \ldots A_{n+1}$. The $n+1$ circular arcs $A_{n+1}A_1$, A_1A_2, ... then bound a finite simply connected plane figure which we will denote provisionally by P. Suppose now that P is inverted in each of its sides, that the resulting figures are inverted in each of their *new* sides, and so on continually. Then from their mode of formation no two of the figures thus arising can overlap either wholly or in part; and when the process is continued without limit, every point in the interior of the orthogonal circle $A_1A_2 \ldots A_{n+1}$ will lie in one and only one of the figures thus formed from P by successive inversions.

If AB, AC, AD are consecutive sides of three polygons having a common corner at A, an inversion at AD is the same as three consecutive inversions at AC, AB, AC. Hence inversions at the new sides of the new polygons may be expressed in terms of inversions at the sides of P.

If P' is any one of the new figures or polygons, the set of inversions at the sides of P by which it is derived from P is perfectly definite. For suppose, if possible, that P' is derived

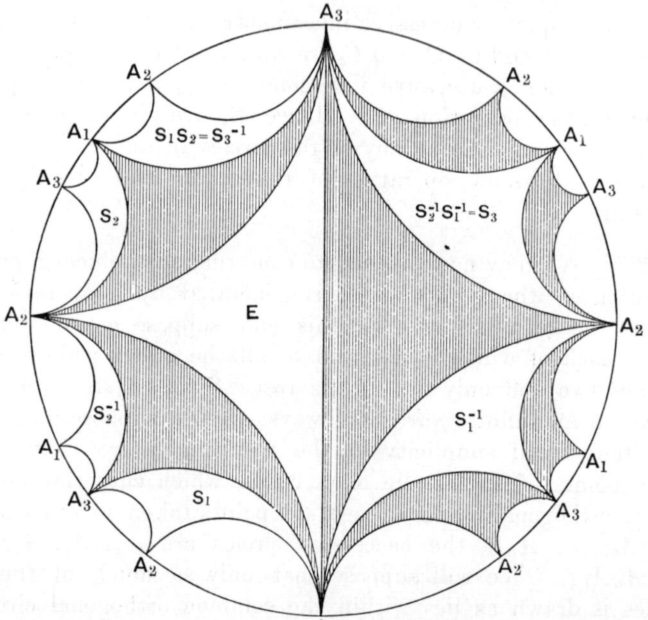

Fig. 3.

from P by two distinct sets of inversions represented by Σ and Σ'. Then $\Sigma\Sigma'^{-1}$ is a set of inversions in the sides of P which transforms P into itself. But every such set of inversions, which does not reduce to identity, necessarily transforms P into some polygon lying outside it, and therefore

$$\Sigma\Sigma'^{-1} = E;$$

or the set of inversions composing Σ is identical term for term with the set composing Σ'. It immediately follows that the polygons can be divided into two sets, according as they are derived from P by an even or an odd number of inversions.

The latter we shall suppose coloured black, and the former (including P) left white. Every white polygon will be surrounded by black polygons and vice versâ. Since there is only one definite set of inversions that will transform P into any other white polygon P', the $n+1$ corners of P' will correspond one by one to the $n+1$ corners of P; and when the perimeters of the two polygons are described in the same direction of rotation with regard to their interiors, the angular points that correspond will occur in the same cyclical order. On the other hand, in order that the corresponding angular points of a white and a black polygon may occur in the same cyclical order, their perimeters must be described in opposite directions. In consequence of these results, we may complete our figure (fig. 3) by lettering every angular point of every polygon with the same letter that occurs at the corresponding angular point of the polygon P.

278. If now $T_1, T_2, \ldots, T_{n+1}$ represent inversions at $A_1A_2, A_2A_3, \ldots A_{n+1}A_1$, the operation $T_{r-1}T_r$ leaves the corner A_r of P unchanged and it transforms P into the next white polygon which has the corner A_r in common with P, the direction of turning round A_r coinciding with the direction $A_{n+1}A_n \ldots A_1$ of describing the perimeter of P. For brevity, we shall describe this transformation of P as a positive rotation round A_r. If then we denote the operation $T_{r-1}T_r$ by the single symbol S_r, we may say that S_r produces a positive rotation of P round A_r. Let P_1 be the new polygon so obtained; and let P_1' be the polygon into which any other white polygon P' is changed by a positive rotation round the corner of P' that corresponds to A_r. Then if Σ is the set of inversions that changes P into P', it also changes P_1 into P_1': so that $\Sigma^{-1}S_r\Sigma$ changes P' into P_1', i.e. produces a positive rotation round the corner A_r of P'; and $S_r\Sigma$ changes P into P_1'.

Let us now represent the operations

$$T_{n+1}T_1,\ T_1T_2,\ \ldots,\ T_nT_{n+1},$$

by

$$S_1,\ S_2,\ \ldots,\ S_{n+1},$$

so that

$$S_1S_2\ldots S_nS_{n+1} = E.$$

Then every operation, consisting of a pair of inversions in the sides of P, can be represented in terms of

$$S_1,\ S_2,\ S_3,\ \ldots,\ S_n.$$

For an inversion at A_rA_{r+1}, followed by an inversion at A_sA_{s+1}, is given by T_rT_s; and

$$T_rT_s = T_rT_{r+1} \,.\, T_{r+1}T_{r+2} \ldots T_{s-1}T_s$$
$$= S_{r+1}S_{r+2} \ldots S_s.$$

If $s > r$, this is of the form required. If $s < r$, the term S_{n+1} that then occurs may be replaced by

$$S_n^{-1}S_{n-1}^{-1} \ldots S_2^{-1}S_1^{-1}.$$

Hence finally, every operation consisting of an even number of inversions in the sides of P can be expressed in terms of

$$S_1,\ S_2,\ S_3,\ \ldots,\ S_n;$$

and with a restriction to positive indices, every such operation can be expressed in terms of

$$S_1,\ S_2,\ \ldots,\ S_n,\ S_{n+1}.$$

Now it has been seen that no two operations, each consisting of a set of inversions in the sides of P, can be identical unless the component inversions are identical term for term. Hence no two reduced operations of the form

$$f(S_i)$$

are identical; in other words, the n generating operations

$$S_1,\ S_2,\ \ldots,\ S_n$$

are subject to no relations.

If then we take the polygon P to correspond to the identical operation of the group G generated by

$$S_1,\ S_2, \ldots,\ S_n,$$

each white polygon may be taken as associated with the operation which will transform P into it. The foregoing discussion makes it clear that in this way a unique correspondence is established between the operations of G and the system of white polygons; or in other words, that the geometrical figure gives a complete graphical representation of the group.

Moreover, since the operation $\Sigma^{-1}S_r\Sigma$ is a positive rotation round the corner A_r of the polygon Σ (calling now P the polygon E), a simple rule may be formulated for determining by a mere inspection of the figure what operation of the group any given white polygon corresponds to.

This rule may be stated as follows. Let a continuous line be drawn inside the orthogonal circle from a point in the white polygon E to a point in any other white polygon, so that every consecutive pair of white polygons through which the line passes have a common corner, a positive rotation round which leads from the first to the second of the pair. This is always possible. Then if the common corners of each consecutive pair of white polygons through which the line passes, starting from E, are $A_p, A_q, \dots, A_r, A_s$, the final white polygon corresponds to the operation

$$S_s S_r \dots S_q S_p{}^*.$$

279. The graphical representation of a general group we have thus arrived at is only one of an infinite number that could be constructed; and we choose this in preference to others mainly because the form of the figure and the relative positions of the successive polygons are readily apprehended by the eye. As regards the mere establishment of such a representation we might, still using the process of inversion for the purpose of forming a definite figure, have started with $n+1$ circles each exterior to and having no point in common with any of the others. Taking as the figure P the space external to all the circles and inverting it continually in the circles, we should form a series of black and white spaces of which the latter would again give a complete picture of the group. It is however only necessary to begin the construction of such a figure in order to convince ourselves that it would not appeal to the eye in the same way as the figure actually chosen.

Moreover, as in the representation of a cyclical group, the process of inversion is in no way essential to the representation at which we arrive. Any arbitrary construction, which would give us the series of white and black polygons having, in the sense of the geometry of position, the same relative configuration as our actual figure, would serve our purpose equally well.

280. If Σ is the operation which transforms P into P', and if Q is the black polygon which has the side $A_r A_{r+1}$ in common with P, then Σ transforms Q into the black polygon which has in common with P' the side corresponding to $A_r A_{r+1}$. If then we take Q to correspond to the identical operation, any black polygon will correspond to the same operation as that white

* The reader who refers to Prof. Dyck's memoir should notice that the definition of the operation S_r above given is not exactly equivalent to that used by Prof. Dyck. With his notation, the white polygon here considered would correspond to the operation $S_p S_q \dots\dots S_r S_s$.

polygon with which it has the side $A_r A_{r+1}$ in common. In this way we may regard our figure as divided in a definite way into double-polygons, each of which represents a single operation of the group.

281. We have next to consider how, from the representation of a general group whose n generating operations are subject to no relations, we may obtain the representation of a special group generated by n operations connected by a series of relations

$$F_j(S_i) = E, \quad (j = 1, 2, \ldots, m).$$

It has been seen (§ 274) that to the identical operation of the special group there corresponds a self-conjugate sub-group H of the general group; or in other words, that the set of operations ΣH of the general group give one and only one operation in the special group.

Hence, to obtain from our figure for the general group one that will apply to the special group, we must regard all the double-polygons of the set ΣH as equivalent to each other; and if from each such set of double-polygons we choose one as a representative of the set, the totality of these representative polygons will have a unique correspondence with the operations of the special group.

We shall first shew that a set of representative double-polygons can always be chosen so as to form a single simply connected figure. Starting with the double-polygon, P_1, that corresponds to the identical operation of the general group as the one which shall correspond to the identical operation of the special group, we take as a representative of some other operation of the special group a double-polygon, P_2, which has a side in common with P_1. Next we take as a representative of some third operation of the special group a double-polygon which has a side in common with either P_1 or P_2; and we continue the choice of double-polygons in this way until it can be carried no further. The set of double-polygons thus arrived at of necessity forms a single simply connected figure C, bounded by circular arcs; and no two of the double-polygons belonging to it correspond to the same operation of the special group. Moreover, in C there is one double-polygon corresponding to each operation of the special group. To shew this, let C' be the figure formed by combining with C every double-polygon which has a side in common with C; and form C'' from C', C''' from C'', and so on, as C' has been formed from C. From the construction of C it follows that every polygon in C' is equivalent, in respect of the special group, to some polygon in C. Similarly, every polygon in C'' is equivalent to some polygon in C' and therefore to some polygon in C; and so on. Hence finally, every polygon in the complete figure of the general group is equivalent to some polygon in C, in respect of the special group; and therefore, since no two polygons of C are equivalent in respect of the special group, the figure C is formed of a complete set of representative double-polygons for the special group.

Suppose now that S is a double-polygon outside C, with a side $A_r'A'_{r+1}$ belonging to the boundary of C. Within C there must be just one polygon, say ST, of the set SH. If this polygon lay entirely inside C, so as to have no side on the boundary of C, every polygon having a side in common with it would belong to C. Now since S and ST are equivalent, every polygon having a side in common with S is equivalent to some polygon having a side in common with ST. Hence since C contains no two equivalent polygons, ST must have a side on the boundary of C; and if this side is $A_r''A''_{r+1}$, the operation T of H transforms $A_r'A'_{r+1}$ into $A_r''A''_{r+1}$. Moreover, no operation of H can transform $A_r'A'_{r+1}$ into another side of C; for if this were possible, C would contain two polygons equivalent to S. It is also clear that, regarded as sides of polygons within C, $A_r'A'_{r+1}$ and $A_r''A''_{r+1}$ belong to polygons of different colours. Hence a correspondence in pairs of the sides of C is established: to each portion $A_r'A'_{r+1}$ of the boundary of C, which forms a side of a white (or black) polygon of C, there corresponds another definite portion $A_r''A''_{r+1}$, forming a side of a black (or white) polygon of C, such that a certain operation of H and its inverse will change one into the other, while no other operation of H will change either into any other portion of the boundary of C.

The system of double-polygons forming the figure C, and the correspondence of the sides of C in pairs, will now give a complete graphical representation of the figure. For the figure has been formed so that there is a unique correspondence between the white polygons of C and the operations of the group, such that until we arrive at the boundary the previously obtained rule will apply; and when we arrive at a polygon on the boundary, the correspondence of the sides in pairs enables the process to be continued.

282. From the mode in which the figure C has been formed, no two of the figures CH can have a polygon in common, when for H is taken in turn each operation of the self-conjugate sub-group H of the general group G; also the complete set contains every double-polygon of our original figure. This set of figures, or rather the division of the original figure into this set, will then represent in a graphical form the self-conjugate sub-group H of G. Moreover, the operations which transform corresponding pairs of sides of C into each other will, when combined and repeated, clearly suffice to transform C into any one of the figures CH and will therefore form a set of generating operations of H.

283. A simple example, in which the process described in the preceding paragraphs is actually carried out, will help to familiarize the reader with the nature of the process and will also serve to introduce a further modification of our figure. The example we propose to consider is the special group with two generating operations which are connected by the relations

$$S_1^3 = E, \quad S_2^3 = E, \quad S_1 S_2 = S_2 S_1.$$

As a first step, we will take account only of the relation

$$S_1 S_2 = S_2 S_1,$$

and form for this special group the figure C. All operations

$$\ldots\ldots S_1^{\alpha_n} S_2^{\beta_n} \ldots\ldots,$$

for which $\Sigma\alpha_n$ and $\Sigma\beta_n$ have given values, are in the special group identical. We may thus select from the figure for the general group the set of polygons

$$S_2^{\alpha} S_1^{\beta} \quad (\alpha, \beta = -\infty \text{ to } +\infty)$$

as a set of representative polygons; and a reference to the diagram* (fig. 4) makes it clear that this set of polygons forms a figure with a single bounding curve. The black polygon which corresponds to the operation Σ has here been chosen as that which has the side A_1A_2 in common with the white polygon Σ.

* In fig. 4 the orthogonal circle, which is not shewn, is taken to be a straight line.

Each double-polygon, except those of the set S_1^m, contributes two sides to the boundary of C, one belonging to a white polygon and one to a black. The polygons, which border C and have sides in common with $S_2^\alpha S_1^\beta$, are $S_1 S_2^\alpha S_1^\beta$ and $S_1^{-1} S_2^\alpha S_1^\beta$; and these, regarded as operations of the special group, are equivalent to $S_2^\alpha S_1^{\beta+1}$ and $S_2^\alpha S_1^{\beta-1}$. Hence the correspondence between the sides of C is such that

(i) to the side $A_1 A_3$ of the white polygon $S_2^\alpha S_1^\beta$ corresponds the side $A_1 A_3$ of the black polygon $S_2^\alpha S_1^{\beta-1}$;

(ii) to the side $A_1 A_3$ of the black polygon $S_2^\alpha S_1^\beta$ corresponds the side $A_1 A_3$ of the white polygon $S_2^\alpha S_1^{\beta+1}$.

When we now take account of the additional relations

$$S_1^3 = E, \quad S_2^3 = E,$$

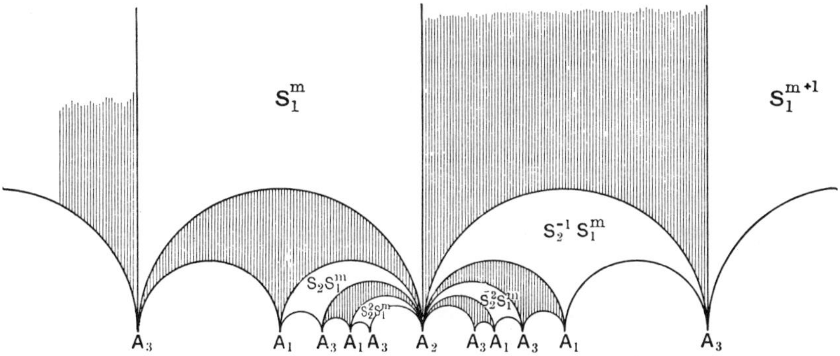

Fig. 4.

the figure C is found to reduce to a set of nine double-polygons, which is completely represented by fig. 5.

In addition to the correspondences between the sides of C to which those just written simplify when the indices of S_1 and S_2 are reduced (mod. 3), we have now also the correspondences, indicated in the figure by curved lines with arrowheads, which also result from the new relations. Our figure may be further modified in such a way that its form takes direct account of these four new correspondences. Thus without in any way altering the configuration of the double-polygons, from the point of view of geometry of position, we may continuously deform the figure so that the pairs of corresponding sides indicated by the curved arrowheads are brought to actual coincidence. When this is done, the resulting figure will have the form shewn in fig. 6. The correspondence in pairs of the sides of the boundary is indicated in the figure by full and dotted lines.

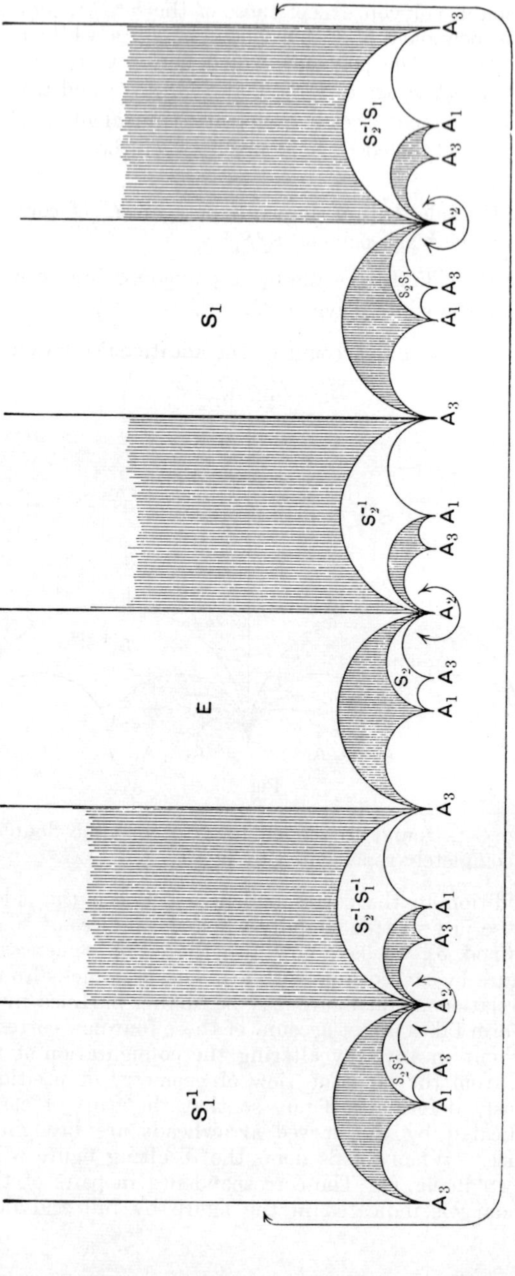

Fig. 5.

The two unmarked portions $A_1A_3A_1$ correspond, as also do the two similar portions marked with a full line, and the two marked with a dotted line.

It will be noticed that, in this final form of the figure for the special group, direct account is taken of the finite order of the generating operations S_1 and S_2 and also of the operation S_1S_2. The simplification of the figure that results by thus taking account directly of the finite order of the generating operations, and the greater ease with which the eye follows this simplified representation, are immediately obvious on a comparison of figs. 5 and 6.

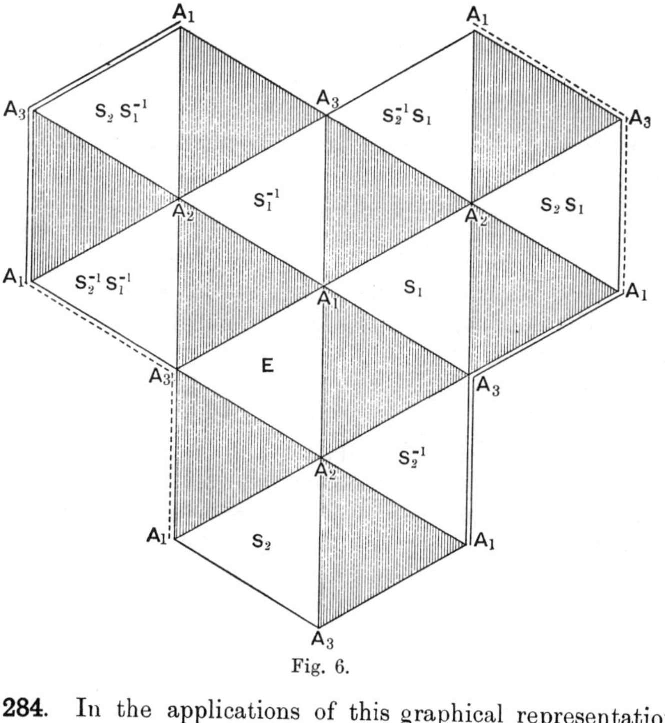

Fig. 6.

284. In the applications of this graphical representation of a group that we have specially in view, namely to groups of finite order, the generating operations themselves are necessarily of finite order. The generating operations

$$S_1, S_2, \ldots, S_n.$$

of such a group may be taken as of orders

$$m_1, m_2, \ldots, m_n;$$

and if $$S_1 S_2 \dots S_n S_{n+1} = E,$$
then S_{n+1} will be of finite order m_{n+1}. We shall therefore next consider a group generated by n operations which satisfy the relations

$$S_1^{m_1} = E,\ S_2^{m_2} = E,\ \dots,\ S_n^{m_n} = E,\ (S_1 S_2 \dots S_n)^{m_{n+1}} = E.$$

The simple example we have given makes it clear that, at least in some particular cases, relations of this form may be directly taken into account in constructing our figure; in such a way that in the complete figure, consisting of a finite or an infinite number of double-polygons, the correspondence in pairs of the sides of the boundary, if any, will depend upon further relations between the generating operations.

We may, in fact, always take account of relations of the form in question in the construction of our figure as follows.

Let us take as before $n+1$ arcs of circles

$$A_{n+1}A_1,\ A_1A_2,\ \dots,\ A_{n-1}A_n,\ A_nA_{n+1},$$

bounding a polygonal figure P of $n+1$ corners; but now, instead of supposing the circles $A_{r-1}A_r$ and A_rA_{r+1} to touch at A_r, let them cut at an angle (measured inside P) of π/m_r, $(r = 1, 2, \dots, n)$, while A_nA_{n+1} and $A_{n+1}A_1$ cut at an angle π/m_{n+1}. Such a figure can again be chosen in an infinite variety of ways; and we will suppose that it is drawn so that the $n+1$ circles have a common orthogonal circle. This clearly is always possible; but it is not now necessarily the case that this orthogonal circle is real. Let the figure P be now inverted in each of its sides; let the new figures so formed be inverted in each of their new sides; and so on continually. Then since the angles of P are sub-multiples of two right angles, no two of the figures thus formed can overlap in part without coinciding entirely. Moreover, when the process is completely carried out, every point within the orthogonal circle when it is real, and every point in the plane of the figure when the orthogonal circle is evanescent or imaginary, will lie in one and in only one of the polygons thus formed from P by successive inversions.

285. Exactly as with the general group, these polygons are coloured white or black according as they are derivable from P by an even or an odd number of inversions. The corners of any white polygon correspond one by one to the corners of P; so that, when the perimeters of the polygons are described in the same direction, corresponding corners occur in the same cyclical order.

If now the operation of successive inversions at $A_{n+1}A_1$ and A_1A_2 is represented by S_1, and that of successive inversions at $A_{r-1}A_r$ and A_rA_{r+1} by S_r, $(r = 2, 3, \ldots, n)$; all operations, consisting of an even number of inversions in the sides of P, can be represented in terms of

$$S_1, S_2, \ldots, S_n.$$

Moreover, from the construction of the polygon P, these operations satisfy the relations

$$S_1^{m_1} = E,\quad S_2^{m_2} = E,\quad \ldots,\quad S_n^{m_n} = E,\quad S_{n+1}^{m_{n+1}} = E,$$

where

$$S_1S_2 \ldots S_nS_{n+1} = E.$$

Again, if P' is any white polygon of the figure, which can be derived from P by the operation Σ, a positive rotation (§ 278) of P' round its corner A_r' is effected by the operation $\Sigma^{-1}S_r\Sigma$; and, if P'' is the polygon so obtained, P'' is derived from P by the operation $S_r\Sigma$. It is to be observed that a positive rotation of a polygon round its A_r corner is now an operation of finite order m_r.

Suppose now that two operations Σ and Σ' transform P into the same polygon P', so that $\Sigma\Sigma'^{-1}$ leaves P unchanged. If this operation, written at length, is

$$S_p^{\alpha} \ldots S_q^{\beta} S_r^{\gamma} S_s^{\delta},$$

and if P is transformed into P_1 by a positive rotation round A_s repeated δ times, P_1 into P_2 by a rotation round its corner A_r repeated γ times, and so on; then the operation may be indicated by a broken line drawn from P to P_1, from P_1 to P_2, and so on, the line returning at last to P. But the operation indicated by such a line is clearly equivalent to complete rotations (i.e. rotations each of which lead to identity), round each of the corners which the broken line includes. In other words, $\Sigma\Sigma'^{-1}$ reduces to identity when account is taken of the relations which the generating operations satisfy. Hence finally, to every white polygon P' will correspond one and only one of the operations of the group, namely that operation which transforms P into P'. The same is clearly true of the black polygons; and by taking P and a chosen black polygon which has a side in common with P as corresponding to the identical operation, the required unique correspondence is established between the complete set of double-polygons in the figure and the operations of the group, the relations which the generating operations satisfy being directly indicated by the configuration of the figure. Moreover, as with the general group (§ 278), a simple rule may be stated for determining, from an inspection of the figure, the polygon that corresponds to any given operation of the group.

286. The number of polygons in the figure and therefore the order of the group will still, in general, be infinite. We may now proceed, just as in the previous case of a quite general group, to derive from the figure representing the group G, generated by n operations satisfying the relations

$$S_1^{m_1}=E,\ S_2^{m_2}=E,\ \ldots,\ S_n^{m_n}=E,\ (S_1S_2\ldots S_n)^{m_{n+1}}=E,$$

a suitable representation of the more special group $\bar{G}$, generated by n operations which satisfy the above relations and in addition the further m relations

$$f_j(S_i)=E,\quad (j=1,\,2,\,\ldots,\,m).$$

As has been seen in § 275, if H is the self-conjugate subgroup of G which is formed by combining all possible operations of the form

$$R^{-1}f_j(S_i)\,R,$$

and if Σ is any operation of G, then the set of operations ΣH, regarded as operations of $\bar{G}$, are all equivalent to each other. From each set of polygons ΣH in the figure of G, we may therefore choose one to represent the corresponding operation of $\bar{G}$; and, as was shewn with the general group, a complete set of such representative polygons may be selected to form a connected figure, i.e. a figure which does not consist of two or more portions which are either isolated or connected only by corners. Moreover, as in the former case, the sides of this figure C will be connected in pairs $A_r'A'_{r+1}$ and $A_r''A''_{r+1}$, which are transformed into each other by some operation T of H and its inverse, while no other operation of H will transform either $A_r'A'_{r+1}$ or $A_r''A''_{r+1}$ into any other side of C.

It is not now however necessarily the case that the figure C, as thus constructed, is simply connected. Let us suppose then that C has one or more inner boundaries as well as an outer boundary, and denote one of these inner boundaries by L. If the sides of L do not all correspond in pairs, and if $A_r'A'_{r+1}$ is a side of L such that the other side $A_r''A''_{r+1}$ corresponding to it does not belong to L, we may replace the double-polygon P'' in C of which $A_r''A''_{r+1}$ is a side by the double-polygon, not previously belonging to C, of which $A_r'A'_{r+1}$ is a side. If P'' has a side on the boundary L, the new figure C' thus obtained will have one inner boundary less than C; and if P'' has no side on the boundary L, the new inner boundary L' that is thus formed from L will contain one double-polygon less than L, while the number of inner boundaries is not increased. This process may be continued till the new inner boundary L_1 which replaces L is such that all of its sides correspond in pairs.

Let now A_sA_{s+1} and $A_s'A'_{s+1}$ be a pair of corresponding sides of L_1, such that A_sA_{s+1} is transformed into $A_s'A'_{s+1}$ by an operation h of the self-conjugate sub-group H. A side A_tA_{t+1} of another boundary of C may be chosen such that A_sA_{s+1} and A_tA_{t+1} are sides of a simply connected portion, say B, of C; while no side of L_1 except A_sA_{s+1} forms part of the boundary of B. The polygons of B are equivalent, in respect of the special group, to those of Bh. Moreover, since the sides of L_1 correspond in pairs, no side of Bh, except $A_s'A'_{s+1}$, can coincide with a side of L_1. Hence when B is replaced by Bh, the inner boundary L_1 will be got rid of and no new inner boundary will be formed. Finally then, C may always be chosen so as to form a single simply connected figure.

The simply connected plane figure C, which has thus been constructed, with the correspondence of the sides of its boundary in pairs, will now give a complete graphical representation of the special group. The rule already formulated will determine the operation of the group to which each white polygon corresponds; and when, in carrying out this rule, we come to a polygon on the boundary, the correspondence of the sides of the boundary in pairs will enable the process to be continued.

The correspondence of the sides of C in pairs involves a correspondence of the corners in sets of two or more. Thus if A_r is a corner of C and if, of the m_r white polygons which in the complete figure have a corner at A_r, n_1 lie within C, there must within C be $m_r - n_1$ white polygons equivalent to the remainder, and each of these must have an A_r corner on the boundary. If A_r' is a corner of C such that there are n_2 white polygons, lying within C and having a corner at A_r', and if one of the sides of the boundary with a corner at A_r' corresponds to one of the sides of the boundary with a corner at A_r, these n_2 white polygons must be equivalent to n_2 of the white polygons, lying outside C and having a corner at A_r. If

$$n_1 + n_2 < m_r,$$

there must be a third corner A_r'', contributing n_3 more white polygons towards the set. With this we proceed as before; and the process may be continued till the whole of the m_r white polygons surrounding A_r are accounted for. The set of corners $A_r, A_r', A_r'', \ldots$ will then form a set of corresponding corners, which are equivalent to each other in respect of the special group; and the whole of the corners of C may be divided into such sets. At each set of corresponding corners A_r of C there must clearly be also m_r black polygons belonging to C; and the sum of the angles of C at a set of corresponding corners must be equal to four right angles.

287. When the order of the group is finite, we may still further so modify our figure as to take account of the correspondence of the sides of the boundary in pairs. We may, in fact, by a suitable bending and stretching of the figure, bring corresponding sides of the boundary to actual coincidence. When this is done, the figure will no longer be a piece of a plane with a single boundary, but will form a continuous surface, which is unbounded and in general is multiply connected. Every point A_r on the surface, which in the plane figure did not lie on the boundary, will be a corner common to $2m_r$ polygons alternately black and white; and, in consequence of what has just been seen in regard to the correspondence of corners of the boundary, the same is true for every point A_r on the surface which in the plane figure consisted of a set of corresponding corners of the boundary. If N is the order of the group, the continuous unbounded surface will be divided into $2N$ polygons, black and white. The configuration of the set of white polygons with respect to any one of them will, from the point of view of geometry of position, be the same as that with respect to any other; and the like is

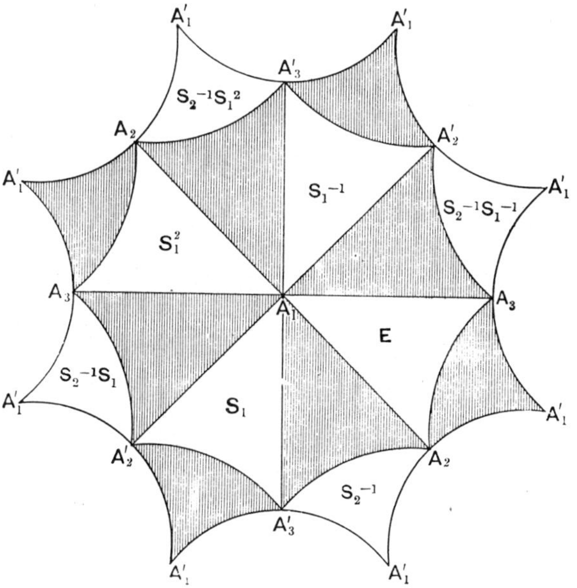

Fig. 7.

true for the black polygons. Such a division of a continuous unbounded surface is described as a *regular* division; and we have finally, as a graphical representation of any group of finite order N, a division of a continuous surface into $2N$ polygons, half black and half white, which is regular with respect to each set. The correspondence between the operations of the group and the white polygons on the surface is given by the rule that a single positive rotation of the white polygon Σ round its corner A_r leads to the white polygon $S_r\Sigma$.

288. We may again here illustrate this final modification of the graphical representation of a finite group by a simple example. For this purpose, we choose the quaternion group defined by

$$S_1^4 = E, \quad S_2^4 = E, \quad S_3^4 = E,$$

$$S_1S_2S_3 = E, \quad S_2^{-1}S_1S_2S_1 = E, \quad S_1^2 = S_2^2.$$

This group (§ 118) is a non-Abelian group of order 8, containing a single operation of order 2. The reader will have no difficulty in verifying that the plane figure for this group is given by fig. 7; and that opposite sides of the octagonal boundary correspond. The single operation of order 2 is

$$S_1^2 \,(= S_2^2 = S_3^2);$$

Fig. 8.

this corresponds to a displacement of the triangles among themselves in which all the six corners remain fixed If now corresponding sides of the boundary are brought to coincidence, the continuous surface formed will be a double-holed anchor-ring, or sphere with two holes through it. A view of one half of the surface divided into black and white triangles, is given in fig. 8. The half of the surface, not shewn, is divided up in a similar manner; and the operation of order 2 replaces each white triangle of one half by the corresponding white triangle of the other, an operation which clearly leaves the six corners of the polygons undisplaced.

289. The form of the plane figure C, which with the correspondence of its bounding sides in pairs represents the group, is capable of indefinite modification by replacing individual polygons on the boundary by equivalent polygons. If however we reckon a pair of corresponding sides of the boundary as a single side and a set of corresponding corners of the boundary as a single corner, it is clear that, however the figure may be modified, the numbers of its corners, sides and polygons remain each constant. This may be immediately verified on replacing any single boundary polygon by its equivalent.

If now A be the number of corners, and S the number of sides in the figure C when reckoned as above, $2N$ being the number of polygons, then the genus* p of the closed surface is given by the equation

$$2p = 2 + S - 2N - A.$$

When the group and its generating operations are given, the integer p is independent of the form of the plane figure C, which as has been seen is capable of considerable modification. The plane figure C however depends directly on the set of generating operations that is chosen for the group. For a given group of finite order, such a set is not in general unique; and the number of generating operations as well as their order will in general vary from one set to another. It does not necessarily follow, and in fact it is not generally the case, that the genus of the surface by whose regular division the group is represented, is independent of the choice of generating operations. There must however obviously be a lower limit to the number p for any given group of finite order, whatever generating operations are chosen; this we shall call the *genus* of the group†.

290. We shall now shew that there is a limit to the order of a group which can be represented by the regular division of

* Forsyth, *Theory of Functions* (second edition), p. 353.

† Hurwitz, "Algebraische Gebilde mit eindeutigen Transformationen in sich," *Math. Ann.* XLI (1893), p. 426.

a surface of given genus p. If N is the order of such a group, generated by the n operations

$$S_1, S_2, \ldots, S_n,$$

which satisfy the relations

$$S_1^{m_1} = E, \quad S_2^{m_2} = E, \quad \ldots, \quad S_n^{m_n} = E,$$

$$S_1 S_2 \ldots S_n = E;$$

the surface will be divided in $2N$ polygons of n sides each. Let $A_1, A_2, \ldots, A_n$ be the angular points of one of these polygons; and suppose that on the surface there are C_1 corners in the set to which A_1 belongs, C_2 in the set to which A_2 belongs, and so on. Round each corner A_r there are $2m_r$ polygons; and each polygon has one and only one corner of the set to which A_r belongs. Hence

$$C_r m_r = N,$$

and so

$$C_1 + C_2 + \ldots + C_n = N \sum_1^n \frac{1}{m_r}.$$

Again, each side belongs to two and only to two polygons, so that the number of sides is

$$Nn.$$

Using these values for A and S in the formula of § 289, we obtain the equation

$$2(p-1) = N\left(n - 2 - \sum_1^n \frac{1}{m_r}\right).$$

A complete discussion of this equation for the cases $p = 0$ and $p = 1$ will be given in the next chapter.

When p is a given integer greater than unity, we can determine the greatest value that is possible for N by finding the least possible positive value of the expression

$$n - 2 - \sum_1^n \frac{1}{m_r}.$$

If $n > 4$, this quantity is not less than $\frac{1}{2}$, since m_r cannot be less than 2.

If $n = 4$, the simultaneous values

$$m_1 = m_2 = m_3 = m_4 = 2$$

are not admissible, since they make the expression zero. Its least value in this case will therefore be given by

$$m_1 = m_2 = m_3 = 2, \quad m_4 = 3;$$

and the expression is then equal to $\frac{1}{6}$.

If $n = 3$, we require the least positive value of

$$K = 1 - \frac{1}{m_1} - \frac{1}{m_2} - \frac{1}{m_3}.$$

Now the three sets of values

$$m_1 = 3, \quad m_2 = 3, \quad m_3 = 3,$$
$$m_1 = 2, \quad m_2 = 4, \quad m_3 = 4,$$
and
$$m_1 = 2, \quad m_2 = 3, \quad m_3 = 6,$$

each make K zero; and therefore no positive value of K can be less than the least of those given by

$$m_1 = 3, \quad m_2 = 3, \quad m_3 = 4,$$
$$m_1 = 2, \quad m_2 = 4, \quad m_3 = 5,$$
and
$$m_1 = 2, \quad m_2 = 3, \quad m_3 = 7.$$

These sets of values give for K the values $\frac{1}{12}$, $\frac{1}{20}$ and $\frac{1}{42}$. Hence finally, the absolutely least positive value of the expression is $\frac{1}{42}$, and therefore the greatest admissible value of N is

$$84(p-1).$$

Hence*:—

THEOREM II. *The order of a group, that can be represented by the regular division of a surface of genus p, cannot exceed* $84(p-1)$, *p being greater than unity.*

291. If, when a group is represented by the regular division of an unbounded surface, we draw a line from any point inside the white polygon E (or any other polygon) returning after any path on the surface to the point from which it started, it will represent a relation between the generating operations of the group. For in following out along the line so drawn the rule that determines the operation of the group corresponding to each white polygon, some operation

$$F(S_i)$$

* Hurwitz, *loc. cit.* p. 424.

will be found to correspond to the final polygon; and this being the white polygon E, it follows that

$$F(S_i) = E.$$

If the surface is simply connected, any such line can be continuously altered till it shrinks to a point; and therefore the $n+1$ relations between the n generating operations completely define the group, since all other relations can be deduced from them.

If however the surface is of genus p, there are $2p$ independent closed paths that can be drawn on the surface, no one of which can by continuous displacement either be shrunk up to a point or brought to coincidence with another; and every closed path on the surface can by continuous displacement either be brought to a point or to coincidence with a path constructed by combination and repetition of the $2p$ independent paths*. Any one of these $2p$ independent paths will give a relation between the n generating operations of the group, which cannot be deduced from the $n+1$ relations on which the angles of the polygons depend. Moreover, every relation between the generating operations can be represented by a closed path on the surface; and therefore there can be no further relation independent of the original relations and those obtained from the $2p$ independent paths. There cannot therefore be more than $2p$ independent relations between the n generating operations of a group, in addition to the $n+1$ relations that give the order of the generating operations and of their product; p being the genus of the surface by whose regular division into n-sided polygons the group is represented.

The $2p$ relations given by $2p$ independent paths on the surface are not, however, necessarily independent. In fact we have already had an example to the contrary in § 288. On the closed surface, by the regular division of which the group there considered is represented, four independent closed paths can be drawn. Two of the corresponding relations are therefore necessary consequences of the other two.

The only known cases in which the $2p$ relations are independent are those of a class of groups of genus one (§ 298).

* Forsyth, *Theory of Functions* (second edition), p. 358.

Ex. Draw the figure of the group generated by S_1, S_2, S_3, where

$$S_1^2 = E, \quad S_2^3 = E, \quad S_3^8 = E, \quad S_1 S_2 S_3 = E.$$

Shew from the figure that the special group, given by the additional relation

$$(S_1 S_3^4)^2 = E,$$

is a finite group of order 48; and that it can be represented by the regular division of a surface of genus 2.

Note to § 287.

If in the process of bending and stretching, described in § 287, by means of which the plane figure C is changed into an unbounded surface, the angles of the polygons all remain unaltered, the circles of the plane figure will become continuous curves on the surface. These curves on the surface, which we will still call circles, are necessarily re-entrant. It is not however necessarily the case that, on the surface, a circle will not cut itself.

In the plane figure for the general group, an inversion at any circle of the figure leaves the figure unchanged geometrically but interchanges the black and white polygons. Each circle is, in fact, a line of symmetry for the figure such that, in respect of it, there is corresponding to every white polygon a symmetric black polygon and vice versâ.

Similarly on the surface a circle which does not cut itself may be a line of symmetry, such that a reflection at it is an operation of order two which leaves the surface and its division into polygons unchanged, but interchanges black and white polygons. When this is the case, every circle on the surface will be a line of symmetry and no circle will cut itself. On the other hand no such operation can ever be connected with a circle which cuts itself.

When such lines of symmetry exist, Prof. Dyck speaks of the division of the surface as regular and symmetric.

CHAPTER XIX.

ON THE GRAPHICAL REPRESENTATION OF GROUPS: GROUPS OF GENUS ZERO AND UNITY; CAYLEY'S COLOUR GROUPS.

292. WE shall now proceed to a discussion in the cases $p=0$ and $p=1$ of the relation

$$2(p-1)=N\left(n-2-\sum_{1}^{n}\frac{1}{m_r}\right),$$

which connects the number and the orders of the generating operations of a group with the order of the group itself; and to the consideration of the corresponding groups.

For any given value of p, other than $p=1$, we may regard this relation as an equation connecting the positive integers N, n, m_1, m_2, ... m_n. It does not however follow from the investigations of the last Chapter that there is always a group or a set of groups corresponding to a given solution of the equation. In fact, for values of p greater than 1, this is not necessarily the case. We shall however find that, when $p=0$, there is a single type of group corresponding to each solution of the equation; and that, when $p=1$, there is an infinite number of types of group, all characterized by a common property, corresponding to each solution of the equation.

When $p=0$, the groups are (§ 289) of genus zero; and all possible groups of genus zero are found by putting $p=0$ in the equation. The groups thus obtained are of special importance in many applications of group-theory; for this reason, they will be dealt with in considerable detail.

293. When $p=0$, the equation may be written in the form

$$2\left(1-\frac{1}{N}\right)=\sum_1^n\left(1-\frac{1}{m_r}\right);$$

in this form, it is clear that the only admissible values of n are 2 and 3.

First, let $n=2$. The only possible solution then is

$$m_1=m_2=N,$$

N being any integer. The corresponding group is a cyclical group of order N.

Secondly, let $n=3$. In this case, one at least of the three integers m_1, m_2, m_3 must be equal to 2, as otherwise the right-hand side of the equation would be not less than 2. We may therefore without loss of generality put $m_1=2$. If now both m_2 and m_3 were greater than 3, the right-hand side would still be not less than 2; and therefore we may take m_2 to be either 2 or 3. When m_1 and m_2 are both 2, the equation becomes

$$\frac{2}{N}=\frac{1}{m_3};$$

giving $$m_3=n,\quad N=2n,$$

where n is any integer.

When m_1 is 2 and m_2 is 3, the equation is

$$\frac{2}{N}+\frac{1}{6}=\frac{1}{m_3}.$$

This has three solutions in positive integers; namely,

$$m_3=3,\quad N=12;$$

$$m_3=4,\quad N=24;$$

and $$m_3=5,\quad N=60.$$

The solutions of the equation for the case $p=0$ may therefore be tabulated in the form:—

	m_1	m_2	m_3	N
I	n	n		n
II	2	2	n	$2n$
III	2	3	3	12
IV	2	3	4	24
V	2	3	5	60

294. That a single type of group actually exists, corresponding to each of these solutions, may be seen at once by returning to our plane figure. The sum of the internal angles of the triangle $A_1A_2A_3$ formed by circular arcs is, in each of these cases, greater than two right angles; and the common orthogonal circle is therefore imaginary. The complete figure will therefore divide the whole plane into black and white triangles, so that there are no boundaries to consider. Moreover, the number of white triangles in each case must be equal to the corresponding value of N; for the preceding investigation shews that this is a possible value, and on the other hand the process, by which the figure is completed from a given original triangle, is a unique one. There is therefore a group corresponding to each solution; and the correspondence which has been established in any case between the operations of a group and the polygons of a figure, proves that there cannot be two distinct types of group corresponding to the same solution.

295. The plane figure for $p=0$ does not, in fact, differ essentially from the figure drawn on a continuous simply connected surface in space. The former may be regarded as the stereographic projection of the latter. The five distinct types are represented graphically by the following figures.

The first is a cyclical group, and the figure (fig. 9) agrees with fig. 2 in § 276, when one point of intersection of the circles is at infinity.

The group given by the second solution of the equation is called the dihedral group. It is represented by fig. 10.

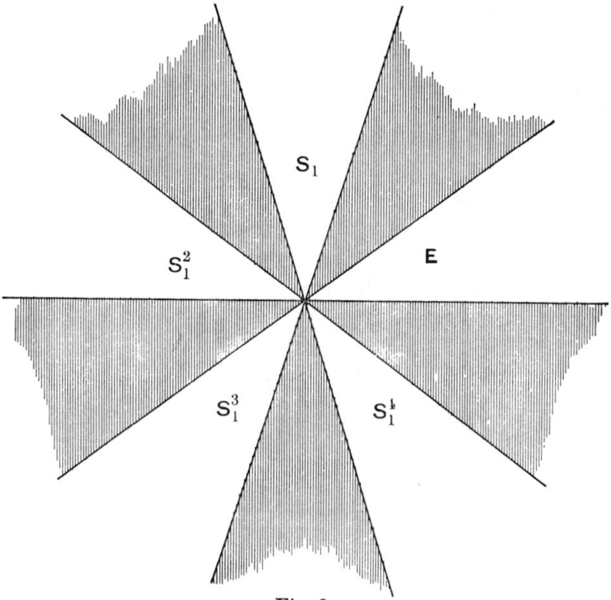

Fig. 9.

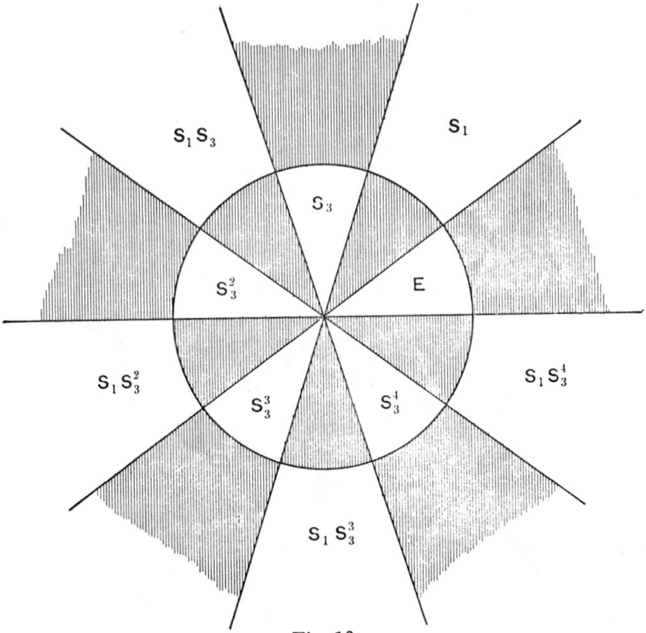

Fig. 10.

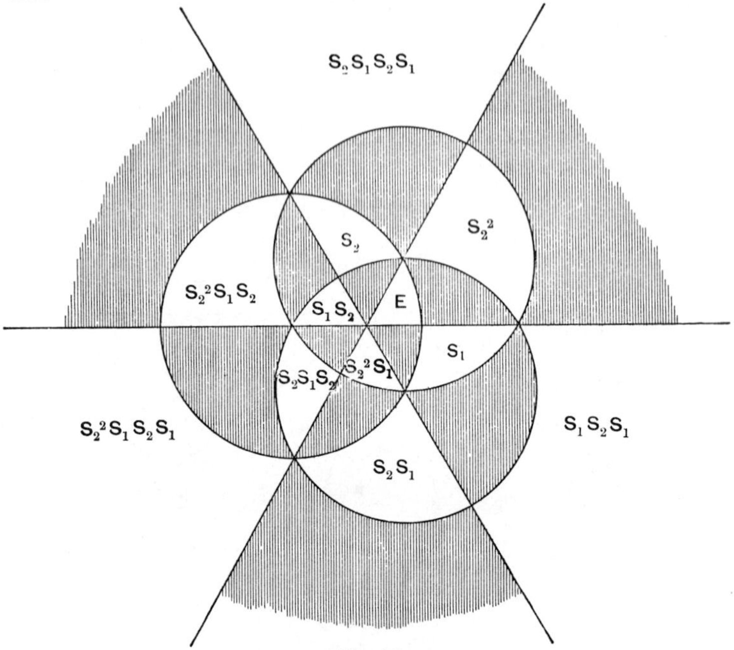
S₂ S₁ S₂ S₁
S₂
S₂²
S₂²S₁S₂
S₁ S₂
E
S₁
S₂S₁S₂
S₂² S₁
S₂²S₁S₂S₁
S₁S₂S₁
S₂S₁

Fig. 11.

Fig. 12.

The group given by the third solution of the equation is represented in fig. 11. It is known as the tetrahedral group.

To the fourth solution of the equation corresponds the group represented in fig. 12. It is known as the octohedral group.

To the fifth solution of the equation corresponds the group represented in fig. 13. It is known as the icosahedral group.

Fig. 13.

The four last groups are identical with the groups of rotations which will bring respectively a double pyramid on an n-sided base, a tetrahedron, an octohedron, and an icosahedron to coincidence with itself*.

When the figures are drawn on a sphere, and the three circles of the original triangle and therefore also all the circles of the figure are taken to be great-circles of the sphere, the actual dis-

* Klein, "Vorlesungen über das Ikosaeder," Chap. I.

placements of the triangles among themselves which correspond to the operations of the group can be effected by real rotations about diameters of the sphere; thus the statement of the preceding sentence may be directly verified.

296. In terms of their generating operations, the five types of group of genus zero are given by the relations:—

I. $S_1^n = E,\quad S_2^n = E,\qquad\qquad S_1S_2 = E;$

II. $S_1^2 = E,\quad S_2^2 = E,\quad S_3^n = E,\quad S_1S_2S_3 = E;$

III. $S_1^2 = E,\quad S_2^3 = E,\quad S_3^3 = E,\quad S_1S_2S_3 = E;$

IV. $S_1^2 = E,\quad S_2^3 = E,\quad S_3^4 = E,\quad S_1S_2S_3 = E;$

V. $S_1^2 = E,\quad S_2^3 = E,\quad S_3^5 = E,\quad S_1S_2S_3 = E.$

The first of these does not require special discussion.

In the dihedral group, we have

$$S_1S_3S_1 = S_1S_2 = S_3^{-1}.$$

The dihedral group of order $2n$ therefore contains a cyclical sub-group of order n self-conjugately; and every operation of the group which does not belong to this self-conjugate sub-group is of order 2. The operations of the group are given, each once and once only, by the form

$$S_1^\alpha S_3^\beta,\quad (\alpha = 0, 1;\ \beta = 0, 1, 2, \ldots, n-1).$$

When $n = 3$, this group is simply isomorphic with the symmetric group of three symbols.

In the tetrahedral group, since

$$(S_1S_2)^3 = E,$$

$$S_2^{-1}S_1S_2S_1 = S_2S_1S_2^{-1},$$

and therefore S_1, $S_2^{-1}S_1S_2$, $S_2S_1S_2^{-1}$ are permutable with each other. These operations of order 2 (with identity) form a self-conjugate sub-group of order 4; and the 12 operations of the group are therefore given by the form

$$S_2^{\alpha'}(S_2^{-1}S_1S_2)^\beta S_1^\gamma,$$

or $$S_2^\alpha S_1^\beta S_2 S_1^\gamma,\quad (\alpha = 0, 1, 2;\ \beta, \gamma = 0, 1).$$

If $$S_1 = (12)(34),\quad S_2 = (123),$$

then $$S_1S_2 = (134);$$

and therefore the tetrahedral group is simply isomorphic with the alternating group of four symbols.

If, in the octohedral group, we write

$$S_3^2 = S',$$

then $$S_2S' = S_1S_3 = S_1S_2^2S_1;$$

and therefore $$(S_2S')^3 = E.$$

Hence S_2 and S' generate a tetrahedral group.

Again $$S_1S_2S_1 = (S_2S')^2,$$

and $$S_1S'S_1 = S_2S'S_2^{-1},$$

so that this is a self-conjugate sub-group. The operations of the group are given, each once and once only, in the form

$$S_1^{\alpha}S_2^{\beta}S_3^{2\gamma}S_2S_3^{2\delta}, \quad (\alpha, \gamma, \delta = 0, 1; \ \beta = 0, 1, 2).$$

If $$S_1 = (12), \quad S_2 = (234),$$

then $$S_1S_2 = (1342);$$

and therefore the octohedral group is simply isomorphic with the symmetric group of four symbols.

The icosahedral group is simple. It is, in fact, simply isomorphic with the alternating group of five symbols which has been shewn (§ 139) to be a simple group. Thus if

$$S_1 = (12)(34), \quad S_2 = (135),$$

then $$S_1S_2 = (12345);$$

so that the substitutions S_1 and S_2 satisfy the relations

$$S_1^2 = E, \quad S_2^3 = E, \quad (S_1S_2)^5 = E.$$

They must therefore generate an icosahedral group or one of its sub-groups. On the other hand, from the substitutions S_1 and S_2 all the even substitutions of five symbols may be formed, and these are 60 in number. The group therefore cannot be a sub-group of the icosahedral group; the only alternative is that the two are identical.

As the icosahedral group has no self-conjugate group, we cannot in this case so easily construct a form which will represent each operation of the group just once in terms of the generating operations. It is however not difficult to verify that this is true of the set of forms*

$$\begin{matrix} S_3^{\alpha}, \quad S_3^{\alpha}S_1S_3^{\beta}, \quad S_3^{\alpha}S_1S_3^2S_1S_3^{\beta}, \\ S_3^{\alpha}S_1S_3^2S_1S_3^3S_1, \end{matrix} \qquad (\alpha, \beta = 0, 1, 2, 3, 4).$$

* Dyck, "Gruppentheoretische Studien," *Math. Ann.* xx (1882), p. 35, and Klein, *loc. cit.* p. 26.

297. We shall next deal with the equation in the case $p=1$. In this case alone, the order of the group disappears from the equation, which merely gives a relation between the number and order of the generating operations. This may be written in the form

$$2=\sum_1^n\left(1-\frac{1}{m_r}\right);$$

and n must therefore be either 4 or 3.

When n is 4, the equation becomes

$$2=\frac{1}{m_1}+\frac{1}{m_2}+\frac{1}{m_3}+\frac{1}{m_4},$$

and the only solution is clearly

$$m_1=m_2=m_3=m_4=2.$$

When n is 3, the equation takes the form

$$1=\frac{1}{m_1}+\frac{1}{m_2}+\frac{1}{m_3},$$

and is easily seen to have three solutions, viz.

$$m_1=3,\quad m_2=3,\quad m_3=3;$$

$$m_1=2,\quad m_2=4,\quad m_3=4;$$

and $$m_1=2,\quad m_2=3,\quad m_3=6.$$

298. Take first the solution

$$n=4,\quad m_1=m_2=m_3=m_4=2.$$

The corresponding general group is defined by the relations

$$S_1^2=E,\quad S_2^2=E,\quad S_3^2=E,\quad S_4^2=E,$$
$$S_1S_2S_3S_4=E.$$

If we proceed to form the plane figure representing this group, the sum of the internal angles of the quadrilateral $A_1A_2A_3A_4$ is equal to four right angles, and the four circles that form it therefore pass through a point. If this point be taken at infinity, the four circles (and therefore all the circles of the figure) become straight lines. The plane figure will now take the form given in fig. 14, and the four generating operations are actual rotations through two right angles about lines through A_1, A_2, A_3 and A_4, perpendicular to the plane of the figure.

Every operation of the group is therefore, in this form of representation, either a rotation through two right angles about a corner of the figure or a translation; and it will clearly be the former or the latter according as it consists of an odd or an even number of factors, when expressed in terms of the generating operations. The operations which correspond to translations form a sub-group; for if two operations each consist of an even number of factors, so also does their product. Moreover, this sub-group is self-conjugate, since the number of factors in $\Sigma^{-1}S\Sigma$ is even if the number in S is

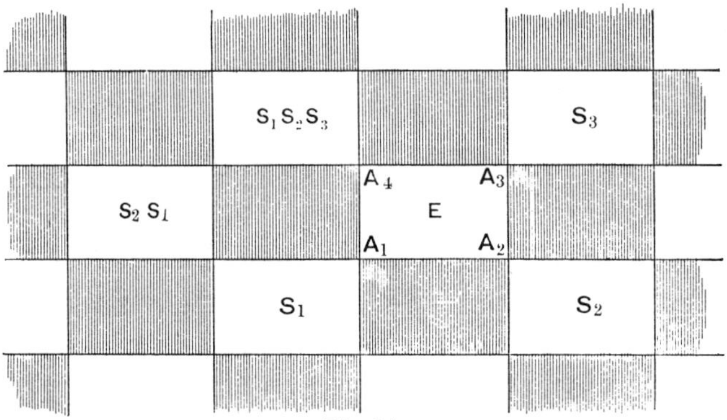

Fig. 14.

even. This self-conjugate sub-group is generated by the two operations

$$S_1S_2 \text{ and } S_2S_3;$$

for

$$S_1S_3 = S_1S_2 \,.\, S_2S_3,$$

$$S_2S_1 = (S_1S_2)^{-1}, \quad S_3S_2 = (S_2S_3)^{-1}, \quad S_3S_1 = (S_2S_3)^{-1}(S_1S_2)^{-1};$$

and therefore every operation containing an even number of factors can be represented in terms of S_1S_2 and S_2S_3. Lastly, these two operations are permutable with each other; for

$$S_2S_3 \,.\, S_1S_2 = S_2S_3 \,.\, S_4S_3 = S_1S_3 = S_1S_2 \,.\, S_2S_3;$$

and therefore every operation of the group is contained, once and only once, in the form

$$S_1^{\alpha}(S_1S_2)^{\beta}(S_2S_3)^{\gamma}, \quad (\alpha = 0, 1;\ \beta, \gamma = -\infty, \ldots, 0, \ldots, \infty).$$

The results thus arrived at may also be verified very simply by purely kinematical considerations. If a group generated by S_1, S_2, S_3 and S_4 is of finite order, there must, since it is of genus 1, be either one or two additional relations between the generating operations; and any such relation is expressible by equating the symbol of some operation of the general group to unity. Such a relation is therefore either of the form

$$S_1 (S_1S_2)^b (S_2S_3)^c = E,$$

or

$$(S_1S_2)^b (S_2S_3)^c = E.$$

The operation $S_1 (S_1S_2)^b (S_2S_3)^c$ of the general group, consisting of an odd number of factors, must be a rotation round some corner of the figure, say a rotation round the corner A_r of the white quadrilateral Σ; it is therefore identical with $\Sigma^{-1}S_r\Sigma$.

Now the relation

$$\Sigma^{-1}S_r\Sigma = E$$

gives

$$S_r = E.$$

A relation of the first of the two forms is therefore inconsistent with the supposition that the group is actually generated by S_1, S_2 and S_3. It, in fact, reduces the generating operations and the relations among them to

$$S_1^2 = E, \quad S_2^2 = E, \quad S_3^2 = E, \quad S_1S_2S_3 = E,$$

which define a group of genus zero.

The only admissible relations for a group of genus 1 are therefore those of the form

$$(S_1S_2)^b (S_2S_3)^c = E.$$

A single relation of this form reduces the operations of the general group to those contained in

$$S_1^{\alpha} (S_1S_2)^{\beta} (S_2S_3)^{\gamma},$$

$$(\alpha = 0, 1\,;\ \beta = 0, 1, \ldots, b-1\,;\ \gamma = -\infty, \ldots, 0, \ldots, \infty\,);$$

and the group so defined is still of infinite order.

Finally, two independent relations

$$(S_1S_2)^b (S_2S_3)^c = E,$$
$$(S_1S_2)^{b'} (S_2S_3)^{c'} = E,$$

where

$$\frac{b}{b'} \neq \frac{c}{c'},$$

must necessarily lead to a group of finite order. If m is the greatest common factor of b and b', so that

$$b = b_1m, \quad b' = b_1'm,$$

where b_1 and b_1' are relatively prime; and if

$$b_1 x - b_1' y = 1;$$

the two relations give

$$(S_2 S_3)^{cb_1' - c'b_1} = E$$

and
$$(S_1 S_2)^m = (S_2 S_3)^{c'y - cx}.$$

Every operation of the group is now contained, once and only once, in the form

$$S_1^{\alpha}(S_1 S_2)^{\beta}(S_2 S_3)^{\gamma},$$

$$(\alpha = 0, 1;\ \beta = 0, 1, \ldots, m-1;\ \gamma = 0, 1, \ldots, cb_1' - b_1 c' - 1);$$

and the order of the group is $2(bc' \sim b'c)$.

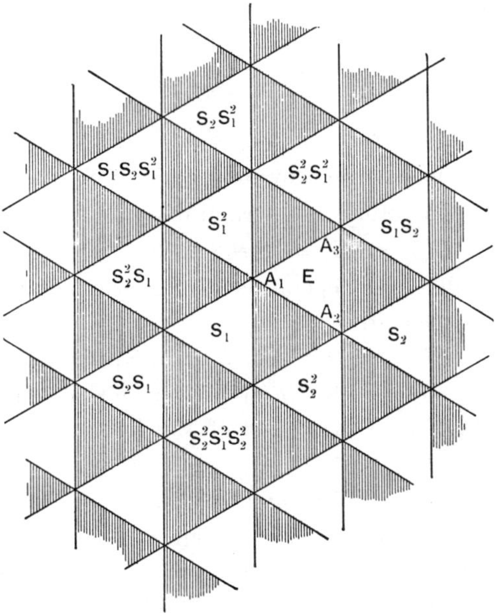

Fig. 15.

299. Corresponding to the solution

$$n = 3, \quad m_1 = m_2 = m_3 = 3,$$

we have the general group generated by S_1, S_2, S_3, where

$$S_1^3 = E, \quad S_2^3 = E, \quad S_3^3 = E,$$

$$S_1 S_2 S_3 = E.$$

The sum of the three angles of the triangle $A_1A_2A_3$ is two right angles, and therefore again the circles in the plane figure (fig. 15) may be taken to be straight lines. When the figure is thus chosen, the generating operations are rotations through $\frac{2}{3}\pi$ about the angles of an equilateral triangle; and every operation of the group is either a translation or a rotation.

The three operations

$$S_1S_2^2, \quad S_2S_1S_2, \quad S_2^2S_1,$$

when transformed by S_2, are interchanged among themselves. When transformed by S_1, they become

$$S_2^2S_1, \quad S_1^2S_2S_1S_2S_1, \quad S_1^2S_2^2S_1^2,$$

and since

$$(S_1S_2)^3 = E,$$

the two latter are $S_1S_2^2$ and $S_2S_1S_2$ respectively.

Hence the three operations generate a self-conjugate sub-group; and since

$$S_1S_2^2 \,.\, S_2S_1S_2 \,.\, S_2^2S_1 = E,$$

this sub-group is generated by $S_1S_2^2$ and $S_2S_1S_2$.

These two operations are permutable; for

$$S_1S_2^2 \,.\, S_2S_1S_2 = S_1^2S_2 = S_2S_1S_2S_1S_2 \,.\, S_2 = S_2S_1S_2 \,.\, S_1S_2^2.$$

Hence finally, every operation of the group is represented, once and only once, by the form

$$S_1^{\alpha}(S_1S_2^2)^{\beta}(S_2S_1S_2)^{\gamma}, \quad (\alpha = 0, 1, 2;\ \beta, \gamma = -\infty, \ldots, 0, \ldots, \infty).$$

This result might also be arrived at by purely kinematical considerations; for an inspection of the figure shews that the two simplest translations are

$$S_1S_2^2 \text{ and } S_2S_1S_2,$$

and that every translation in the group can be obtained by the combination and repetition of these. Every operation in which the index α is not zero must be a rotation through $\frac{2}{3}\pi$ or $\frac{4}{3}\pi$ about one of the angles of the figure; it is therefore necessarily identical with an operation of the form

$$\Sigma^{-1}S_r^{\alpha}\Sigma.$$

If now the group generated by S_1, S_2, S_3 is of finite order, there must be either one or two additional relations between them. A relation of the form

$$S_1^{a}(S_1S_2^2)^{b}(S_2S_1S_2)^{c} = E,$$

whether a is either 1 or 2, is equivalent to

$$\Sigma^{-1} S_r^{\,a} \Sigma = E,$$

so that

$$S_r = E.$$

Such a relation would reduce the group to a cyclical group of order 3. This is not admissible, if the group is actually to be generated by two distinct operations S_1 and S_2.

A relation $$(S_1 S_2^{\,2})^b (S_2 S_1 S_2)^c = E,$$

gives, on transformation by S_2^{-1},

$$(S_2 S_1 S_2)^b (S_2^{\,2} S_1)^c = E,$$

or

$$(S_1 S_2^{\,2})^{-c} (S_2 S_1 S_2)^{b-c} = E.$$

If m is the greatest common factor of b and c, so that

$$b = b'm, \quad c = c'm,$$

where b' and c' are relatively prime; and if

$$b'x - c'y = 1,$$

the two relations

$$(S_1 S_2^{\,2})^b (S_2 S_1 S_2)^c = E,$$

and

$$(S_1 S_2^{\,2})^{-c} (S_2 S_1 S_2)^{b-c} = E,$$

lead to

$$(S_2 S_1 S_2)^{m(b'^2 - b'c' + c'^2)} = E,$$

and

$$(S_1 S_2)^m = (S_2 S_1 S_2)^{m\{(c'-b')y - c'x\}};$$

so that every operation of the group is contained, once and only once, in the form

$$S_1^{\,\alpha} (S_1 S_2^{\,2})^\beta (S_2 S_1 S_2)^\gamma,$$

where

$$\alpha = 0, 1, 2; \ \beta = 0, 1, \ldots, m-1; \ \gamma = 0, 1, \ldots, m(b'^2 - b'c' + c'^2) - 1.$$

Thus the group is of finite order $3(b^2 - bc + c^2)$. In this case then, unlike the previous one, a single additional relation is sufficient to ensure that the group is of finite order. Any further relation, which is independent, must of necessity reduce the group to a cyclical group of order 3 or to the identical operation. The case $b = c = 1$ reduces the group to a cyclical group of order 3 and must be excluded.

300. The two remaining solutions may now be treated in less detail. The general group corresponding to the solution

$$n = 3, \quad m_1 = 2, \quad m_2 = m_3 = 4,$$

is given by $$S_1^2 = E, \quad S_2^4 = E, \quad S_3^4 = E,$$
$$S_1S_2S_3 = E,$$
and is represented graphically by fig. 16.

All the translations of the group can be generated from the two operations
$$S_1S_2^2, \quad S_2S_1S_2;$$
and every operation of the group is given, once and only once, by the form
$$S_2^{\alpha}(S_1S_2^2)^{\beta}(S_2S_1S_2)^{\gamma}, \quad (\alpha = 0, 1, 2, 3; \ \beta, \gamma = -\infty, \ldots, 0, \ldots, \infty).$$

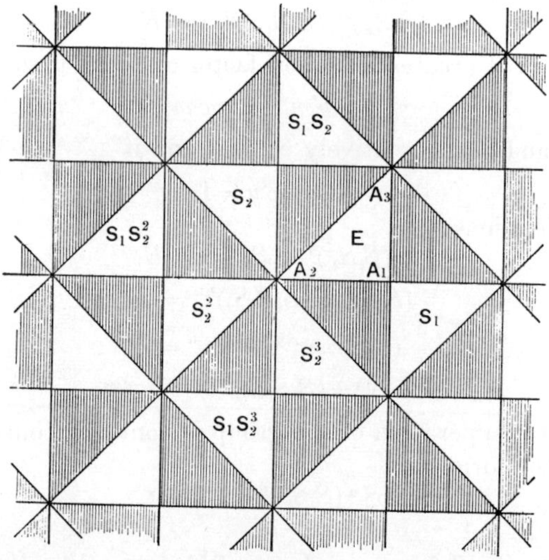

Fig. 16.

An additional relation of the form
$$S_2^a(S_1S_2^2)^b(S_2S_1S_2)^c = E,$$
where a is 1, 2 or 3, leads either to
$$S_1 = E, \quad S_2 = E, \text{ or } S_3 = E,$$
and is therefore inconsistent with the supposition that the group is generated by two distinct operations of orders two and four.

An additional relation
$$(S_1S_2^2)^b(S_2S_1S_2)^c = E,$$
gives $$(S_1S_2^2)^{-c}(S_2S_1S_2)^b = E:$$

and if
$$b = b_1m, \quad c = c_1m,$$
$$b_1x + c_1y = 1,$$
where b_1 and c_1 are relatively prime, these relations are equivalent to
$$(S_2S_1S_2)^{m(b_1^2+c_1^2)} = E,$$
$$(S_1S_2^2)^m = (S_2S_1S_2)^{m(b_1y-c_1x)}.$$

Every operation of the group is then contained, once and only once, in the form
$$S_2^\alpha (S_1S_2^2)^\beta (S_2S_1S_2)^\gamma,$$
$(\alpha = 0, 1, 2, 3;\ \beta = 0, 1, \ldots, m-1;\ \gamma = 0, 1, \ldots, m(b_1^2 + c_1^2) - 1)$; and the order of the group is $4(b^2 + c^2)$.

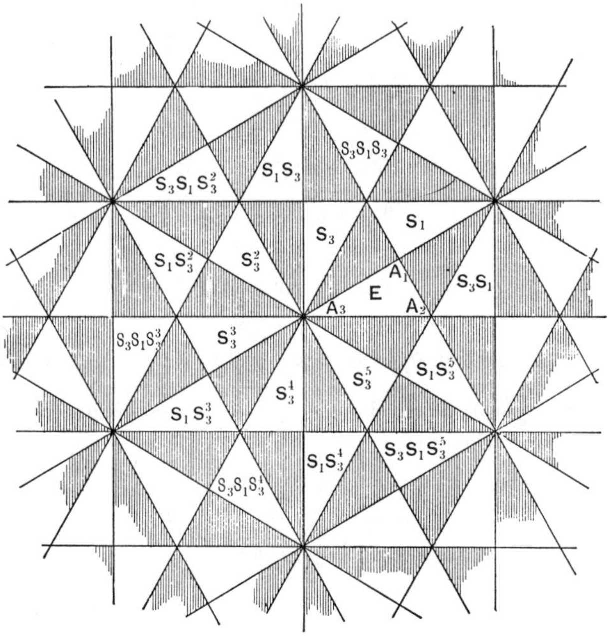

Fig. 17.

301. Lastly, the general group corresponding to the solution
$$n = 3, \quad m_1 = 2, \quad m_2 = 3, \quad m_3 = 6,$$
is given by
$$S_1^2 = E, \quad S_2^3 = E, \quad S_3^6 = E,$$
$$S_1S_2S_3 = E;$$
and it is represented graphically by fig. 17.

Now it may again be verified, either from the generating relations or from the figure, that the two operations

$$S_2^2 S_3^2 \text{ and } S_3 S_2^2 S_3,$$

which are permutable with each other, generate all the operations which in the kinematical form of the group are translations; and that every operation of the group is represented, once and only once, by the form

$$S_3^\alpha (S_2^2 S_3^2)^\beta (S_3 S_2^2 S_3)^\gamma,$$

$$(\alpha = 0, 1, \ldots, 5; \ \beta, \gamma = -\infty, \ldots, 0, \ldots, \infty).$$

Also as before any further relation, which does not reduce S_3 to an operation of lower order, is necessarily of the form

$$(S_2^2 S_3^2)^b (S_3 S_2^2 S_3)^c = E.$$

On transforming this relation by S_3^{-1}, we obtain

$$(S_3 S_2^2 S_3)^b (S_3^2 S_2^2)^c = E.$$

Now $\qquad S_3^2 S_2^2 = (S_2^2 S_3^2)^{-1} (S_3 S_2^2 S_3);$

so that $\qquad (S_2^2 S_3^2)^{-c} (S_3 S_2 S_3)^{b+c} = E.$

If then $\qquad b = b_1 m, \quad c = c_1 m,$

$$b_1 x + c_1 y = 1,$$

where b_1 and c_1 are relatively prime, it follows that

$$(S_3 S_2^2 S_3)^{m(b_1^2 + b_1 c_1 + c_1^2)} = E,$$

and $\qquad (S_2^2 S_3^2)^m = (S_3 S_2 S_3)^{m\{b_1 y + c_1 (y - x)\}}.$

Every operation of the group is then contained, once and only once, in the form

$$S_3^\alpha (S_2^2 S_3^2)^\beta (S_3 S_2^2 S_3)^\gamma,$$

$$(\alpha = 0, 1, \ldots, 5; \ \beta = 0, 1 \ldots, m - 1; \ \gamma = 0, 1, \ldots, m(b_1^2 + b_1 c_1 + c_1^2) - 1;$$

and the order of the group is $6(b^2 + bc + c^2)$.

302. There are thus four distinct classes of groups* of genus 1, which are defined in terms of their generating operations by the following sets of relations:—

I. $\qquad S_1^2 = E, \quad S_2^2 = E, \quad S_3^2 = E, \quad (S_1 S_2 S_3)^2 = E,$

$$(S_1 S_2)^a (S_2 S_3)^b = E, \quad (S_1 S_2)^{a'} (S_2 S_3)^{b'} = E, \quad (ab' - a'b \neq 0);$$

$$N = 2(ab' - a'b).$$

* Dyck, "Ueber Aufstellung und Untersuchung von Gruppe und Irrationalität regulärer Riemann'scher Flächen," *Math. Ann.* XVII (1880), pp. 501—509.

II.
$$S_1^3 = E, \quad S_2^3 = E, \quad (S_1S_2)^3 = E,$$
$$(S_1S_2^2)^a (S_2S_1S_2)^b = E;$$
$$N = 3(a^2 - ab + b^2).$$

III.
$$S_1^2 = E, \quad S_2^4 = E, \quad (S_1S_2)^4 = E,$$
$$(S_1S_2^2)^a (S_2S_1S_2)^b = E;$$
$$N = 4(a^2 + b^2).$$

IV.
$$S_1^6 = E, \quad S_2^3 = E, \quad (S_1S_2)^2 = E,$$
$$(S_1^2S_2^2)^a (S_1S_2^2S_1)^b = E;$$
$$N = 6(a^2 + ab + b^2).$$

For special values of a and b, some of these groups may be groups of genus zero; for instance, in Class I, if $ab' - a'b$ is a prime, the group is a dihedral group. It is left as an exercise to the reader to determine all such exceptional cases.

Ex. Prove that the number of distinct types of group, of genus two, is four; viz. the groups defined by

(i) $A^4 = E,\ B^2 = A^2,\ B^{-1}AB = A^{-1}$; (ii) $A^8 = E,\ B^2 = E,\ B^{-1}AB = A^3$;

(iii) $A^4 = E,\ B^3 = E,\ A^{-1}BA = B^2$;

(iv) $A^8 = E,\ B^2 = E,\ (AB)^3 = E,\ (A^4B)^2 = E.$

303. As a final illustration of the present method of graphical representation, we will consider the simple group of order 168 (§ 166), given by

$$\{(1236457),\quad (234)(567),\quad (2763)(45)\}.$$

The operations of this group are of orders 7, 4, 3 and 2; and it is easy to verify that three operations of orders 2, 3, and 7 can be chosen such that their product is identity.

In fact, if

$$S_2 = (16)(34), \quad S_3 = (253)(476), \quad S_7 = (1673524);$$

then
$$S_2S_3S_7 = E.$$

Moreover, these three operations generate the group. The genus of the corresponding surface, by the regular division of which the group can be represented, is p; where

$$2p - 2 = 168\left(3 - 2 - \tfrac{1}{2} - \tfrac{1}{3} - \tfrac{1}{7}\right).$$

This gives $p = 3$;

it follows from Theorem II, § 290, that the genus of the group is 3.

The figure for the general group, generated by S_2, S_3, and S_7, where

$$S_2^2 = E, \quad S_3^3 = E, \quad S_7^7 = E,$$
$$S_2 S_3 S_7 = E,$$

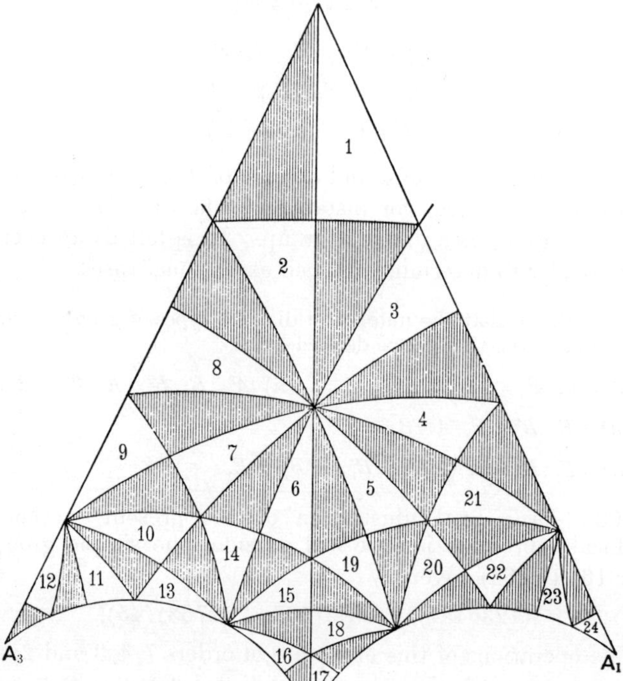

Fig. 18.

acquires as symmetrical a form as possible, by taking the centre of the orthogonal circle for that angular point of the triangle E at which the angle is $\frac{1}{7}\pi$. In fig. 18 a portion of the general figure, which is contained between two radii of the orthogonal circle inclined at an angle $\frac{2}{7}\pi$, is shewn. The remainder may be filled in by inversions at the different portions of the boundary.

The operations, which correspond to the white triangles of the figure, are given by the following table:—

1	E	9	$S_2S_7^5S_2$	17	$S_2S_7^5S_2S_7^3S_2$
2	S_2	10	$S_7S_2S_7^5S_2$	18	$S_7^6S_2S_7^3S_2$
3	S_7S_2	11	$S_7^2S_2S_7^5S_2$	19	$S_2S_7^3S_2$
4	$S_7^2S_2$	12	$S_7^3S_2S_7^5S_2$	20	$S_7S_2S_7^3S_2$
5	$S_7^3S_2$	13	$S_7^6S_2S_7^4S_2$	21	$S_2S_7^2S_2$
6	$S_7^4S_2$	14	$S_2S_7^4S_2$	22	$S_7^6S_2S_7^2S_2$
7	$S_7^5S_2$	15	$S_7S_2S_7^4S_2$	23	$S_7^5S_2S_7^2S_2$
8	$S_7^6S_2$	16	$S_7^2S_2S_7^4S_2$	24	$S_2S_7^4S_2S_7^2S_2$

The representation of the special group is derived from this general figure by retaining only a set of 168 white (and corresponding black) triangles, which are distinct when S_2, S_3 and S_7 are replaced by the corresponding substitutions given on p. 419. When each white triangle is thus marked with the corresponding substitution, it is found that a complete set of 168 distinct white (and black) triangles is given by the portion of the figure actually drawn and the six other distinct portions obtained by rotating it round the centre of the orthogonal circle through multiples of $\frac{2}{7}\pi$.

To complete the graphical representation of the group of order 168, it is necessary to determine the correspondence in pairs of the sides of the boundary. This is facilitated by noticing that the angular points A_1, A_2, A_3, ... of the boundary must correspond in sets. Now the white triangle, which has an angle at A_1 and lies inside the polygon, is given by

$$S_2S_7^4S_2S_7^2S_2.$$

This must be equivalent to a white triangle, which lies outside the polygon, and has a side on the boundary and an angle at one of the points A_2, A_3, ...

The triangle, which satisfies these conditions and has an angle at A_{2n+1}, is given by

$$S_7S_2S_7^4S_2S_7^2S_2S_7^n;$$

while the triangle, which satisfies the conditions and has an angle at A_{2n+2}, is given by

$$S_7^6S_2S_7^5S_2S_7^3S_2S_7^n.$$

When (16) (34) and (1673524) are written for S_2 and S_7, we find that

$$S_2S_7^4S_2S_7^2S_2 = S_7S_2S_7^4S_2S_7^2S_2S_7^5.$$

The white triangle with an angle at A_1 inside the polygon is therefore equivalent to the white triangle with an angle at A_{11}, which lies outside the polygon and has a side on the boundary. It follows, from the continuity of the figure, that the arcs A_1A_2 and $A_{11}A_{10}$ of the boundary correspond. Since the operation S_7 changes the figure and the boundary into themselves, it follows that A_3A_4, $A_{13}A_{12}$; A_5A_6, A_1A_{14}; A_7A_8, A_3A_2; A_9A_{10}, A_5A_4; $A_{11}A_{12}$, A_7A_6; and $A_{13}A_{14}$, A_9A_8; are pairs of corresponding sides. Hence the above single condition is sufficient to ensure that the general group shall reduce to the special group of order 168.

By taking account of the relation

$$(S_7S_2)^3 = E, \text{ or } (S_2S_7)^3 = E,$$

the form of the condition may be simplified. Thus it may be written

$$S_7^4S_2S_7^2S_2 = S_2S_7S_2S_7 \, . \, S_7^3S_2S_7^2S_2S_7^5$$
$$= S_7^6S_2S_7^3S_2S_7^2S_2S_7^5,$$

or

$$S_2S_7^2S_2 = S_7^2S_2S_7^3S_2S_7^2S_2S_7^5.$$

Now

$$S_2S_7 \, . \, S_7S_2 = S_7^6S_2S_7^6S_2 \, . \, S_2S_7^6S_2S_7^6$$
$$= S_7^6S_2S_7^5S_2S_7^6.$$

Hence

$$S_7^4S_2S_7^5S_2S_7 = S_2S_7^3S_2S_7^2S_2,$$

or

$$S_7^4S_2S_7^4 \, . \, S_2S_7^6S_2 = S_2S_7^3S_2S_7^2S_2,$$

or

$$S_7^4S_2S_7^4S_2S_7^4 = S_2S_7^3S_2,$$

or finally

$$(S_7^4S_2)^4 = E.$$

The simple group of order 168 is therefore defined abstractly by the relations*

$$S_2^2 = E, \quad S_7^7 = E, \quad (S_7S_2)^3 = E, \quad (S_7^4S_2)^4 = E.$$

Ex. Shew that the symmetric group of degree five is a group of genus four; and that it is completely defined by the relations

$$S_2^2 = E, \quad S_5^5 = E, \quad (S_2S_5)^4 = E, \quad (S_5^{-1}S_2S_5S_2)^3 = E.$$

* This agrees with the result as stated by Dyck, "Gruppentheoretische Studien," *Math. Ann.* Vol. xx (1882), p. 41.

304. The regular division of a continuous surface into $2N$ black and white polygons is only one of many methods that may be conceived for representing a group graphically.

We shall now describe shortly another such mode of representation, due to Cayley*, who has called it the method of *colour-groups*. As given by Cayley, this method is entirely independent of the one we have been hitherto dealing with; but there is an intimate relation between them, and the new method can be most readily presented to the reader by deriving it from the old one.

Let
$$E, S_1, S_2, \ldots, S_{N-1}$$
be the operations of a group G of order N. We may take the $N-1$ operations other than identity as a set of generating operations. Their continued product
$$S_1S_2 \ldots S_{N-1}$$
is some definite operation of the group. If it is the identical operation, the only modification in the figure, which represents the group by the regular division of a continuous surface, will be that the Nth corner of the polygon has an angle of two right angles.

With this set of generating operations, the representation of the group is given by a regular division of a continuous surface into N white and N black polygons $A_1A_2 \ldots A_N$, the angle at A_r being $\frac{2\pi}{m_r}$, m_r being the order of S_r. Suppose now that in each white polygon we mark a definite point. From the marked point in the polygon Σ, draw a line to the marked point in the polygon derived from it by a positive rotation round its angle A_r. Call this line an S_r-line, and denote the direction in which it is drawn by means of an arrow. Carry out this construction for each polygon Σ, and for each of its angles except A_N. We thus form a figure which, disregarding the original surface, consists of N points connected by $N(N-1)$ directed lines, two distinct lines joining each pair of points. Now if the line drawn from *a*

* *American Journal of Mathematics*, Vol. I (1878), pp. 174—176, Vol. XI (1889), pp. 139—157; *Proceedings of the London Mathematical Society*, Vol. IX (1878), pp. 126—133; *Collected Papers*, Vols. X, XII.

to b, where a and b are two of the points, is an S-line, then the line drawn from b to a is from the construction an S^{-1}-line. We may then at once modify our diagram, in the direction of simplification, by dropping out one of the two lines between a and b, say the S^{-1}-line, on the understanding that the remaining line, with the arrow-head reversed, will give the line omitted. If S is an operation of order 2, S and S^{-1} are identical, and the arrow-head drawn on such a line may be omitted. The modified figure will now consist of N points connected by $\frac{1}{2}N(N-1)$ lines. From the construction it follows at once that, for every value of r, a single S_r-line ends at each point of the figure and a single S_r-line begins at each point of the figure; these two lines being identical when the order of S_r is 2.

We may pass from one point of the figure to another along the lines in various ways; but any path between two points of the figure will be specified completely by such directions as: follow first an S_r-line, then an S_s-line, then an S_t^{-1}-line, and so on. Such a set of directions is said to define a route. It is an immediate consequence of the construction that, if starting from some one particular point a given route leads back to the starting point, then it will lead back to the starting point from whatever point we begin. In fact, a route will be specified symbolically by a symbol

$$S_u \dots S_t^{-1} S_s S_r,$$

and if $$S_u \dots S_t^{-1} S_s S_r \Sigma = \Sigma,$$

then $$S_u \dots S_t^{-1} S_s S_r = E,$$

and therefore $$S_u \dots S_t^{-1} S_s S_r \Sigma' = \Sigma',$$

whatever operation Σ' may be.

305. If the diagram of N points connected by $\frac{1}{2}N(N-1)$ directed lines is to appeal readily to the eye, some method must be adopted of easily distinguishing an S_r-line from an S_s-line. To effect this purpose, Cayley suggested that all the S_r-lines should be of one colour, all the S_s-lines of another, and so on.

Suppose now that, independently of any previous consideration, we have a diagram of N points connected by $\frac{1}{2}N(N-1)$ coloured directed lines satisfying the following conditions:—

(i) all the lines of any one colour have either (*a*) a single arrow-head denoting their directions: or (*b*) no arrow-head, in which case the line may be regarded as equivalent to two coincident lines in opposite directions;

(ii) there is a single line of any given colour leading to every point in the diagram, and a single line of the colour leading from every point: if the colour is one without arrow-heads, the two lines coincide;

(iii) every route which, starting from some one given point in the diagram, is closed, i.e. leads back again to the given point, is closed whatever the starting point.

Then, under these conditions, the diagram represents in graphical form a definite group of order N.

It is to be noticed that the first two conditions are necessary in order that the phrase "a route" used in the third shall have a definite meaning. Suppose that R and R' are two routes leading from a to b. Then RR'^{-1} is a closed route and will lead back to the initial point whatever it may be. Hence if R leads from c to d, so also must R'; and therefore R and R' are equivalent routes in the sense that from any given starting point they lead to the same final point. There are then, with identity which displaces no point, just N non-equivalent routes on the diagram, and the product of any two of these is a definite route of the set. The N routes may be regarded as operations performed on the N points; on account of the last property which has been pointed out, they form a group. Moreover, the diagram gives in explicit form the complete multiplication table of the group, for a mere inspection will immediately determine the one-line route which is equivalent to any given route; i.e. the operation of the group which is the same as the product of any set of operations in any given order.

From a slightly different point of view, every route will give a permutation of the N points, regarded as a set of symbols, among themselves; no symbol remaining unchanged unless they all do. To the set of N independent routes, there will correspond a set of N permutations performed on N symbols; and we can therefore immediately from the diagram represent the group as a transitive permutation-group of degree N.

306. It cannot be denied that, even for groups of small order, the diagram we have been describing would not be easily grasped by the eye. It may however still be considerably simplified since, so far as a graphical definition of the group is concerned, a large number of the lines are always redundant.

If in the diagram consisting of N points and $\frac{1}{2}N(N-1)$ coloured lines, which satisfies the conditions of § 305, all the lines of one or more colours are omitted, two cases may occur. We may still have a figure in which it is possible to pass along lines from one point to any other; or the points may break up into sets such that those of any one set are connected by lines, while there are no lines which enable us to pass from one set to another.

Suppose, to begin with, that the first is the case. There will then, as before, be N non-equivalent routes in the figure, which form a group when they are regarded as operations; it is obviously the same group as is given by the general figure. The sole difference is that there will not now be a one-line route leading from every point to every other point, and therefore the diagram will no longer give directly the result of the product of any number of operations of the group.

If on the other hand the points break up into sets, the new diagram will no longer represent the same group as the original diagram. Some of the routes of the original diagram will not be possible on the new one, but every route on the new one will be a route on the original diagram. Hence the new diagram will give a sub-group; and since it is still the case that no route, except identity, can leave any point unchanged, the number of points in each of the sets must be the same. The reader may verify that the sub-group thus obtained will be self-conjugate, only if the omitted colours interchange these sets bodily among themselves.

307. The simplest diagram that will represent the group will be that which contains the smallest number of colours and at the same time connects all the points. To each colour corresponds a definite operation of the group (and its inverse). Hence the smallest number of colours is the smallest number of operations that will generate the group. It may be noticed that this simplified diagram can be actually constructed from the previously obtained representation of the group by the regular division of a surface, the process being exactly the same as that by which the general diagram was obtained. For if

$$S_1, S_2, \ldots, S_n$$

are a set of independent generating operations, and if

$$S_1 S_2 \ldots S_n S_{n+1} = E,$$

we may represent the group by the regular division of a surface into $2N$ black and white $(n+1)$-sided polygons. When we draw on this surface the S_1-, S_2-, ..., S_n-lines, the N points will be connected by lines in a single set, since from

$$S_1, S_2, \ldots, S_n$$

every operation of the group can be constructed; and the set of points and directed coloured lines so obtained is clearly the diagram required.

As an illustration of this form of graphical representation, we may consider the octohedral group (§ 295), defined by

$$S_1^2 = E, \quad S_2^3 = E, \quad S_3^4 = E,$$

$$S_1 S_2 S_3 = E.$$

On the diagram already given (p. 406), we may at once draw S_1-, S_2- and S_3-lines. These in the present figure are coloured respectively red, yellow, and green. By omitting successively the red, the yellow, and the green lines we form from this the three simplest colour diagrams which will represent the group*.

* For further illustrations, the reader may refer to Young, *Amer. Journal*, Vol. XV (1893), pp. 164—167; Maschke, *Amer. Journal*, Vol. XVIII (1896), pp. 156—188; and Hilton, *An introduction to groups of finite order* (1908), pp. 84—89.

CHAPTER XX.

ON CONGRUENCE GROUPS*.

308. In §§ 88, 89 and again in §§ 140, 141 we have incidentally used systems of congruences to define a group of finite order. This method of presenting a group in a concrete form has been found to lend itself very readily to the discussion and analysis of certain large classes of groups. With the space at our disposal it is impossible to do more than illustrate the application of the method in a few particular cases.

The first that we choose for this purpose is the group of isomorphisms of an Abelian group of order p^n and type (1, 1, ... to n units). This group has been defined and its order determined in §§ 88, 89. It is there shewn that the group is

* The homogeneous linear group and its sub-groups forms the subject of the greater part of Jordan's *Traité des Substitutions.* The investigation of its composition-series, given in the text, is due to Jordan.

The complete analysis of the fractional linear group, defined by

$$y \equiv \frac{\alpha x + \beta}{\gamma x + \delta}, \qquad (\text{mod. } p),$$

where

$$\alpha\delta - \beta\gamma \equiv 1,$$

is due originally to Gierster, "Die Untergruppen der Galois'schen Gruppe der Modulargleichungen für den Fall eines primzahligen Transformationsgrades," *Math. Ann.* Vol. XVIII (1881), pp. 319—365. With a few unimportant modifications, the investigation in the text follows the lines of Gierster's memoir.

In connection with the theory of congruence groups the reader should consult Prof. L. E. Dickson's treatise on *Linear groups with an exposition of the Galois field theory* (1901). This book, which is entirely devoted to the study of groups defined by congruences, gives an admirable and complete account of the theory.

simply isomorphic with the homogeneous linear group defined by all sets of congruences

$$\left.\begin{array}{l} y_1 \equiv a_{11}x_1 + a_{12}x_2 + \ldots + a_{1n}x_n, \\ y_2 \equiv a_{22}x_1 + a_{22}x_2 + \ldots + a_{2n}x_n, \\ \ldots\ldots\ldots\ldots\ldots\ldots\ldots\ldots\ldots\ldots \\ y_n \equiv a_{n1}x_1 + a_{n2}x_2 + \ldots + a_{nn}x_n, \end{array}\right\} \quad (\text{mod. } p),$$

whose determinants are not congruent to zero; and that its order is

$$N = (p^n - 1)(p^n - p) \ldots (p^n - p^{n-1}).$$

The operation given by the above set of congruences will be denoted in future by the symbol

$$(a_{11}x_1 + \ldots + a_{1n}x_n,\ a_{21}x_1 + \ldots + a_{2n}x_n,\ \ldots,\ a_{n1}x_1 + \ldots + a_{nn}x_n).$$

309. The determinant of any operation of the group is congruent (mod. p) to one of the numbers $1, 2, \ldots, p-1$; and if D and D' are the determinants of S and S', the determinant of SS' is congruent (mod. p) to DD'. We have seen (note, p. 268) that those substitutions of a group of linear substitutions, whose determinant is unity, constitute a self-conjugate sub-group. From this it at once follows that those operations of the homogeneous linear group whose determinants are congruent to unity (mod. p) constitute a self-conjugate sub-group. This self-conjugate sub-group will be denoted by Γ, the group itself being G.

Suppose now that S is an operation* of G whose determinant is congruent to z, a primitive root of the congruence

$$z^{p-1} \equiv 1 \quad (\text{mod. } p).$$

Then the determinant of every operation of the set

$$S^r\Gamma$$

is congruent to z^r; and therefore, if r and s are not congruent (mod. p), the two sets

$$S^r\Gamma \text{ and } S^s\Gamma$$

can have no operation in common. Moreover, if S' is any operation of G whose determinant is congruent to z^r, then $S^{-r}S'$ belongs to Γ, and therefore S' belongs to the set $S^r\Gamma$. Hence finally, the sets

$$\Gamma,\ S\Gamma,\ S^2\Gamma,\ \ldots,\ S^{p-2}\Gamma$$

* The operation $(zx_1, x_2, \ldots, x_n)$ has z for its determinant.

are all distinct, and they include every operation of G; so that

$$G = \{S, \Gamma\}.$$

The factor-group G/Γ is therefore cyclical and of order $p-1$.

310. It may be very readily verified that the operations of the cyclical sub-group generated by

$$(zx_1, zx_2, \ldots, zx_n)$$

are self-conjugate operations of G. To prove that these are the only self-conjugate operations of G, we will deal with the case $n = 3$: it will be seen that the method is perfectly general. Suppose then that

$$T = (\alpha x_1 + \beta x_2 + \gamma x_3,\ \alpha' x_1 + \beta' x_2 + \gamma' x_3,\ \alpha'' x_1 + \beta'' x_2 + \gamma'' x_3)$$

is a self-conjugate operation of G, while

$$S = (ax_1 + bx_2 + cx_3,\ a'x_1 + b'x_2 + c'x_3,\ a''x_1 + b''x_2 + c''x_3)$$

is any operation. The relation

$$ST = TS$$

involves the nine simultaneous congruences*

$$a\alpha + b\alpha' + c\alpha'' \equiv \alpha a + \beta a' + \gamma a'',$$

$$a\beta + b\beta' + c\beta'' \equiv \alpha b + \beta b' + \gamma b'',$$

$$a\gamma + b\gamma' + c\gamma'' \equiv \alpha c + \beta c' + \gamma c'',$$

etc., etc.;

and these must be satisfied for all possible values of the coefficients of S. Now

$$b \equiv c \equiv a' \equiv 0$$

is a possible relation between the coefficients of S, whether regarded as an operation of G or Γ; and therefore

$$\gamma \equiv 0.$$

In the same way, it may be shewn that

$$\beta \equiv \alpha' \equiv \gamma' \equiv \alpha'' \equiv \beta'' \equiv 0,$$

and that $\alpha \equiv \beta' \equiv \gamma''$;

so that T is a power of the operation

$$(zx_1, zx_2, zx_3).$$

* These and all succeeding congruences are to be taken mod. p, unless the contrary is stated.

The only self-conjugate operations of G are therefore the powers of A, where A denotes

$$(zx_1,\ zx_2,\ \ldots,\ zx_n);$$

and the only self-conjugate operations of Γ are those operations of this cyclical sub-group which are contained in Γ. Now the order of A is $p-1$ and its determinant is z^n. Hence the self-conjugate operations of Γ form a cyclical sub-group D of order d, where d is the greatest common factor of $p-1$ and n; and this sub-group is generated by $A^{(p-1)/d}$.

311. To determine completely the composition-series of G, it is necessary to find whether Γ has a self-conjugate sub-group greater than and containing D. A simple calculation will shew that, from

$$(x_1 + x_s,\ x_2,\ x_3,\ \ldots,\ x_n)$$

and its conjugate operations, all the operations of Γ may be generated; and hence no self-conjugate sub-group of Γ which is different from Γ itself can contain an operation of this form. If then it is shewn that any self-conjugate sub-group of Γ, distinct from D, necessarily contains operations of this form, it follows that D is a maximum self-conjugate sub-group of Γ.

We shall first deal with the case $n = 2$.

If $p = 2$, the orders of G, Γ and D are 6, 6 and 1. In this case, Γ is simply isomorphic with the symmetric group of three symbols, which has a self-conjugate sub-group of order 3. The successive factor-groups of the composition-series of G are therefore cyclical groups of orders 2 and 3.

If $p = 3$, the orders of G, Γ and D are 48, 24 and 2. The factor-group Γ/D has 12 for its order, and cannot therefore be a simple group. The reader will have no difficulty in verifying that, in this case, the successive factor-groups of G have orders 2, 3, 2, 2 and 2. We will then, in dealing with the case $n = 2$, assume that p is not less than 5.

Let us suppose now that Γ has a self-conjugate sub-group I that contains D; and let S or

$$(ax_1 + bx_2,\ a'x_1 + b'x_2)$$

be one of its operations, not contained in D.

If b is different from zero, Γ contains Σ, where Σ denotes

$$\left(\alpha a x_1 + \alpha b x_2, \quad -\frac{1+\alpha^2 a^2}{\alpha b} x_1 - \alpha a x_2\right),$$

and therefore I contains $\Sigma^{-1}S\Sigma S$, which is

$$\left(-\alpha^{-2}x_1, \ -\frac{(1+\alpha^2)(b'+a\alpha^2)}{b\alpha^2} x_1 - \alpha^2 x_2\right).$$

If b is zero, b' is congruent with a^{-1}; therefore, in any case, I contains an operation S' of the form

$$(cx_1, \ dx_1 + c^{-1}x_2).$$

Again, Γ contains the operation T, where T denotes

$$(x_1, x_1 + x_2);$$

and I therefore contains $S'T^{-1}S'^{-1}T$, which is

$$(x_1, (1-c^2)\,x_1 + x_2).$$

Hence unless $1 - c^2 \equiv 0$, I must coincide with Γ. Now, when $p > 5$, c can always be chosen so that this congruence is not satisfied. If $p = 5$, the square of the above operation $\Sigma^{-1}S\Sigma S$, when unity is written for α, is

$$\left(x_1, \frac{4}{b}(b'+a)\,x_1 + x_2\right);$$

unless $b' + a \equiv 0$, this again requires that I coincides with Γ. If finally, the condition $b' + a \equiv 0$ is satisfied in S, it is not satisfied in $ST^{-1}S^{-1}T$, another operation belonging to I; and therefore again, in this case, I coincides with Γ.

Hence finally, if $n = 2$, the factor-group Γ/D is simple, except when p is 2 or 3.

312. When n is greater than 2, it will be found that it is sufficient to deal in detail with the case $n = 3$, as the method will apply equally well for any greater value of n. Suppose here again that Γ has a self-conjugate sub-group I which contains D; and let S, denoting

$$(ax_1 + bx_2 + cx_3, \ a'x_1 + b'x_2 + c'x_3, \ a''x_1 + b''x_2 + c''x_3),$$

be one of the operations of I which is not contained in D. S cannot be permutable with all operations of the form $(x_1, x_2, x_3 + x_1)$, as it would then be permutable with every operation of Γ. We may therefore suppose without loss of generality that S and T are not permutable, T denoting $(x_1, x_2, x_3 + x_1)$. Then $S^{-1}T^{-1}ST$ is an operation, distinct from identity, belonging to I. Now a simple calculation shews that this operation, say U, is of the form

$$(x_1 - cX,\ x_2 - c'X,\ Ax_1 + Bx_2 + Cx_3),$$

where X is the symbol with which S^{-1} replaces x_1.

If c and c' are both different from zero, Γ will contain an operation V of the form

$$\left(x_1 - \frac{c}{c'}x_2,\ x_2,\ x_2\right);$$

and I contains $V^{-1}UV$, which is of the form

$$(x_1,\ \alpha x_1 + \beta x_2 + \gamma x_3,\ \alpha' x_2 + \beta' x_2 + \gamma' x_3).$$

Moreover, if either c or c' is zero, the operation U itself leaves one symbol unaltered. Hence I always contains operations, other than the identical one, by which one symbol is unaltered.

If now W, or

$$(x_1,\ \alpha x_1 + \beta x_2 + \gamma x_3,\ \alpha' x_1 + \beta' x_2 + \gamma' x_3)$$

is such an operation contained in I, and if R is

$$(x_1,\ x_2 + Ax_1,\ x_3 + Bx_1),$$

then $R^{-1}WRW^{-1}$ is

$$(x_1,\ x_2 + ax_1,\ x_3 + bx_1),$$

where

$$a \equiv A(\gamma' - 1) - B\gamma,$$
$$b \equiv -A\beta' + B(\beta - 1).$$

Hence, unless $\beta \equiv \gamma' \equiv 1$ and $\beta' \equiv \gamma \equiv 0$, I has operations of the form

$$(x_1,\ x_2 + ax_1,\ x_3 + bx_1),$$

and, if these conditions hold, W is already of this form. Still denoting this operation by W, if S is

$$(x_1,\ cx_2,\ c^{-1}x_3),$$

then $S^{-1}WSW^{-c}$ is

$$(x_1,\ x_2,\ x_3 + b(c^{-1} - c)x_1);$$

and it has been seen that Γ can be generated from this operation and its conjugates. Hence finally, if $n > 2$, the factor-group Γ/D is simple for all prime values of p.

313. The composition-series of G is now, except as regards the constitution of the simple group Γ/D, perfectly definite. It has, in fact, been seen that G/Γ and D are cyclical groups of orders $p-1$ and d; and therefore if $\alpha, \beta, \gamma, \ldots$ are primes whose product is $p-1$, and if $\alpha', \beta', \gamma', \ldots$ are primes whose product is d; the successive factor-groups of G are first, a series of simple groups of prime orders $\alpha, \beta, \gamma, \ldots$: then a simple group of composite order $N/(p-1)d$: and lastly, a series of simple groups of prime orders $\alpha', \beta', \gamma', \ldots$.

The sequence in which the set of simple groups of orders $\alpha, \beta, \gamma, \ldots$ are taken in the composition-series may be clearly any whatever, and the same is true of the set of factor-groups of orders $\alpha', \beta', \gamma', \ldots$, but it is to be noticed that, when d is not equal to $p-1$, the composition-series is capable of further modifications. In this case, $\{A, \Gamma\}$ is a self-conjugate sub-group of G of order N/d, which has a maximum self-conjugate sub-group $\{A\}$ of order $p-1$. The successive composition-factors of G may therefore be taken in the sequence

$$\alpha', \beta', \gamma', \ldots : N/(p-1)d : \alpha, \beta, \gamma, \ldots :$$

and their arrangement may be yet further changed by considering the self-conjugate sub-group $\{A^m, \Gamma\}$, where m is a factor of $p-1$ less than $(p-1)/d$.

314. For every value of p^n, except 2^2 and 3^2, it thus appears that the linear group may be regarded as defining a simple group of composite order. We shall now proceed to a discussion of the constitution of the simple groups thus defined when $n=2$, p being greater than 3. In this case, the group Γ is defined by the congruences

$$\begin{aligned} y_1 &\equiv \alpha x_1 + \beta x_2, \\ y_2 &\equiv \gamma x_1 + \delta x_2, \qquad (\text{mod. } p); \\ \alpha\delta - \beta\gamma &\equiv 1, \end{aligned}$$

and since $p-1$ is divisible by 2 when p is an odd prime, d is equal to 2. Hence the self-conjugate operations of Γ are

$$(x_1, x_2) \text{ and } (-x_1, -x_2).$$

The order of Γ is $p(p^2-1)$, and therefore the order of the simple group, H, which it defines is $\frac{1}{2}p(p^2-1)$. Suppose now, if possible, that Γ contains a sub-group g simply isomorphic with H. If S is any operation of Γ, not contained in g, the whole of the operations of Γ are contained in the two sets

$$g, Sg.$$

Now $(x_2, -x_1)$, whose square $(-x_1, -x_2)$ is a self-conjugate operation, cannot be contained in the simple group g. Hence both $(x_2, -x_1)$ and $(-x_1, -x_2)$ are contained in Sg, an obvious contradiction. Therefore Γ contains no sub-group simply isomorphic with H.

For a discussion of the properties of H, some concrete representation of the group itself is necessary; this may be obtained in the following way. Instead of the pair of homogeneous congruences that define each operation of Γ, let us, as in § 141, consider the single non-homogeneous congruence

$$y \equiv \frac{\alpha x + \beta}{\gamma x + \delta}, \quad (\text{mod. } p),$$

where

$$\alpha\delta - \beta\gamma \equiv 1.$$

Corresponding to every operation

$$(\alpha x_1 + \beta x_2, \gamma x_1 + \delta x_2)$$

of Γ, there will be a single operation of this new set; namely that in which $\alpha, \beta, \gamma, \delta$ have respectively the same values. But since the operations

$$y \equiv \frac{\alpha x + \beta}{\gamma x + \delta} \text{ and } y \equiv \frac{-\alpha x - \beta}{-\gamma x - \delta}$$

are identical, two operations

$$(\alpha x_1 + \beta x_2, \gamma x_2 + \delta x_2) \text{ and } (-\alpha x_1 - \beta x_2, -\gamma x_1 - \delta x_2)$$

of Γ will correspond to each operation

$$y \equiv \frac{\alpha x + \beta}{\gamma x + \delta}$$

of the new set; the two self-conjugate operations

$$(x_1, x_2) \text{ and } (-x_1, -x_2),$$

in particular, corresponding to the identical operation of the new set. Moreover, direct calculation immediately verifies that, to the product of any two operations of Γ, corresponds the product of the two corresponding operations of the new set. Hence the new set of operations forms a group of order $\frac{1}{2}p(p^2-1)$, with which Γ is multiply isomorphic; the group of order 2 formed by the self-conjugate operations of Γ corresponding to the identical operation of the new group.

The simple group H, of order $\frac{1}{2}p(p^2-1)$, which we propose to discuss, can therefore be represented by the set of operations

$$y \equiv \frac{\alpha x+\beta}{\gamma x+\delta}, \quad (\text{mod. } p);$$

where

$$\alpha\delta-\beta\gamma \equiv 1,$$

$\alpha, \beta, \gamma, \delta$ being integers reduced to modulus p.

315. Since the order of H is divisible by p and not by p^2, the group must contain a single conjugate set of sub-groups of order p. Now the operation

$$y \equiv x+1,$$

or $(x+1)$ as we will write it in future, is clearly an operation of order p: for its nth power is $(x+n)$, and p is the smallest value of n for which this is the identical operation. If $(x+1)$ and $\left(\frac{\alpha x+\beta}{\gamma x+\delta}\right)$ are represented by P and S, then

$$S^{-1}PS=\left(\frac{(1-\alpha\gamma)\,x+\alpha^2}{-\gamma^2x+1+\alpha\gamma}\right).$$

This is identical with P, only if

$$\gamma \equiv 0, \quad \alpha^2 \equiv 1;$$

and therefore P is permutable with no operations except its own powers. On the other hand, if

$$\gamma \equiv 0,$$

then

$$S^{-1}PS=P^{\alpha^2};$$

and therefore every operation, for which $\gamma \equiv 0$, transforms the sub-group $\{P\}$ into itself. These operations therefore form a sub-group: a result that may also be easily verified directly.

The order of this sub-group is the number of distinct operations $\left(\frac{\alpha x+\beta}{\delta}\right)$ for which $\alpha\delta \equiv 1$. The ratio $\frac{\alpha}{\delta}$ must be a quadratic residue, while β may have any value whatever. Hence the order of the sub-group is $\frac{1}{2}(p-1)p$; and H therefore contains $p+1$ sub-groups of order p. Since H is a simple group, it follows (§ 177) that it can be represented as a transitive permutation-group of degree $p+1$.

This representation of the group can be directly derived, as in § 141, from the congruences already used to define it. Thus if, in

$$y \equiv \frac{\alpha x+\beta}{\gamma x+\delta},$$

we write for x successively $0, 1, 2, \ldots, p-1, \infty$, the $p+1$ values obtained for y, when reduced mod. p, will be the same $p+1$ symbols in some other sequence. For if

$$\frac{\alpha x_1+\beta}{\gamma x_1+\delta} \equiv \frac{\alpha x_2+\beta}{\gamma x_2+\delta},$$

then

$$(\alpha\delta-\beta\gamma)(x_1-x_2) \equiv 0,$$

and therefore $x_1 \equiv x_2$.

Each operation of H gives therefore a distinct permutation performed on the symbols $0, 1, \ldots, p-1, \infty$; and the complete set of permutations thus obtained gives the representation of H as a transitive permutation-group of degree $p+1$. Since H contains operations of order p, this permutation-group must be doubly transitive. That this is the case may also be shewn directly. Thus

$$\frac{y-a}{y-b} \equiv m\,\frac{x-a'}{x-b'}$$

is an operation changing a' into a and b' into b. This operation may be written

$$y \equiv \frac{k(bm-a)x+k(ab'-ma'b)}{k(m-1)x+k(b'-ma')},$$

and its determinant is

$$k^2m(b-a)(b'-a').$$

If now $(b-a)(b'-a')$ is a quadratic residue (or non-residue) mod. p, m may be any quadratic residue (or non-residue); and k can always be chosen so that the determinant is unity. There are therefore $\frac{1}{2}(p-1)$ permutations in the group, changing any two symbols a', b' into any other two given symbols a, b. Further, if the operation $\left(\frac{\alpha x+\beta}{\gamma x+\delta}\right)$ keeps x unchanged in the permutation-group, x must satisfy the congruence

$$x \equiv \frac{\alpha x+\beta}{\gamma x+\delta},$$

that is $$\gamma x^2+(\delta-\alpha)x-\beta \equiv 0.$$

Such a congruence cannot have more than two roots; and therefore every permutation displaces all, all but one, or all but two, of the $p+1$ symbols.

316. The permutations, which keep either one or two symbols fixed, must therefore be regular in the remaining p or $p-1$ symbols. Hence the order of every permutation which keeps just one symbol fixed must be p; and the order of every permutation that keeps two symbols fixed must be equal to or be a factor of $p-1$. Now it was seen in the last paragraph that the order of the sub-group that keeps two symbols fixed is $\frac{1}{2}(p-1)$. Moreover, if z is a primitive root mod. p, the sub-group that keeps a and b fixed contains the operation

$$\frac{y-a}{y-b} = z^2 \frac{x-a}{x-b},$$

and the order of this operation is $\frac{1}{2}(p-1)$. Hence, the sub-group that keeps any two symbols fixed is a cyclical group of order $\frac{1}{2}(p-1)$; and every operation that keeps two symbols fixed is some power of an operation of order $\frac{1}{2}(p-1)$. Since the group is a doubly transitive group of degree $p+1$, there must be $\frac{1}{2}(p+1)p$ sub-groups which keep two symbols fixed; and these must form a conjugate set. Each is therefore self-conjugate in a sub-group of order $p-1$. To determine the type of this sub-group, we may consider the sub-group keeping 0 and ∞ fixed: this is generated by Q, where Q denotes $\left(\frac{zx}{z^{-1}}\right)$.

If $\left(\frac{\alpha x+\beta}{\gamma x+\delta}\right)$ is represented by S, then

$$S^{-1}QS=\left(\frac{(z\alpha\delta-z^{-1}\beta\gamma)\,x-(z-z^{-1})\,\alpha\beta}{(z-z^{-1})\,\gamma\delta x+z^{-1}\alpha\delta-z\beta\gamma}\right),$$

which can be a power of Q only if

$$\alpha\beta\equiv 0,\quad \gamma\delta\equiv 0.$$

Hence either $$\beta\equiv\gamma\equiv 0,$$
in which case S is a power of Q: or

$$\alpha\equiv\delta\equiv 0,\quad \gamma\equiv-\beta^{-1}.$$

In the latter case, we have

$$S=\left(\frac{-\beta}{\beta^{-1}x}\right),$$

which is an operation of order 2; and then

$$S^{-1}QS=\left(\frac{z^{-1}x}{z}\right)=Q^{-1}.$$

The group of order $p-1$, which contains self-conjugately a cyclical sub-group of order $\frac{1}{2}(p-1)$ that keeps two symbols fixed, is therefore a group of dihedral (§ 295) type. Moreover, if t is any factor of $p-1$, this investigation shews that $\{S, Q\}$ is the greatest sub-group that contains $\{Q^t\}$ self-conjugately.

317. A permutation that changes all the symbols must either be regular in the $p+1$ symbols, or must be such that one of its powers keeps two symbols fixed. The latter case however cannot occur; for we have just seen that, if Q is an operation, of order $\frac{1}{2}(p-1)$, which keeps two symbols fixed, the only operations permutable with Q^r are the powers of Q. Hence the permutations that change all the symbols must be regular in the $p+1$ symbols, and their orders must be equal to or be factors of $p+1$.

Suppose now that i is a primitive root of the congruence

$$i^{p^2-1}-1\equiv 0 \pmod{p},$$

so that i and i^p are the roots of a quadratic congruence with real coefficients; and consider the operation K, denoting

$$\frac{y-i^k}{y-i^{kp}}\equiv i^{2(p-1)}\,\frac{x-i^k}{x-i^{kp}},$$

where k is not a multiple of $p+1$. On solving with respect to y, K is expressed in the form

$$y \equiv \frac{\dfrac{i^{\left(\frac{k}{2}+1\right)(p-1)} - i^{-\left(\frac{k}{2}+1\right)(p-1)}}{i^{\frac{k}{2}(p-1)} - i^{-\frac{k}{2}(p-1)}} x - \dfrac{i^{(p-1)} - i^{-(p-1)}}{i^{\frac{k}{2}(p-1)} - i^{-\frac{k}{2}(p-1)}} i^{\frac{k}{2}(p+1)}}{\dfrac{i^{(p-1)} - i^{-(p-1)}}{i^{\frac{k}{2}(p-1)} - i^{-\frac{k}{2}(p-1)}} x i^{-\frac{k}{2}(p+1)} + \dfrac{i^{\left(\frac{k}{2}-1\right)(p-1)} - i^{-\left(\frac{k}{2}-1\right)(p-1)}}{i^{\frac{k}{2}(p-1)} - i^{-\frac{k}{2}(p-1)}}},$$

an operation of determinant unity. It will be found, on writing i^p for i in the coefficients of this operation, that they remain unaltered; therefore, since they are symmetric functions of i and i^p, they must be real numbers. The operation therefore belongs to H. The nth power of this operation is given by

$$\frac{y - i^k}{y - i^{kp}} \equiv i^{2n(p-1)} \frac{x - i^k}{x - i^{kp}},$$

and therefore, since the first power of i which is congruent to unity, mod. p, is the (p^2-1)th, the order of the operation is $\frac{1}{2}(p+1)$. If we write kp for k in the operation K, the new operation is K^{-1}; but if k is replaced by any other number k', which is not a multiple of $p+1$, the new operation K', given by

$$\frac{y - i^{k'}}{y - i^{k'p}} \equiv i^{2(p-1)} \frac{x - i^{k'}}{x - i^{k'p}},$$

generates a new sub-group of order $\frac{1}{2}(p+1)$, which has no operation except identity in common with $\{K\}$. Now there are p^2-p numbers less than p^2-1 which are not multiples of $p+1$; therefore H contains $\frac{1}{2}(p^2-p)$ cyclical sub-groups of order $\frac{1}{2}(p+1)$, no two of which have a common operation except identity. The corresponding permutations displace all the symbols.

318. A simple enumeration shews that the operations of the cyclical sub-groups of orders $\frac{1}{2}(p-1)$, p and $\frac{1}{2}(p+1)$, exhaust all the operations of the group. Thus there are, omitting identity from each sub-group:

(i) $\frac{1}{2}p(p+1)$ sub-groups of order $\frac{1}{2}(p-1)$, containing $\frac{1}{4}p(p^2-1) - \frac{1}{2}p^2 - \frac{1}{2}p$ distinct operations;

(ii) $\frac{1}{2}p(p-1)$ sub-groups of order $\frac{1}{2}(p+1)$, containing $\frac{1}{4}p(p^2-1)-\frac{1}{2}p^2+\frac{1}{2}p$ distinct operations;

(iii) $p+1$ sub-groups of order p, containing p^2-1 distinct operations;

and the sum of these numbers, with 1 for the identical operation, gives $\frac{1}{2}p(p^2-1)$, which is the order of the group.

Every operation that displaces all the symbols is therefore the power of an operation of order $\frac{1}{2}(p+1)$.

319. We shall now further shew that the $\frac{1}{2}p(p-1)$ sub-groups of order $\frac{1}{2}(p+1)$ form a single conjugate set, and that each is contained self-conjugately in a dihedral group of order $p+1$. Let S be any operation of H, which is permutable with $\{K\}$ and replaces i^k by some other symbol j. Then $S^{-1}KS$ is an operation which leaves j unaltered; it may therefore be expressed in the form

$$\frac{y-j}{y-j'}=m\frac{x-j}{x-j'}.$$

This can belong to the sub-group generated by K, only if j and j' are the same pair as i^k and i^{kp}. Hence j must be either i^k or i^{kp}; and similarly, if S replaces i^{kp} by j', the latter must be either i^{kp} or i^k. Hence either S must keep both the symbols i^k and i^{kp} unchanged or it must interchange them; and conversely, every operation which either keeps both the symbols unchanged or interchanges them, must transform $\{K\}$ into itself. If S keeps both of them unchanged, it is a power of K. If S interchanges them, it is of the form

$$\frac{y-i^k}{y-i^{kp}}\equiv m\frac{x-i^{kp}}{x-i^k};$$

and a simple calculation shews that

$$S^{-1}KS=K^{-1}.$$

If we take $m=1$, S becomes

$$x+y\equiv i^k+i^{kp},$$

an operation belonging to H. Hence the cyclical sub-group $\{K\}$ is contained self-conjugately in the sub-group of $\{S, K\}$ which is of dihedral type. If there were any other operation S', not contained in $\{S, K\}$, which transformed K into its inverse, then

SS' would be an operation permutable with K and not contained in $\{K\}$. It has just been seen that no such operation exists. Hence $\{S, K\}$, of order $p+1$, is the greatest sub-group that contains $\{K\}$ self-conjugately; and $\{K\}$ must be one of $\frac{1}{2}p(p-1)$ conjugate sub-groups.

320. The distribution of the operations of H in conjugate sets is now known. A sub-group of order p is contained self-conjugately in a group of order $\frac{1}{2}p(p-1)$, while an operation of order p is permutable only with its own powers. There are therefore two conjugate sets of operations of order p, each set containing $\frac{1}{2}(p^2-1)$ operations. Again, each of the operations of a cyclical sub-group of order $\frac{1}{2}(p-1)$ or $\frac{1}{2}(p+1)$ is conjugate to its own inverse and to no other of its powers. Hence if $\frac{1}{2}(p+1)$ is even and therefore $\frac{1}{2}(p-1)$ odd, there are $\frac{1}{4}(p-3)$ conjugate sets of operations whose orders are factors of $\frac{1}{2}(p-1)$, each set containing p^2+p operations; $\frac{1}{4}(p-3)$ conjugate sets of operations whose orders are factors of $\frac{1}{2}(p+1)$, other than the factor 2, each set containing p^2-p operations; and a single set of operations of order 2, containing $\frac{1}{2}(p^2-p)$ operations. If $\frac{1}{2}(p-1)$ is even and $\frac{1}{2}(p+1)$ odd, there are $\frac{1}{4}(p-1)$ conjugate sets of operations whose orders are factors of $\frac{1}{2}(p+1)$, each containing p^2-p operations; $\frac{1}{4}(p-5)$ conjugate sets whose orders are factors of $\frac{1}{2}(p-1)$, other than the factor 2, each set containing p^2+p operations; and a single set of $\frac{1}{2}(p^2+p)$ conjugate operations of order 2. In either case, the group contains, inclusive of identity, $\frac{1}{2}(p+5)$ conjugate sets of operations.

321. Since $p-1$ and $p+1$ can have no common factor except 2, it follows that, if q^m denote the highest power of an odd prime, other than p, which divides the order of H, q^m must be a factor of $\frac{1}{2}(p-1)$ or of $\frac{1}{2}(p+1)$; and the sub-groups of order q^m must be cyclical. Moreover, since no two cyclical sub-groups of order $\frac{1}{2}(p-1)$, or $\frac{1}{2}(p+1)$, have a common operation except identity, the same must be true of the sub-groups of order q^m.

If 2^m is the highest power of 2 that divides $\frac{1}{2}(p-1)$ or $\frac{1}{2}(p+1)$, 2^{m+1} will be the highest power of 2 that divides the order of H. Moreover, a sub-group of order 2^{m+1} must contain a cyclical sub-group of order 2^m self-conjugately, and it must contain an operation of order 2 that transforms every operation of this cyclical sub-group into its own inverse; in other words, the sub-groups of order 2^{m+1} are of dihedral type.

Suppose $m > 1$ and that two sub-groups of order 2^{m+1} have a common sub-group of order 2^r $(r > 2)$. Such a sub-group must be either cyclical or dihedral: in the latter case, it contains self-conjugately a single cyclical sub-group of order 2^{r-1}. Hence, on the supposition made, a cyclical sub-group of order 4 at least would be contained self-conjugately in two distinct cyclical sub-groups of order 2^m. It has been seen that this is not the case; and therefore the greatest sub-group, that two sub-groups of order 2^{m+1} can have in common, must be a sub-group of order 4, whose operations, except identity, are all of order 2. Now every group of order 2^{m+1} contains one self-conjugate operation of order 2, and 2^m operations of order 2 falling into 2 conjugate sets of 2^{m-1} each. Moreover, the group of order $p \pm 1$, which has a cyclical sub-group of order 2^m and contains the operation A of order 2 of this cyclical group self-conjugately, has $\frac{1}{2}(p \pm 1)$ other operations of order 2; and therefore it contains $(p \pm 1)/2^{m+1}$ sub-groups of order 2^{m+1}, each of which has A for its self-conjugate operation. If now B is any operation of order 2 of this sub-group of order $p \pm 1$, and if it is distinct from A, then B enters into a sub-group of order 2^{m+1} that contains A self-conjugately. But since A is permutable with B, A must belong to the sub-group of order $p \pm 1$, which contains B self-conjugately; hence A enters into a sub-group of order 2^{m+1} which contains B self-conjugately. The sub-group $\{A, B\}$ is therefore common to two distinct sub-groups of order 2^{m+1}. Now no group of order 2^r $(r > 2)$ can be common to two sub-groups of order 2^{m+1}; and therefore $\{A, B\}$ must (§ 122) be permutable with some operation S whose order s is prime to 2. If s is not 3, S must be permutable with A and B: and then $\{A, S\}$ and $\{B, S\}$ would be two distinct sub-groups of orders $2s$, whose operations are permutable with each other. It has been seen that H does not contain such sub-groups. Hence $s = 3$; and S transforms A, B and AB cyclically, or $\{S, A, B\}$ is a sub-group of tetrahedral type (§ 295).

The number of quadratic* sub-groups contained in H may be directly enumerated. A group of order 2^{m+1} contains 2^{m-1} such sub-groups, which fall into 2 conjugate sets of 2^{m-2} each; a single group of order 8 containing each quadratic group self-conjugately. The quadratic groups, contained in the $(p \pm 1)/2^{m+1}$ sub-groups of order 2^{m+1} of a sub-group of order $p \pm 1$, are clearly all distinct, and each quadratic group belongs to just 3 groups of order $p \pm 1$; thus $\{A, B\}$ belongs to the 3 groups which contain A, B and AB respectively as self-conjugate operations. Hence the total number of quadratic groups contained in H is

$$\tfrac{1}{2}p(p \mp 1)\frac{p \pm 1}{2^{m+1}} 2^{m-1} \tfrac{1}{3} = \frac{\tfrac{1}{2}p(p^2-1)}{12}.$$

322. The greatest sub-group of a group of order 2^{m+1}, that contains a quadratic group self-conjugately, is a group of order 8 and dihedral type; and it has been shewn that 3 is the only factor, prime to 2, that occurs in the order of the sub-group containing a quadratic group self-conjugately. Hence finally, the order of the greatest group containing a quadratic group self-conjugately is 24, and the $\tfrac{1}{2}p(p^2-1)/12$ quadratic groups fall into two conjugate sets of $\tfrac{1}{2}p(p^2-1)/24$ each. The group of order 24, that contains a quadratic group self-conjugately, contains also a self-conjugate tetrahedral sub-group, while the sub-groups of order 8 are dihedral. Hence (§§ 126, 295) this group must be of octohedral type.

Since every tetrahedral sub-group of H contains a quadratic sub-group self-conjugately, and every octohedral sub-group contains a tetrahedral sub-group self-conjugately, there must also be two conjugate sets of tetrahedral sub-groups and two conjugate sets of octohedral sub-groups, the number in each set being $\tfrac{1}{2}p(p^2-1)/24$.

323. In the last two paragraphs we have supposed $m > 1$, or what is the same thing, $p \equiv \pm 1 \pmod{8}$. If now $m = 1$, so that $p \equiv \pm 3 \pmod{8}$, the highest power of 2 that divides the order of H is 2^2; and, since 2^2 is not a factor of $\tfrac{1}{2}(p \pm 1)$, the sub-groups of order 2^2 are quadratic. Moreover, since 2^2 is the highest power

* A non-cyclical group of order 4 is called a *quadratic* group.

of 2 dividing the order of H, the quadratic sub-groups form a single conjugate set. Each sub-group of order $p \pm 1$, which has a self-conjugate operation of order 2, contains $\frac{1}{4}(p \pm 1)$ sub-groups of order 4, and each of the latter belongs to 3 of the former. The total number is as before $\frac{1}{2}p(p^2-1)/12$, and since they form a single conjugate set, each quadratic group is self-conjugate in a group of order 12. Also, for the same reason as in the previous case, this sub-group is of tetrahedral type.

Finally, since every sub-group of H of tetrahedral type must contain a quadratic sub-group self-conjugately, H must contain a single conjugate set of $\frac{1}{2}p(p^2-1)/12$ tetrahedral sub-groups. In this case the order of H is not divisible by 24, and therefore the question of octohedral sub-groups does not arise.

324. The group H always contains tetrahedral sub-groups; when its order is divisible by 24, it contains also octohedral sub-groups. Now if $p \equiv \pm 1 \pmod{5}$, the order of H is divisible by 60; and it may be shewn as follows that, in these cases, H contains sub-groups of icosahedral type.

Let us suppose, first, that $p \equiv 1 \pmod{5}$; and let j be a primitive root of the congruence

$$j^5 \equiv 1 \pmod{p}.$$

Then $\left(\dfrac{jx}{j^{-1}}\right)$, which we will denote by A, is an operation of order 5. The operations of order 2 of H are all of the form B, where B denotes $\left(\dfrac{\alpha x+\beta}{\gamma x-\alpha}\right)$, since each is its own inverse. Now

$$AB = \left(\frac{\alpha jx+\beta j^{-1}}{\gamma jx - \alpha j^{-1}}\right);$$

and (§ 295) A and B will generate an icosahedral group, if

$$(AB)^3 = E.$$

A simple calculation shews that this condition is satisfied, if

$$\alpha^2 (j-j^{-1})^2 \equiv 1.$$

Also, since the determinant of B is unity,

$$\alpha^2 + \beta\gamma \equiv -1.$$

These two congruences have just $p-1$ distinct solutions, the solutions α, β, γ and $-\alpha, -\beta, -\gamma$ being regarded as identical. There are therefore $p-1$ operations of order two in H, namely the operations

$$\left(\frac{\frac{1}{j-j^{-1}}x+\beta}{\gamma x-\frac{1}{j-j^{-1}}}\right),$$

where
$$\beta\gamma \equiv -1-\frac{1}{(j-j^{-1})^2},$$

which with A generate an icosahedral sub-group.

The group generated by

$$\left(\frac{jx}{j^{-1}}\right) \text{ and } \left(\frac{\frac{1}{j-j^{-1}}x+\beta_0}{\gamma_0 x-\frac{1}{j-j^{-1}}}\right),$$

contains 5 of the $p-1$ operations of order 2 of the form

$$\left(\frac{\frac{1}{j-j^{-1}}x+\beta}{\gamma x-\frac{1}{j-j^{-1}}}\right),$$

viz. those for which

$$\beta \equiv \beta_0 j^n, \quad \gamma \equiv \gamma_0 j^{-n}, \quad (n=0, 1, 2, 3, 4).$$

Hence the sub-group $\{A\}$, of order 5, belongs to $\frac{1}{5}(p-1)$ distinct icosahedral sub-groups. Now each icosahedral sub-group has 6 sub-groups of order 5; and H contains $\frac{1}{2}p(p+1)$ sub-groups of order 5 forming a single conjugate set. The number of icosahedral sub-groups in H is therefore

$$\tfrac{1}{6}\frac{p-1}{5}\,\tfrac{1}{2}p(p+1)=\frac{\frac{1}{2}p(p^2-1)}{30}.$$

The group of isomorphisms of the icosahedral group is the symmetric group of degree 5 (§ 162). Now H can contain no sub-group simply isomorphic with the symmetric group of degree 5. For if it contained such a sub-group, an operation of order 5 would be conjugate to its own square; and this is not the case.

Hence (§ 70), if an icosahedral sub-group K of H is contained self-conjugately in a greater sub-group L, then L must be the direct product of K and some other sub-group. This also is impossible; for the greatest sub-group of H in which any cyclical sub-group, except those of order p, is contained self-conjugately, is of dihedral type. Hence L must coincide with K, and K must be one of $\frac{1}{2}p(p^2-1)/60$ conjugate sub-groups. The icosahedral sub-groups of H therefore fall into two conjugate sets of $\frac{1}{2}p(p^2-1)/60$ each.

In a similar manner, when $p \equiv -1$ (mod. 5), we may take as a typical operation A, of order 5,

$$\frac{y-i}{y-i^p} \equiv i^{\frac{p^2-1}{5}} \frac{x-i}{x-i^p};$$

and it may be shewn, the calculation being rather more cumbrous than in the previous case, that there are just $p+1$ operations B, of the form $\left(\frac{\alpha x+\beta}{\gamma x-\alpha}\right)$, such that

$$(AB)^3 = E,$$

and that five of these belong to the icosahedral group generated by A and any one of them. It follows, exactly as in the previous case, that H contains $\frac{1}{2}p(p^2-1)/30$ icosahedral sub-groups, which fall into two conjugate sets, each set containing $\frac{1}{2}p(p^2-1)/60$ groups.

325. Finally, we proceed to shew that H has no other sub-groups than those which have been already determined. Suppose, first, that a sub-group h of H contains two distinct sub-groups of order p. These must, by Sylow's theorem, form part of a set of $kp+1$ sub-groups of order p conjugate within h. Now H contains only $p+1$ sub-groups of order p, and therefore k must be unity and h must contain all the sub-groups of order p; or since H is simple, h must contain and therefore coincide with H. Hence the only sub-groups of H, whose orders are divisible by p, are those that contain a sub-group of order p self-conjugately. They are of known types.

Suppose next that g is a sub-group of H, whose order n is not divisible by p, and let S_1 be an operation of g whose order q_1 is not less than the order of any other operation of g. In H the sub-group $\{S_1\}$ is self-conjugate in a dihedral group of order $p \pm 1$; and the greatest sub-group of this group, which contains no operation of order greater than q_1, is a dihedral group of order $2q_1$. Hence in g the sub-group $\{S_1\}$ is self-conjugate in a group of order q_1 or $2q_1$, and therefore it forms one of n/q_1 or of $n/2q_1$ conjugate sub-groups. Moreover, no two of these sub-groups contain a common operation except identity; and they therefore contain, excluding identity, $n(q_1 - 1)/\epsilon_1 q_1$ distinct operations, where ϵ_1 is either 1 or 2.

Of the remaining operations of g, let S_2 be one whose order q_2 is not less than that of any of the others. The operation S_2 cannot be permutable with any of the $n(q_1 - 1)/\epsilon_1 q_1$ operations already accounted for, since S_2 is not a power of any one of these operations. Hence, exactly as before, $\{S_2\}$ must form one of $n/\epsilon_2 q_2$ conjugate sub-groups in g, ϵ_2 being either 1 or 2; and these sub-groups contain $n(q_2 - 1)/\epsilon_2 q_2$ operations which are distinct from identity, from each other, and from those of the previous set. This process may be continued till the identical operation only remains. Hence, finally, n being the total number of operations of g, we must have

$$n = 1 + \sum_\nu \frac{n(q_\nu - 1)}{\epsilon_\nu q_\nu}$$

or

$$\frac{1}{n} = 1 - \sum_\nu \frac{q_\nu - 1}{\epsilon_\nu q_\nu}.$$

326. In this equation, let r of the ϵ's be 1 and s of them be 2. Then

$$\begin{aligned}
\frac{1}{n} &= 1 - \Sigma\left(1 - \frac{1}{q_\lambda}\right) - \Sigma\left(\tfrac{1}{2} - \frac{1}{2q_\mu}\right) \\
&= 1 - r + \Sigma\frac{1}{q_\lambda} - \tfrac{1}{2}s + \Sigma\frac{1}{2q_\mu} \\
&\leqslant 1 - r + \tfrac{1}{2}r - \tfrac{1}{2}s + \tfrac{1}{4}s \\
&\leqslant 1 - \tfrac{1}{2}r - \tfrac{1}{4}s.
\end{aligned}$$

Hence, since n is a positive integer, r cannot be greater than 1, and therefore not more than one of the ϵ's can be unity. Also, when one of the ϵ's is unity, we have

$$\begin{aligned}\frac{1}{n} &= \frac{1}{q} - \tfrac{1}{2}s + \Sigma\frac{1}{2q_\mu} \\ &\leqslant \tfrac{1}{2} - \tfrac{1}{2}s + \tfrac{1}{4}s \\ &\leqslant \tfrac{1}{4}(2-s),\end{aligned}$$

so that, in this case, s cannot be greater than unity. The solutions are now easily obtained by trial.

(i) For one term in the sum, the only possible solution is

$$\epsilon_1 = 1,\ n = q_1,$$

and the corresponding group is cyclical.

(ii) For two terms in the sum, the solutions are

$$(\alpha)\quad \epsilon_1 = \epsilon_2 = 2,\ n = \frac{2q_1q_2}{q_1+q_2};$$

$$(\beta)\quad \epsilon_1 = 2,\ \epsilon_2 = 1,\ q_2 = 2,\ n = 2q_1;$$

$$(\gamma)\quad \epsilon_1 = 1,\ \epsilon_2 = 2,\ q_1 = 3,\ q_2 = 2,\ n = 12.$$

To the solution (α) there corresponds no sub-group; for $n < 2q_1$, and the values $q_1 = q_1$, $\epsilon_1 = 2$ imply that g has a sub-group of order $2q_1$.

To the solution (β) correspond the sub-groups of order $2q_1$ of dihedral type, for which q_1 is odd, so that the operations of order 2 form a single conjugate set.

To the solution (γ) corresponds a sub-group of order 12 containing 8 operations of order 3 and 3 operations of order 2, i.e. a tetrahedral sub-group.

(iii) For three terms in the sum, the solutions are

(α)	$\epsilon_1 = \epsilon_2 = \epsilon_3 = 2$,		$q_2 = 2$,	$q_3 = 2$,	$n = 2q_1$;
(β)	,, ,,	$q_1 = 3$,	$q_2 = 3$,	$q_3 = 2$,	$n = 12$;
(γ)	,, ,,	$q_1 = 4$,	$q_2 = 3$,	$q_3 = 2$,	$n = 24$;
(δ)	,, ,,	$q_1 = 5$,	$q_2 = 3$,	$q_3 = 2$,	$n = 60$.

To the solution (α) correspond the sub-groups of order $2q_1$

of dihedral type, in which q_1 is even, so that the operations of order 2, which do not belong to the cyclical sub-group of order q_1, fall into two distinct conjugate sets.

To the solution (β) would correspond a group of order 12 containing 3 operations of order 2 and 4 sub-groups of order 3 which fall into two conjugate sets of 2 each. Sylow's theorem shews that such a group cannot exist; and therefore there is no sub-group of H corresponding to this solution.

Solution (γ) gives a group of order 24, with 3 conjugate cyclical sub-groups of order 4, 4 conjugate cyclical sub-groups of order 3, and 6 other operations of order 2 forming a single conjugate set. No operation of this group is permutable with each of the 4 sub-groups of order 3; and therefore, if the group exists, it can be represented as a transitive group of 4 symbols. On the other hand, the order of the symmetric group of 4 symbols, which (§ 296) is simply isomorphic with the octohedral group, is 24; and its cyclical sub-groups are distributed as above. Hence to the solution (γ) there correspond the octohedral sub-groups of H.

Solution (δ) gives a group of order 60, with 6 conjugate sub-groups of order 5, 10 conjugate sub-groups of order 3, and a conjugate set of 15 operations of order 2. It has been shewn, in § 127, that there is only one type of group of order 60 that has 6 sub-groups of order 5; viz. the alternating group of degree 5: and that, in this group, the distribution of sub-groups in conjugate sets agrees with that just given. Moreover, the alternating group of degree 5 is simply isomorphic with the icosahedral group. Hence to this solution there correspond the icosahedral sub-groups of H.

(iv) For more than three terms in the sum there are no solutions.

327. When $p > 11$, then $\frac{1}{2}p(p-1) > 60$; and, when $p > 3$, $\frac{1}{2}p(p-1) > p+1$. Hence when $p > 11$, the order of the greatest sub-group of H is $\frac{1}{2}p(p-1)$, and the least number of symbols in which H can be expressed as a transitive group is $p+1$.

When p is 5, 7 or 11, however, H can be expressed as a transitive group of p symbols*.

For, when $p=5$, H contains a tetrahedral sub-group of order 12, forming one of 5 conjugate sub-groups; therefore H can be expressed as a transitive group of 5 symbols. It is to be noticed that in this case H is an icosahedral group.

When $p=7$, H contains an octohedral sub-group of order 24, which is one of 7 conjugate sub-groups; and H can therefore be expressed as a transitive group of 7 symbols. Similarly, when $p=11$, H contains an icosahedral sub-group of order 60, which is one of 11 conjugate sub-groups; and the group can be expressed transitively in 11 symbols.

328. The simple groups, of the class we have been discussing in the foregoing sections, are self-conjugate sub-groups of the triply transitive groups of degree $p+1$, defined by

$$y \equiv \frac{\alpha x+\beta}{\gamma x+\delta}, \quad (\text{mod. } p),$$

the existence of which was demonstrated in § 141. In fact, since $\left(\frac{\alpha x+\beta}{\gamma x+\delta}\right)$ and $\left(\frac{k\alpha x+k\beta}{k\gamma x+k\delta}\right)$ represents the same transformation, the determinant, $\alpha\delta-\beta\gamma$, of any transformation may always be taken as either unity or a given non-residue; and it follows at once that the transformations of determinant unity form a self-conjugate sub-group of the whole group of transformations.

If, as in § 141, α, β, γ, δ are powers of i, where i is a primitive root of the congruence

$$i^{p^n-1} \equiv 1, \quad (\text{mod. } p),$$

the triply transitive group G of degree p^n+1, which is defined by the transformations, has again, when p is an odd prime, a self-conjugate sub-group H of order $\frac{1}{2}p^n(p^{2n}-1)$, which is given by the transformations of determinant unity. It follows from Theorem XIII, § 154, that G, being a triply transitive group of degree p^n+1, must have, as a self-conjugate sub-group, a

* This is another of the results stated in the letter of Galois referred to in the footnote on p. 202.

doubly transitive simple group; and it is easy to shew that H is this sub-group.

In fact, if a simple group h is a self-conjugate sub-group of G it must be contained in H. Also, since h is a doubly transitive group of degree p^n+1, it must contain every operation of order p that occurs in G. Now we may shew that these operations generate H. Thus $\left(\frac{2x+1}{-x}\right)$ and $(x+2-i-i^{-1})$ are operations of order p belonging to G. Therefore $\left(\frac{(i+i^{-1})x+1}{-x}\right)$ belongs to h. But this operation is transformed into $\left(\frac{ix}{i^{-1}}\right)$ by $\left(\frac{x+i^{-1}}{x+i}\right)$. Hence $\left(\frac{ix}{i^{-1}}\right)$ belongs to h; and a sub-group of h which keeps one symbol unchanged is the group of order $\frac{1}{2}p^n(p^n-1)$ generated by $(x+1)$ and $\left(\frac{ix}{i^{-1}}\right)$. The order of h therefore is not less than $\frac{1}{2}p^n(p^{2n}-1)$; in other words h is identical with H.

When $p=2$, every power of i is a quadratic residue, and the determinant of every transformation is unity. In this case it may be shewn, by an argument similar to the above, that the group G of order $2^n(2^{2n}-1)$ is itself a simple group.

We are thus led to recognize the existence of a doubly-infinite series of simple groups of orders $2^n(2^{2n}-1)$ and $\frac{1}{2}p^n(p^{2n}-1)$, which are closely analogous to the groups of order $\frac{1}{2}p(p^2-1)$ already discussed. For an independent proof of the existence of these simple groups and for an investigation of their properties, the reader is referred to the memoirs mentioned below*.

329. We will now return to the linear homogeneous group G of transformations of n symbols, taken to a prime modulus p; and consider it more directly as the group of isomorphisms of an Abelian group of order p^n and type (1, 1, ... to n units). As in § 63 it may be expressed in the form of a substitution

* Moore, "On a doubly-infinite series of simple groups," *Chicago Congress Mathematical Papers* (1893); Burnside, "On a class of groups defined by congruences," *Proc. L. M. S.* Vol. xxv (1894), pp. 113—139.

group performed on the $p^n - 1$ symbols of the operations, other than identity, of the Abelian group. In this form it is clearly transitive, since there are isomorphisms changing any operation of the Abelian group into any other operation. If P is any operation of the Abelian group, an isomorphism which changes any one of the $p-1$ operations

$$P,\ P^2, \dots, P^{p-1}$$

into any other, will certainly interchange the set among themselves. Hence, when expressed as a group of degree $p^n - 1$, G is imprimitive; and the symbols forming an imprimitive system are those of the operations, other than identity, of any sub-group of order p of the Abelian group. If

$$P_1,\ P_2, \dots, P_n$$

are a set of generating operations of the Abelian group, an isomorphism, which changes each of the sub-groups

$$\{P_1\},\ \{P_2\},\ \dots,\ \{P_n\}$$

into itself, must be of the form

$$\begin{pmatrix} P_1, & P_2, & \dots, & P_n \\ P_1^{\alpha_1}, & P_2^{\alpha_2}, & \dots, & P_n^{\alpha_n} \end{pmatrix}.$$

This isomorphism changes P_1P_2 into $(P_1P_2^{\frac{\alpha_2}{\alpha_1}})^{\alpha_1}$; therefore it will only transform the sub-group $\{P_1P_2\}$ into itself when $\alpha_1 \equiv \alpha_2$, (mod. p). If then the given isomorphism changes every sub-group of order p into itself, we must have

$$\alpha_1 \equiv \alpha_2 \equiv \dots \equiv \alpha_n, \quad (\text{mod. } p).$$

Hence the only operations of G, which interchange the symbols of each imprimitive system among themselves, are those given by the powers of

$$\begin{pmatrix} P_1, & P_2, & \dots, & P_n \\ P_1^{\alpha}, & P_2^{\alpha}, & \dots, & P_n^{\alpha} \end{pmatrix},$$

where α is a primitive root of p. This operation is the same as that denoted by A in § 310. It follows immediately that the factor-group $G/\{A\}$ can be represented as a transitive group in $(p^n - 1)/(p-1)$ symbols. In fact, the operations of $\{A\}$ are the only operations of G which transform each of the

$$(p^n - 1)/(p-1)$$

sub-groups of order p into itself; and these $(p^n-1)/(p-1)$ sub-groups must be permuted among themselves by every operation of G. The substitution group thus obtained is doubly transitive; for if P and P' are any two operations of the Abelian group such that P' is not a power of P, and if Q and Q' are any other two operations of the Abelian group subject to the same condition, there certainly exists an isomorphism of the form

$$\begin{pmatrix} P, & P', \dots \\ Q, & Q', \dots \end{pmatrix},$$

and this isomorphism changes the sub-groups $\{P\}$ and $\{P'\}$ into the sub-groups $\{Q\}$ and $\{Q'\}$.

These results will still hold if, instead of considering G the total group of isomorphisms, we take Γ the group of isomorphisms of determinant unity. Thus the determinant of

$$\begin{pmatrix} P, & P', \dots \\ Q^{\alpha}, & Q', \dots \end{pmatrix}$$

is α times the determinant of

$$\begin{pmatrix} P, & P', \dots \\ Q, & Q', \dots \end{pmatrix}.$$

It is therefore possible always to choose α so that the determinant of

$$\begin{pmatrix} P, & P', \dots \\ Q^{\alpha}, & Q', \dots \end{pmatrix}$$

shall be unity; and this isomorphism still changes the sub-groups $\{P\}$ and $\{P'\}$ into $\{Q\}$ and $\{Q'\}$ respectively.

The lowest power of A contained in Γ is (§ 310) $A^{(p-1)/d}$. Hence the group $\Gamma/\{A^{(p-1)/d}\}$ can be represented as a doubly transitive group of degree $(p^n-1)/(p-1)$. This group is (§ 313) simply isomorphic with the simple group of order $N/(p-1)d$, which is defined by the composition-series of G.

We may sum up these results as follows:—

THEOREM. *The homogeneous linear group of order*

$$N=(p^n-1)(p^n-p)\dots(p^n-p^{n-1})$$

when p^n is neither 2^2 nor 3^2, defines, by its composition-series, a simple group of order $N/(p-1)d$, where d is the greatest common *factor of $p-1$ and n. This simple group can be represented as a doubly transitive group of degree $p^{n-1}+p^{n-2}+\ldots+p+1$.*

330. The $(p^n-1)/(p-1)$ symbols, permuted by one of these doubly transitive simple groups, may be regarded as the sub-groups of order p of an Abelian group of order p^n and type (1, 1, ... to n units). Now every pair of sub-groups of such an Abelian group enters in one, and only in one, sub-group of order p^2; and every sub-group of order p^2 contains $p+1$ sub-groups of order p. Hence from the $(p^n-1)/(p-1)$ symbols permuted by the doubly transitive group, $(p^n-1)(p^{n-1}-1)/(p-1)(p^2-1)$ sets of $p+1$ symbols each may be formed, such that every pair of symbols occurs in one set and no pair in more than one set, while the sets are permuted transitively by the operations of the group. These groups therefore belong to the class of groups referred to in § 168. The sub-group, that leaves two symbols unchanged, permutes the remaining symbols in two transitive systems of $p-1$ and $p^{n-1}+p^{n-2}+\ldots+p^2$; and the sub-group, that leaves unchanged each of the symbols of one of the sets of $p+1$, is contained self-conjugately in a sub-group whose order is $(p+1)p$ times that of a sub-group leaving two symbols unchanged. This latter sub-group permutes the symbols in two transitive systems of $p+1$ and

$$p^{n-1}+p^{n-2}+\ldots+p^2.$$

It may be pointed out that, when n is 3, such a sub-group is simply isomorphic with, but is not conjugate to, the sub-groups that leave one symbol unchanged: this may be seen at once by noticing that an Abelian group, of order p^3 and type (1, 1, 1), has the same number of sub-groups of orders p and p^2.

331. Some special cases may be noticed. First, when $p=2$, both $p-1$ and d are unity, and the homogeneous linear group is itself a simple group.

If $n=3$, then $N=168$; so that the group of isomorphisms of a group of order 8, whose operations are all of order 2, is the simple group of order 168 (§ 166).

If $n=4$, then $N=2^6 . 3^2 . 5 . 7$. This is the order of the alternating group of 8 symbols; and it may be shewn that this group is simply isomorphic with the group of isomorphisms*.

* This result is due to Jordan, *Traité des Substitutions*, pp. 380—382.

It has been seen in § 166 that the symmetric group of degree 8 contains a sub-group of order 8 . 7 . 6 . 4 which can be expressed as a primitive group of degree 8. The only sub-group of greater order is the alternating group. The sub-group is therefore one of 30 conjugate sub-groups; and in the alternating group, to which they belong, these sub-groups fall into two distinct conjugate sets of 15 each.

The alternating group of degree 8 can therefore be represented as a transitive group of degree 15; and the sub-groups that then leave one symbol unchanged constitute one of the above two sets of conjugate sub-groups. In this form of the group the other set of sub-groups of order 8 . 7 . 6 . 4 must be intransitive (since their order is not divisible by 5), and must therefore permute the symbols in two transitive sets of 7 and 8 symbols respectively.

When the alternating group of degree 8 is represented as a transitive group of degree 15 it is therefore possible to choose a set of 7 out of the 15 symbols which only takes 15 values under the permutations of the group.

When the alternating group of degree 8 is represented as a transitive group of degree 15, an alternating group of degree 6 contained in it is necessarily transitive, because there are no representations of the alternating group of degree 6 as a transitive group of degree 9. The alternating group of degree 6 contains a doubly transitive sub-group simply isomorphic with the alternating group of degree 5. When the alternating group of degree 6 is represented as a transitive group of degree 15, this sub-group is necessarily transitive. Hence when the alternating group of degree 8 is represented as a transitive group of degree 15 it contains transitive icosahedral sub-groups. Such a sub-group is generated by

$$S \text{ or } (123)(456)(7ab)(cde)(fgh),$$

and

$$T \text{ or } (1f6c2)(4hbd5)(3ea7g).$$

For ST is

$$(2e)(3f)(5c)(6h)(ad)(bg),$$

so that

$$S^3 = E, \quad T^5 = E, \quad (ST)^2 = E.$$

The sub-group that leaves 1 unchanged consists of identity and

$$(2e)(3f)(5c)(6h)(ad)(bg),$$
$$(2f)(3e)(5h)(6c)(ag)(bd),$$
$$(23)(ef)(56)(ch)(ab)(dg).$$

If a set of 7 symbols takes only 15 values under the permutations of the group, one of the values must be invariant for this sub-group; and therefore it must be

$$14723ef,$$
$$14756ch,$$

or

$$147abdg.$$

Now each of these lead to the same set of 15, viz.

14723*ef*,	24*f*56*ad*,
14756*ch*,	24*fbcgh*,
147*abdg*,	27*e*5*abh*,
1235*acg*,	27*e*6*cdg*,
1236*bdh*,	34*eacdh*,
1*ef*6*agh*,	34*e*56*bg*,
1*ef*5*bcd*,	37*f*6*abc*,
	37*f*5*dgh*.

Hence, since this set is unique for the icosahedral sub-group, it must be the set for the alternating group of degree 8 in 15 symbols which contains the icosahedral sub-group.

Consider now the linear substitutions formed by multiplying each of the 7 symbols in one of the sets by 1, and each of the remaining 8 symbols by -1. Fifteen linear substitutions thus arise of order 2, and they are permuted among themselves by every permutation of the transitive group of degree 15.

But these fifteen substitutions with identity constitute an Abelian group of order 16. Thus, if A multiplies each of 14723*ef* by $+1$ and each of 56*abcdgh* by -1, and if B multiplies each of 34*e*56*bg* by $+1$ and each of 127*acdfh* by -1, then AB multiplies each of 34*eacdh* by $+1$ and each of 12567*bfg* by -1; so that AB belongs to the set. Moreover this completes the verification since the group of permutations of the 15 sets is doubly transitive. The group of permutations is thus actually exhibited as a group of isomorphisms of an Abelian group of order 16. Since the alternating group is simple none of its permutations, except identity, can give the identical isomorphism. Hence the order of the group of isomorphisms being the same as that of the group of permutations, the two must be simply isomorphic.

An alternative proof of this result may be based upon Ex. 2, p. 230. The reader will find it instructive to develop this proof.

If $p^n = 3^3$, then $p^{n-1} + \ldots + p + 1 = 13$, $d = 1$, and $N = 2^4 . 3^3 . 13$. There is therefore a doubly transitive simple group of degree 13 and order $2^4 . 3^3 . 13$ (§§ 164, 169).

332. The homogeneous linear group may be generalized by taking for the coefficients powers of a primitive root of

$$i^{p^\nu - 1} \equiv 1, \quad (\text{mod. } p),$$

instead of powers of a primitive root of

$$i^{p-1} \equiv 1, \quad (\text{mod. } p).$$

When the coefficients are thus chosen, the order of the group $G_{p,n,\nu}$, defined by all sets of transformations

$$\begin{aligned} x_1' &\equiv a_{11}x_1 + a_{12}x_2 + \ldots + a_{1n}x_n, \\ x_2' &\equiv a_{21}x_1 + a_{22}x_2 + \ldots + a_{2n}x_n, \\ &\ldots\ldots\ldots\ldots\ldots\ldots \\ x_n' &\equiv a_{n1}x_1 + a_{n2}x_2 + \ldots + x_{nn}x_n, \end{aligned} \quad (\text{mod. } p),$$

whose determinant differs from zero, may be shewn, as in § 85, to be

$$N = (p^{n\nu} - 1)(p^{n\nu} - p^{\nu})(p^{n\nu} - p^{2\nu}) \ldots (p^{n\nu} - p^{(n-1)\nu});$$

and the order of the sub-group Γ, formed of those transformations whose determinant is unity, is $N/(p^{\nu} - 1)$. The only self-conjugate operations of Γ are the operations of the sub-group generated by $(ix_1, ix_2, \ldots, ix_n)$, which are contained in Γ. If δ is the greatest common factor of $p^{\nu} - 1$ and n, these self-conjugate operations of Γ form a cyclical sub-group γ of order δ. Finally it may be shewn by a process similar to that of § 312 that Γ/γ is a simple group.

The homogeneous linear group $G_{p,n,\nu}$, when values of ν greater than unity are admitted, thus defines a triply infinite system of simple groups; and it may be proved that these groups can, for all values of ν, be expressed as doubly transitive groups of degree $(p^{n\nu} - 1)/(p^{\nu} - 1)$.

333. We may shew, in conclusion, that the group $G_{p,n,\nu}$ is simply isomorphic with a sub-group of $G_{p,n\nu,1}$. For this purpose, we consider the group defined by

$$x_1' \equiv x_1 + i_{r_1},\ x_2' \equiv x_2 + i_{r_2},\ \ldots\ldots,\ x_n' \equiv x_n + i_{r_n},$$
$$(i_{r_1},\ i_{r_2},\ \ldots\ldots,\ i_{r_n} = 0,\ i,\ i^2,\ \ldots\ldots,\ i^{p^{\nu}-1});$$

the congruences being taken to modulus p. This is an Abelian group of order $p^{n\nu}$ and type (1, 1, ... to $n\nu$ units). Moreover, the operation

$$\begin{aligned} x_1' &\equiv a_{11}x_1 + \ldots\ldots + a_{1n}x_n, \\ &\ldots\ldots\ldots\ldots\ldots\ldots \\ x_n' &\equiv a_{n1}x_1 + \ldots\ldots + a_{nn}x_n, \end{aligned}$$

of $G_{p,n,\nu}$ transforms the given operation of the Abelian group into

$$x_1' \equiv x_1 + i_{s_1},\ x_2' \equiv x_2 + i_{s_2},\ \ldots\ldots,\ x_n' \equiv x_n + i_{s_n};$$

where
$$\begin{aligned} i_{s_1} &\equiv a_{11}i_{r_1} + a_{12}i_{r_2} + \ldots\ldots + a_{1n}i_{r_n}, \\ &\ldots\ldots\ldots\ldots\ldots\ldots \\ i_{s_n} &\equiv a_{n1}i_{r_1} + a_{n2}i_{r_2} + \ldots\ldots + a_{nn}i_{r_n}. \end{aligned}$$

Every operation of $G_{p,n,\nu}$, as defined in § 332, is therefore permutable with the Abelian group, and gives a distinct isomorphism of it; or in other words, as stated above, $G_{p,n,\nu}$ is simply isomorphic with a sub-group of $G_{p,n\nu,1}$.

Further, the sub-group

$$x_1' \equiv x_1 + i_r, \quad x_2' \equiv x_2, \ \ldots\ldots, \ x_n' \equiv x_n,$$
$$(i_r = 0, \ i, \ i^2, \ \ldots\ldots, \ i^{p^\nu - 1}),$$

is transformed by the given operation of $G_{p,n,\nu}$ into the sub-group

$$x_1' \equiv x_1 + a_{11} i_r, \quad x_2' \equiv x_2 + a_{21} i_r, \ \ldots\ldots, \ x_n' \equiv x_n + a_{n1} i_r,$$
$$(i_r = 0, \ i, \ i^2, \ \ldots\ldots, \ i^{p^\nu - 1}).$$

If
$$a_{21} \equiv a_{31} \equiv \ldots\ldots \equiv a_{n1} \equiv 0,$$

the two sub-groups are identical; but if these conditions are not satisfied, they have no operation in common except identity. Moreover,

$$a_{11}, \ a_{21}, \ \ldots\ldots, \ a_{n1}$$

may each have any value from 0 to $i^{p^\nu - 1}$, simultaneous zero values alone excluded. Hence the sub-group of order p^ν defined by

$$x_1' \equiv x_1 + i_r, \quad x_2' \equiv x_2, \ \ldots\ldots, \ x_n' \equiv x_n,$$
$$(i_r = 0, \ i, \ i^2, \ \ldots\ldots, \ i^{p^\nu - 1}),$$

is one of $(p^{n\nu} - 1)/(p^\nu - 1)$ conjugate sub-groups in the group formed by combining the Abelian group with $G_{p,n,\nu}$; and no two of these conjugate sub-groups have a common operation except identity.

The $p^{n\nu} - 1$ operations, other than identity, of an Abelian group of order $p^{n\nu}$ and type (1, 1, ... to $n\nu$ units), can therefore be divided into $(p^{n\nu} - 1)/(p^\nu - 1)$ sets of $p^\nu - 1$ each, such that each set, with identity, forms a sub-group of order p^ν; and the group $G_{p,n,\nu}$ is isomorphic with a group of isomorphisms of the Abelian group which permutes among themselves such a set of $(p^{n\nu} - 1)/(p^\nu - 1)$ sub-groups of order p^ν.

Ex. 1. Shew that the $\dfrac{p^{n\nu} - 1 \,.\, p^{n\nu} - p \ \ldots\ldots \ p^{n\nu} - p^\nu}{p - 1 \,.\, p^2 - 1 \ \ldots\ldots \ p^\nu - 1}$ sub-groups of order p^ν of an Abelian group of order $p^{n\nu}$ and type (1, 1, ... to $n\nu$ units) can be divided into sets of $(p^{n\nu} - 1)/(p^\nu - 1)$ each, such that each set contains every operation of the group, other than identity, once and once only; and discuss in how many distinct ways such a division may be carried out.

Ex. 2. Shew that the simple group, defined by the group of isomorphisms of an Abelian group of order p^n and type (1, 1, ..., 1), admits a class of outer isomorphisms, which change the operations of the simple group, that correspond to isomorphisms leaving a sub-group of order p of the Abelian group unaltered, into operations that correspond to isomorphisms leaving a sub-group of order p^{n-1} of the Abelian group unaltered.

Ex. 3. Prove that the group G, of order $2^n(2^{2n}-1)$, defined by all congruences of the form

$$x' \equiv \frac{\alpha x + \beta}{\gamma x + \delta}, \quad (\text{mod. } 2),$$

where each coefficient is either zero or a power of a primitive root of the congruence

$$z^{2^n-1} - 1 \equiv 0, \quad (\text{mod. } 2),$$

has $2^n + 1$ conjugate sets of operations.

If H' is a sub-group of order 2^n and S an operation of order $2^n - 1$ which transforms H' into itself, shew that the group of monomial substitutions $G_{\omega S, H'}$ (note D), where ω is an imaginary (2^n-1)th root of unity, is an irreducible representation of G.

Shew also that $2^{n-1} - 1$ distinct irreducible representations of G thus arise; and that they are the only ones which can be expressed as groups of monomial substitutions.

NOTE A.

ON THE EQUATION $N = h_1 + h_2 + \ldots + h_r$.

If h_i is the number of operations in the ith conjugate set of a group of order N, each one of them is contained self-conjugately in a sub-group of order m_i, where

$$m_i h_i = N.$$

The equation of § 26 may therefore be written

$$\frac{1}{m_1} + \frac{1}{m_2} + \ldots + \frac{1}{m_r} = 1.$$

When r is a given positive integer, this equation has only a finite number of solutions in positive integers. Hence for a group of finite order with a given number of conjugate sets, this condition alone limits the possible sets of values of $h_1, h_2, \ldots, h_r$. A further limitation is immediately given by the condition that if

$$m_1 \geqslant m_2 \geqslant \ldots \geqslant m_r,$$

then each m must be equal to or a factor of m_1, since the order of any sub-group is a factor of the order of the group. Other limitations suggest themselves. For instance, if m_i is a prime, m_1 is divisible only by the first power of m_i; and no other m, which is not equal to m_i, can be divisible by m_i. The number of solutions of the equation which can correspond to a group may thus be further limited; but eventually a detailed examination of each separate solution will be necessary, before it can be decided whether one or more types of group correspond to it. One solution, which always gives a group, is

$$m_1 = m_2 = \ldots = m_r = r,$$

so that

$$h_1 = h_2 = \ldots = h_r = 1.$$

In this case every operation is self-conjugate and any Abelian group of order r satisfies the conditions. Putting this case on one side, it will be found that for values of r not exceeding 5, the only solutions which correspond to groups are

$$\tfrac{1}{6}+\tfrac{1}{3}+\tfrac{1}{2}=1,$$
$$\tfrac{1}{10}+\tfrac{1}{5}+\tfrac{1}{5}+\tfrac{1}{2}=1,$$
$$\tfrac{1}{12}+\tfrac{1}{4}+\tfrac{1}{3}+\tfrac{1}{3}=1,$$
$$\tfrac{1}{14}+\tfrac{1}{7}+\tfrac{1}{7}+\tfrac{1}{7}+\tfrac{1}{2}=1,$$
$$\tfrac{1}{21}+\tfrac{1}{7}+\tfrac{1}{7}+\tfrac{1}{3}+\tfrac{1}{3}=1,$$
$$\tfrac{1}{24}+\tfrac{1}{8}+\tfrac{1}{4}+\tfrac{1}{4}+\tfrac{1}{3}=1,$$
$$\tfrac{1}{60}+\tfrac{1}{5}+\tfrac{1}{5}+\tfrac{1}{4}+\tfrac{1}{3}=1,$$
$$\tfrac{1}{8}+\tfrac{1}{8}+\tfrac{1}{4}+\tfrac{1}{4}+\tfrac{1}{4}=1,$$
$$\tfrac{1}{20}+\tfrac{1}{5}+\tfrac{1}{4}+\tfrac{1}{4}+\tfrac{1}{4}=1.$$

Each of these, except the last but one, corresponds to a single type of group, while the last but one gives two types.

If $m_r=2$, the order of the group must be $2n$, where n is odd, and it must contain n operations of order 2. We have seen (§ 66) that in such a case the group has an Abelian sub-group of order n, every operation of which, except identity, belongs to a set of two conjugate operations. Hence if $m_r=2$, the only solution of the equation which gives a group is

$$m_1=2\,(2r-3),\quad m_2=m_3=\ldots=m_{r-1}=2r-3,\quad m_r=2\,;$$

and the number of distinct groups is the same as the number of distinct Abelian groups of order $2r-3$.

If $m_r=r-1$, the greatest possible value of m_1 is clearly $r\,(r-1)$, and the corresponding solution of the equation is

$$m_1=r\,(r-1),\quad m_2=r,\quad m_3=m_4=\ldots=m_r=r-1.$$

Hence if the order of the sub-group which contains an operation of the greatest conjugate set self-conjugately is $r-1$, the order of the group cannot exceed $r\,(r-1)$. When r is the power of a prime, there are always groups corresponding to this solution (§ 140).

NOTE B.

ON THE GROUP OF ISOMORPHISMS OF A GROUP.

The analysis of the group of isomorphisms of a given group may be carried a step further than in the text. It is there shewn that the isomorphisms which change every conjugate set into itself constitute a self-conjugate sub-group of the group of isomorphisms.

Using the notation of § 234, the system of conjugate sets $C^{(\mu)}$, where μ is any number relatively prime to N, may be called a "family" of sets. Suppose that

$$\begin{pmatrix} S \\ S' \end{pmatrix}$$

is an isomorphism which changes each family of sets into itself, while

$$\begin{pmatrix} S \\ S'' \end{pmatrix}$$

is any isomorphism. If the latter changes the set C_i into the set C_j, it also changes $C_i^{(\mu)}$ into $C_j^{(\mu)}$. Hence, if the former changes C_i into $C_i^{(\mu)}$, the isomorphism

$$\begin{pmatrix} S \\ S'' \end{pmatrix}^{-1} \begin{pmatrix} S \\ S' \end{pmatrix} \begin{pmatrix} S \\ S'' \end{pmatrix}$$

changes the set C_j into the set $C_j^{(\mu)}$. It follows that those isomorphisms which change each family of conjugate sets into itself constitute a self-conjugate sub-group of the group of isomorphisms. If I, I_f, I_s, I_i are respectively the group of isomorphisms, the group of isomorphisms which change each family of conjugate sets into itself, the group of isomorphisms which change each conjugate set into itself and the group of inner isomorphisms, each of the latter three are self-conjugate sub-groups of the first. Moreover the group I_f/I_s is clearly an Abelian group; and it may be shewn by an extension of the method of § 249 that I_s/I_i is an Abelian group.

The chief outstanding problems in connection with the isomorphisms of a group are, (i) whether I_s and I_i are necessarily identical; and (ii) whether a group of linear substitutions in which S and S^μ (μ relatively prime to the order of S) have different characteristics necessarily admits an outer isomorphism for which S^μ corresponds to S.

NOTE C.

ON THE SYMMETRIC GROUP.

The symmetric group is of great importance in many branches of analysis; and we shall devote this note to dealing with some points connected with it that have not been referred to in the text.

We consider first its abstract definition by means of a number of generating operations connected by relations. The most symmetrical form into which the abstract definition can be thrown is probably given by a system of generating operations S_i $(i=1, 2 \ldots, n-1)$, satisfying the relations

$$S_i^2 = E, \quad (S_iS_j)^3 = E, \quad (S_iS_jS_iS_k)^2 = E,$$
$$(i \neq j \neq k;\ i, j, k = 1, 2, \ldots, n-1).$$

In this form however a large number of the relations are redundant, being consequences of the remainder. The form actually given below is due to Prof. E. H. Moore (*Proc. L. M. S.*, Vol. XXVIII (1897), pp. 357—366). In Professor Moore's paper an alternative form of definition will be found; and in a paper by the author in the same volume (pp. 119—129) another form is given.

The n operations S_i $(i=1, 2, \ldots, n)$, subject to the relations

$$S_i^2 = E, \quad (i = 1, 2, \ldots, n),$$
$$(S_iS_{i+1})^3 = E, \quad (i = 1, 2, \ldots, n-1),$$
$$(S_iS_j)^2 = E, \quad (i = 1, 2, \ldots, n-2;\ j > i+1),$$

generate a group G simply isomorphic with the symmetric group of $n+1$ symbols.

Let H be the sub-group of G which is generated by

$$S_1, S_2, \ldots, S_{n-1};$$

and consider the $n+1$ sets of operations

$$H,\ HS_n,\ HS_nS_{n-1},\ HS_nS_{n-1}S_{n-2}, \ldots,\ HS_nS_{n-1} \ldots S_2S_1.$$

On post-multiplication by any S they are permuted among themselves. To verify this statement consider the operation

$$S_nS_{n-1} \ldots S_{i+1}S_iS_j.$$

If $j < i-1$, S_j is permutable with each of the previous operations, and

$$S_nS_{n-1}\dots S_{i+1}S_iS_j = S_jS_nS_{n-1}\dots S_{i+1}S_i.$$

If $j > i$, since S_j is permutable with $S_{j-2}, S_{j-3}, \dots, S_i$,

$$\begin{aligned} S_nS_{n-1}\dots S_{i+1}S_iS_j &= S_nS_{n-1}\dots S_{j+1}S_jS_{j-1}S_jS_{j-2}\dots S_i \\ &= S_nS_{n-1}\dots S_{j+1}S_{j-1}S_jS_{j-1}S_{j-2}\dots S_i \\ (\text{since } S_jS_{j-1}S_j = S_{j-1}S_jS_{j-1}) \quad &= S_{j-1}S_nS_{n-1}\dots S_i, \end{aligned}$$

since S_{j-1} is permutable with S_k if k is greater than j.

Hence when the $n+1$ sets of operations are post-multiplied by S_j, all remain unchanged except

$$HS_nS_{n-1}\dots S_{j+2}S_{j+1}S_j \text{ and } HS_nS_{n-1}\dots S_{j+2}S_{j+1},$$

while these two are permuted.

Every operation of G is therefore contained in the $n+1$ sets; and if H is a group of finite order, the order of G does not exceed $n+1$ times the order of H. Now when $n=2$ the order of H is 2. Hence G is a group of finite order not exceeding $(n+1)!$. Further G is isomorphic with a group of permutations of the $n+1$ symbols

$$H,\ HS_n,\ HS_nS_{n-1},\ HS_nS_{n-1}S_{n-2},\ \dots,\ HS_nS_{n-1}\dots S_2S_1;$$

and if these be denoted respectively by

$$a_{n+1},\ a_n,\ a_{n-1},\ a_{n-2},\ \dots,\ a_1,$$

it has been shewn that the permutations corresponding to

$$S_1,\ S_2,\ \dots,\ S_n \text{ are } (a_1a_2),\ (a_2a_3),\ \dots,\ (a_na_{n+1}).$$

Now these permutations generate the symmetric group in the $n+1$ symbols. Hence G is isomorphic with the symmetric group of $n+1$ symbols; and, since the order of G does not exceed $(n+1)!$, the isomorphism must be simple.

Although not directly connected with the subject of the present note, we add the system of relations defining abstractly the alternating group which Prof. Moore gives.

The $n-1$ operations S_i $(i = 1, 2, \dots, n-1)$, subject to the relations

$$\begin{aligned} &S_1^3 = E,\ S_i^2 = E, && (i = 2, 3, \dots, n-1), \\ &(S_iS_{i+1})^3 = E, && (i = 1, 2, \dots, n-2), \\ &(S_iS_j)^2 = E, && (i = 1, 2, \dots, n-3;\ j > i+1), \end{aligned}$$

generate a group G simply isomorphic with the alternating group of $n+1$ symbols.

The proof of this theorem follows precisely the same lines as that of the previous one, the $n+1$ sets of operations used being

$$H,\ HS_n,\ HS_nS_{n-1},\ \dots,\ HS_n\dots S_2,\ HS_n\dots S_2S_1,\ HS_n\dots S_2S_1^2,$$

where H denotes the sub-group generated by $S_1, S_2, \dots, S_{n-2}$. It is not necessary to give it at length.

We now proceed to consider certain irreducible representations of the symmetric group, with the view of proving that, when $n > 4$, there is no irreducible representation in a number of symbols lying between 1 and $n-1$. When n is a prime this follows necessarily from the fact that every characteristic is rational. Herr Wiman has proved* that, with certain exceptions for small values of n, there is no group of linear substitutions simply or multiply isomorphic with either the symmetric or the alternating group of degree n in a number of variables lying between 1 and $n-1$.

It is an immediate consequence of Theorem V, Chap. XIV, that the symmetric group of degree n has just two representations in a single symbol. One of these is Γ_1, the identical representation; the other is a representation† Γ_1', in which the operations not belonging to the alternating group correspond to $x' = -x$. If Γ is any irreducible representation, then the representation denoted by $\Gamma_1'\Gamma$ (§ 220) is also irreducible. It is distinct from Γ unless the characteristic in Γ of every operation which does not belong to the alternating group is zero. In any case it may be denoted by Γ'.

When the symmetric group G, of degree n, is expressed by the permutations of $a_1, a_2, \ldots, a_n$, we will denote the sub-groups

$$\{(a_2a_3), (a_3a_4), \ldots, (a_{n-1}a_n)\},\ \{(a_3a_4), (a_4a_5), \ldots, (a_{n-1}a_n)\}$$

and
$$\{(a_1a_2), (a_3a_4), (a_4a_5), \ldots, (a_{n-1}a_n)\}$$

by H, I and J. Then the transitive representation G_H (§ 177) is the ordinary representation of the symmetric group in n symbols. It is multiply transitive and has therefore just two irreducible representations, of which one is Γ_1, and the other is a representation in $n-1$ symbols which may be denoted by Γ_{n-1}. There are therefore only two representations in which H has linear invariants and in each it has one. In G_H, J has obviously 2 linear invariants and I has 3. Hence in Γ_{n-1} J has 1 and I has 2.

Consider next the transitive representation G_J. It is the group of permutations of the $\frac{1}{2}n(n-1)$ symbols ab,

$$(a, b = 1, 2, \ldots, n),\ a \neq b,\ ab = ba$$

that arises when $1, 2, \ldots, n$ undergo all permutations. In this group J has just three linear invariants, viz.

$$12,\quad \begin{matrix} 13 + 14 + \ldots + 1n \\ + 23 + 24 + \ldots + 2n \end{matrix},\quad 34 + 35 + \ldots + n-1, n.$$

* "Über die Darstellung der symmetrischen und alternirenden Vertauschungsgruppen als Collineationsgruppen von möglichst geringer Dimensionenzahl" (*Math. Ann.* Vol. XLV (1899), pp. 243—270).

† Since every representation of the symmetric group is self-inverse, the accent may here, without risk of confusion, be used in a sense different from that of Chap. XV.

Hence G_J has just three irreducible components. Now it has been seen that J has one linear invariant in Γ_{n-1}, so that Γ_1 and Γ_{n-1} must be two of the irreducible components. The other therefore affects $\frac{1}{2}n(n-3)$ symbols and may be denoted by $\Gamma_{\frac{1}{2}n(n-3)}$. The only representations in which J has a linear invariant are therefore Γ_1, Γ_{n-1} and $\Gamma_{\frac{1}{2}n(n-3)}$; and from this it follows that the only representations in which J can have a linear relative invariant are Γ_1', Γ'_{n-1} $\Gamma'_{\frac{1}{2}n(n-3)}$.

Consider further the transitive representation G_I. It is the group of permutations of the $n(n-1)$ symbols ab,

$$(a, b = 1, 2, \ldots, n), \quad a \neq b, \quad ab \neq ba.$$

In this group I has just seven linear invariants, viz.

$$\begin{matrix} 12, & 13+14+\ldots+1n, & 23+24+\ldots+2n, \\ 21, & 31+41+\ldots+n1, & 32+42+\ldots+n2, \end{matrix} \quad 34+43+\ldots+n-1, n+n, n-1.$$

Now I has two linear invariants in Γ_{n-1}; and therefore Γ_{n-1} enters twice among the irreducible components of G_I. There must therefore be just three others of which Γ_1 is one, and $\Gamma_{\frac{1}{2}n(n-3)}$ another; for J having a linear invariant in the latter group, I necessarily has one. The remaining one then must affect

$$n(n-1)-1-2(n-1)-\tfrac{1}{2}n(n-3) = \tfrac{1}{2}n(n-3)+1$$

symbols. It may be denoted by $\Gamma_{\frac{1}{2}n(n-3)+1}$. The only irreducible representations of G in which I has linear invariants are therefore Γ_1, Γ_{n-1}, $\Gamma_{\frac{1}{2}n(n-3)}$ and $\Gamma_{\frac{1}{2}n(n-3)+1}$; and the only representations in which I can have a linear relative invariant are Γ_1', Γ'_{n-1}, $\Gamma'_{\frac{1}{2}n(n-3)}$ and $\Gamma'_{\frac{1}{2}n(n-3)+1}$.

In every irreducible representation of G, I is necessarily reducible. In fact every operation of I is permutable with (a_1a_2). Hence if, in an irreducible representation Γ of G in $\nu_1+\nu_2$ symbols, the substitution corresponding to (a_1a_2) leaves ν_1 symbols unchanged and multiplies the other ν_2 by -1, the substitutions of I must transform the ν_1 symbols and the ν_2 symbols each among themselves. If the substitutions corresponding to (a_3a_4), (a_4a_5), ... $(a_{n-1}a_n)$ either leave all the ν_1 symbols unchanged or multiply all of them by -1, I will have at least ν_1 linear invariants (absolute or relative) in Γ. In every other case the group of linear substitutions in the ν_1 symbols, corresponding to the operations of I, is simply isomorphic with I. Suppose now, if possible, that $\nu_1+\nu_2$ were less than $n-1$ $(n>4)$. Then it has been seen above that, in Γ, there is neither an absolute nor a relative invariant for I; and therefore the groups of linear substitutions in the ν_1 symbols and in the ν_2 symbols must be simply isomorphic with I, while either ν_1 or ν_2 is equal to or less than $\frac{1}{2}(n-2)$.

Hence, if the symmetric group in n symbols ($n > 4$) admits an irreducible representation in ν symbols ($1 < \nu < n-1$), the symmetric group of $n-2$ symbols must be simply isomorphic with a group of linear substitutions in not more than $\frac{1}{2}\nu$ symbols. Now for the smaller values of n it is easy to verify directly that the symmetric group of degree n cannot be simply isomorphic with a group of linear substitutions in less than $n-1$ symbols. Hence, *when $n > 4$, the symmetric group of degree n admits no irreducible representation in ν symbols where ν is greater than* 1 *and less than* $n-1$.

Since the symmetric group of degree n admits of no irreducible representation, with which it is simply isomorphic in fewer than $n-1$ symbols as a group of linear substitutions, any concrete representation involving a smaller number of symbols possesses a certain interest. It may be shewn that for all values of n greater than 4, there is a group of birational substitutions in $n-3$ symbols with which the symmetric group is simply isomorphic*.

It is well known that the expression α_1 or

$$\frac{(a_1-a_2)(a_3-a_4)}{(a_1-a_3)(a_4-a_2)}$$

is changed into a linear function of itself by every permutation of the four symbols a_1, a_2, a_3, a_4. It is unaltered by the permutations

$$E,\ (a_1a_2)(a_3a_4),\ (a_1a_3)(a_2a_4),\ (a_1a_4)(a_2a_3);$$

so that the group of birational substitutions of a single symbol that thus arises is simply isomorphic with the symmetric group of three symbols.

From α_1 there arise, under all the permutations of $a_1, a_2, \dots, a_n$, a set of $\frac{1}{4}n!$ expressions. These cannot all be independent, and it may in fact be shewn that they are all rationally expressible in terms of a suitably chosen set of $n-3$.

Let $$\alpha_r = \frac{(a_r - a_{r+1})(a_{r+2}-a_{r+3})}{(a_r - a_{r+2})(a_{r+3}-a_{r+1})} \qquad (r = 1, 2, \dots, n-3).$$

Under the permutation (a_1a_2), $\alpha_3, \alpha_n, \dots, \alpha_{n-3}$ remain unchanged. If α_1 and α_2 become α_1' and α_2', then

$$\alpha_1' = \frac{(a_2-a_1)(a_3-a_4)}{(a_2-a_3)(a_4-a_1)} = -\frac{\alpha_1}{\alpha_1+1},$$

and $$\alpha_2' = \frac{(a_1-a_3)(a_4-a_5)}{(a_1-a_4)(a_5-a_3)} = \frac{\alpha_2}{\alpha_1+1}.$$

* See E. H. Moore, "The cross-ratio group of $n!$ Cremona Transformations of order $n-3$ in flat space of $n-3$ dimensions," *Amer. Journ. Math.* Vol. XXII, pp. 279—291 (1900); and W. Burnside, "Note on the Symmetric Group," *Mess. of Math.* Vol. XXX, pp. 148—153 (1901).

Under the permutation $(a_1 a_2 \dots a_{n-1} a_n)$, a_i becomes a_{i+1} $(i = 1, 2, \dots, n-4)$; and if a_{n-3} becomes a'_{n-3}, then

$$\begin{aligned} a'_{n-3} &= \frac{(a_{n-2}-a_{n-1})(a_n-a_1)}{(a_{n-2}-a_n)(a_1-a_{n-1})} \\ &= -1 - \frac{(a_{n-2}-a_1)(a_{n-1}-a_n)}{(a_{n-2}-a_n)(a_1-a_{n-1})} \\ &= -1 + \frac{(a_{n-3}-a_{n-2})(a_{n-1}-a_n)}{(a_{n-3}-a_{n-1})(a_n-a_{n-2})} \frac{(a_{n-3}-a_{n-1})(a_{n-2}-a_1)}{(a_{n-3}-a_{n-2})(a_1-a_{n-1})} \\ &= -1 + \frac{a_{n-3}}{\dfrac{(a_{n-3}-a_{n-2})(a_{n-1}-a_1)}{(a_{n-3}-a_{n-1})(a_1-a_{n-2})}}. \end{aligned}$$

Similarly

$$\frac{(a_{n-3}-a_{n-2})(a_{n-1}-a_1)}{(a_{n-3}-a_{n-1})(a_1-a_{n-2})} = -1 + \frac{a_{n-4}}{\dfrac{(a_{n-4}-a_{n-3})(a_{n-2}-a_1)}{(a_{n-4}-a_{n-2})(a_1-a_{n-3})}},$$

and so on. Hence

$$a'_{n-3} = -1 + \frac{a_{n-3}}{-1+} \frac{a_{n-4}}{-1+} \cdots \frac{a_1}{-1}.$$

To the two permutations $(a_1 a_2)$ and $(a_1 a_2 \dots a_{n-1} a_n)$ which generate the symmetric group, there therefore correspond the two substitutions

$$a_1' = \frac{-a_1}{a_1+1}, \quad a_2' = \frac{a_2}{a_1+1}, \quad a_3' = a_3, \; \dots, \; a'_{n-3} = a_{n-3};$$

and

$$a_1' = a_2, \; a_2' = a_3, \; \dots, \; a'_{n-4} = a_{n-3}, \; a'_{n-3} = -1 + \frac{a_{n-3}}{-1+} \cdots \frac{a_1}{-1}.$$

Now these two substitutions are obviously birational; that is to say, if the accented symbols are regarded as given, the unaccented symbols are uniquely determined. Hence the totality of the birational substitutions formed by combining these two in all possible ways constitute a group simply isomorphic with the symmetric group of n symbols.

NOTE D.

ON THE COMPLETELY REDUCED FORM OF A GROUP OF MONOMIAL SUBSTITUTIONS.

The representation of a group of finite order as a group of monomial substitutions, given in § 242, may be expressed in terms of the irreducible representations of the group by a formula closely analogous to that given in § 207 for any representation as a transitive permutation-group.

We will denote the representation of G established in § 242 by $G_{\omega S, H'}$, and assume that the completely reduced form of this representation is given by

$$G_{\omega S, H'} = \Sigma b_i \Gamma_i.$$

Let $x_1, x_2, \ldots, x_n$ be the symbols operated on by $G_{\omega S, H'}$; and suppose that the sub-group $\{S, H'\}$ permutes the symbols, with factors, in m transitive sets, viz.

$$x_1\,;\; x_2, x_3, \ldots x_s\,;\; x_{s+1}, x_{s+2}, \ldots, x_t\,;\ldots.$$

The conjugate group will be set up by taking ω^{-1} for the multiplier in the place of ω. The Hermitian invariant for $G_{\omega S, H'}$ and $G_{\omega^{-1}S, H'}$ that arises from $x_1\bar{x}_2 + \bar{x}_1 x_2$ is the same as that which arises from $x_1\bar{x}_3 + \bar{x}_1 x_3$; and, unless it is identically zero, is distinct from that given by $x_1\bar{x}_{s+1} + \bar{x}_1 x_{s+1}$. The condition that the Hermitian invariant form arising from $x_1\bar{x}_2 + \bar{x}_1 x_2$ shall not be identically zero is that the group of monomial substitutions on $x_2, x_3, \ldots, x_s$ corresponding to $\{S, H'\}$ shall have a linear invariant for H', which is changed into ω times itself by S. Hence the number of independent Hermitian invariants for $G_{\omega S, H'}$ and $G_{\omega^{-1}S, H'}$ is equal to the number of independent linear invariants for H' in $G_{\omega S, H'}$, each of which is changed into ω times itself by S. Such a linear function of the variables may, for shortness, be called an ω-invariant for $\{S, H'\}$.

Denote by n_i the number of ω-invariants for $\{S, H'\}$ in Γ_i. Then what has just been proved takes the form

$$\sum_i b_i^2 = \sum_i b_i n_i.$$

Now it may be shewn, by considering the expression of x_1 in terms of the reduced variables exactly as in § 207, that

$$n_i \geqslant b_i.$$

Combining this with the immediately previous result, it follows that

$$n_i = b_i,$$

and therefore the completely reduced form of $G_{\omega S, H'}$ is given by

$$G_{\omega S, H'} = \sum_i n_i \Gamma_i,$$

where n_i is the number of independent ω-invariants for $\{S, H'\}$ in Γ_i.

From this result it may be shewn that every representation of a group G as an irreducible group of monomial substitutions can be set up by the method used in § 242.

Let Γ, an irreducible group of monomial substitutions on the symbols $x_1, x_2, \ldots, x_n$, be a representation of G. Denote by H the sub-group of G which changes x_1 into a multiple of itself. Let ω be a primitive mth root of unity, m being taken as small as possible consistently with the condition that, if an operation of H changes x_1 into αx_1, then α is a power of ω. Then the operations of H which leave x_1 unchanged form a self-conjugate sub-group H' of H, and H/H' is a cyclical group of order m. Let S be an operation of H such that S^m is the lowest power of S that occurs in H', and as in § 242 form the representation denoted by $G_{\omega S, H'}$. The number of times that any irreducible representation of G enters in $G_{\omega S, H'}$ is equal to the number of ω-invariants for $\{S, H'\}$ in the irreducible representation. Now in Γ x_1 is an ω-invariant for $\{S, H'\}$. Hence Γ enters as an irreducible component in $G_{\omega S, H'}$. But the number of symbols operated on by these two groups is the same. Hence Γ is equivalent to $G_{\omega S, H'}$; and, further, this representation has only one ω-invariant for $\{S, H'\}$.

It has been shewn in § 258 that every irreducible group of linear substitutions whose order is a power of a prime p can be expressed as a group of monomial substitutions. The result that has just been proved shews further that the variables may always be chosen so that the coefficients in the group of monomial substitutions are p^mth $(m \geqslant 1)$ roots of unity. Moreover for a given representation of a given group there must be a minimum value of m such that it is *not* possible to express the representation in a form in which all the coefficients are p^{m-1}th roots of unity.

NOTE E.

ON THE IRREDUCIBLE REPRESENTATIONS OF A GROUP WHICH HAS A SELF-CONJUGATE SUB-GROUP OF PRIME INDEX.

Let a group G, of order N, with r conjugate sets be contained self-conjugately in a group H of order Np, where p is prime. Suppose further that the isomorphism of G, given by an operation J of H which does not belong to G, leaves r_1 conjugate sets of G unchanged and permutes the remaining $r - r_1$ sets in cyclical sets of p. If S_i ($i = 1, 2, \ldots, N$) are the operations of G, the N operations

$$JS_1, JS_2, \ldots, JS_N \quad \ldots\ldots\ldots\ldots\ldots\ldots\ldots\ldots(1)$$

when transformed by any operation of H are permuted among themselves. If S is an operation of G, belonging to a conjugate set which is unchanged on transformation by J, just N/h_S of the operations of the set (1) are unchanged on transformation by S. If S is an operation of G, belonging to a conjugate set which is changed on transformation by J, none of the set (1) are unchanged on transformation by S. Hence in the permutation-group that arises when the set (1) is transformed by all the operations of G, Nr_1 is the total number of unchanged symbols in all the permutations. It follows (Theorem XII, Chapter X) that the N symbols are permuted, on transformation by the operations of G, in r_1 transitive sets.

If $$JS_1, JS_2, \ldots, JS_t$$

is one of these sets, it must on transformation by any operation of H that does not belong to G be changed either into itself or into another of the sets. Hence, since JS_1 transforms JS_1 into itself, the operations of the set are permuted among themselves on transformation by any operation of H. They therefore form a conjugate set for H, and the operations of the set JG fall into r_1 conjugate sets. The same is true for the operations of each of the sets J^iG ($i = 1, 2, \ldots, p-1$). Now by supposition the operations of G fall into $r_1 + \dfrac{r - r_1}{p}$ conjugate sets in H. Hence r', the number of conjugate sets in H, is given by

$$r' = pr_1 + \frac{r - r_1}{p}$$

Denote now by $\Delta_t (t=1, 2, \ldots, r')$ the irreducible representations of H, Δ_1 being the identical representation. Also let $\Delta_2, \Delta_3, \ldots, \Delta_p$ be the other $p-1$ representations in a single symbol, in which every operation of G corresponds to the identical substitution.

Suppose that G is irreducible in the representation $\Delta_i (i>p)$ of H. Then in the representation $\Delta_i \Delta_{i'}$, when reduced, the representations $\Delta_2, \ldots, \Delta_p$ do not occur. For if they did G would have p bilinear invariants in $\Delta_i \Delta_{i'}$, in contradiction of the assumption that G is irreducible in Δ_i.

Hence
$$\Delta_i, \Delta_2\Delta_i, \ldots, \Delta_p\Delta_i$$
are p distinct representations of H, each containing the same irreducible representation of G.

Suppose next that, in Δ_j, G is reducible. Then in $\Delta_j \Delta_{j'}$ there must be more than one bilinear invariant for G. Hence, in the reduced form of $\Delta_j \Delta_{j'}$ at least one, and therefore all, of the representations $\Delta_2, \Delta_3, \ldots, \Delta_p$ occur. It follows that, in Δ_j, G must have at least p irreducible components. Since (§ 218) $\sum_S \chi_S \chi_{S^{-1}}$ is equal to the order of the group, G cannot have more than p irreducible components in Δ_j, and its p irreducible components must be all distinct. Moreover, for the same reason, the characteristic in Δ_j of every operation of H, which does not belong to G, must be zero.

Consider now the representation H_E of H as a regular permutation-group. In it G has the representation pG_E; and any irreducible representation of G in χ_1 symbols occurs $p\chi_1$ times. From this it at once follows that the irreducible representation of G that occurs in
$$\Delta_i, \Delta_2\Delta_i, \ldots, \Delta_p\Delta_i$$
can occur in no other irreducible representation of H; and similarly that the irreducible representations of G, that occur in Δ_j, occur in no other irreducible representation of H.

Denote by x the number of the irreducible representations of G that occur in representations of H in which G is irreducible. Then
$$r' = px + \frac{r-x}{p},$$
for either side of this equation is the number of distinct irreducible representations of H. Hence $x = r_1$.

Let $C_1, C_2, \ldots, C_{r_1}$ be the conjugate sets of G each of which is transformed into itself by J; and $C_{s1}, C_{s2}, \ldots, C_{sp}$, $(s=1, 2, \ldots, (r-r_1)/p)$ be the cyclical sets of p each, in which the remaining $r-r_1$ conjugate sets are permuted on transformation by J^{-1}.

In Δ_i the sets $C_{s1}, C_{s2}, \ldots, C_{sp}$ form a single conjugate set, and therefore the characteristics of all the operations contained in these sets are the same. Now, in Δ_i, G is irreducible. Hence in this irreducible representation of G, the p sets $C_{s1}, C_{s2}, \ldots, C_{sp}$ have the same characteristic for each s. There are therefore r_1 irreducible representations of G in each of which the p sets $C_{s1}, C_{s2}, \ldots, C_{sp}$ $(s=1, 2, \ldots, (r-r_1)/p)$ have the same characteristic.

Consider next the irreducible representation Δ_j of H. Let $\Gamma_{i_1}, \Gamma_{i_2}, \ldots, \Gamma_{i_p}$ be the p distinct irreducible representations of G that occur in it, and

$$x_{t,1}, x_{t,2}, \ldots, x_{t,n} \; (t=1, 2, \ldots, p)$$

the corresponding reduced variables. The operation J of H must change $x_{t,1}, x_{t,2}, \ldots, x_{t,n}$ into another set of n variables which are transformed among themselves by G. Since H is irreducible, J cannot change $x_{t,1}, x_{t,2}, \ldots, x_{t,n}$ into linear functions of themselves; and therefore it must change them into linear functions of another of the sets of reduced variables. Hence, since J^p is the lowest power of J that occurs in G, J must permute the p sets of variables, and we may take J to be

$$x'_{i,u} = \Sigma\, c_{iuv}\, x_{i+1,v}, \quad (u, v=1, 2, \ldots, n\,;\; i=1, 2, \ldots, p).$$

It follows that on replacing each reduced set by suitable linear functions of themselves, J will be

$$x'_{i,u} = x_{i+1,u}, \quad (i=1, 2, \ldots, p-1\,;\; u=1, 2, \ldots, n),$$
$$x'_{p,u} = \Sigma\, a_{uv}\, x_{1,v}, \quad (u, v=1, 2, \ldots, n)\,;$$

while J^p is

$$x'_{i,u} = \Sigma\, a_{uv}\, x_{i,v} \quad (u, v=1, 2, \ldots, n\,;\; i=1, 2, \ldots, p).$$

When J has this form it is clear that the sets of linear substitutions which form the representations $\Gamma_{i_1}, \Gamma_{i_2}, \ldots, \Gamma_{i_p}$ are the same, though of course the correspondence between the substitutions and the operations of G is different for each representation.

Let
$$x_{1,u} = s_{uvK}\, x_{1,v}, \quad (u, v=1, 2, \ldots, n)$$
be the substitution of Γ_{i_1} that corresponds to the operation K of G; and let

$$\begin{pmatrix} S \\ S' \end{pmatrix}$$

be the isomorphism of G given by J^{-1}, so that

$$JSJ^{-1} = S', \quad JS'J^{-1} = S'', \ldots.$$

Then the substitution of Δ_j that corresponds to K is

$$x'_{1,u} = \Sigma\, s_{uvK}\, x_{1,v},$$
$$x'_{2,u} = \Sigma\, s_{uvK'}\, x_{2,v}, \quad (u, v=1, 2, \ldots, n)$$
$$\cdots\cdots\cdots\cdots\cdots\cdots$$
$$x'_{p,u} = \Sigma\, s_{uvK^{(p-1)}}\, x_{p,v}.$$

Now if K belongs to one of the first r_1 conjugate sets, K' and K are conjugate in G, and therefore from the form of the above substitution K has the same characteristic in each of the p representations $\Gamma_{i_1}, \Gamma_{i_2}, \ldots, \Gamma_{i_p}$. On the other hand the characteristics of an operation of C'_{s1} in $\Gamma_{i_1}, \Gamma_{i_2}, \ldots, \Gamma_{i_p}$ are the same as those of operations of $C_{s1}, C_{s2}, \ldots, C_{sp}$ in Γ_{i_1}; and, for some value of s, these must be all different, as otherwise the p representations would not be distinct.

These results may be summed up as follows :

If a group with r conjugate sets admits an isomorphism which leaves the first r_1 sets unaltered and permutes the remaining sets in cycles of p (prime), whose pth power is an inner isomorphism; then there are r_1 irreducible representations in each of which each of the p conjugate sets belonging to the same cycle have the same characteristics. The remaining $r-r_1$ irreducible representations fall into $(r-r_1)/p$ systems of p each, such that the p representations of each system are given by the same set of linear substitutions, while in each of the p representations of a system any one of the first r_1 conjugate sets has the same characteristic.

NOTE F.

ON GROUPS OF FINITE ORDER WHICH ARE SIMPLY ISOMORPHIC WITH IRREDUCIBLE GROUPS OF LINEAR SUBSTITUTIONS.

The self-conjugate substitutions of an irreducible group of linear substitutions have the same multipliers (§ 202), and therefore the central, i.e. the sub-group formed of the self-conjugate substitutions, of such a group is necessarily cyclical. It follows that a group of finite order, whose central is not cyclical, cannot be simply isomorphic with an irreducible group of linear substitutions. It may however be the case that the central of a group is cyclical, or even consists of the identical operation only, and still the group may not be simply isomorphic with any irreducible group of linear substitutions.

Consider, for instance, the group of order 18 defined by

$$P^3 = E,\ Q^3 = E,\ A^2 = E,\ PQ = QP,\ APA = P^{-1},\ AQA = Q^{-1}.$$

The conjugate sets are E; P, P^{-1}; Q, Q^{-1}; $PQ, P^{-1}Q^{-1}$; $PQ^{-1}, P^{-1}Q$; $A, AP, AP^{-1}, AQ, AQ^{-1}, APQ, AP^{-1}Q^{-1}, AP^{-1}Q, APQ^{-1}$; so that r is 6. There are two irreducible representations in a single symbol, and four in two symbols. The latter four representations may be set up by taking the substitutions

$$\begin{matrix} x' = \omega x\ ; & x' = x\ ; & x' = y\ ; \\ y' = \omega^{-1} y\ ; & y' = y\ ; & y' = x\ ; \end{matrix} \quad \omega^3 = 1$$

to correspond to P, Q, A for (i), P, QP, A for (ii), P, QP^{-1}, A for (iii), and Q, P, A for (iv).

Hence in every irreducible representation of the group there are operations, other than E, which correspond to the identical substitution. The group is therefore multiply isormorphic with each of its irreducible representations and at the same time has no self-conjugate operations other than E.

The conditions necessary and sufficient to ensure that a group of finite order may be simply isomorphic with an irreducible group of linear substitutions are not yet known. The following investigation gives a sufficient condition in a simple form.

Let G be a group of finite order which is multiply isomorphic with each of its irreducible representations. Then in each representation there must be conjugate sets such that their operations correspond to the identical substitution. Choose the conjugate set C_a, so that in some irreducible representation the operations of C_a correspond to identity, while at the same time the self-conjugate sub-group $\{C_a\}$ generated by the operations of the set is of as small an order as possible.

Further let $\Gamma_1, \Gamma_{a_2}, \Gamma_{a_3}, \ldots, \Gamma_{a_s}$ be the irreducible representations in which the operations of C_a correspond to identity. These then are the irreducible representations of $G/\{C_a\}$. They cannot include all the irreducible representations; in each of them all the operations of $\{C_a\}$ correspond to identity; and in no other irreducible representation does any operation of $\{C_a\}$ correspond to identity. From the conjugate sets that correspond to identity in the remaining representations choose C_b so that the order of $\{C_b\}$ is as small as possible. Let $\Gamma_1, \Gamma_{b_2}, \Gamma_{b_3}, \ldots, \Gamma_{b_t}$ be the irreducible representations in which the operations of C_b correspond to identity. The self-conjugate sub-group $\{C_b\}$ can have no operation except E in common with $\{C_a\}$. For if it had it would contain $\{C_a\}$ (which is generated by any conjugate set entering into it), and the operations of C_a would correspond to identity in other representations besides $\Gamma_1, \Gamma_{a_2}, \ldots, \Gamma_{a_s}$, contrary to supposition. If all the irreducible representations do not enter in the two sets

$$\Gamma_1, \Gamma_{a_2}, \ldots, \Gamma_{a_s},$$

and

$$\Gamma_1, \Gamma_{b_2}, \ldots, \Gamma_{b_t},$$

choose C_c in connection with the remaining ones as C_a and C_b have been chosen; and continue the process till all the irreducible representations have been accounted for. The self-conjugate subgroups $\{C_a\}, \{C_b\}, \{C_c\}, \ldots, \{C_d\}$ so chosen are such that (i) no two have a common operation except E, and (ii) in every irreducible representation the operations of one or more of them correspond to identity.

Since $\{C_a\}$ and $\{C_b\}$ are self-conjugate sub-groups of G with no common operation except E, $\{C_a, C_b\}$ is their direct product. From the way in which $\{C_c\}$ is chosen it follows that either $\{C_c\}$ belongs to $\{C_a, C_b\}$ or the two groups have no operation except E in common.

Hence $\{C_a, C_b, C_c, \ldots, C_d\}$ is the direct product of a certain number of the groups $\{C_a\}, \{C_b\}, \ldots, \{C_d\}$. Now in the irreducible representations of G every irreducible representation of the self-conjugate sub-group $\{C_a, C_b, \ldots, C_d\}$ must occur. But in every representation of G all the operations of at least one of the component groups $\{C_a\}, \{C_b\}, \ldots$ correspond to identity. Hence in every irreducible representation of $\{C_a, C_b, \ldots, C_d\}$ all the operations of at least one of the component groups must correspond to identity.

Lastly, the groups $\{C_a\}$, $\{C_b\}$, ... are minimum (§ 52) self-conjugate sub-groups of G. Each of them is therefore either a simple group or the direct product of simply isomorphic simple groups.

Suppose now that simple groups G_x, G_y, G_z, of composite order, are represented by irreducible groups of linear substitutions on the symbols

$$x_1,\ x_2,\ \ldots,\ x_u,$$

$$y_1,\ y_2,\ \ldots,\ y_v,$$

$$z_1,\ z_2,\ \ldots,\ z_w,$$

respectively. Then when the x's undergo the substitutions of G_x, the y's those of G_y and the z's those of G_z independently, the uvw products $x_i y_j z_k$ undergo a group of linear substitutions which is easily seen to be irreducible and simply isomorphic with the direct product of G_x, G_y and G_z. The direct product of any number of simple groups of composite order is therefore always simply isomorphic with an irreducible group of linear substitutions. Moreover the same is true of the direct product of a number of simple groups of composite order and a number of cyclical groups the order of each of which is a different prime.

Suppose now that $\{C_a\}$ is the only one of the groups $\{C_a\}$, $\{C_b\}$, ... whose order is a power of p, and that $\{C_b, C_c, \ldots, C_d\}$ is simply isomorphic with an irreducible group of linear substitutions. Then the order of $\{C_a\}$ were p, $\{C_a, C_b, \ldots, C_d\}$ would be simply isomorphic with a group of linear substitutions; and if the order of $\{C_a\}$ were greater than p, there would be irreducible representations of $\{C_a, C_b, \ldots, C_d\}$ in which some of the operations of $\{C_a\}$ correspond to identity and some do not. If G is not simply isomorphic with an irreducible group, neither of these cases is possible; and therefore the orders of at least two of the groups $\{C_a\}$, $\{C_b\}$, ... must be powers of the same prime.

Hence, *unless G has two distinct minimum self-conjugate sub-groups whose orders are powers of the same prime, it is simply isomorphic with an irreducible group of linear substitutions.* In particular, a group of prime power order, whose central is cyclical is simply isomorphic with an irreducible group.

NOTE G.

ON THE REPRESENTATION OF A GROUP OF FINITE ORDER AS A GROUP OF LINEAR SUBSTITUTIONS WITH RATIONAL COEFFICIENTS.

If $\Gamma_{i_1}, \Gamma_{i_2}, \ldots, \Gamma_{i_t}$ form a family (§ 234) of irreducible representations of a group G, the representation of G denoted by

$$\Gamma_{i_1} + \Gamma_{i_2} + \ldots + \Gamma_{i_t}$$

has all its characteristics rational. It does not necessarily follow that this representation can be thrown into a form in which all the coefficients are rational; but, if m is the number of symbols on which Γ_{i_1} operates,

$$m\,(\Gamma_{i_1} + \Gamma_{i_2} + \ldots + \Gamma_{i_t})$$

can certainly be thrown into such a form. This follows immediately from the fact that $m\Gamma_{i_1}$ can be expressed in a form in which the coefficients are rational functions of the characteristics of Γ_{i_1}.

Let $a\ (\leqslant m)$ be the smallest integer such that

$$a\,(\Gamma_{i_1} + \Gamma_{i_2} + \ldots + \Gamma_{i_t})$$

can be represented in a form in which all the coefficients are rational numbers. This representation of G may be called a rationally irreducible rational representation. Unless both a and t are unity, it is a reducible representation when there is no limitation on the field of rationality; but when the field is restricted to rational numbers, it is irreducible. In fact a reduced component of the form $\Sigma a_s\Gamma_{i_s}$ $(a_s \leqslant a)$ has some of its characteristics irrational unless the a_s's are all equal, and therefore certainly some of the coefficients must be irrational. On the other hand if the a_s's are all equal, the statement follows from the assumption that has been made in respect of a.

Each family of representations will give such a rationally irreducible rational representation; and the ρ representations so arising are necessarily distinct, because the r irreducible representations are distinct.

Let
$$a'(\Gamma_{j_1}+\Gamma_{j_2}+\ldots+\Gamma_{j_{t'}})$$
be another rationally irreducible rational representation, and denote this and the previous one by Δ' and Δ. Suppose now that
$$a(\Gamma_{i_1}+\Gamma_{i_2}+\ldots+\Gamma_{i_t})+a'(\Gamma_{j_1}+\Gamma_{j_2}+\ldots+\Gamma_{j_{t'}})$$
is a rationally irreducible representation D of G, in which a is not a multiple of a. Take n such that $na=pa$ and $na'=p'a'$, where n, p, p' are integers. Then the representation nD is rationally reducible into n representations D and also into p representations Δ and p' representations Δ'. A consideration of the reduced symbols immediately shews that this is not possible.

It follows that the ρ rational representations $\Delta_1, \Delta_2, \ldots, \Delta_\rho$ that arise from the ρ families of irreducible representations are the only rationally irreducible rational representations; and therefore that every rational representation is included in
$$\Sigma b_i \Delta_i,$$
where the b's are positive integers. The number ρ is the number of distinct conjugate sets of cyclical sub-groups in G.

A very remarkable property of groups of linear substitutions of finite order with rational coefficients is that they can always be so transformed that the coefficients are integers.

Let
$$x_i' = \sum_j c_{ijk} x_j \ (i, j = 1, 2, \ldots, n)$$
$$(k = 1, 2, \ldots)$$
be the substitutions of a group of linear substitutions, and suppose that the coefficients c_{ijk} are rational numbers with a finite least common denominator d. (If the group is one of finite order, the latter part of the condition follows from the former, since the number of coefficients is finite.) A particular set of values of the variables
$$(a_1, a_2, \ldots, a_n)$$
may be called a point. If, for each value of i and k, $\sum_j c_{ijk} a_j$ is an integer, the point $(a_1, a_2, \ldots, a_n)$ will be called an "integral" point. It is clear that such integral points always exist, for $(d, d, \ldots, d)$ is an integral point. Moreover it follows from the definition that if $(a_1, a_2, \ldots, a_n)$ and $(b_1, b_2, \ldots, b_n)$ are integral points, then
$$(a_1+b_1, a_2+b_2, \ldots, a_n+b_n)$$
is an integral point.

Suppose that a_{11} is the smallest positive integer such that $(a_{11}, 0, 0, \ldots, 0)$ is an integral point. Then if $(a, 0, 0, \ldots, 0)$ is an integral point a must be a multiple of a_{11}. For if it were not integers l, m could be found such that $la_{11}+ma$ is a positive integer less than a_{11}, and then $(la_{11}+m\alpha, 0, 0, \ldots, 0)$ would be an integral point, contrary to the supposition made.

Let a_{22} be the smallest positive integer such that $(a_{21}, a_{22}, 0, \ldots, 0)$ is an integral point. Then it follows as above that if $(\alpha, \beta, 0, \ldots, 0)$ is an integral point, β must be a multiple of a_{22}. (It is clear that a_{21} may be taken to be equal to or less than a_{11}, but this is not material for the present purpose.)

Similarly let $a_{33}, a_{44}, \ldots, a_{nn}$ be the smallest positive integers such that

$$(a_{31}, a_{32}, a_{33}, 0, 0, \ldots, 0),$$
$$(a_{41}, a_{42}, a_{43}, a_{44}, 0, \ldots, 0),$$
$$\cdots\cdots\cdots\cdots\cdots\cdots$$
$$(a_{n1}, a_{n2}, a_{n3}, a_{n4}, a_{n5}, \ldots, a_{nn}),$$

are integral points.

Then if $(A_1, A_2, \ldots, A_n)$ is an integral point, A_n is a multiple of a_{nn}.

If
$$A_n = X_n a_{nn},$$
then $(A_1 - X_n a_{n1}, A_2 - X_n a_{n2}, \ldots, A_{n-1} - X_n a_{n,n-1}, 0)$ is an integral point, and therefore $A_{n-1} - X_n a_{n,n-1}$ is a multiple of $a_{n-1,n-1}$. Continuing thus, we find that

$$\begin{aligned} A_1 &= X_1 a_{11} + X_2 a_{21} + X_3 a_{31} + \ldots + X_n a_{n1}, \\ A_2 &= \phantom{X_1 a_{11} +{}} X_2 a_{22} + X_3 a_{32} + \ldots + X_n a_{n2}, \\ A_3 &= \phantom{X_1 a_{11} + X_2 a_{21} +{}} X_3 a_{33} + \ldots + X_n a_{n3}, \\ &\cdots\cdots\cdots\cdots\cdots\cdots \\ A_n &= \phantom{X_1 a_{11} + X_2 a_{21} + X_3 a_{31} + \ldots +{}} X_n a_{nn}. \end{aligned}$$

If a point is an integral point, its A's must be given by these equations with integral values of the X's; and conversely every point whose A's are given by these equations with integral values for the X's is an integral point. Moreover the totality of integral points are permuted among themselves by every substitution of the group.

Suppose now that new variables $X_1, X_2, \ldots, X_n$ are taken connected with the original variables by the equations

$$\begin{aligned} x_1 &= X_1 a_{11} + X_2 a_{21} + \ldots + X_n a_{n1}, \\ x_2 &= \phantom{X_1 a_{11} +{}} X_2 a_{22} + \ldots + X_n a_{n2}, \\ &\cdots\cdots\cdots\cdots\cdots\cdots \\ &\cdots\cdots\cdots\cdots\cdots\cdots \\ x_n &= \phantom{X_1 a_{11} + X_2 a_{21} + \ldots +{}} X_n a_{nn}, \end{aligned}$$

and with these new variables let

$$X_i' = \sum_j C_{ijk} X_j, \quad (i, j = 1, 2, \ldots, n)$$
$$(k = 1, 2, \ldots)$$

be the substitutions of the group. If $X_1, X_2, \ldots, X_n$ are integers, $(x_1, x_2, \ldots, x_n)$ is an integral point, and therefore $(x_1', x_2', \ldots, x_n')$ is an integral point, and $X_1', X_2', \ldots X_n'$ are integers.

Put $\quad X_1 = X_2 = \ldots = X_{j-1} = X_{j+1} = \ldots = X_n = 0, \; X_j = 1.$

Then $\quad X_i' = C_{ijk},$

and therefore C_{ijk} is an integer. Hence in the transformed group all the coefficients are integers.

For a group of rational linear substitutions on n variables it is possible to determine in a comparatively simple manner an upper limit for the order. To this end we find the highest power of a prime p that can be a factor of the order.

It has been seen in Note D that an irreducible group of linear substitutions whose order is a power of p can be expressed as a group of monomial substitutions whose coefficients are powers of ω, a p^mth root of unity ($m \geqslant 1$), while they cannot be expressed as powers of a p^{m-1}th root of unity. Denote such a group by Γ_ω, and the group that arises on writing ω' for ω in all the coefficients by $\Gamma_{\omega'}$. Then the group denoted by

$$\sum_\mu \Gamma_{\omega^\mu},$$

where for μ each of the $p^{m-1}(p-1)$ numbers less than and prime to p^m is taken, can obviously be expressed as a group of rational linear substitutions. Moreover, since ω satisfies an irreducible equation of degree $p^{m-1}(p-1)$, any rational group of linear substitutions which contains Γ_ω as an irreducible component must contain each of the groups Γ_{ω^μ} as an irreducible component.

If p^n is the number of variables operated on by Γ_ω, $p^{n+m-1}(p-1)$ is the number of symbols operated on by $\sum_\mu \Gamma_{\omega^\mu}$. The number of symbols operated on by any rationally irreducible group of rational linear substitutions, whose order is a power of p, is therefore of the form $p^{n+m-1}(p-1)$. Suppose now conversely that such a group has $p^{m-1}(p-1)$ irreducible components. In each of them the coefficients are necessarily p^mth roots of unity, and the number of variables is p^n. Now the order of the greatest group on p^n variables, each of whose substitutions replaces every variable by a multiple of itself, the factors being p^mth roots of unity, is clearly p^{mp^n}. Also we have seen in § 172 that the order of the greatest permutation-group on p^n symbols, the order being a power of p, is p^a, where

$$a = 1 + p + p^2 + \ldots + p^{n-1}.$$

Hence on the supposition made the order of the group of rational substitutions is

$$p^{1+p+p^2+\dots+p^{n-1}+mp^n}.$$

If

$$n+m-1=\mu,$$

and n and m take all possible values for a given μ, the greatest value of this order corresponds to $m=1$, $n=\mu$. Hence the greatest possible value for the order of a rationally irreducible group of rational linear substitutions on $p^\mu(p-1)$ variables (the order being a power of p), is p^{M_μ}, where

$$M_\mu = 1+p+p^2+\dots+p^\mu;$$

and such a group actually exists. Moreover it is easily seen that if the group were rationally reducible its maximum order would be less than the above value. Thus if there were p rationally irreducible rational components in $p^{\mu-1}(p-1)$ variables each, the maximum order would be $1/p$th of that determined.

Now suppose μ chosen so that $p^{\mu+1}(p-1) > n > p^\mu(p-1)$, where n is the number of symbols operated on by the rational group of linear substitutions, and express n in the form

$$n = a_\mu p^\mu(p-1) + a_{\mu-1}p^{\mu-1}(p-1) + \dots + a_1 p(p-1) + a_0(p-1) + b,$$

where $a_\mu, a_{\mu-1}, \dots, a_0$ are positive numbers less than p and b is less than $p-1$.

A rational group of linear substitutions in n variables whose order is a power of p must then be rationally reducible. The greatest number of variables in a rationally irreducible component is $p^\mu(p-1)$, and the greatest possible order of this component is p^{M_μ}. It follows from the preceding discussion that the greatest possible order for the group is obtained by taking the number of variables in each rationally irreducible component as great as possible. Moreover the order of the direct product of the rationally irreducible components is clearly greater than that of the group that results by establishing any isomorphism between them. Hence finally the maximum order for the group is p^M, where

$$M = a_\mu M_\mu + a_{\mu-1}M_{\mu-1} + \dots + a_1 M_1 + a_0 M_0.$$

It also follows that a rational group on the n variables of this maximum order actually exists.

If the symbol $\left[\frac{n}{m}\right]$ be used to denote the greatest integer contained in $\frac{n}{m}$, the number M may be expressed in a form in which it is easily calculated.

Thus

$$\left[\frac{n}{p^\mu(p-1)}\right] = a_\mu,$$

$$\left[\frac{n}{p^{\mu-1}(p-1)}\right] = a_\mu p \quad + a_{\mu-1},$$

....

$$\left[\frac{n}{p(p-1)}\right] = a_\mu p^{\mu-1} + a_{\mu-1}p^{\mu-2} + \dots + a_1,$$

$$\left[\frac{n}{p-1}\right] = a_\mu p^\mu \quad + a_{\mu-1}p^{\mu-1} + \dots + a_1 p + a_0;$$

and therefore $$M = \sum_{i=0}^{i=\infty} \left[\frac{n}{p^i(p-1)}\right].$$

The expression thus arrived at as an upper limit to the order of a group of rational linear substitutions in n variables* is $\Pi_p p^M$, the product being extended to all primes equal to or less than $n+1$.

When $n=3$ this upper limit is $2^4.3$, and the group generated by

$$x_1' = -x_1,\ x_2' = x_2,\ x_3' = x_3;$$
$$x_1' = x_2,\ x_2' = x_1,\ x_3' = x_3;$$
$$x_1' = x_3,\ x_2' = x_2,\ x_3' = x_1;$$

has actually this order. In no other case is a group of rational substitutions on n variables known to exist whose order is equal to $\Pi_p p^M$.

For all values of n there are groups of rational linear substitutions of orders $n+1\,!$ and $2^n.n\,!$ respectively. In fact we have seen in Note C that the symmetric group of degree $n+1$ has a rational representation in n symbols; while the symmetric group in $x_1, x_2, \dots, x_n$, together with the substitution

$$x_1' = -x_1,\ x_2' = x_2,\ \dots,\ x_n' = x_n,$$

obviously generate a group of order $2^n.n\,!$ which contains an Abelian group of order 2^n and type (1, 1, ... to n symbols) self-conjugately. These two groups are not only rationally but also absolutely irreducible.

Outside these two classes of groups the first group of rational substitutions of relatively high order that presents itself for the smaller values of n is one of order $2^8.3^4.5$ on six variables that we consider in the next note.

* Minkowski (*Crelle's Journal*, Vol. CI) obtains this expression for the upper limit of the order in another way. He does not shew that the order of any one of the Sylow sub-groups may actually attain its upper limit.

NOTE H.

ON THE GROUP OF THE TWENTY-SEVEN LINES OF A CUBIC SURFACE.

Many of the most important and interesting groups of finite order arise in connection with geometrical configurations. From this point of view the groups are directly given as permutation-groups. Thus the Hessian configuration of 9 points lying 3 by 3 on 12 straight lines (§ 169) determines a doubly transitive permutation-group of 9 symbols for which the set of 12 triplets which give the lines is invariant. We will consider here the group that arises in this way in connection with the configuration of the 27 lines on a cubic surface. This group has formed the subject of a very large number of investigations. The earliest is due to M. Jordan (*Traité des Substitutions*, pp. 316–329). Various forms of the group are given by Herr Burkhardt ("Hyperelliptische Modulfunctionen," *Math. Ann.* Vols. XXXVIII and XLI). Prof. L. E. Dickson has analysed the group exhaustively in a number of memoirs (see also, *Linear Groups*, Chap. XIV); and the author has considered it directly as a group of collineations of ordinary space (*Proc. R. S.*, Vol. LXXVII). Our object here is to present the group in as simple a form as possible, and to illustrate in doing so a method for the rational reduction of a permutation-group.

To define the configuration we shall use Schläfli's notation, replacing numbers by letters. The 27 lines are denoted by the 12 single symbols

$$a,\ b,\ c,\ d,\ e,\ f,$$
$$a',\ b',\ c',\ d',\ e',\ f',$$

and the 15 double symbols ab, ..., ef, the sequence in which a double symbol is written being immaterial so that ab and ba denote the same line. With this notation it is known that the 45 triangles formed from the 27 lines may be denoted by

$$a,\ b',\ ab\ ;\quad ab,\ cd,\ ef\ ;$$

and the triplets that arise from these by any permutation of a, b, c, d, e, f and the consequent permutations. By consequent permutation is meant that if a is changed into c and b into f, then a' is changed into c', b' into f' and ab into cf.

The group of the configuration is then the group of permutations of the 27 symbols of the lines for which the set of 45 triplets is invariant.

The 36 double sixes formed by the lines are given by

$$\left.\begin{matrix} a, & b, & c, & d, & e, & f \\ a', & b', & c', & d', & e', & f' \end{matrix}\right\} \quad \ldots\ldots\ldots\ldots\ldots\ldots\ldots 1,$$

$$\left.\begin{matrix} a, & b, & c, & ef, & fd, & de \\ d', & e', & f', & bc, & ca, & ab \end{matrix}\right\} \quad \ldots\ldots\ldots\ldots\ldots 20,$$

$$\left.\begin{matrix} a, & a', & bc, & bd, & be, & bf \\ b, & b', & ac, & ad, & ae, & af \end{matrix}\right\} \quad \ldots\ldots\ldots\ldots\ldots 15,$$

where the 20 of the second set and the 15 of the third arise from those written by any permutation of a, b, c, d, e, f and the consequent permutations.

The geometrical configuration suggests that this set of double sixes must be invariant under the same permutations that leave the 45 triangles invariant, and it is actually found that this is the case. Moreover, if the two sets of symbols in the first and second line of any double six are called its two halves, it is found that any permutation of the group which changes one double six into another, changes the first half of the one into either the first half or the second half of the other.

Some of the permissible permutations are obvious. Thus any permutation of a, b, c, d, e, f with the consequent permutations must form part of the group, and leaves the first half of the first double six unchanged. Again, a permutation that leaves all the double symbols unchanged and permutes a with a', b with b', ..., f with f' belongs to the group and permutes the two halves of the first double six. A permutation interchanging d and ef, e and fd, f and de, a' and bc, b' and ca, c' and ab, and leaving all the other symbols unchanged belongs to the group and changes the first half of the first double six into the first half of the second. Again, the permutation interchanging a' and b, c and bc, d and bd, e and be, f and bf, c' and ac, d' and ad, e' and ae, f' and af, cd and ef, ce and df, cf and de, and leaving a, b' and ab unchanged belongs to the group and changes the first half of the first double six into the first half of the third. There are therefore permutations changing the first half of the first double six into either half of any other.

Now, every permutation must either leave the first half of the first double six unchanged or must change it into one half of another. Hence the 72 halves of the double sixes are transitively permuted by the group. The order of the sub-group which leaves one unchanged being $6!$, the order of the group must be $72 . 6!$. It is a simply transitive group of degree 27 and therefore has at least three irreducible components.

Suppose now that L is a linear function of the 27 symbols which, when expressed in terms of the reduced variables, does not contain the variables of one or more irreducible components Γ, Γ', etc. The equation

$$L=0$$

and those derived from it by the permutations of the group will then not make all the variables vanish, but will express them in terms of the reduced variables of Γ, Γ', ... Take $L=a+b'+ab$. The system of relations that arise under the permutations of the group are

$$a+b'+ab=0, \quad ab+cd+ef=0,$$

and those given by permutations of a, b, c, d, e, f and the consequent permutations. Those arising from the first obviously give

$$a-a'=b-b'=\ldots=f-f'=k \quad \text{and} \quad ab=k-a-b,$$

for all values of a and b. Those arising from the second then reduce to

$$3k-a-b-c-d-e-f=0.$$

Hence if s denotes $a+b+c+d+e+f$, the system of relations expresses the other 21 symbols in terms of a, b, c, d, e, f in the form

$$a'=a-\tfrac{1}{3}s \text{ ....6 equations,}$$
$$ab=\tfrac{1}{3}s-a-b \text{ ....15 equations.}$$

By means of these relations a component of the transitive permutation-group in six symbols with rational coefficients is set up. The 72 halves of the double sixes expressed in terms of a, b, c, d, e, f are

$$a,\ b,\ c,\ d,\ e,\ f, \text{ ....1 set,}$$
$$a-\tfrac{1}{3}s,\ b-\tfrac{1}{3}s,\ c-\tfrac{1}{3}s,\ d-\tfrac{1}{3}s,\ e-\tfrac{1}{3}s,\ f-\tfrac{1}{3}s, \text{ ... 1 set,}$$
$$a,\ b,\ c,\ \tfrac{1}{3}s-e-f,\ \tfrac{1}{3}s-f-d,\ \tfrac{1}{3}s-d-e, \text{ ......20 sets,}$$
$$a-\tfrac{1}{3}s,\ b-\tfrac{1}{3}s,\ c-\tfrac{1}{3}s,\ \tfrac{1}{3}s-e-f,\ \tfrac{1}{3}s-f-d,\ \tfrac{1}{3}s-d-e, \text{...20 sets,}$$
$$a,\ a-\tfrac{1}{3}s,\ \tfrac{1}{3}s-b-c,\ \tfrac{1}{3}s-b-d,\ \tfrac{1}{3}s-b-e,\ \tfrac{1}{3}s-b-f, \text{ ...30 sets.}$$

And if α, β, γ, δ, ϵ, ζ are the symbols of any one of these sets in any sequence, the $72 . 6!$ operations of the group are the linear substitutions

$$a'=\alpha,\ b'=\beta,\ c'=\gamma,\ d'=\delta,\ e'=\epsilon,\ f'=\zeta.$$

The group is thus expressed as a group of rational linear substitutions on 6 symbols, the whole of the substitutions being exhibited in explicit form.

The substitution $(abcdef)$ has -1 for its determinant. Hence the group contains a self-conjugate sub-group H of order $72 \cdot \frac{1}{2} 6\,!$, in which the sub-group that permutes the six symbols is the alternating group of degree 6.

Suppose now that H has a self-conjugate sub-group I. Since the alternating group of six symbols is simple, I can have no operation except E in common with the group of permutations of $a, b, c, d, e\, f$. The order of I is therefore equal to or a factor of 72. A group of order 72 has one or four sub-groups of order 9. If there were four they could not be permuted on transformation by the operations of the alternating group of degree 6; and a group of order 9 does not admit a group of isomorphisms isomorphic with the alternating group of degree 6. Hence if the order of I were 72, each of its operations whose order is a power of 3 would be permutable with every operation of the alternating group of degree 6. This is impossible. Similar but simpler reasoning shews that the order of I cannot be a factor of 72. The group H is therefore a simple group.

The group itself does not contain the substitution

$$a' = -a,\ b' = -b,\ \ldots,\ f' = -f.$$

Combining this with it there results a group of rational linear substitutions in six variables of order $2^8 \cdot 3^4 \cdot 5$.

The method of the preceding note shews that the group is transformed into one with integral coefficients by the substitution

$$a = 3x - y,\ b = y - z,\ c = z - u,\ d = u - v,\ e = v - w,\ f = w.$$

NOTE I.

ON THE CONDITIONS OF REDUCIBILITY OF A GROUP OF LINEAR SUBSTITUTIONS OF FINITE ORDER.

Let $x_i' = \sum_j a_{ijk} x_j$, $(i, j = 1, 2, \ldots, \chi_1)$, $(k = 1, 2, \ldots, N)$,

be any irreducible group of linear substitutions of finite order. If G is the abstract group with which it is simply isomorphic, the group of linear substitutions is an irreducible representation of G, for which we will use the usual notation.

In this representation the linear substitution that corresponds to C_j is (§ 213)

$$x_i' = \frac{h_j \chi_j}{\chi_1} x_i \quad (i = 1, 2, \ldots, \chi_1).$$

Hence the linear substitution that corresponds to $\Sigma \chi_{j'} C_j$, or K (§ 229), is

$$x_i' = \frac{N}{\chi_1} x_i \quad (i = 1, 2, \ldots, \chi_1);$$

and therefore the linear substitution which corresponds to KS_x is

$$x_i' = \frac{N}{\chi_1} \sum_j a_{ijx} x_j \quad (i, j = 1, 2, \ldots, \chi_1).$$

Now we have seen in § 230 that of the N symbols KS_x $(x = 1, 2, \ldots, N)$, just $(\chi_1)^2$ are linearly independent. Also if KS_x $(x = 1, 2, \ldots, (\chi_1)^2)$ is such an independent set, then any other symbol of the set can be expressed linearly in terms of KS_x $(x = 1, 2, \ldots, (\chi_1)^2)$ with coefficients which are rational in the characteristics of the representation.

It follows (§ 213) that the $(\chi_1)^2$ linear substitutions

$$x_i' = \frac{N}{\chi_1} \Sigma a_{ijx} x_j \quad (i, j = 1, 2, \ldots, \chi_1) \quad (x = 1, 2, \ldots, (\chi_1)^2)$$

must be linearly independent in the sense that there is no linear relation

$$\sum_{x=1}^{x=(\chi_1)^2} d_x a_{ijx} = 0$$

connecting the coefficients of the substitutions for all values of the suffixes i, j.

Hence any irreducible group of linear substitutions of finite order in n variables must contain a set of n^2 substitutions which are linearly independent in the above sense. Moreover the coefficients in every other substitution can be expressed in the form

$$a_{ijt} = \sum_{x=1}^{x=n^2} d_{xt}\, a_{ijx},$$

where the coefficients d_{xt} are rational functions of the characteristics.

Now if a group of linear substitutions is reducible, it is possible to transform it so that in the transformed group the coefficients a'_{ij} are zero in all the substitutions for certain values of i and j. But if s_{ij} and S_{ij} are the coefficients in the transforming substitution and its inverse

$$a'_{ij} = \sum_{u,\, v} s_{iu}\, a_{uv}\, S_{vj}.$$

Hence a necessary condition that a group should be reducible is that the coefficients of all its substitutions should satisfy one or more linear relations of the form

$$\sum_{i,\, j} d_{ij}\, a_{ijk} = 0 \quad (k = 1, 2, \ldots, N).$$

The preceding considerations shew that this condition is also sufficient, since if one such relation holds there cannot be n^2 substitutions whose coefficients are linearly independent.

NOTE J.

ON CONDITIONS FOR THE FINITENESS OF THE ORDER OF A GROUP OF LINEAR SUBSTITUTIONS.

In the group of linear substitutions with real coefficients

$$x_i' = \sum_j a_{ijk} x_j \quad (i, j = 1, 2, \dots, n)$$

suppose that each coefficient which is not zero satisfies the inequalities

$$M > |a_{ijk}| > m,$$

where M and m are assigned positive quantities. The sum of the squares of the coefficients of any substitution is then less than n^2M^2. Hence if the coefficients be regarded as the co-ordinates of a point in space of n^2 dimensions, the points so constructed must all lie within a sphere of radius nM. If the number of points is not finite, there must be some point $(A_{11}, A_{12}, \dots, A_{nn})$ within the sphere such that an infinite number of the points lie within a sphere of radius $\frac{1}{2}\epsilon$ described round it, however small ϵ may be. Let $(a_{11}, a_{12}, \dots, a_{nn})$ and $(b_{11}, b_{12}, \dots, b_{nn})$ be two of these points, so that

$$|a_{ij} - b_{ij}| < \epsilon.$$

If A and B be the corresponding substitutions and if C be the substitution $A^{-1}B$, it follows that

$$|c_{ii} - 1| < nM\epsilon,$$

$$|c_{ij}| < nM\epsilon, \quad (i \neq j),$$

and the group has an infinite number of substitutions whose coefficients satisfy these relations. If c_{ij} is not zero for all values of i and j, ϵ may be taken so small that $|c_{ij}|$ is less than m, contrary to supposition. If c_{ij} is zero for all values of i and j, the substitution replaces each variable by a multiple of itself. Since there is an infinite number of such substitutions the multipliers cannot all be $+1$ or -1. But in a sufficiently high power of such a substitution some of the coefficients must be either numerically greater than M or less than m, again contrary to supposition.

Hence under the given conditions the group is one of finite order.

If Γ is a group of linear substitutions whose coefficients are not real, $\Gamma + \overline{\Gamma}$ can, by taking $\frac{1}{2}(x_i + \bar{x}_i)$, $\frac{1}{2\sqrt{-1}}(x_i - \bar{x}_i)$ $(i = 1, 2, \ldots, n)$ as variables, be represented as a group of real substitutions the coefficients of which are $\frac{1}{2}(a_{ij} + \bar{a}_{ij})$, $\frac{1}{2\sqrt{-1}}(a_{ij} - \bar{a}_{ij})$, or α_{ij} and β_{ij},

where
$$a_{ij} = \alpha_{ij} + \beta_{ij}\sqrt{-1}.$$

Hence, if
$$M > |\alpha_{ij}| > m$$
$$M > |\beta_{ij}| > m$$

hold for all non-zero values of α_{ij} and β_{ij}, Γ is a group of finite order.

It may also be shewn that a group of linear substitutions in n variables, which has only a finite number of conjugate sets, is of finite order. Suppose first that the group is irreducible and let $a_{ij}^{(t)}$ $(t = 1, 2, \ldots, n^2)$ be the coefficients of a set of n^2 linearly independent substitutions A_t (Note I) contained in it. If s_{ij} are the coefficients of any other substitution S, $\sum_{i,j} a_{ji}^{(t)} s_{ij}$ is the characteristic of A_tS. The system of n^2 independent linear equations

$$\sum_{i,j} a_{ji}^{(t)} s_{ij} = \chi_{A_tS} \quad (t = 1, 2, \ldots, n^2)$$

determine the s's when the χ's are known. Now by supposition there are only a finite number of values that the χ's can take. Hence the group contains only a finite number of substitutions.

If the group is reducible, suppose that the first s x's are transformed irreducibly among themselves. Then so far as it affects these variables the group is one of finite order, and it must have a self-conjugate sub-group which leaves each of the first s x's unchanged. Let

$$x_i' = x_i \quad (i = 1, 2, \ldots, s),$$

$$x'_{s+u} = \sum_{i=1}^{i=s} a_{ui} x_i + \sum_{v=1}^{v=t} b_{uv} x_{s+v}, \quad (u = 1, 2, \ldots, t)$$

be a typical substitution of this sub-group.

The set of substitutions

$$x'_{s+u} = \sum_{v=1}^{v=t} b_{uv} x_{s+v} \quad (u = 1, 2, \ldots, t)$$

constitutes a group and satisfies the condition of having only a finite number of characteristics. If it is irreducible, it is of finite order; and the original group has a self-conjugate sub-group whose substitutions are of the form

$$x_i' = x_i \quad (i = 1, 2, \ldots, s),$$

$$x'_{s+u} = x_{s+u} + \sum_{i=1}^{i=s} a_{ui} x_i \quad (u = 1, 2, \ldots, t).$$

This is an Abelian group, and if it be denoted by H, while S is any substitution not belonging to H, the set of substitutions SH all give the same isomorphism of H. Hence the number of operations in H belonging to one conjugate set is finite; and unless the order of H is finite the number of conjugate sets is infinite. But if the order of H is finite it must consist of E alone. Hence if the set of substitutions

$$x'_{s+u} = \sum_{b=1}^{v=t} b_{uv} x_{s+v} \quad (u = 1, 2, \ldots, t)$$

is irreducible, the group is of finite order. If it is reducible the same reasoning may be repeated. The group is therefore one of finite order.

If, in a group of linear substitutions on n variables, the order of every substitution is equal to or is less than a given finite number m, there can only be a finite number of distinct characteristics. In fact every characteristic is the sum of n roots of unity whose indices do not exceed m, and these can only be chosen in a finite number of ways. If the group is irreducible it follows, as in the previous investigation, that it must be of finite order. If it is reducible, it may be shewn as above that there is an Abelian self-conjugate sub-group of the form

$$x_i' = x_i \quad (i = 1, 2, \ldots, s),$$

$$x'_{s+u} = x_{s+u} + \sum_{i=1}^{i=s} a_{ui} x_i \quad (u = 1, 2, \ldots, t).$$

If this sub-group contains operations other than E, their orders are certainly not finite. Hence again the group must be one of finite order.

Let Γ_1 be a group of linear substitutions, the coefficients in which are integers in an algebraic field of finite order m. Let ξ_1 be a number, satisfying an irreducible equation of degree m with rational coefficients, which defines the field, and let $\omega_1, \omega_2, \ldots, \omega_m$ be an integral basis of the field. Suppose further that when ξ_i, another root of the equation satisfied by ξ_1, is written for ξ_1, $\omega_1, \omega_2, \ldots, \omega_m$ become $\omega_1^{(i)}, \omega_2^{(i)}, \ldots, \omega_m^{(i)}$.

If
$$x_u' = \sum_v a_{uv} x_v \quad (u, v = 1, 2, \dots, n)$$

is any substitution of the group, each coefficient is expressible in the form

$$a_{uv} = a_{uv1}\,\omega_1 + a_{uv2}\,\omega_2 + \dots + a_{uvm}\,\omega_m,$$

where $a_{uv1}, a_{uv2}, \dots, a_{uvm}$ are rational integers. If in each coefficient of each substitution $\omega_1^{(i)}, \omega_2^{(i)}, \dots, \omega_m^{(i)}$ are written for $\omega_1, \omega_2, \dots, \omega_m$, the set of substitutions form a group Γ_i simply isomorphic with Γ_1. If the m sets of symbols

$$x_{i1}, x_{i2}, \dots, x_{in}$$
$$(i = 1, 2, \dots, m)$$

undergo simultaneously corresponding substitutions of the m groups $\Gamma_1, \Gamma_2, \dots, \Gamma_m$, the resulting group on the mn symbols can clearly be expressed as a group of rational substitutions. Moreover if

$$x_{uv} = y_{v1}\,\omega_1^{(u)} + y_{v2}\,\omega_2^{(u)} + \dots + y_{vm}\,\omega_m^{(u)},$$
$$\begin{pmatrix} u = 1, 2, \dots, m \\ v = 1, 2, \dots, n \end{pmatrix}$$

and the y's are taken for new variables, the group will be actually so expressed; for the y's clearly undergo a group of linear substitutions with rational integral coefficients. That this is the case follows from the fact that, if in

$$y'_{v1}\,\omega_1^{(u)} + y'_{v2}\,\omega_2^{(u)} + \dots + y'_{vm}\,\omega_m^{(u)}$$
$$= \sum_w \left(a_{vw1}\,\omega_1^{(u)} + a_{vw2}\,\omega_2^{(u)} + \dots + a_{vwm}\,\omega_m^{(u)}\right)\left(y_{w1}\,\omega_1^{(u)} + y_{w2}\,\omega_2^{(u)} + \dots + y_{wm}\omega_m^{(u)}\right),$$

the y's and y''s are assumed rational, a linear substitution, with integral coefficients, on the y's arises which is the same whatever value be assigned to the symbol (u).

Suppose now that there is a non-zero definite Hermitian form invariant for Γ_1 and $\overline{\Gamma}_1$, and denote it by

$$\sum a_{uv}^{(1)} x_{1u} \overline{x}_{1v}.$$

Then for Γ_i and $\overline{\Gamma}_i$ the non-zero form

$$\sum a_{uv}^{(i)} x_{iu} \overline{x}_{iv}$$

is invariant; and for the group on the mn variables and its conjugate

$$\sum_{i, u, v} a_{uv}^{(i)} x_{iu} \overline{x}_{iv}$$

is invariant. This is a quadratic form in the mn y's. It can only vanish if

$$x_{iu}=0 \quad (i=1,\ 2,\ \ldots,\ m;\ u=1,\ 2,\ \ldots,\ n),$$

which involves that each of the mn y's, assumed real, must vanish.

Hence for the group of rational integral substitutions on the mn y's, there is an invariant quadratic form $f(y_{11}, y_{12}, \ldots, y_{mn})$, which, assuming the y's real, vanishes only for simultaneous zero values. If N is an assigned number there is only a finite number of integral sets of values of the y's, for which $f(y_{11}, y_{12}, \ldots, y_{mn}) \leqslant N$. These integral sets of values, or points, are permuted among themselves by the substitutions of the group; and if N is sufficiently great a substitution which leaves each point unaltered is certainly the identical substitution. The group of substitutions on the y's is then simply isomorphic with a permutation-group of finite degree, and is therefore a group of finite order.

Hence, lastly, if the coefficients in a group of linear substitutions are integers in an algebraic field of finite order, and if for the group and its conjugate there is an invariant non-zero definite Hermitian form, then the order of the group is finite.

NOTE K.

ON THE REPRESENTATION OF A GROUP OF FINITE ORDER AS A GROUP OF BIRATIONAL TRANSFORMATIONS OF AN ALGEBRAIC CURVE.

The multiply-connected surface by whose regular division a group is represented graphically may be conceived of as a Riemann's surface. To the regular division of the surface will correspond a group of birational transformations of the algebraic functions of the surface, and a group of linear substitutions on the integrals of the first kind of the surface.

That every group of finite order admits a representation of this kind may be shewn directly as follows. Let G be a group of linear substitutions of finite order on the variables

$$x_1, x_2, \ldots, x_n,$$

and let $I_1, I_2, \ldots, I_{n-1}$ be $n-1$ algebraically independent invariants of the group, so chosen that when equated to zero they do not completely determine the ratios of the variables. Take $f(x_1, x_2, \ldots, x_n)$, a rational function of the n variables which is not invariant for G or for any self-conjugate sub-group of G; and consider the system of equations

$$z=f(x_1, x_2, \ldots, x_n),\ I_1=0,\ I_2=0,\ \ldots,\ I_{n-1}=0.$$

Let M be the greatest number of sets of values for the x's which they determine, however z is chosen. It is always possible, by taking for $g(x_1, x_2, \ldots, x_n)$ a polynomial in the variables of sufficiently high degree, to ensure that the M values which g takes for the M sets of values of the x's given by the solution of the foregoing set of n equations are all different. Put

$$w=g(x_1, x_2, \ldots, x_n),$$

and denote the result of eliminating $x_1, x_2, \ldots, x_n$ from the system of $n+1$ equations

$$w=g(x_1, x_2, \ldots, x_n),\ z=f(x_1, x_2, \ldots, x_n),\ I_1=0, \ldots, I_{n-1}=0 \ldots \text{(i)}$$

by

$$F(w, z)=0.$$

Then, corresponding to any pair of values of w and z which satisfy the last equation, there is just one set of values of $x_1, x_2, \ldots, x_n$ which satisfy equations (i). In other words, when w and z satisfy

$$F(w, z) = 0,$$

the equations (i) determine each x as a rational function of w and z.

Let $x_i^{(s)}$ $(i = 1, 2, \ldots, n)$ denote what the x's become under any substitution S of G; and put

$$z^{(s)} = f(x_1^{(s)}, x_2^{(s)}, \ldots, x_n^{(s)}),$$
$$w^{(s)} = g(x_1^{(s)}, x_2^{(s)}, \ldots, x_n^{(s)}).$$

Then since $I_1, I_2, \ldots, I_{n-1}$ are invariants of the group

$$F(w^{(s)}, z^{(s)}) = 0.$$

Now $w^{(s)}$ and $z^{(s)}$ are rational functions of $x_1, x_2, \ldots, x_n$; and the latter when the equations (i) hold are rational functions of w and z. Hence

$$w^{(s)} = g_1(w, z),$$
$$z^{(s)} = f_1(w, z),$$

where f_1 and g_1 are rational functions. Moreover, by considering the substitution S^{-1}, it follows that w and z can be expressed as rational functions of $w^{(s)}$ and $z^{(s)}$. Hence the algebraic curve (or Riemann's surface)

$$F(w, z) = 0$$

admits a group of birational transformations into itself simply isomorphic with G.

For a given group of linear substitutions the set of $n-1$ invariants may be chosen in an infinite variety of ways, and there are an infinite number of groups of linear substitutions simply isomorphic with G. Still however the invariants or the representation of the group are chosen the genus or deficiency of the resulting algebraic curve must have some definite smallest value, and this must be the genus of the group.

The group of birational transformations into itself which the algebraic curve admits may, but will not in general, be a group of collineations. Thus we have seen in § 267 that the algebraic curve

$$x_1x_2^3 + x_2x_3^3 + x_3x_1^3 = 0$$

admits, as a group of collineations, the simple group of order 168, whose genus was shewn in § 303 to be 3.

As an example we will consider the curve of genus 2, which admits as large a group of birational transformations as possible. It has been stated on pp. 401, 419 that the group defined by

$$S_1^2 = E,\ S_2^3 = E,\ S_3^8 = E,\ S_1S_2S_3 = E,\ (S_1S_3^4)^2 = E,$$

is a group of genus 2; and it will now be shewn that the curve

$$y^2 = x(x^4 - 1),$$

which is obviously a curve of genus or deficiency 2, admits a group of birational transformations into itself defined by the above relations.

If α is a primitive eighth root of unity, the curve obviously admits the transformation

$$x' = \alpha^2 x, \quad y' = \alpha y,$$

whose order is 8, and which may be taken for S_3.

Now

$$x' = \frac{-x + \alpha^2}{1 - \alpha^2 x}$$

gives

$$x'(x'^4 - 1) = \frac{8x(x^4 - 1)}{(1 - \alpha^2 x)^6}.$$

Hence

$$x' = \frac{-x + \alpha^2}{1 - \alpha^2 x}, \quad y' = \frac{-2\sqrt{2}y}{(1 - \alpha^2 x)^3}$$

is a birational transformation of order 2 which transforms the curve into itself. If this be taken for S_1, it is easily verified that

$$(S_3 S_1)^3 = E, \quad (S_3{}^4 S_1)^2 = E,$$

so that the two transformations S_1 and S_3 generate a group simply isomorphic with that defined.

Lastly a pair of independent integrals of the first kind are determined by

$$di_1 = \frac{dx}{y}, \quad di_2 = \frac{x\,dx}{y}.$$

Corresponding to S_3 these obviously undergo the transformation

$$di_1' = \alpha\, di_1, \quad di_2' = \alpha^3 di_2;$$

and corresponding to S_1 it will be found that they undergo the transformation

$$di_1' = \frac{1}{\sqrt{2}} di_1 - \frac{\alpha^2}{\sqrt{2}} di_2, \quad di_2' = \frac{\alpha^2}{\sqrt{2}} di_1 - \frac{1}{\sqrt{2}} di_2.$$

The pair of integrals of the first kind therefore undergo the substitutions of a group of linear substitutions simply isomorphic with that defined.

It should be noticed that in this simple example the two variables undergo a group of birational transformations independently of any relation between x and y. In fact the equations defining S_1 and S_3 can be solved rationally with respect to x and y, in each case a unique solution resulting.

In general this will not be so; and the equations expressing x' and y' in terms of x and y will only be rationally soluble with respect to x and y when account is taken of the equation to the curve.

NOTE L.

ON THE GROUP-CHARACTERISTICS OF THE FRACTIONAL LINEAR GROUP.

In the fractional linear group G of order $\frac{1}{2}p(p^2-1)$, let P be an operation of order p, and Q an operation of order $\frac{1}{2}(p-1)$, such that

$$Q^{-1}PQ = P^{g^2}$$

where g is a primitive root of p. Further let R be an operation of order $\frac{1}{2}(p+1)$. Every operation of the group is then conjugate to either P, P^g, Q^x or R^y with suitably chosen values of the indices x and y.

When G is represented in respect of the sub-group $\{S, P\}$ as a doubly transitive group of degree $p+1$, the characteristics of P, P^g, Q^x, R^y are respectively 1, 1, 2, 0. This doubly transitive representation has just two irreducible components (§ 250), of which one is the identical representation Γ_1 and the other is a representation in p symbols that will be denoted by Γ_p. In the latter the characteristics of E, P, P^g, Q^x, R^y are (from the above values) p, 0, 0, 1, -1 respectively.

Consider now the representation of G as a group of monomial substitutions denoted by $G_{\alpha Q, \{P\}}$ in the notation of Note D, where α is a $\frac{1}{2}(p-1)$th root of unity. In this representation the substitution corresponding to R permutes the symbols in two cycles of $\frac{1}{2}(p+1)$ each; the substitution corresponding to P leaves one symbol unchanged and permutes the remainder in a cycle of p; and the substitution corresponding to Q changes two symbols into α and α^{-1} times themselves and permutes the remainder in two cycles of $\frac{1}{2}(p-1)$ each. Hence, if ψ denotes a characteristic in this representation,

$$\psi_E = p+1, \quad \psi_P = 1, \quad \psi_{R^x} = 0, \quad \psi_{Q^y} = \alpha^y + \alpha^{-y}.$$

We will consider in detail the case in which $p \equiv 1 \pmod{4}$, when -1 is a possible value for α. If α is unity the representation is the one already considered. If α is any $\frac{1}{2}(p-1)$th root of unity except 1 or -1, it is found by a simple calculation that

$$\sum_S \psi_S \psi_{S^{-1}} = \frac{1}{2}p(p^2-1).$$

For these values of a the representation under consideration is therefore an irreducible representation. In it the characteristics are (we now use the symbol χ),

$$\chi_E = p + 1,\ \chi_P = 1,\ \chi_{P^g} = 1,\ \chi_{R^x} = 0,\ \chi_{Q^y} = a^y + a^{-y}.$$

Since, omitting the values 1 and -1 for a, the quantity $a + a^{-1}$ takes $\frac{1}{4}(p-5)$ values, this representation belongs to a set of $\frac{1}{4}(p-5)$ representations that arise by taking the different available values of a.

When the value -1 is used for a, it is found that

$$\sum_S \psi_S \psi_{S^{-1}} = p(p^2-1),$$

so that $G_{-Q,\{P\}}$ has two distinct irreducible components. It is obvious that Γ_1 is not one of these, so that in each the characteristic of P is irrational. Hence since the group of monomial substitutions has rational coefficients, the two irreducible components must be in the same number, $\frac{1}{2}(p+1)$, of variables. Since P and P^{g^2} have the same characteristic, the characteristics of P in these two representations must be

$$1 + \omega + \omega^{g^2} + \ldots + \omega^{g^{\frac{1}{2}(p-1)}},$$

and

$$1 + \omega^g + \omega^{g^3} + \ldots + \omega^{g^{1+\frac{1}{2}(p-1)}},$$

or $\frac{1}{2}(1+\sqrt{p})$ and $\frac{1}{2}(1-\sqrt{p})$ respectively. The operations whose orders are not p have rational and therefore equal characteristics in these two representations. The characteristics in the two are therefore

$$\chi_E = \tfrac{1}{2}(p+1),\ \chi_P = \tfrac{1}{2}(1+\sqrt{p}),\ \chi_{P^g} = \tfrac{1}{2}(1-\sqrt{p}),\ \chi_{R^x} = 0,\ \chi_{Q^y} = (-1)^y,$$

$$\chi_E = \tfrac{1}{2}(p+1),\ \chi_P = \tfrac{1}{2}(1-\sqrt{p}),\ \chi_{P^g} = \tfrac{1}{2}(1+\sqrt{p}),\ \chi_{R^x} = 0,\ \chi_{Q^y} = (-1)^y.$$

The total number of irreducible representations is equal to the number of conjugate sets, viz. $\frac{1}{2}(p+5)$ (§ 320). Of these $\frac{1}{4}(p+11)$ have been determined and there remain $\frac{1}{4}(p-1)$. When in the equation

$$N = \sum_i (\chi_1^i)^2$$

the values of the $\frac{1}{4}(p+11)$ χ_1's that have been determined are entered, it is found that the sum of the squares of the remaining $\frac{1}{4}(p-1)$ $(\chi_1)^2$'s is $\frac{1}{4}(p-1)^3$. Hence unless each of the remaining χ_1's is $p-1$ some must be smaller. Now for a representation in less than $p-1$ symbols, χ_P must be irrational, and if χ_P is irrational in any other representation than the two already found in $\frac{1}{2}(p+1)$ symbols, $\sum_i \chi_P^i \chi_P^{i'}$ would certainly be greater than p, which is its actual value. Hence for each of the remaining $\frac{1}{4}(p-1)$ representations χ_1 is equal to $p-1$.

Now $\Sigma\chi_Q\chi_{Q^{-1}}$ for the $\frac{1}{4}(p+11)$ representations that have been determined is $\frac{1}{2}(p-1)$. Hence Q and each of its powers have zero characteristics in the remaining $\frac{1}{4}(p-1)$. Also P and P^g clearly have -1 for characteristic in all of them.

Let Γ_u and Γ_v be any two of the remaining representations, and suppose that in them

$$\chi_R^u = 2a_0 + a_1(\beta+\beta^{-1}) + a_2(\beta^2+\beta^{-2}) + \ldots + a_{\frac{1}{4}(p-1)}(\beta^{\frac{1}{4}(p-1)} + \beta^{-\frac{1}{4}(p-1)})$$

and

$$\chi_R^v = 2b_0 + b_1(\beta+\beta^{-1}) + b_2(\beta^2+\beta^{-2}) + \ldots + b_{\frac{1}{4}(p-1)}(\beta^{\frac{1}{4}(p-1)} + \beta^{-\frac{1}{4}(p-1)})$$

are the characteristics of R expressed as the sum of its multipliers, so that each a and each b is zero or a positive integer, β being a primitive $\frac{1}{2}(p+1)$th of unity.

After simple reductions the equations

$$\sum_S \chi_S^u = 0, \qquad \sum_S \chi_S^v = 0,$$

$$\sum_S (\chi_S^u)^2 = \tfrac{1}{2}p(p^2-1), \quad \sum_S (\chi_S^v)^2 = \tfrac{1}{2}p(p^2-1),$$

and

$$\sum_S \chi_S^u \chi_S^v = 0,$$

give

$$a_0 = 1, \qquad b_0 = 1,$$

$$\sum_1^{\frac{1}{4}(p-1)} a_i^2 = p-4, \qquad \sum_1^{\frac{1}{4}(p-1)} b_i^2 = p-4, \qquad \sum_1^{\frac{1}{4}(p-1)} a_i b_i = p-5.$$

Hence

$$\sum_1^{\frac{1}{4}(p-1)} (a_i - b_i)^2 = 2,$$

so that of the $\frac{1}{4}(p-1)$ differences $a_i \sim b_i$ only two can be different from zero, and these two must be unity. Moreover this result holds for each pair Γ_u and Γ_v of the $\frac{1}{4}(p-1)$ representations in $p-1$ symbols.

Now

$$2(a_0 + a_1 + \ldots + a_{\frac{1}{4}(p-1)}) = p-1,$$

so that

$$\sum_1^{\frac{1}{4}(p-1)} a_i = \sum_1^{\frac{1}{4}(p-1)} b_i = \tfrac{1}{2}(p-3).$$

From these and the previous equations it immediately follows that of the $\frac{1}{4}(p-1)$ numbers a_i one is unity and all the others are 2. Moreover if a_i is unity b_i must be 2. Hence, since

$$1 + \beta + \beta^{-1} + \beta^2 + \beta^{-2} + \ldots + \beta^{\frac{1}{4}(p-1)} + \beta^{-\frac{1}{4}(p-1)} = 0,$$

the characteristic of R in any one of the $\frac{1}{4}(p-1)$ remaining representations is $-(\beta+\beta^{-1})$, where β is any $\frac{1}{2}(p+1)$th root of unity except 1. The group-characteristics may now be exhibited in tabular form*

χ_E	1	$\frac{1}{2}(p+1)$	$\frac{1}{2}(p+1)$	p	$p-1$	$p+1$
χ_P	1	$\frac{1}{2}(1+\sqrt{p})$	$\frac{1}{2}(1-\sqrt{p})$	0	-1	1
χ_{P^g}	1	$\frac{1}{2}(1-\sqrt{p})$	$\frac{1}{2}(1+\sqrt{p})$	0	-1	1
χ_{Q^y}	1	$(-1)^y$	$(-1)^y$	1	0	$\alpha^y+\alpha^{-y}$
χ_{R^x}	1	0	0	-1	$-(\beta^x+\beta^{-x})$	0

The first four columns each give a single representation, the fifth gives $\frac{1}{4}(p-1)$ according to the $\frac{1}{2}(p+1)$th root of unity taken for β, and the sixth gives $\frac{1}{4}(p-5)$ according to the $\frac{1}{2}(p-1)$th root of unity, other than -1, taken for α.

It may be shewn in a closely similar manner that if $p\equiv 3$ (mod. 4) the table of characteristics is

χ_E	1	$\frac{1}{2}(p-1)$	$\frac{1}{2}(p-1)$	p	$p-1$	$p+1$
χ_P	1	$\frac{1}{2}(-1+\sqrt{-p})$	$\frac{1}{2}(-1+\sqrt{-p})$	0	-1	1
χ_{P^g}	1	$\frac{1}{2}(-1-\sqrt{-p})$	$\frac{1}{2}(-1-\sqrt{-p})$	0	-1	1
χ_{Q^y}	1	0	0	1	0	$\alpha^y+\alpha^{-y}$
χ_{R^x}	1	$(-1)^{x+1}$	$(-1)^{x+1}$	-1	$-(\beta^x+\beta^{-x})$	0

Here again the first four columns each give a single representation, while the fifth and sixth each give $\frac{1}{4}(p-3)$ representations.

* These tables are given by Prof. Frobenius, "Über Gruppencharaktore" (*Berliner Sitzungsberichte* (1896) p. 1021), where however they are established in an entirely different way.

NOTE M.

ON GROUPS OF ODD ORDER.

It has been seen that there is in some respects a marked difference between groups of even and those of odd order. The most noticeable property of groups of odd order is perhaps that they admit no self-inverse irreducible representation, except the identical one. From this property combined with that denoted by the relation

$$\Gamma^2 = \Gamma_{(2)} + \Sigma c_i \Gamma_i$$

of § 253, it is not difficult to shew that all irreducible groups of odd order in 3, 5 or 7 symbols are soluble.

Prof. G. A. Miller was the first to examine the possibility of a simple group of odd order under given conditions. In a paper in Vol. XXXIII (1901) of the *Proceedings of the London Mathematical Society* he proved that no group of odd order with a conjugate set of operations containing fewer than 50 members could be simple. In the same volume, working from a somewhat different point of view, the author proved that all transitive groups of odd order whose degree is less than 100 are soluble; and in his thesis (Baltimore, 1904) Mr H. L. Rietz extended this result to groups whose degrees are less than 243. The author has also shewn (*l.c.*) that the number of prime factors in the order of a simple group of odd order cannot be less than 7; and thence, by an examination of some particular cases, that 40,000 is a lower limit for the order of a group of odd degree, if simple. The contrast that these results shew between groups of odd and of even order suggests inevitably that simple groups of odd order do not exist. A discussion of the possibility of their existence must in any case lead to interesting results. Among other methods the problem might be approached by a detailed examination of the properties of irreducible groups of linear substitutions of odd order, or by regarding the group as a group of isomorphisms of an Abelian group of type (1, 1, ..., 1) whose order is a power of 2.

NOTE N.

ON THE ORDERS OF SIMPLE GROUPS.

The only numbers less than 1000 which are the orders of simple groups are 60, 168, 360, 504 and 660. In each case there is one type of simple group corresponding to the order. Those of orders 60 and 360 are the alternating groups of 5 symbols and of 6 symbols. Those of orders 168 and 660 are the linear fractional groups for $p=7$ and $p=11$; and that of order 504 is the triply transitive group of degree 9, whose existence is proved in § 141. These results have been proved by a direct examination of the possibility of a simple group for each order within the given range. The investigation was carried out by Prof. Hölder (*Math. Ann.*, Vol. XL (1892)) for orders up to 200; by Dr Cole (*Amer. Journal of Mathematics*, Vol. XV (1893)) for orders from 200 to 660; and by the author (*Proc. L. M. S.*, Vol. XXVI (1895)) for orders from 660 to 1000. The labour involved in such a direct examination increases very rapidly with the order, and puts a practical limit on carrying it on to considerable values of the order. Prof. Dickson has given in his *Linear Groups* a table of all known simple groups whose orders do not exceed 1,000,000. Their number is 53. Among them there occur two distinct types of simple group corresponding to one and the same order, viz. 20160. Prof. Dickson has also shewn (*l.c.*) hat there is an infinite series of numbers corresponding to which as order there exists more than one type of simple group. Of the 53 simple groups whose orders are less than 1,000,000 all, except three, belong to known systems of simple groups, each system having an infinite number of members. These three which appear to belong to no system are the quintuply transitive group of degree 12 and order 12 . 11 . 10 . 9 . 8 given on p. 229, the quadruply transitive group of degree 11 and order 11 . 10 . 9 . 8 which it contains and a transitive group of degree 22. These apparently sporadic simple groups would probably repay a closer examination than they have yet received.

NOTE O.

ON ALGEBRAIC NUMBERS.

In dealing with groups of linear substitutions it has been necessary to assume the reader acquainted with some of the fundamental ideas of the theory of algebraic numbers. A real or imaginary quantity x, which satisfies an equation

$$a_0 x^n + a_1 x^{n-1} + \dots + a_{n-1} x + a_n = 0,$$

of finite degree, in which $a_0, a_1, \dots, a_n$ are rational integers is called an algebraic number. From this it follows at once that the sum, difference, product and quotient of two algebraic numbers are algebraic numbers. If a_0 is unity, x is called an algebraic integer. An algebraic integer which is a rational number is necessarily a rational integer. The above equation is spoken of as rationally irreducible when it is not possible to express the left-hand side in the form

$$(b_0 x^m + b_1 x^{m-1} + \dots + b_m)(c_0 x^{n-m} + c_1 x^{n-m+1} + \dots + c_{n-m}),$$

where the b's and c's are rational integers, while neither m nor $n-m$ is less than 1. When this condition is satisfied the totality of the rational functions of x with rational coefficients is called an algebraic field of the nth degree, and is denoted by $R(x)$.

Every algebraic number contained in this algebraic field is expressible in the form

$$\alpha_1 x^{n-1} + \alpha_2 x^{n-2} + \dots + \alpha_{n-1} x + \alpha_n,$$

where the α's are rational numbers. A fundamental property of an algebraic field of the nth degree is that a set of algebraic integers of the field $\omega_1, \omega_2, \dots, \omega_n$ can always be found, so that every integer of the field is expressible in the form

$$i_1 \omega_1 + i_2 \omega_2 + \dots + i_n \omega_n,$$

where the i's are rational integers, while at the same time this expression can only vanish for simultaneous zero values of the i's, assuming them to be rational numbers. The set of integers $\omega_1, \omega_2, \ldots, \omega_n$ is called an integral basis of the field.

If x' is another root of the irreducible equation satisfied by x, the field $R(x')$, consisting of all rational functions of x' with rational coefficients, is distinct from $R(x)$, unless x' belongs to $R(x)$. If when x' is written for x, $\omega_1, \omega_2, \ldots, \omega_n$ become $\omega_1', \omega_2', \ldots, \omega_n'$, the latter set of quantities is a rational basis of $R(x')$.

There is unfortunately no English book to which reference can be made for proofs of the above statements and for the general theory of algebraic fields. The reader who wishes for a complete account of the theory should consult "Die Theorie der algebraischen Zahlkörper," by Prof. Hilbert (*Jahresbericht der Deutschen Mathematiker-Vereinigung*, Vol. IV (1897)). The first part of a French translation of Prof. Hilbert's memoir has just been published in the *Annales de la Faculté des Sciences de l'Université de Toulouse* (1909). An admirable account of the theory is also given in Prof. Weber's *Lehrbuch der Algebra*, Vol. II (1899). For an introduction to the subject there is no better book than Prof. Minkowski's *Diophantische Approximationen* (1907), or Dr Sommer's *Vorlesungen über Zahlentheorie* (1907), where the theory of cubic and quadratic fields are dealt with.

INDEX OF TECHNICAL TERMS.

(*The numbers refer to sections.*)

INDEX OF AUTHORS QUOTED.

(The numbers refer to pages.)

GENERAL INDEX.

(The numbers refer to sections.)

INTRODUCTION TO THE THEORY OF NUMBERS
by Leonard Eugene Dickson

Written by one of the foremost modern theoreticians in this area o modern mathematics, this book is an introduction to the theory of numbers. While the author's approach is thorough and comprehensive, with adequate coverage of classical literature, it is written in terms that a beginner can follow.

Beginning with three chapters on divisibility, congruences, quadratic residues and reciprocity law, Professor Dickson covers such basic principles as the infinitude of primes, least residues, Fermat's theorem, Euler's phi function, the Chinese remainder theorem, Legendre's symbol, Gauss's lemma, and others.

Four chapters are devoted to a full treatment of binary quadratic forms, without the usual restriction to integral coefficients—for example, automorphs, Kronecker's symbol, relations between roots of equivalent forms, reduced forms, Gauss's celebrated theorem on duplication, the minima of real, indefinite, binary quadratic forms, etc. Interspersed are four chapters on Diophantine equations: the first elementary; the second treating the notion of reduced binary quadratic forms; the last two, though elementary, involve long chains of arguments. Such topics are covered here as equal sums of two fourth powers, methods of Euler and Lagrange, recent theorems of Thue and Siegel, the rational approximation to a root of an algebraic equation, and many others.

Besides providing an easily followed account of general theory of numbers, this volume contains considerable original material not readily available elsewhere. 239 problems of gradually increasing difficulty are included.

Index. 1 figure. viii+183 pp. 5⅜ x 8.

S342 Paperbound **$1.65**

A TREATISE ON ADVANCED TRIGONOMETRY

by E. W. Hobson

This reprint of Hobson's classic formerly entitled A TREATISE ON PLANE TRIGONOMETRY, will be appreciated by the mathematician, the engineer, the mathematics instructor and everybody interested in a formal exposition of trigonometry and the related topics of complex variables and infinite series. Historically of great importance, this work continues to provide much stimulating and valuable material not easily obtainable elsewhere. One of the few books on advanced trigonometry, it goes far beyond the usual college level. It is the most complete analytic treatment of the subject available in English. The variety of trigonometric relations, is unusually wide and complete. A wealth of problems and formulae, fully worked out, is found throughout the body of the book and hundreds of additional examples are given in special sections.

Partial contents. CIRCULAR FUNCTIONS: GENERAL, OF 2 OR MORE ANGLES, OF SUBMULTIPLE ANGLES. Identities & transformations, solution of equations, maximan & minima, porismatic systems of equations, summation of series. EXPANSION OF FUNCTIONS OF MULTIPLE ANGLES. Series in descending, ascending powers of sine or cosine. Euler's product. Relation between trigonometrical & algrebraic identities. TRIGONOMETRICAL TABLES. RELATIONS BETWEEN SIDES & ANGLES OF A TRIANGLE. SOLUTION OF TRIANGLE. PROPERTIES OF TRIANGLES & QUADRILATERALS. Medians, bisectos of angles, pedal triangle. COMPLEX NUMBERS: geometrical representation, powers, de Moivre's theorem, factorization, etc. THEORY OF INFINITE SERIES. Convergence of real and complex series, continuous functions, uniform convergence, geometrical series, etc. EXPONENTIAL FUNCTION, LOGARITHMS. Exponential series, generalized logarithms, Gregory's series, summation of series. HYPERBOLIC SERIES. Solution of cubic equations, table of Godermannian functions. INFINITE PRODUCTS. Convergence of infinite products, series for tangent, cotangent, secant, cosecant, etc. CONTINUED FRACTIONS: proof of irrationality of pi, Euler's transformations, etc.

Many problems are solved completely in the text. 689 examples, at chapter ends. 66 figures. xvi + 383pp. 5 3/8 x 8.

S353 Paperbound **$1.95**

Catalogue of Dover SCIENCE BOOKS

BOOKS THAT EXPLAIN SCIENCE

THE NATURE OF LIGHT AND COLOUR IN THE OPEN AIR, M. Minnaert. Why is falling snow sometimes black? What causes mirages, the fata morgana, multiple suns and moons in the sky; how are shadows formed? Prof. Minnaert of U. of Utrecht answers these and similar questions in optics, light, colour, for non-specialists. Particularly valuable to nature, science students, painters, photographers. "Can best be described in one word—fascinating!" Physics Today. Translated by H. M. Kremer-Priest, K. Jay. 202 illustrations, including 42 photos. xvi + 362pp. 5⅜ x 8. T196 Paperbound **$1.95**

THE RESTLESS UNIVERSE, Max Born. New enlarged version of this remarkably readable account by a Nobel laureate. Moving from sub-atomic particles to universe, the author explains in very simple terms the latest theories of wave mechanics. Partial contents: air and its relatives, electrons and ions, waves and particles, electronic structure of the atom, nuclear physics. Nearly 1000 illustrations, including 7 animated sequences. 325pp. 6 x 9. T412 Paperbound **$2.00**

MATTER AND LIGHT, THE NEW PHYSICS, L. de Broglie. Non-technical papers by a Nobel laureate explain electromagnetic theory, relativity, matter, light, radiation, wave mechanics, quantum physics, philosophy of science. Einstein, Planck, Bohr, others explained so easily that no mathematical training is needed for all but 2 of the 21 chapters. "Easy simplicity and lucidity . . . should make this source-book of modern physcis available to a wide public," Saturday Review. Unabridged. 300pp. 5⅜ x 8. T35 Paperbound **$1.60**

THE COMMON SENSE OF THE EXACT SCIENCES, W. K. Clifford. Introduction by James Newman, edited by Karl Pearson. For 70 years this has been a guide to classical scientific, mathematical thought. Explains with unusual clarity basic concepts such as extension of meaning of symbols, characteristics of surface boundaries, properties of plane figures, vectors, Cartesian method of determining position, etc. Long preface by Bertrand Russell. Bibliography of Clifford. Corrected. 130 diagrams redrawn. 249pp. 5⅜ x 8. T61 Paperbound **$1.60**

THE EVOLUTION OF SCIENTIFIC THOUGHT FROM NEWTON TO EINSTEIN, A. d'Abro. Einstein's special, general theories of relativity, with historical implications, analyzed in non-technical terms. Excellent accounts of contributions of Newton, Riemann, Weyl, Planck, Eddington, Maxwell, Lorentz, etc., are treated in terms of space, time, equations of electromagnetics, finiteness of universe, methodology of science. "Has become a standard work," Nature. 21 diagrams. 482pp. 5⅜ x 8. T2 Paperbound **$2.00**

BRIDGES AND THEIR BUILDERS, D. Steinman, S. R. Watson. Engineers, historians, everyone ever fascinated by great spans will find this an endless source of information and interest. Dr. Steinman, recent recipient of Louis Levy Medal, is one of the great bridge architects, engineers of all time. His analysis of great bridges of history is both authoritative and easily followed. Greek, Roman, medieval, oriental bridges; modern works such as Brooklyn Bridge, Golden Gate Bridge, etc. described in terms of history, constructional principles, artistry, function. Most comprehensive, accurate semi-popular history of bridges in print in English. New, greatly revised, enlarged edition. 23 photographs, 26 line drawings. xvii + 401pp. 5⅜ x 8. T431 Paperbound **$1.95**

CONCERNING THE NATURE OF THINGS, Sir William Bragg. Christmas lectures at Royal Society by Nobel laureate, dealing with atoms, gases, liquids, and various types of crystals. No scientific background is needed to understand this remarkably clear introduction to basic processes and aspects of modern science. "More interesting than any bestseller," London Morning Post. 32pp. of photos. 57 figures. xii + 232pp. 5⅜ x 8. T31 Paperbound **$1.35**

THE RISE OF THE NEW PHYSICS, A. d'Abro. Half million word exposition, formerly titled "The Decline of Mechanism," for readers not versed in higher mathematics. Only thorough explanation in everyday language of core of modern mathematical physical theory, treating both classical, modern views. Scientifically impeccable coverage of thought from Newtonian system through theories of Dirac, Heisenberg, Fermi's statistics. Combines history, exposition; broad but unified, detailed view, with constant comparison of classical, modern views. "A must for anyone doing serious study in the physical sciences," J. of the Franklin Inst. "Extraordinary faculty . . . to explain ideas and theories . . . in language of everyday life," Isis. Part I of set: philosophy of science, from practice of Newton, Maxwell, Poincaré, Einstein, etc. Modes of thought, experiment, causality, etc. Part II: 100 pp. on grammar, vocabulary of mathematics, discussions of functions, groups, series, Fourier series, etc. Remainder treats concrete, detailed coverage of both classical, quantum physics: analytic mechanics, Hamilton's principle, electromagnetic waves, thermodynamics, Brownian movement, special relativity, Bohr's atom, de Broglie's wave mechanics, Heisenberg's uncertainty, scores of other important topics. Covers discoveries, theories of d'Alembert, Born, Cantor, Debye, Euler, Foucault, Galois, Gauss, Hadamard, Kelvin, Kepler Laplace, Maxwell, Pauli, Rayleigh Volterra, Weyl, more than 180 others. 97 illustrations. ix + 982pp. 5⅜ x 8.
T3 Vol. 1 Paperbound **$2.00**
T4 Vol. II Paperbound **$2.00**

SPINNING TOPS AND GYROSCOPIC MOTION, John Perry. Well-known classic of science still unsurpassed for lucid, accurate, delightful exposition. How quasi-rigidity is induced in flexible, fluid bodies by rapid motions; why gyrostat falls, top rises; nature, effect of internal fluidity on rotating bodies; etc. Appendixes describe practical use of gyroscopes in ships, compasses, monorail transportation. 62 figures. 128pp. 5⅜ x 8.
T416 Paperbound **$1.00**

FOUNDATIONS OF PHYSICS, R. B. Lindsay, H. Margenau. Excellent bridge between semi-popular and technical writings. Discussion of methods of physical description, construction of theory; valuable to physicist with elementary calculus. Gives meaning to data, tools of modern physics. Contents: symbolism, mathematical equations; space and time; foundations of mechanics; probability; physics, continua; electron theory; relativity; quantum mechanics; causality; etc. "Thorough and yet not overdetailed. Unreservedly recommended," Nature. Unabridged corrected edition. 35 illustrations. xi + 537pp. 5⅜ x 8. S377 Paperbound **$2.45**

FADS AND FALLACIES IN THE NAME OF SCIENCE, Martin Gardner. Formerly entitled "In the Name of Science," the standard account of various cults, quack systems, delusions which have masqueraded as science: hollow earth fanatics, orgone sex energy, dianetics, Atlantis, Forteanism, flying saucers, medical fallacies like zone therapy, etc. New chapter on Bridey Murphy, psionics, other recent manifestations. A fair reasoned appraisal of eccentric theory which provides excellent innoculation. "Should be read by everyone, scientist or non-scientist alike," R. T. Birge, Prof. Emeritus of Physics, Univ. of Calif; Former Pres., Amer. Physical Soc. x + 365pp. 5⅜ x 8. T394 Paperbound **$1.50**

ON MATHEMATICS AND MATHEMATICIANS, R. E. Moritz. A 10 year labor of love by discerning, discriminating Prof. Moritz, this collection conveys the full sense of mathematics and personalities of great mathematicians. Anecdotes, aphorisms, reminiscences, philosophies, definitions, speculations, biographical insights, etc. by great mathematicians, writers: Descartes, Mill, Locke, Kant, Coleridge, Whitehead, etc. Glimpses into lives of great mathematicians, from Archimedes to Euler, Gauss, Weierstrass. To mathematicians, a superb browsing-book. To laymen, exciting revelation of fullness of mathematics. Extensive cross index. 410pp. 5⅜ x 8.
T489 Paperbound **$1.95**

GUIDE TO THE LITERATURE OF MATHEMATICS AND PHYSICS, N. G. Parke III. Over 5000 entries under approximately 120 major subject headings, of selected most important books, monographs, periodicals, articles in English, plus important works in German, French, Italian, Spanish, Russian (many recently available works). Covers every branch of physics, math, related engineering. Includes author, title, edition, publisher, place, date, number of volumes, number of pages. 40 page introduction on basic problems of research, study provides useful information on organization, use of libraries, psychology of learning, etc. Will save you hours of time. 2nd revised edition. Indices of authors, subjects. 464pp. 5⅜ x 8.
S447 Paperbound **$2.49**

THE STRANGE STORY OF THE QUANTUM, An Account for the General Reader of the Growth of Ideas Underlying Our Present Atomic Knowledge, B. Hoffmann. Presents lucidly, expertly, with barest amount of mathematics, problems and theories which led to modern quantum physics. Begins with late 1800's when discrepancies were noticed; with illuminating analogies, examples, goes through concepts of Planck, Einstein, Pauli, Schroedinger, Dirac, Sommerfield, Feynman, etc. New postscript through 1958. "Of the books attempting an account of the history and contents of modern atomic physics which have come to my attention, this is the best," H. Margenau, Yale U., in Amer. J. of Physics. 2nd edition. 32 tables, illustrations. 275pp. 5⅜ x 8. T518 Paperbound **$1.45**

HISTORY OF SCIENCE AND PHILOSOPHY OF SCIENCE

THE VALUE OF SCIENCE, Henri Poincaré. Many of most mature ideas of "last scientific universalist" for both beginning, advanced workers. Nature of scientific truth, whether order is innate in universe or imposed by man, logical thought vs. intuition (relating to Weierstrass, Lie, Riemann, etc), time and space (relativity, psychological time, simultaneity), Herz's concept of force, values within disciplines of Maxwell, Carnot, Mayer, Newton, Lorentz, etc. iii + 147pp. 5⅜ x 8. S469 Paperbound **$1.35**

PHILOSOPHY AND THE PHYSICISTS, L. S. Stebbing. Philosophical aspects of modern science examined in terms of lively critical attack on ideas of Jeans, Eddington. Tasks of science, causality, determinism, probability, relation of world physics to that of everyday experience, philosophical significance of Planck-Bohr concept of discontinuous energy levels, inferences to be drawn from Uncertainty Principle, implications of "becoming" involved in 2nd law of thermodynamics, other problems posed by discarding of Laplacean determinism. 285pp. 5⅜ x 8. T480 Paperbound **$1.65**

THE PRINCIPLES OF SCIENCE, A TREATISE ON LOGIC AND THE SCIENTIFIC METHOD, W. S. Jevons. Milestone in development of symbolic logic remains stimulating contribution to investigation of inferential validity in sciences. Treats inductive, deductive logic, theory of number, probability, limits of scientific method; significantly advances Boole's logic, contains detailed introduction to nature and methods of probability in physics, astronomy, everyday affairs, etc. In introduction, Ernest Nagel of Columbia U. says, "[Jevons] continues to be of interest as an attempt to articulate the logic of scientific inquiry." liii + 786pp. 5⅜ x 8. S446 Paperbound **$2.98**

A HISTORY OF ASTRONOMY FROM THALES TO KEPLER, J. L. E. Dreyer. Only work in English to give complete history of cosmological views from prehistoric times to Kepler. Partial contents: Near Eastern astronomical systems, Early Greeks, Homocentric spheres of Euxodus, Epicycles, Ptolemaic system, Medieval cosmology, Copernicus, Kepler, much more. "Especially useful to teachers and students of the history of science . . . unsurpassed in its field," Isis. Formerly "A History of Planetary Systems from Thales to Kepler." Revised foreword by W. H. Stahl. xvii + 430pp. 5⅜ x 8. S79 Paperbound **$1.98**

A CONCISE HISTORY OF MATHEMATICS, D. Struik. Lucid study of development of ideas, techniques, from Ancient Near East, Greece, Islamic science, Middle Ages, Renaissance, modern times. Important mathematicians described in detail. Treatment not anecdotal, but analytical development of ideas. Non-technical—no math training needed. "Rich in content, thoughtful in interpretations," U.S. Quarterly Booklist. 60 illustrations including Greek, Egyptian manuscripts, portraits of 31 mathematicians. 2nd edition. xix + 299pp. 5⅜ x 8. S255 Paperbound **$1.75**

THE PHILOSOPHICAL WRITINGS OF PEIRCE, edited by Justus Buchler. A carefully balanced expositon of Peirce's complete system, written by Peirce himself. It covers such matters as scientific method, pure chance vs. law, symbolic logic, theory of signs, pragmatism, experiment, and other topics. "Excellent selection . . . gives more than adequate evidence of the range and greatness," Personalist. Formerly entitled "The Philosophy of Peirce." xvi + 368pp. T217 Paperbound **$1.95**

SCIENCE AND METHOD, Henri Poincaré. Procedure of scientific discovery, methodology, experiment, idea-germination—processes by which discoveries come into being. Most significant and interesting aspects of development, application of ideas. Chapters cover selection of facts, chance, mathematical reasoning, mathematics and logic; Whitehead, Russell, Cantor, the new mechanics, etc. 288pp. 5⅜ x 8. S222 Paperbound **$1.35**

SCIENCE AND HYPOTHESIS, Henri Poincaré. Creative psychology in science. How such concepts as number, magnitude, space, force, classical mechanics developed, how modern scientist uses them in his thought. Hypothesis in physics, theories of modern physics. Introduction by Sir James Larmor. "Few mathematicians have had the breadth of vision of Poincaré, and none is his superior in the gift of clear exposition," E. T. Bell. 272pp. 5⅜ x 8. S221 Paperbound **$1.35**

ESSAYS IN EXPERIMENTAL LOGIC, John Dewey. Stimulating series of essays by one of most influential minds in American philosophy presents some of his most mature thoughts on wide range of subjects. Partial contents: Relationship between inquiry and experience; dependence of knowledge upon thought; character logic; judgments of practice, data, and meanings; stimuli of thought, etc. viii + 444pp. 5⅜ x 8. T73 Paperbound **$1.95**

WHAT IS SCIENCE, Norman Campbell. Excellent introduction explains scientific method, role of mathematics, types of scientific laws. Contents: 2 aspects of science, science and nature, laws of chance, discovery of laws, explanation of laws, measurement and numerical laws, applications of science. 192pp. 5⅜ x 8. S43 Paperbound **$1.25**

FROM EUCLID TO EDDINGTON: A STUDY OF THE CONCEPTIONS OF THE EXTERNAL WORLD, Sir Edmund Whittaker. Foremost British scientist traces development of theories of natural philosophy from western rediscovery of Euclid to Eddington, Einstein, Dirac, etc. 5 major divisions: Space, Time and Movement; Concepts of Classical Physics; Concepts of Quantum Mechanics; Eddington Universe. Contrasts inadequacy of classical physics to understand physical world with present day attempts of relativity, non-Euclidean geometry, space curvature, etc. 212pp. 5⅜ x 8. T491 Paperbound **$1.35**

THE ANALYSIS OF MATTER, Bertrand Russell. How do our senses accord with the new physics? This volume covers such topics as logical analysis of physics, prerelativity physics, causality, scientific inference, physics and perception, special and general relativity, Weyl's theory, tensors, invariants and their physical interpretation, periodicity and qualitative series. "The most thorough treatment of the subject that has yet been published," The Nation. Introduction by L. E. Denonn. 422pp. 5⅜ x 8. T231 Paperbound **$1.95**

LANGUAGE, TRUTH, AND LOGIC, A. Ayer. A clear introduction to the Vienna and Cambridge schools of Logical Positivism. Specific tests to evaluate validity of ideas, etc. Contents: function of philosophy, elimination of metaphysics, nature of analysis, a priori, truth and probability, etc. 10th printing. "I should like to have written it myself," Bertrand Russell. 160pp. 5⅜ x 8. T10 Paperbound **$1.25**

THE PSYCHOLOGY OF INVENTION IN THE MATHEMATICAL FIELD, J. Hadamard. Where do ideas come from? What role does the unconscious play? Are ideas best developed by mathematical reasoning, word reasoning, visualization? What are the methods used by Einstein, Poincaré, Galton, Riemann? How can these techniques be applied by others? One of the world's leading mathematicians discusses these and other questions. xiii + 145pp. 5⅜ x 8. T107 Paperbound **$1.25**

GUIDE TO PHILOSOPHY, C. E. M. Joad. By one of the ablest expositors of all time, this is not simply a history or a typological survey, but an examination of central problems in terms of answers afforded by the greatest thinkers: Plato, Aristotle, Scholastics, Leibniz, Kant, Whitehead, Russell, and many others. Especially valuable to persons in the physical sciences; over 100 pages devoted to Jeans, Eddington, and others, the philosophy of modern physics, scientific materialism, pragmatism, etc. Classified bibliography. 592pp. 5⅜ x 8. T50 Paperbound **$2.00**

SUBSTANCE AND FUNCTION, and **EINSTEIN'S THEORY OF RELATIVITY, Ernst Cassirer.** Two books bound as one. Cassirer establishes a philosophy of the exact sciences that takes into consideration new developments in mathematics, shows historical connections. Partial contents: Aristotelian logic, Mill's analysis, Helmholtz and Kronecker, Russell and cardinal numbers, Euclidean vs. non-Euclidean geometry, Einstein's relativity. Bibliography. Index. xxi + 464pp. 5⅜ x 8. T50 Paperbound **$2.00**

FOUNDATIONS OF GEOMETRY, Bertrand Russell. Nobel laureate analyzes basic problems in the overlap area between mathematics and philosophy: the nature of geometrical knowledge, the nature of geometry, and the applications of geometry to space. Covers history of non-Euclidean geometry, philosophic interpretations of geometry, especially Kant, projective and metrical geometry. Most interesting as the solution offered in 1897 by a great mind to a problem still current. New introduction by Prof. Morris Kline, N.Y. University. "Admirably clear, precise, and elegantly reasoned analysis," International Math. News. xii + 201pp. 5⅜ x 8. S233 Paperbound **$1.60**

THE NATURE OF PHYSICAL THEORY, P. W. Bridgman. How modern physics looks to a highly unorthodox physicist—a Nobel laureate. Pointing out many absurdities of science, demonstrating inadequacies of various physical theories, weighs and analyzes contributions of Einstein, Bohr, Heisenberg, many others. A non-technical consideration of correlation of science and reality. xi + 138pp. 5⅜ x 8. S33 Paperbound **$1.25**

EXPERIMENT AND THEORY IN PHYSICS, Max Born. A Nobel laureate examines the nature and value of the counterclaims of experiment and theory in physics. Synthetic versus analytical scientific advances are analyzed in works of Einstein, Bohr, Heisenberg, Planck, Eddington, Milne, others, by a fellow scientist. 44pp. 5⅜ x 8. S308 Paperbound **60¢**

A SHORT HISTORY OF ANATOMY AND PHYSIOLOGY FROM THE GREEKS TO HARVEY, Charles Singer. Corrected edition of "The Evolution of Anatomy." Classic traces anatomy, physiology from prescientific times through Greek, Roman periods, dark ages, Renaissance, to beginning of modern concepts. Centers on individuals, movements, that definitely advanced anatomical knowledge. Plato, Diocles, Erasistratus, Galen, da Vinci, etc. Special section on Vesalius. 20 plates. 270 extremely interesting illustrations of ancient, Medieval, Renaissance, Oriental origin. xii + 209pp. 5⅜ x 8. T389 Paperbound **$1.75**

SPACE-TIME-MATTER, Hermann Weyl. "The standard treatise on the general theory of relativity," (Nature), by world renowned scientist. Deep, clear discussion of logical coherence of general theory, introducing all needed tools: Maxwell, analytical geometry, non-Euclidean geometry, tensor calculus, etc. Basis is classical space-time, before absorption of relativity. Contents: Euclidean space, mathematical form, metrical continuum, general theory, etc. 15 diagrams. xviii + 330pp. 5⅜ x 8. S267 Paperbound **$1.75**

FOUNDATIONS OF SCIENCE: THE PHILOSOPHY OF THEORY AND EXPERIMENT, N. Campbell. A critique of the most fundamental concepts of science, particularly physics. Examines why certain propositions are accepted without question, demarcates science from philosophy, etc. Part I analyzes presuppositions of scientific thought: existence of material world, nature of laws, probability, etc; part 2 covers nature of experiment and applications of mathematics: conditions for measurement, relations between numerical laws and theories, error, etc. An appendix covers problems arising from relativity, force, motion, space, time. A classic in its field. "A real grasp of what science is," Higher Educational Journal. xiii + 565pp. 5⅝ x 8⅜. S372 Paperbound **$2.95**

THE STUDY OF THE HISTORY OF MATHEMATICS and **THE STUDY OF THE HISTORY OF SCIENCE, G. Sarton.** Excellent introductions, orientation, for beginning or mature worker. Describes duty of mathematical historian, incessant efforts and genius of previous generations. Explains how today's discipline differs from previous methods. 200 item bibliography with critical evaluations, best available biographies of modern mathematicians, best treatises on historical methods is especially valuable. 10 illustrations. 2 volumes bound as one. 113pp. + 75pp. 5⅜ x 8. T240 Paperbound **$1.25**

MATHEMATICAL PUZZLES

MATHEMATICAL PUZZLES OF SAM LOYD, selected and edited by **Martin Gardner.** 117 choice puzzles by greatest American puzzle creator and innovator, from his famous "Cyclopedia of Puzzles." All unique style, historical flavor of originals. Based on arithmetic, algebra, probability, game theory, route tracing, topology, sliding block, operations research, geometrical dissection. Includes famous "14-15" puzzle which was national craze, "Horse of a Different Color" which sold millions of copies. 120 line drawings, diagrams. Solutions. xx + 167pp. 5⅜ x 8. T498 Paperbound **$1.00**

SYMBOLIC LOGIC and THE GAME OF LOGIC, Lewis Carroll. "Symbolic Logic" is not concerned with modern symbolic logic, but is instead a collection of over 380 problems posed with charm and imagination, using the syllogism, and a fascinating diagrammatic method of drawing conclusions. In "The Game of Logic" Carroll's whimsical imagination devises a logical game played with 2 diagrams and counters (included) to manipulate hundreds of tricky syllogisms. The final section, "Hit or Miss" is a lagniappe of 101 additional puzzles in the delightful Carroll manner. Until this reprint edition, both of these books were rarities costing up to $15 each. Symbolic Logic: Index. xxxi + 199pp. The Game of Logic: 96pp. 2 vols. bound as one. 5⅜ x 8. T492 Paperbound **$1.50**

PILLOW PROBLEMS and A TANGLED TALE, Lewis Carroll. One of the rarest of all Carroll's works, "Pillow Problems" contains 72 original math puzzles, all typically ingenious. Particularly fascinating are Carroll's answers which remain exactly as he thought them out, reflecting his actual mental process. The problems in "A Tangled Tale" are in story form, originally appearing as a monthly magazine serial. Carroll not only gives the solutions, but uses answers sent in by readers to discuss wrong approaches and misleading paths, and grades them for insight. Both of these books were rarities until this edition, "Pillow Problems" costing up to $25, and "A Tangled Tale" $15. Pillow Problems: Preface and Introduction by Lewis Carroll. xx + 109pp. A Tangled Tale: 6 illustrations. 152pp. Two vols. bound as one. 5⅜ x 8. T493 Paperbound **$1.50**

NEW WORD PUZZLES, G. L. Kaufman. 100 brand new challenging puzzles on words, combinations, never before published. Most are new types invented by author, for beginners and experts both. Squares of letters follow chess moves to build words; symmetrical designs made of synonyms; rhymed crostics; double word squares; syllable puzzles where you fill in missing syllables instead of missing letter; many other types, all new. Solutions. "Excellent," Recreation. 100 puzzles. 196 figures. vi + 122pp. 5⅜ x 8. T344 Paperbound **$1.00**

MATHEMATICAL EXCURSIONS, H. A. Merrill. Fun, recreation, insights into elementary problem solving. Math expert guides you on by-paths not generally travelled in elementary math courses—divide by inspection, Russian peasant multiplication; memory systems for pi; odd, even magic squares; dyadic systems; square roots by geometry; Tchebichev's machine; dozens more. Solutions to more difficult ones. "Brain stirring stuff . . . a classic," Genie. 50 illustrations. 145pp. 5⅜ x 8. T350 Paperbound **$1.00**

THE BOOK OF MODERN PUZZLES, G. L. Kaufman. Over 150 puzzles, absolutely all new material based on same appeal as crosswords, deduction puzzles, but with different principles, techniques. 2-minute teasers, word labyrinths, design, pattern, logic, observation puzzles, puzzles testing ability to apply general knowledge to peculiar situations, many others. Solutions. 116 illustrations. 192pp. 5⅜ x 8. T143 Paperbound **$1.00**

MATHEMAGIC, MAGIC PUZZLES, AND GAMES WITH NUMBERS, R. V. Heath. Over 60 puzzles, stunts, on properties of numbers. Easy techniques for multiplying large numbers mentally, identifying unknown numbers, finding date of any day in any year. Includes The Lost Digit, 3 Acrobats, Psychic Bridge, magic squares, triangles, cubes, others not easily found elsewhere. Edited by J. S. Meyer. 76 illustrations. 128pp. 5⅜ x 8. T110 Paperbound **$1.00**

PUZZLE QUIZ AND STUNT FUN, J. Meyer. 238 high-priority puzzles, stunts, tricks—math puzzles like The Clever Carpenter, Atom Bomb, Please Help Alice; mysteries, deductions like The Bridge of Sighs, Secret Code; observation puzzlers like The American Flag, Playing Cards, Telephone Dial; over 200 others with magic squares, tongue twisters, puns, anagrams. Solutions. Revised, enlarged edition of "Fun-To-Do." Over 100 illustrations. 238 puzzles, stunts, tricks. 256pp. 5⅜ x 8. T337 Paperbound **$1.00**

101 PUZZLES IN THOUGHT AND LOGIC, C. R. Wylie, Jr. For readers who enjoy challenge, stimulation of logical puzzles without specialized math or scientific knowledge. Problems entirely new, range from relatively easy to brainteasers for hours of subtle entertainment. Detective puzzles, find the lying fisherman, how a blind man identifies color by logic, many more. Easy-to-understand introduction to logic of puzzle solving and general scientific method. 128pp. 5⅜ x 8. T367 Paperbound **$1.00**

CRYPTANALYSIS, H. F. Gaines. Standard elementary, intermediate text for serious students. Not just old material, but much not generally known, except to experts. Concealment, Transposition, Substitution ciphers; Vigenere, Kasiski, Playfair, multafid, dozens of other techniques. Formerly "Elementary Cryptanalysis." Appendix with sequence charts, letter frequencies in English, 5 other languages, English word frequencies. Bibliography. 167 codes. New to this edition: solutions to codes. vi + 230pp. 5⅜ x 8⅜. T97 Paperbound **$1.95**

CRYPTOGRAPY, L. D. Smith. Excellent elementary introduction to enciphering, deciphering secret writing. Explains transposition, substitution ciphers; codes; solutions; geometrical patterns, route transcription, columnar transposition, other methods. Mixed cipher systems; single, polyalphabetical substitutions; mechanical devices; Vigenere; etc. Enciphering Japanese; explanation of Baconian biliteral cipher; frequency tables. Over 150 problems. Bibliography. Index. 164pp. 5⅜ x 8. T247 Paperbound **$1.00**

MATHEMATICS, MAGIC AND MYSTERY, M. Gardner. Card tricks, metal mathematics, stage mind-reading, other "magic" explained as applications of probability, sets, number theory, etc. Creative examination of laws, applications. Scores of new tricks, insights. 115 sections on cards, dice, coins; vanishing tricks, many others. No sleight of hand—math guarantees success. "Could hardly get more entertainment . . . easy to follow," Mathematics Teacher. 115 illustrations. xii + 174pp. 5⅜ x 8. T335 Paperbound **$1.00**

AMUSEMENTS IN MATHEMATICS, H. E. Dudeney. Foremost British originator of math puzzles, always witty, intriguing, paradoxical in this classic. One of largest collections. More than 430 puzzles, problems, paradoxes. Mazes, games, problems on number manipulations, unicursal, other route problems, puzzles on measuring, weighing, packing, age, kinship, chessboards, joiners', crossing river, plane figure dissection, many others. Solutions. More than 450 illustrations. viii + 258pp. 5⅜ x 8. T473 Paperbound **$1.25**

THE CANTERBURY PUZZLES H. E. Dudeney. Chaucer's pilgrims set one another problems in story form. Also Adventures of the Puzzle Club, the Strange Escape of the King's Jester, the Monks of Riddlewell, the Squire's Christmas Puzzle Party, others. All puzzles are original, based on dissecting plane figures, arithmetic, algebra, elementary calculus, other branches of mathematics, and purely logical ingenuity. "The limit of ingenuity and intricacy," The Observer. Over 110 puzzles, full solutions. 150 illustrations. viii + 225 pp. 5⅜ x 8. T474 Paperbound **$1.25**

MATHEMATICAL PUZZLES FOR BEGINNERS AND ENTHUSIASTS, G. Mott-Smith. 188 puzzles to test mental agility. Inference, interpretation, algebra, dissection of plane figures, geometry, properties of numbers, decimation, permutations, probability, all are in these delightful problems. Includes the Odic Force, How to Draw an Ellipse, Spider's Cousin, more than 180 others. Detailed solutions. Appendix with square roots, triangular numbers, primes, etc. 135 illustrations. 2nd revised edition. 248pp. 5⅜ x 8. T198 Paperbound **$1.00**

MATHEMATICAL RECREATIONS, M. Kraitchik. Some 250 puzzles, problems, demonstrations of recreation mathematics on relatively advanced level. Unusual historical problems from Greek, Medieval, Arabic, Hindu sources; modern problems on "mathematics without numbers," geometry, topology, arithmetic, etc. Pastimes derived from figurative, Mersenne, Fermat numbers: fairy chess; latruncles: reversi; etc. Full solutions. Excellent insights into special fields of math. "Strongly recommended to all who are interested in the lighter side of mathematics," Mathematical Gaz. 181 illustrations. 330pp. 5⅜ x 8. T163 Paperbound **$1.75**

FICTION

FLATLAND, E. A. Abbott. A perennially popular science-fiction classic about life in a 2-dimensional world, and the impingement of higher dimensions. Political, satiric, humorous, moral overtones. This land where women are straight lines and the lowest and most dangerous classes are isosceles triangles with 3° vertices conveys brilliantly a feeling for many concepts of modern science. 7th edition. New introduction by Banesh Hoffmann. 128pp. 5⅜ x 8. T1 Paperbound **$1.00**

SEVEN SCIENCE FICTION NOVELS OF H. G. WELLS. Complete texts, unabridged, of seven of Wells' greatest novels: The War of the Worlds, The Invisible Man, The Island of Dr. Moreau, The Food of the Gods, First Men in the Moon, In the Days of the Comet, The Time Machine. Still considered by many experts to be the best science-fiction ever written, they will offer amusements and instruction to the scientific minded reader. "The great master," Sky and Telescope. 1051pp. 5⅜ x 8. T264 Clothbound **$3.95**

28 SCIENCE FICTION STORIES OF H. G. WELLS. Unabridged! This enormous omnibus contains 2 full length novels—Men Like Gods, Star Begotten—plus 26 short stories of space, time, invention, biology, etc. The Crystal Egg, The Country of the Blind, Empire of the Ants, The Man Who Could Work Miracles, Aepyornis Island, A Story of the Days to Come, and 20 others "A master . . . not surpassed by . . . writers of today," The English Journal. 915pp. 5⅜ x 8. T265 Clothbound **$3.95**

FIVE ADVENTURE NOVELS OF H. RIDER HAGGARD. All the mystery and adventure of darkest Africa captured accurately by a man who lived among Zulus for years, who knew African ethnology, folkways as did few of his contemporaries. They have been regarded as examples of the very best high adventure by such critics as Orwell, Andrew Lang, Kipling. Contents: She, King Solomon's Mines, Allan Quatermain, Allan's Wife, Maiwa's Revenge. "Could spin a yarn so full of suspense and color that you couldn't put the story down," Sat. Review. 821pp. 5⅜ x 8. T108 Clothbound **$3.95**

CHESS AND CHECKERS

LEARN CHESS FROM THE MASTERS, Fred Reinfeld. Easiest, most instructive way to improve your game—play 10 games against such masters as Marshall, Znosko-Borovsky, Bronstein, Najdorf, etc., with each move graded by easy system. Includes ratings for alternate moves possible. Games selected for interest, clarity, easily isolated principles. Covers Ruy Lopez, Dutch Defense, Vienna Game openings; subtle, intricate middle game variations; all-important end game. Full annotations. Formerly "Chess by Yourself." 91 diagrams. viii + 144pp. 5⅜ x 8. T362 Paperbound **$1.00**

REINFELD ON THE END GAME IN CHESS, Fred Reinfeld. Analyzes 62 end games by Alekhine, Flohr, Tarrasch, Morphy, Capablanca, Rubinstein, Lasker, Reshevsky, other masters. Only 1st rate book with extensive coverage of error—tell exactly what is wrong with each move you might have made. Centers around transitions from middle play to end play. King and pawn, minor pieces, queen endings; blockage, weak, passed pawns, etc. "Excellent . . . a boon," Chess Life. Formerly "Practical End Play." 62 figures. vi + 177pp. 5⅜ x 8. T417 Paperbound **$1.25**

HYPERMODERN CHESS as developed in the games of its greatest exponent, ÅRON NIMZOVICH, edited by Fred Reinfeld. An intensely original player, analyst, Nimzovich's approaches startled, often angered the chess world. This volume, designed for the average player, shows how his iconoclastic methods won him victories over Alekhine, Lasker, Marshall, Rubinstein, Spielmann, others, and infused new life into the game. Use his methods to startle opponents, invigorate play. "Annotations and introductions to each game . . . are excellent," Times (London). 180 diagrams. viii + 220pp. 5⅜ x 8. T448 Paperbound **$1.35**

THE ADVENTURE OF CHESS, Edward Lasker. Lively reader, by one of America's finest chess masters, including: history of chess, from ancient Indian 4-handed game of Chaturanga to great players of today; such delights and oddities as Maelzel's chess-playing automaton that beat Napoleon 3 times; etc. One of most valuable features is author's personal recollections of men he has played against—Nimzovich, Emanuel Lasker, Capablanca, Alekhine, etc. Discussion of chess-playing machines (newly revised). 5 page chess primer. 11 illustrations. 53 diagrams. 296pp. 5⅜ x 8. S510 Paperbound **$1.45**

THE ART OF CHESS, James Mason. Unabridged reprinting of latest revised edition of most famous general study ever written. Mason, early 20th century master, teaches beginning, intermediate player over 90 openings; middle game, end game, to see more moves ahead, to plan purposefully, attack, sacrifice, defend, exchange, govern general strategy. "Classic . . . one of the clearest and best developed studies," Publishers Weekly. Also included, a complete supplement by F. Reinfeld, "How Do You Play Chess?", invaluable to beginners for its lively question-and-answer method. 448 diagrams. 1947 Reinfeld-Bernstein text. Bibliography. xvi + 340pp. 5⅜ x 8. T463 Paperbound **$1.85**

MORPHY'S GAMES OF CHESS, edited by P. W. Sergeant. Put boldness into your game by flowing brilliant, forceful moves of the greatest chess player of all time. 300 of Morphy's best games, carefully annotated to reveal principles. 54 classics against masters like Anderssen, Harrwitz, Bird, Paulsen, and others. 52 games at odds; 54 blindfold games; plus over 100 others. Follow his interpretation of Dutch Defense, Evans Gambit, Giuoco Piano, Ruy Lopez, many more. Unabridged reissue of latest revised edition. New introduction by F. Reinfeld. Annotations, introduction by Sergeant. 235 diagrams. x + 352pp. 5⅜ x 8. T386 Paperbound **$1.75**

WIN AT CHECKERS, M. Hopper. (Formerly "Checkers.") Former World's Unrestricted Checker Champion discusses principles of game, expert's shots, traps, problems for beginner, standard openings, locating best move, end game, opening "blitzkrieg" moves to draw when behind, etc. Over 100 detailed questions, answers anticipate problems. Appendix. 75 problems with solutions, diagrams. 79 figures. xi + 107pp. 5⅜ x 8. T363 Paperbound **$1.00**

HOW TO FORCE CHECKMATE, Fred Reinfeld. If you have trouble finishing off your opponent, here is a collection of lightning strokes and combinations from actual tournament play. Starts with 1-move checkmates, works up to 3-move mates. Develops ability to look ahead, gain new insights into combinations, complex or deceptive positions; ways to estimate weaknesses, strengths of you and your opponent. "A good deal of amusement and instruction," Times, (London). 300 diagrams. Solutions to all positions. Formerly "Challenge to Chess Players." 111pp. 5⅜ x 8. T417 Paperbound **$1.25**

A TREASURY OF CHESS LORE, edited by Fred Reinfeld. Delightful collection of anecdotes, short stories, aphorisms by, about masters; poems, accounts of games, tournaments, photographs; hundreds of humorous, pithy, satirical, wise, historical episodes, comments, word portraits. Fascinating "must" for chess players; revealing and perhaps seductive to those who wonder what their friends see in game. 49 photographs (14 full page plates). 12 diagrams. xi + 306pp. 5⅜ x 8. T458 Paperbound **$1.75**

WIN AT CHESS, Fred Reinfeld. 300 practical chess situations, to sharpen your eye, test skill against masters. Start with simple examples, progress at own pace to complexities. This selected series of crucial moments in chess will stimulate imagination, develop stronger, more versatile game. Simple grading system enables you to judge progress. "Extensive use of diagrams is a great attraction," Chess. 300 diagrams. Notes, solutions to every situation. Formerly "Chess Quiz." vi + 120pp. 5⅜ x 8. T433 Paperbound **$1.00**

MATHEMATICS: ELEMENTARY TO INTERMEDIATE

HOW TO CALCULATE QUICKLY, H. Sticker. Tried and true method to help mathematics of everyday life. Awakens "number sense"—ability to see relationships between numbers as whole quantities. A serious course of over 9000 problems and their solutions through techniques not taught in schools: left-to-right multiplications, new fast division, etc. 10 minutes a day will double or triple calculation speed. Excellent for scientist at home in higher math, but dissatisfied with speed and accuracy in lower math. 256pp. 5 x 7¼. Paperbound **$1.00**

FAMOUS PROBLEMS OF ELEMENTARY GEOMETRY, Felix Klein. Expanded version of 1894 Easter lectures at Göttingen. 3 problems of classical geometry: squaring the circle, trisecting angle, doubling cube, considered with full modern implications: transcendental numbers, pi, etc. "A modern classic . . . no knowledge of higher mathematics is required," Scientia. Notes by R. Archibald. 16 figures. xi + 92pp. 5⅜ x 8. T298 Paperbound **$1.00**

HIGHER MATHEMATICS FOR STUDENTS OF CHEMISTRY AND PHYSICS, J. W. Mellor. Practical, not abstract, building problems out of familiar laboratory material. Covers differential calculus, coordinate, analytical geometry, functions, integral calculus, infinite series, numerical equations, differential equations, Fourier's theorem probability, theory of errors, calculus of variations, determinants. "If the reader is not familiar with this book, it will repay him to examine it," Chem. and Engineering News. 800 problems. 189 figures. xxi + 641pp. 5⅜ x 8. S193 Paperbound **$2.25**

TRIGONOMETRY REFRESHER FOR TECHNICAL MEN, A. A. Klaf. 913 detailed questions, answers cover most important aspects of plane, spherical trigonometry—particularly useful in clearing up difficulties in special areas. Part I: plane trig, angles, quadrants, functions, graphical representation, interpolation, equations, logs, solution of triangle, use of slide rule, etc. Next 188 pages discuss applications to navigation, surveying, elasticity, architecture, other special fields. Part 3: spherical trig, applications to terrestrial, astronomical problems. Methods of time-saving, simplification of principal angles, make book most useful. 913 questions answered. 1738 problems, answers to odd numbers. 494 figures. 24 pages of formulas, functions. x + 629pp. 5⅜ x 8. T371 Paperbound **$2.00**

CALCULUS REFRESHER FOR TECHNICAL MEN, A. A. Klaf. 756 questions examine most important aspects of integral, differential calculus. Part I: simple differential calculus, constants, variables, functions, increments, logs, curves, etc. Part 2: fundamental ideas of integrations, inspection, substitution, areas, volumes, mean value, double, triple integration, etc. Practical aspects stressed. 50 pages illustrate applications to specific problems of civil, nautical engineering, electricity, stress, strain, elasticity, similar fields. 756 questions answered. 566 problems, mostly answered. 36pp. of useful constants, formulas. v + 431pp. 5⅜ x 8. T370 Paperbound **$2.00**

MONOGRAPHS ON TOPICS OF MODERN MATHEMATICS, edited by J. W. A. Young. Advanced mathematics for persons who have forgotten, or not gone beyond, high school algebra. 9 monographs on foundation of geometry, modern pure geometry, non-Euclidean geometry, fundamental propositions of algebra, algebraic equations, functions, calculus, theory of numbers, etc. Each monograph gives proofs of important results, and descriptions of leading methods, to provide wide coverage. "Of high merit," Scientific American. New introduction by Prof. M. Kline, N.Y. Univ. 100 diagrams. xvi + 416pp. 6⅛ x 9¼.
S289 Paperbound **$2.00**

MATHEMATICS IN ACTION, O. G. Sutton. Excellent middle level application of mathematics to study of universe, demonstrates how math is applied to ballistics, theory of computing machines, waves, wave-like phenomena, theory of fluid flow, meteorological problems, statistics, flight, similar phenomena. No knowledge of advanced math required. Differential equations, Fourier series, group concepts, Eigenfunctions, Planck's constant, airfoil theory, and similar topics explained so clearly in everyday language that almost anyone can derive benefit from reading this even if much of high-school math is forgotten. 2nd edition. 88 figures. viii + 236pp. 5⅜ x 8. T450 Clothbound **$3.50**

ELEMENTARY MATHEMATICS FROM AN ADVANCED STANDPOINT, Felix Klein. Classic text, an outgrowth of Klein's famous integration and survey course at Göttingen. Using one field to interpret, adjust another, it covers basic topics in each area, with extensive analysis. Especially valuable in areas of modern mathematics. "A great mathematician, inspiring teacher, . . . deep insight," Bul., Amer. Math Soc.

Vol. I. ARITHMETIC, ALGEBRA, ANALYSIS. Introduces concept of function immediately, enlivens discussion with graphical, geometric methods. Partial contents: natural numbers, special properties, complex numbers. Real equations with real unknowns, complex quantities. Logarithmic, exponential functions, infinitesimal calculus. Transcendence of e and pi, theory of assemblages. Index. 125 figures. ix + 274pp. 5⅜ x 8. S151 Paperbound **$1.75**

Vol. II. GEOMETRY. Comprehensive view, accompanies space perception inherent in geometry with analytic formulas which facilitate precise formulation. Partial contents: Simplest geometric manifold; line segments, Grassman determinant principles, classication of configurations of space. Geometric transformations: affine, projective, higher point transformations, theory of the imaginary. Systematic discussion of geometry and its foundations. 141 illustrations. ix + 214pp. 5⅜ x 8. S151 Paperbound **$1.75**

A TREATISE ON PLANE AND ADVANCED TRIGONOMETRY, E. W. Hobson. Extraordinarily wide coverage, going beyond usual college level, one of few works covering advanced trig in full detail. By a great expositor with unerring anticipation of potentially difficult points. Includes circular functions; expansion of functions of multiple angle; trig tables; relations between sides, angles of triangles; complex numbers; etc. Many problems fully solved. "The best work on the subject," Nature. Formerly entitled "A Treatise on Plane Trigonometry." 689 examples. 66 figures. xvi + 383pp. 5⅜ x 8. S353 Paperbound **$1.95**

NON-EUCLIDEAN GEOMETRY, Roberto Bonola. The standard coverage of non-Euclidean geometry. Examines from both a historical and mathematical point of view geometries which have arisen from a study of Euclid's 5th postulate on parallel lines. Also included are complete texts, translated, of Bolyai's "Theory of Absolute Space," Lobachevsky's "Theory of Parallels." 180 diagrams. 431pp. 5⅜ x 8. S27 Paperbound **$1.95**

GEOMETRY OF FOUR DIMENSIONS, H. P. Manning. Unique in English as a clear, concise introduction. Treatment is synthetic, mostly Euclidean, though in hyperplanes and hyperspheres at infinity, non-Euclidean geometry is used. Historical introduction. Foundations of 4-dimensional geometry. Perpendicularity, simple angles. Angles of planes, higher order. Symmetry, order, motion; hyperpyramids, hypercones, hyperspheres; figures with parallel elements; volume, hypervolume in space; regular polyhedroids. Glossary. 78 figures. ix + 348pp. 5⅜ x 8.
S182 Paperbound **$1.95**

MATHEMATICS: INTERMEDIATE TO ADVANCED

GEOMETRY (EUCLIDEAN AND NON-EUCLIDEAN)

THE GEOMETRY OF RENÉ DESCARTES. With this book, Descartes founded analytical geometry. Original French text, with Descartes's own diagrams, and excellent Smith-Latham translation. Contains: Problems the Construction of Which Requires only Straight Lines and Circles; On the Nature of Curved Lines; On the Construction of Solid or Supersolid Problems. Diagrams. 258pp. 5⅜ x 8. S68 Paperbound **$1.50**

DOVER SCIENCE BOOKS

THE WORKS OF ARCHIMEDES, edited by T. L. Heath. All the known works of the great Greek mathematician, including the recently discovered Method of Archimedes. Contains: On Sphere and Cylinder, Measurement of a Circle, Spirals, Conoids, Spheroids, etc. Definitive edition of greatest mathematical intellect of ancient world. 186 page study by Heath discusses Archimedes and history of Greek mathematics. 563pp. 5⅜ x 8. S9 Paperbound **$2.00**

COLLECTED WORKS OF BERNARD RIEMANN. Important sourcebook, first to contain complete text of 1892 "Werke" and the 1902 supplement, unabridged. 31 monographs, 3 complete lecture courses, 15 miscellaneous papers which have been of enormous importance in relativity, topology, theory of complex variables, other areas of mathematics. Edited by R. Dedekind, H. Weber, M. Noether, W. Wirtinger. German text; English introduction by Hans Lewy. 690pp. 5⅜ x 8. S226 Paperbound **$2.85**

THE THIRTEEN BOOKS OF EUCLID'S ELEMENTS, edited by Sir Thomas Heath. Definitive edition of one of very greatest classics of Western world. Complete translation of Heiberg text, plus spurious Book XIV. 150 page introduction on Greek, Medieval mathematics, Euclid, texts, commentators, etc. Elaborate critical apparatus parallels text, analyzing each definition, postulate, proposition, covering textual matters, refutations, supports, extrapolations, etc. This is the full Euclid. Unabridged reproduction of Cambridge U. 2nd edition. 3 volumes. 995 figures. 1426pp. 5⅜ x 8. S88, 89, 90, 3 volume set, paperbound **$6.00**

AN INTRODUCTION TO GEOMETRY OF N DIMENSIONS, D. M. Y. Sommerville. Presupposes no previous knowledge of field. Only book in English devoted exclusively to higher dimensional geometry. Discusses fundamental ideas of incidence, parallelism, perpendicularity, angles between linear space, enumerative geometry, analytical geometry from projective and metric views, polytopes, elementary ideas in analysis situs, content of hyperspacial figures. 60 diagrams. 196pp. 5⅜ x 8. S494 Paperbound **$1.50**

ELEMENTS OF NON-EUCLIDEAN GEOMETRY, D. M. Y. Sommerville. Unique in proceeding step-by-step. Requires only good knowledge of high-school geometry and algebra, to grasp elementary hyperbolic, elliptic, analytic non-Euclidean Geometries; space curvature and its implications; radical axes; homopethic centres and systems of circles; parataxy and parallelism; Gauss' proof of defect area theorem; much more, with exceptional clarity. 126 problems at chapter ends. 133 figures. xvi + 274pp. 5⅜ x 8. S460 Paperbound **$1.50**

THE FOUNDATIONS OF EUCLIDEAN GEOMETRY, H. G. Forder. First connected, rigorous account in light of modern analysis, establishing propositions without recourse to empiricism, without multiplying hypotheses. Based on tools of 19th and 20th century mathematicians, who made it possible to remedy gaps and complexities, recognize problems not earlier discerned. Begins with important relationship of number systems in geometrical figures. Considers classes, relations, linear order, natural numbers, axioms for magnitudes, groups, quasi-fields, fields, non-Archimedian systems, the axiom system (at length), particular axioms (two chapters on the Parallel Axioms), constructions, congruence, similarity, etc. Lists: axioms employed, constructions, symbols in frequent use. 295pp. 5⅜ x 8. S481 Paperbound **$2.00**

CALCULUS, FUNCTION THEORY (REAL AND COMPLEX), FOURIER THEORY

FIVE VOLUME "THEORY OF FUNCTIONS" SET BY KONRAD KNOPP. Provides complete, readily followed account of theory of functions. Proofs given concisely, yet without sacrifice of completeness or rigor. These volumes used as texts by such universities as M.I.T., Chicago, N.Y. City College, many others. "Excellent introduction . . . remarkably readable, concise, clear, rigorous," J. of the American Statistical Association.

ELEMENTS OF THE THEORY OF FUNCTIONS, Konrad Knopp. Provides background for further volumes in this set, or texts on similar level. Partial contents: Foundations, system of complex numbers and Gaussian plane of numbers, Riemann sphere of numbers, mapping by linear functions, normal forms, the logarithm, cyclometric functions, binomial series. "Not only for the young student, but also for the student who knows all about what is in it," Mathematical Journal. 140pp. 5⅜ x 8. S154 Paperbound **$1.35**

THEORY OF FUNCTIONS, PART I, Konrad Knopp. With volume II, provides coverage of basic concepts and theorems. Partial contents: numbers and points, functions of a complex variable, integral of a continuous function, Cauchy's intergral theorem, Cauchy's integral formulae, series with variable terms, expansion and analytic function in a power series, analytic continuation and complete definition of analytic functions, Laurent expansion, types of singularities. vii + 146pp. 5⅜ x 8. S156 Paperbound **$1.35**

THEORY OF FUNCTIONS, PART II, Konrad Knopp. Application and further development of general theory, special topics. Single valued functions, entire, Weierstrass. Meromorphic functions: Mittag-Leffler. Periodic functions. Multiple valued functions. Riemann surfaces. Algebraic functions. Analytical configurations, Riemann surface. x + 150pp. 5⅜ x 8. S157 Paperbound **$1.35**

PROBLEM BOOK IN THE THEORY OF FUNCTIONS, VOLUME I, Konrad Knopp. Problems in elementary theory, for use with Knopp's "Theory of Functions," or any other text. Arranged according to increasing difficulty. Fundamental concepts, sequences of numbers and infinite series, complex variable, integral theorems, development in series, conformal mapping. Answers. viii + 126pp. 5⅜ x 8. S 158 **Paperbound $1.35**

PROBLEM BOOK IN THE THEORY OF FUNCTIONS, VOLUME II, Konrad Knopp. Advanced theory of functions, to be used with Knopp's "Theory of Functions," or comparable text. Singularities, entire and meromorphic functions, periodic, analytic, continuation, multiple-valued functions, Riemann surfaces, conformal mapping. Includes section of elementary problems. "The difficult task of selecting . . . problems just within the reach of the beginner is here masterfully accomplished," AM. MATH. SOC. Answers. 138pp. 5⅜ x 8.
S159 Paperbound **$1.35**

ADVANCED CALCULUS, E. B. Wilson. Still recognized as one of most comprehensive, useful texts. Immense amount of well-represented, fundamental material, including chapters on vector functions, ordinary differential equations, special functions, calculus of variations, etc., which are excellent introductions to these areas. Requires only one year of calculus. Over 1300 exercises cover both pure math and applications to engineering and physical problems. Ideal reference, refresher. 54 page introductory review. ix + 566pp. 5⅜ x 8.
S504 Paperbound **$2.45**

LECTURES ON THE THEORY OF ELLIPTIC FUNCTIONS, H. Hancock. Reissue of only book in English with so extensive a coverage, especially of Abel, Jacobi, Legendre, Weierstrass, Hermite, Liouville, and Riemann. Unusual fullness of treatment, plus applications as well as theory in discussing universe of elliptic integrals, originating in works of Abel and Jacobi. Use is made of Riemann to provide most general theory. 40-page table of formulas. 76 figures. xxiii + 498pp. 5⅜ x 8. S483 Paperbound **$2.55**

THEORY OF FUNCTIONALS AND OF INTEGRAL AND INTEGRO-DIFFERENTIAL EQUATIONS, Vito Volterra. Unabridged republication of only English translation, General theory of functions depending on continuous set of values of another function. Based on author's concept of transition from finite number of variables to a continually infinite number. Includes much material on calculus of variations. Begins with fundamentals, examines generalization of analytic functions, functional derivative equations, applications, other directions of theory, etc. New introduction by G. C. Evans. Biography, criticism of Volterra's work by E. Whittaker. xxxx + 226pp. 5⅜ x 8. S502 Paperbound **$1.75**

AN INTRODUCTION TO FOURIER METHODS AND THE LAPLACE TRANSFORMATION, Philip Franklin. Concentrates on essentials, gives broad view, suitable for most applications. Requires only knowledge of calculus. Covers complex qualities with methods of computing elementary functions for complex values of argument and finding approximations by charts; Fourier series; harmonic anaylsis; much more. Methods are related to physical problems of heat flow, vibrations, electrical transmission, electromagnetic radiation, etc. 828 problems, answers. Formerly entitled "Fourier Methods." x + 289pp. 5⅜ x 8.
S452 Paperbound **$1.75**

THE ANALYTICAL THEORY OF HEAT, Joseph Fourier. This book, which revolutionized mathematical physics, has been used by generations of mathematicians and physicists interested in heat or application of Fourier integral. Covers cause and reflection of rays of heat, radiant heating, heating of closed spaces, use of trigonometric series in theory of heat, Fourier integral, etc. Translated by Alexander Freeman. 20 figures. xxii + 466pp. 5⅜ x 8.
S93 Paperbound **$2.00**

ELLIPTIC INTEGRALS, H. Hancock. Invaluable in work involving differential equations with cubics, quatrics under root sign, where elementary calculus methods are inadequate. Practical solutions to problems in mathematics, engineering, physics; differential equations requiring integration of Lamé's, Briot's, or Bouquet's equations; determination of arc of ellipse, hyperbola, lemiscate; solutions of problems in elastics; motion of a projectile under resistance varying as the cube of the velocity; pendulums; more. Exposition in accordance with Legendre-Jacobi theory. Rigorous discussion of Legendre transformations. 20 figures. 5 place table. 104pp. 5⅜ x 8. S484 Paperbound **$1.25**

THE TAYLOR SERIES, AN INTRODUCTION TO THE THEORY OF FUNCTIONS OF A COMPLEX VARIABLE, P. Dienes. Uses Taylor series to approach theory of functions, using ordinary calculus only, except in last 2 chapters. Starts with introduction to real variable and complex algebra, derives properties of infinite series, complex differentiation, integration, etc. Covers biuniform mapping, overconvergence and gap theorems, Taylor series on its circle of convergence, etc. Unabridged corrected reissue of first edition. 186 examples, many fully worked out. 67 figures. xii + 555pp. 5⅜ x 8. S391 Paperbound **$2.75**

LINEAR INTEGRAL EQUATIONS, W. V. Lovitt. Systematic survey of general theory, with some application to differential equations, calculus of variations, problems of math, physics. Includes: integral equation of 2nd kind by successive substitutions; Fredholm's equation as ratio of 2 integral series in lambda, applications of the Fredholm theory, Hilbert-Schmidt theory of symmetric kernels, application, etc. Neumann, Dirichlet, vibratory problems. ix + 253pp. 5⅜ x 8.
S175 Clothbound **$3.50**
S176 Paperbound **$1.60**

DICTIONARY OF CONFORMAL REPRESENTATIONS, H. Kober. Developed by British Admiralty to solve Laplace's equation in 2 dimensions. Scores of geometrical forms and transformations for electrical engineers, Joukowski aerofoil for aerodynamics, Schwartz-Christoffel transformations for hydro-dynamics, transcendental functions. Contents classified according to analytical functions describing transformations with corresponding regions. Glossary. Topological index. 447 diagrams. 6⅛ x 9¼. S160 Paperbound **$2.00**

ELEMENTS OF THE THEORY OF REAL FUNCTIONS, J. E. Littlewood. Based on lectures at Trinity College, Cambridge, this book has proved extremely successful in introducing graduate students to modern theory of functions. Offers full and concise coverage of classes and cardinal numbers, well ordered series, other types of series, and elements of the theory of sets of points. 3rd revised edition. vii + 71pp. 5⅜ x 8. S171 Clothbound **$2.85**
S172 Paperbound **$1.25**

INFINITE SEQUENCES AND SERIES, Konrad Knopp. 1st publication in any language. Excellent introduction to 2 topics of modern mathematics, designed to give student background to penetrate further alone. Sequences and sets, real and complex numbers, etc. Functions of a real and complex variable. Sequences and series. Infinite series. Convergent power series. Expansion of elementary functions. Numerical evaluation of series. v + 186pp. 5⅜ x 8.
S152 Clothbound **$3.50**
S153 Paperbound **$1.75**

THE THEORY AND FUNCTIONS OF A REAL VARIABLE AND THE THEORY OF FOURIER'S SERIES, E. W .Hobson. One of the best introductions to set theory and various aspects of functions and Fourier's series. Requires only a good background in calculus. Exhaustive coverage of: metric and descriptive properties of sets of points; transfinite numbers and order types; functions of a real variable; the Riemann and Lebesgue integrals; sequences and series of numbers; power-series; functions representable by series sequences of continuous functions; trigonometrical series; representation of functions by Fourier's series; and much more. "The best possible guide," Nature. Vol. I: 88 detailed examples, 10 figures. Index. xv + 736pp. Vol. II: 117 detailed examples, 13 figures. x + 780pp. 6⅛ x 9¼.
Vol. I: S387 Paperbound **$3.00**
Vol. II: S388 Paperbound **$3.00**

ALMOST PERIODIC FUNCTIONS, A. S. Besicovitch. Unique and important summary by a well known mathematician covers in detail the two stages of development in Bohr's theory of almost periodic functions: (1) as a generalization of pure periodicity, with results and proofs; (2) the work done by Stepanof, Wiener, Weyl, and Bohr in generalizing the theory. xi + 180pp. 5⅜ x 8. S18 Paperbound **$1.75**

INTRODUCTION TO THE THEORY OF FOURIER'S SERIES AND INTEGRALS, H. S. Carslaw. 3rd revised edition, an outgrowth of author's courses at Cambridge. Historical introduction, rational, irrational numbers, infinite sequences and series, functions of a single variable, definite integral, Fourier series, and similar topics. Appendices discuss practical harmonic analysis, periodogram analysis, Lebesgue's theory. 84 examples. xiii + 368pp. 5⅜ x 8.
S48 Paperbound **$2.00**

SYMBOLIC LOGIC

THE ELEMENTS OF MATHEMATICAL LOGIC, Paul Rosenbloom. First publication in any language. For mathematically mature readers with no training in symbolic logic. Development of lectures given at Lund Univ., Sweden, 1948. Partial contents: Logic of classes, fundamental theorems, Boolean algebra, logic of propositions, of propositional functions, expressive languages, combinatory logics, development of math within an object language, paradoxes, theorems of Post, Goedel, Church, and similar topics. iv + 214pp. 5⅜ x 8.
S227 Paperbound **$1.45**

INTRODUCTION TO SYMBOLIC LOGIC AND ITS APPLICATION, R. Carnap. Clear, comprehensive, rigorous, by perhaps greatest living master. Symbolic languages analyzed, one constructed. Applications to math (axiom systems for set theory, real, natural numbers), topology (Dedekind, Cantor continuity explanations), physics (general analysis of determination, causality, space-time topology), biology (axiom system for basic concepts). "A masterpiece," Zentralblatt für Mathematik und Ihre Grenzgebiete. Over 300 exercises. 5 figures. xvi + 241pp. 5⅜ x 8. S453 Paperbound **$1.85**

AN INTRODUCTION TO SYMBOLIC LOGIC, Susanne K. Langer. Probably clearest book for the philosopher, scientist, layman—no special knowledge of math required. Starts with simplest symbols, goes on to give remarkable grasp of Boole-Schroeder, Russell-Whitehead systems, clearly, quickly. Partial Contents: Forms, Generalization, Classes, Deductive System of Classes, Algebra of Logic, Assumptions of Principia Mathematica, Logistics, Proofs of Theorems, etc. "Clearest . . . simplest introduction . . . the intelligent non-mathematician should have no difficulty," MATHEMATICS GAZETTE. Revised, expanded 2nd edition. Truth-value tables. 368pp. 5⅜ 8. S164 Paperbound **$1.75**

TRIGONOMETRICAL SERIES, Antoni Zygmund. On modern advanced level. Contains carefully organized analyses of trigonometric, orthogonal, Fourier systems of functions, with clear adequate descriptions of summability of Fourier series, proximation theory, conjugate series, convergence, divergence of Fourier series. Especially valuable for Russian, Eastern European coverage. 329pp. 5⅜ x 8. S290 Paperbound **$1.50**

THE LAWS OF THOUGHT, George Boole. This book founded symbolic logic some 100 years ago. It is the 1st significant attempt to apply logic to all aspects of human endeavour. Partial contents: derivation of laws, signs and laws, interpretations, eliminations, conditions of a perfect method, analysis, Aristotelian logic, probability, and similar topics. xvii + 424pp. 5⅜ x 8. S28 Paperbound **$2.00**

SYMBOLIC LOGIC, C. I. Lewis, C. H. Langford. 2nd revised edition of probably most cited book in symbolic logic. Wide coverage of entire field; one of fullest treatments of paradoxes; plus much material not available elsewhere. Basic to volume is distinction between logic of extensions and intensions. Considerable emphasis on converse substitution, while matrix system presents supposition of variety of non-Aristotelian logics. Especially valuable sections on strict limitations, existence theorems. Partial contents: Boole-Schroeder algebra; truth value systems, the matrix method; implication and deductibility; general theory of propositions; etc. "Most valuable," Times, London. 506pp. 5⅜ x 8. S170 Paperbound **$2.00**

GROUP THEORY AND LINEAR ALGEBRA, SETS, ETC.

LECTURES ON THE ICOSAHEDRON AND THE SOLUTION OF EQUATIONS OF THE FIFTH DEGREE, Felix Klein. Solution of quintics in terms of rotations of regular icosahedron around its axes of symmetry. A classic, indispensable source for those interested in higher algebra, geometry, crystallography. Considerable explanatory material included. 230 footnotes, mostly bibliography. "Classical monograph . . . detailed, readable book," Math. Gazette. 2nd edition. xvi + 289pp. 5⅜ x 8. S314 Paperbound **$1.85**

INTRODUCTION TO THE THEORY OF GROUPS OF FINITE ORDER, R. Carmichael. Examines fundamental theorems and their applications. Beginning with sets, systems, permutations, etc., progresses in easy stages through important types of groups: Abelian, prime power, permutation, etc. Except 1 chapter where matrices are desirable, no higher math is needed. 783 exercises, problems. xvi + 447pp. 5⅜ x 8. S299 Clothbound **$3.95**
S300 Paperbound **$2.00**

THEORY OF GROUPS OF FINITE ORDER, W. Burnside. First published some 40 years ago, still one of clearest introductions. Partial contents: permutations, groups independent of representation, composition series of a group, isomorphism of a group with itself, Abelian groups, prime power groups, permutation groups, invariants of groups of linear substitution, graphical representation, etc. "Clear and detailed discussion . . . numerous problems which are instructive," Design News. xxiv + 512pp. 5⅜ x 8. S38 Paperbound **$2.45**

COMPUTATIONAL METHODS OF LINEAR ALGEBRA, V. N. Faddeeva, translated by C. D. Benster. 1st English translation of unique, valuable work, only one in English presenting systematic exposition of most important methods of linear algebra—classical, contemporary. Details of deriving numerical solutions of problems in mathematical physics. Theory and practice. Includes survey of necessary background, most important methods of solution, for exact, iterative groups. One of most valuable features is 23 tables, triple checked for accuracy, unavailable elsewhere. Translator's note. x + 252pp. 5⅜ x 8. S424 Paperbound **$1.95**

THE CONTINUUM AND OTHER TYPES OF SERIAL ORDER, E. V. Huntington. This famous book gives a systematic elementary account of the modern theory of the continuum as a type of serial order. Based on the Cantor-Dedekind ordinal theory, which requires no technical knowledge of higher mathematics, it offers an easily followed analysis of ordered classes, discrete and dense series, continuous series, Cantor's transfinite numbers. "Admirable introduction to the rigorous theory of the continuum . . . reading easy," Science Progress. 2nd edition. viii + 82pp. 5⅜ x 8. S129 Clothbound **$2.75**
S130 Paperbound **$1.00**

THEORY OF SETS, E. Kamke. Clearest, amplest introduction in English, well suited for independent study. Subdivisions of main theory, such as theory of sets of points, are discussed, but emphasis is on general theory. Partial contents: rudiments of set theory, arbitrary sets, their cardinal numbers, ordered sets, their order types, well-ordered sets, their cardinal numbers. vii + 144pp. 5⅜ x 8. S141 Paperbound **$1.35**

CONTRIBUTIONS TO THE FOUNDING OF THE THEORY OF TRANSFINITE NUMBERS, Georg Cantor. These papers founded a new branch of mathematics. The famous articles of 1895-7 are translated, with an 82-page introduction by P. E. B. Jourdain dealing with Cantor, the background of his discoveries, their results, future possibiilties. ix + 211pp. 5⅜ x 8. S45 Paperbound **$1.25**

NUMERICAL AND GRAPHICAL METHODS, TABLES

JACOBIAN ELLIPTIC FUNCTION TABLES, L. M. Milne-Thomson. Easy-to-follow, practical, not only useful numerical tables, but complete elementary sketch of application of elliptic functions. Covers description of principle properties; complete elliptic integrals; Fourier series, expansions; periods, zeros, poles, residues, formulas for special values of argument; cubic, quartic polynomials; pendulum problem; etc. Tables, graphs form body of book: Graph, 5 figure table of elliptic function sn (u m); cn (u m); dn (u m). 8 figure table of complete elliptic integrals K, K′, E, E′, nome q. 7 figure table of Jacobian zeta-function Z(u). 3 figures. xi + 123pp. 5⅜ x 8. S194 Paperbound **$1.35**

TABLES OF FUNCTIONS WITH FORMULAE AND CURVES, E. Jahnke, F. Emde. Most comprehensive 1-volume English text collection of tables, formulae, curves of transcendent functions. 4th corrected edition, new 76-page section giving tables, formulae for elementary functions not in other English editions. Partial contents: sine, cosine, logarithmic integral; error integral; elliptic integrals; theta functions; Legendre, Bessel, Riemann, Mathieu, hypergeometric functions; etc. "Out-of-the-way functions for which we know no other source." Scientific Computing Service, Ltd. 212 figures. 400pp. 5⅝ x 8⅜. S133 Paperbound **$2.00**

MATHEMATICAL TABLES, H. B. Dwight. Covers in one volume almost every function of importance in applied mathematics, engineering, physical sciences. Three extremely fine tables of the three trig functions, inverses, to 1000th of radian; natural, common logs; squares, cubes; hyperbolic functions, inverses; $(a^2 + b^2)$ exp. ½a; complete elliptical integrals of 1st, 2nd kind; sine, cosine integrals; exponential integrals; Ei(x) and Ei(—x); binomial coefficients; factorials to 250; surface zonal harmonics, first derivatives; Bernoulli, Euler numbers, their logs to base of 10; Gamma function; normal probability integral; over 60pp. Bessel functions; Riemann zeta function. Each table with formulae generally used, sources of more extensive tables, interpolation data, etc. Over half have columns of differences, to facilitate interpolation. viii + 231pp. 5⅜ x 8. S445 Paperbound **$1.75**

PRACTICAL ANALYSIS, GRAPHICAL AND NUMERICAL METHODS, F. A. Willers. Immensely practical hand-book for engineers. How to interpolate, use various methods of numerical differentiation and integration, determine roots of a single algebraic equation, system of linear equations, use empirical formulas, integrate differential equations, etc. Hundreds of short-cuts for arriving at numerical solutions. Special section on American calculating machines, by T. W. Simpson. Translation by R. T. Beyer. 132 illustrations. 422pp. 5⅜ x 8. S273 Paperbound **$2.00**

NUMERICAL SOLUTIONS OF DIFFERENTIAL EQUATIONS, H. Levy, E. A. Baggott. Comprehensive collection of methods for solving ordinary differential equations of first and higher order. 2 requirements: practical, easy to grasp; more rapid than school methods. Partial contents: graphical integration of differential equations, graphical methods for detailed solution. Numerical solution. Simultaneous equations and equations of 2nd and higher orders. "Should be in the hands of all in research and applied mathematics, teaching," Nature. 21 figures. viii + 238pp. 5⅜ x 8. S168 Paperbound **$1.75**

NUMERICAL INTEGRATION OF DIFFERENTIAL EQUATIONS, Bennet, Milne, Bateman. Unabridged republication of original prepared for National Research Council. New methods of integration by 3 leading mathematicians: "The Interpolational Polynomial," "Successive Approximation," A. A. Bennett, "Step-by-step Methods of Integration," W. W. Milne. "Methods for Partial Differential Equations," H. Bateman. Methods for partial differential equations, solution of differential equations to non-integral values of a parameter will interest mathematicians, physicists. 288 footnotes, mostly bibliographical. 235 item classified bibliography. 108pp. 5⅜ x 8. S305 Paperbound **$1.35**

Write for free catalogs!

Indicate your field of interest. Dover publishes books on physics, earth sciences, mathematics, engineering, chemistry, astronomy, anthropology, biology, psychology, philosophy, religion, history, literature, mathematical recreations, languages, crafts, art, graphic arts, etc.

Write to Dept. catr
Dover Publications, Inc.
180 Varick St., N. Y. 14, N. Y.

Science A